W9-CHN-558

ELEMENTARY DIFFERENTIAL EQUATIONS

İlhan Şener

[illegible]

The University of Texas

September 1963

ELEMENTARY DIFFERENTIAL EQUATIONS

LYMAN M. KELLS, Ph.D.

Professor of Mathematics, Emeritus
U.S. Naval Academy

FIFTH EDITION

McGRAW-HILL BOOK COMPANY, INC.

New York Toronto London

1960

ELEMENTARY DIFFERENTIAL EQUATIONS

Copyright © 1960 by the McGraw-Hill Book Company, Inc.

Copyright, 1932, 1935, 1947, 1954, by the McGraw-Hill Book Company, Inc. Printed in the United States of America. All rights reserved. This book, or parts thereof, may not be reproduced in any form without permission of the publishers. *Library of Congress Catalog Card Number* 60-8029

IV

33528

THE MAPLE PRESS COMPANY, YORK, PA.

PREFACE

Differential equations furnish extremely powerful tools for analyzing functional relations. Moreover, so vast is the field of their applications that the practical side rivals in importance purely theoretical considerations. In this book theory and applications go hand in hand.

The outstanding feature of this treatise is simple presentation of the fundamental types of differential equations with numerous examples and carefully graded exercises. Enough theory is given to provide complete understanding and penetrating intuitional power. A certain unity is obtained by strong emphasis on basic methods, such as those using substitutions, operators, and transforms. For example, in this book nearly all methods of solving equations of the first order and a great many others are based on substitutions. In particular, the same substitution is used in linear equations, Bernoulli's equation, and a generalization of Bernoulli's equation. The general plan is to use fundamental principles and thinking as opposed to memorized particular procedures. This gives basic power and thorough assimilation.

In this revision two new chapters, one on *Laplace transforms* and one on *numerical solutions*, have been added. Laplace transforms give directly short solutions of differential equations satisfying given initial conditions, and they have extensive applications in many fields. The chapter on numerical integration of differential equations is extremely important. It is used to solve practical problems based on observed data and problems for which other methods are complicated or fail completely. In practice, the computation is carried out by means of computing machines.

The lists of problems have been changed in quality and materials. Great care has been taken to arrange the problems so that a student becomes familiar with necessary, fundamental ideas while solving simple problems near the beginning of a list; afterwards he meets more difficult problems, some of which will tax the ingenuity of the best student. New problems have been devised with this general plan in view. While many of these are standard in type, the work has been modernized by others relating to chemistry, electricity, motion in space, rockets, elasticity, fields of force, half-lives of isotopes, nuclear reactors, heat transfer, simple and complex vibrations, and many other topics. At the end of each of the first eleven chapters is a review section for the chapter. These sections are designed primarily for review work but may be used for extra problems or for testing purposes.

Many of the ideas in this revision derive from the excellent suggestions of teachers using previous editions. It is a pleasure to express appreciation and sincere thanks for this valuable assistance.

Lyman M. Kells

CONTENTS

Preface v

Chapter 1. Definitions and Elementary Problems 1

1. General remarks 1
2. Differential equation. Order. Degree 2
3. Solution of a differential equation 3
4. Geometric considerations 5
5. Existence theorems 7
6. General solution. Particular solution 8
7. Finding differential equation from general solution 8
8. Variables separable 11
9. Review exercises 13

Chapter 2. Applications 15

10. Geometric applications using rectangular coordinates 15
11. Orthogonal trajectories 16
12. Geometric applications using polar coordinates 18
13. Use of limits 20
14. Physical applications 21
15. Compound-interest-law problems 22
16. Acceleration. Velocity. Distance 24
17. Other rate problems 27
18. Miscellaneous problems 30

Chapter 3. Differential Equations of the First Order and the First Degree . 33

19. Simple substitutions 33
20. Homogeneous equations 35
21. Equations of the form $(ax + by + c)\,dx + (\alpha x + \beta y + \gamma)\,dy = 0$ . . . 37
22. Exact differentials 38
23. Exact differential equations 39
24. Integrating factors 42
25. Linear differential equation 45
26. Equations reducible to linear form 48
27. Simultaneous equations 49
28. Summary 51

Chapter 4. Applications Involving Differential Equations of the First Order . 54

29. Miscellaneous elementary applications 54
30. Applications involving simultaneous equations 56
31. Applications to the flow of electricity 59
32. Air pressure 60

33. Applications involving forces and velocities 61
34. Review problems 67

Chapter 5. First-order Equations of Degree Higher than the First 70

35. Foreword 70
36. Equations solvable for dy/dx 70
37. Envelopes 72
38. Envelope from differential equation 75
39. Equations solvable for y 78
40. Equations solvable for x 80
41. Review problems 81

Chapter 6. Linear Differential Equations with Constant Coefficients . . . 83

42. Operators 83
43. Linear independence of functions 86
44. Linear differential equation 88
45. Homogeneous linear differential equation with constant coefficients . . 89
46. Auxiliary equation has repeated roots 90
47. Constants of integration from initial conditions 91
48. Auxiliary equation has imaginary roots 92
49. Right-hand member not zero 94
50. Special case when the right-hand member is not zero 96
51. A basic theorem relating to operators 97
52. Methods using symbolic operators 98
53. Variation of parameters 103
54. Simultaneous differential equations. 106
55. Summary and review exercises 108

Chapter 7. Laplace Transforms 110

56. Introduction 110
57. Definition of a Laplace transform 110
58. Some properties of Laplace transforms. 111
59. Deriving transform relations from given ones 114
60. Inverse transforms of products 117
61. Transforms of derivatives 121
62. Solving differential equations by transforms 122
63. Solving systems of differential equations 124
64. Resolving a fraction into partial fractions 126
65. Fractions having repeated factors in the denominator 128
66. Partial fractions. Quadratic factors 130
67. Review problems 133

Chapter 8. Applications of Linear Equations with Constant Coefficients . . 135

68. Harmonic motion. Damping 135
69. Types of damping. Resonance. 137
70. Forces. Accelerations. Moments. 139
71. Some fundamental equations of motion 140
72. Oscillatory motion 141
73. Plane motions of bodies 147
74. Kirchhoff's current law and electromotive-force law 151
75. Simple circuits containing constant electromotive force 153

76. Simple circuits containing a sinusoidal electromotive force 154
77. Resonance 155
78. Applications of Kirchhoff's laws to networks 156
79. Review problems 161

Chapter 9. Miscellaneous Differential Equations of Order Higher than the First 163

80. Reduction of order by substitution 163
81. Dependent variable absent 163
82. Independent variable absent 165
83. Method based on factorization of the operator 166
84. Euler's linear equation 169
85. Second-order linear equation 170
86. Review exercises 171

Chapter 10. Applications 173

87. Radius of curvature 173
88. Cables. The catenary 174
89. Equation of elastic curve. Beams 176
90. Columns 181
91. Motion of a particle in a plane 182
92. Review problems 185

Chapter 11. Existence Theorems and Applications 187

93. Foreword 187
94. Replacement of differential equations by a system of the first order and first degree 187
95. Existence theorems 188
96. Differential equations of the first order and first degree in the unknowns . 191
97. Total differential equations 194
98. Geometrical interpretation 198
99. Fields of force in space 198
100. Review exercises 200

Chapter 12. Solution by Series 202

101. Introduction 202
102. Integration in series 204
103. Solution involving a more general type of series 208
104. Indicial equation has roots differing by an integer 210
105. The gamma function 213
106. Bessel's equation 215
107. Bessel's functions 217
108. Expansion of functions in terms of Bessel's functions 222
109. Legendre's functions 224

Chapter 13. Numerical Solutions of Differential Equations 229

110. Introduction 229
111. Methods of successive approximations 229
112. Newton's interpolation formula 231
113. Interpolation 234
114. Formulas for approximate integration 236

115. Illustration and discussion of formulas (16) to (21), §114 237
116. Halving the interval h of x 240
117. Numerical solution of a system of simultaneous equations 242
118. The Runge-Kutta method 245

Chapter 14. Partial Differential Equations 248

119. Introduction 248
120. Solution of a partial differential equation 248
121. Equations easily integrable 250
122. Equations having the form $Pp + Qq = R$. 251
123. Finding particular solutions satisfying given conditions 254
124. Separation of variables 256
125. Hyperbolic, parabolic, elliptic equations 258

Chapter 15. Applications of Partial Differential Equations 263

126. Fourier series 263
127. Cosine series. Sine series 267
128. Application to nuclear fission 269
129. Vibrations of a string. 272
130. Vibrations of a rod 275
131. Flow of heat 276
132. One-dimensional heat flow 279
133. Vibrations of a membrane 281
134. Telephone, telegraph, and radio equations. 283
135. Fluid motion 286

Answers 291

Index 313

CHAPTER 1

DEFINITIONS AND ELEMENTARY PROBLEMS

1. General remarks

Differential equations furnish a very powerful tool for solving many practical problems of engineering and science generally, as well as a wide range of purely mathematical problems. While this book treats of the most important types of differential equations and gives strong emphasis to outstanding applications to problems of a physical nature, it also takes up many interesting applications to geometry.

The applications to engineering, physics, and science generally are of the greatest importance. A law is conceived and set forth as a system of differential equations; the solution of these equations tells a rather complete story of the states and motions to be expected of the materials obeying that law. For example, we assume the law, suggested by experiment, that radium disintegrates at a rate proportional to the amount present and express this in mathematical symbols by the equation

$$\frac{dQ}{dt} = kQ.$$

By solving this equation for a 100-g lump and using facts found from experiment, the equation

$$Q = 100e^{-0.041t}$$

is easily derived. This tells approximately the amount of radium to be expected in the lump t centuries from now.

Newton conceived the law of gravitation and then solved the corresponding system of differential equations to show that the earth moves about the sun approximately in an ellipse with the sun at one focus. He made a long step forward in the development of celestial mechanics. About 1865, Maxwell conceived a relation between an electric current and the corresponding magnetic field, expressed the relation as a system of partial differential equations, solved them, and from the result predicted the waves of radio. Differential equations have played a prominent role in the development of the theories of radio, radar, television, and electricity generally. Similar remarks apply to nearly every great branch of science. The many applications in this book will show the great power of differential equations and give methods of using it.

2. Differential equation. Order. Degree

The student has already met differential equations of an elementary type in his study of the calculus. Thus,

$$\frac{dy}{dx} = x^2 + 3 \tag{1}$$

is a differential equation. In general, **a differential equation** *is an equation containing differentials or derivatives.* If the equation contains total differentials, total derivatives, or both but does not contain partial derivatives, it is called an **ordinary differential equation**; if it contains partial derivatives, it is called a **partial differential equation.** Thus,

$$x^2 \frac{d^2y}{dx^2} + 2x \frac{dy}{dx} + y = x^2 + 2, \tag{2}$$

$$\left(\frac{d^3y}{dx^3}\right)^2 + 2 \frac{d^2y}{dx^2} \frac{dy}{dx} + x^2 \left(\frac{dy}{dx}\right)^3 = 0, \tag{3}$$

$$\left[1 + \left(\frac{dy}{dx}\right)^2\right]^{\frac{3}{2}} = k \frac{d^2y}{dx^2}, \tag{4}$$

$$(x + y^2 - 3y) + (x^2 + 3x + y) \frac{dy}{dx} = 0 \tag{5}$$

are ordinary differential equations, whereas

$$\frac{\partial z}{\partial x} = y, \tag{6}$$

$$\frac{\partial^2 u}{\partial x^2} + \frac{\partial^2 u}{\partial y^2} + \frac{\partial^2 u}{\partial z^2} = 0 \tag{7}$$

are partial differential equations.

The **order** *of a differential equation is the order of the highest-ordered derivative involved in its expression.* Referring to the differential equations numbered (1) to (5), equations (1) and (5) are of the first order, (2) and (4) are of the second order, and (3) is of the third order.

The **degree** *of an ordinary differential equation algebraic in its derivatives is the algebraic degree of its highest-ordered derivative.*

Consider, for example,

$$\sqrt[3]{\left(\frac{d^2y}{dx^2}\right)^2} = \sqrt{1 + \left(\frac{dy}{dx}\right)^2}. \tag{8}$$

Here the highest-ordered derivative is d^2y/dx^2, and the order of the equation is 2. Equating the sixth powers of the members of (8), obtain

$$\left(\frac{d^2y}{dx^2}\right)^4 = \left[1 + \left(\frac{dy}{dx}\right)^2\right]^3. \tag{9}$$

Here 4, the degree in d^2y/dx^2, is the degree of equation (8). Equations

ln h maybe (−) or (+)
must be (+)

(1), (2), (5), and (6) are of the first degree; (3) and (4) are of the second. Equation (4) is of the second degree; for d^2y/dx^2 appears to the second degree in the equation resulting from clearing (4) of the radical represented by the 2 in the exponent $\frac{3}{2}$.

EXERCISES

State the order and the degree of each of the following differential equations:

1. $\dfrac{dy}{dx} = 5y.$

2. $\left(\dfrac{dy}{dx}\right)^2 = \dfrac{3x}{4y}.$

3. $\left(\dfrac{dy}{dx}\right)^3 = \sqrt{1 + \left(\dfrac{dy}{dx}\right)^2}.$

4. $\dfrac{d^2y}{dx^2} = 3\dfrac{dy}{dx} + xy.$

5. $\sqrt{\dfrac{d^2y}{dx^2}} = 3\dfrac{dy}{dx} + x.$

6. $\dfrac{d^2y}{dx^2} = \sqrt{1 + \left(\dfrac{dy}{dx}\right)^4}.$

7. $\dfrac{d^3y}{dx^3} = \sqrt{\dfrac{dy}{dx}}.$

8. $\left(\dfrac{d^2y}{dx^2}\right)^{\frac{1}{3}} = k\left[1 + \left(\dfrac{dy}{dx}\right)^2\right]^{\frac{5}{2}}.$

3. Solution of a differential equation

A **solution** *of an ordinary differential equation in two variables is a non-derivative relation between the variables which satisfies the equation.* If, in particular, the solution has the form $y = f(x)$, then replacement of y and the derivatives of y with respect to x by $f(x)$ and its derivatives produces an identity. Thus $y = cx^2$ is a solution of

$$x\frac{dy}{dx} = 2y. \tag{10}$$

For, substituting cx^2 for y and $2cx$ for dy/dx in (10), we get

$$x \cdot 2cx = 2cx^2.$$

Example 1. Prove that $y = Ae^x + Be^{-2x} + x^2 + x$, A and B constants, is a solution of $(d^2y/dx^2) + (dy/dx) - 2y = 3 - 2x^2$.

Proof. From $y = Ae^x + Be^{-2x} + x^2 + x$, we obtain

$$\frac{dy}{dx} = Ae^x - 2Be^{-2x} + 2x + 1, \qquad \frac{d^2y}{dx^2} = Ae^x + 4Be^{-2x} + 2.$$

Substituting these values in the differential equation, we get the identity

$$Ae^x + 4Be^{-2x} + 2 + Ae^x - 2Be^{-2x} + 2x + 1 - 2Ae^x - 2Be^{-2x} - 2x^2 - 2x = 3 - 2x^2.$$

Example 2.* Prove that $\ln y + (x/y) = c$ is a solution of

$$(y - x)\frac{dy}{dx} + y = 0. \tag{a}$$

* The symbol $\ln x$, with no base specified, indicates throughout this text a natural logarithm, that is, a logarithm to the base $e = 2.7183$ approximately. Also, the letter e will often be used, without explanation, to represent this base of natural logarithms.

Proof. Using the regular process of differentiating an implicit function, we obtain from $\ln y + (x/y) = c$

$$\frac{1}{y}\frac{dy}{dx} - \frac{x}{y^2}\frac{dy}{dx} + \frac{1}{y} = 0,$$

or, solving for dy/dx,

$$\frac{dy}{dx} = \frac{-y}{y - x}. \qquad (b)$$

Substituting in (a) the value of dy/dx from (b), we obtain

$$(y - x)\left(\frac{-y}{y - x}\right) + y = -y + y = 0.$$

EXERCISES

Prove that each equation is a solution of the differential equation written opposite it:

1. $y = x^2 + x + c,$ $\qquad \dfrac{dy}{dx} = 2x + 1.$

2. $y = x^2 + cx,$ $\qquad x\dfrac{dy}{dx} = x^2 + y.$

3. $y = c,$ $\qquad \dfrac{dy}{dx} = 0.$

4. $cy = x^2,$ $\qquad x\dfrac{dy}{dx} = 2y.$

5. $y = x^5 + ax + b,$ $\qquad \dfrac{d^2y}{dx^2} = 20x^3.$

6. $y = x^4 + ax^2 + bx + c,$ $\qquad \dfrac{d^3y}{dx^3} = 24x.$

7. $y = A \sin x + B \cos x,$ $\qquad \dfrac{d^2y}{dx^2} + y = 0.$

8. $y = A \sin 5x + B \cos 5x,$ $\qquad \dfrac{d^2y}{dx^2} + 25y = 0.$

9. $y = (x + c)e^{-x},$ $\qquad \dfrac{dy}{dx} + y = e^{-x}.$

10. $y = c_1 \sin 3x + c_2 \cos 3x + 9x^2 - 2,$ $\qquad \dfrac{d^2y}{dx^2} + 9y = 81x^2.$

11. $y = c_1e^{2x} + c_2e^{-4x} + 2xe^{2x},$ $\qquad \dfrac{d^2y}{dx^2} + 2\dfrac{dy}{dx} - 8y = 12e^{2x}.$

12. $y = c(x - c)^2,$ $\qquad \left(\dfrac{dy}{dx}\right)^3 - 4xy\dfrac{dy}{dx} + 8y^2 = 0.$

13. $y^{-3} = x^3(3e^x + c),$ $\qquad x\dfrac{dy}{dx} + y + x^4y^4e^x = 0.$

14. $\ln y = c_1e^x + c_2e^{-x},$ $\qquad y\dfrac{d^2y}{dx^2} - \left(\dfrac{dy}{dx}\right)^2 = y^2 \ln y.$

4. Geometric considerations

Any differential equation of the first order and first degree may be written in the form

$$\frac{dy}{dx} = f(x,y). \tag{11}$$

It associates to each point (x_0,y_0) a line having as slope $(dy/dx)_0 = f(x_0,y_0)$; in other words, (11) associates to each point a direction. Observe that every point on the curve

$$f(x,y) = m \tag{12}$$

is associated with the slope m. The curves (12) are called the **isoclines** of (11).

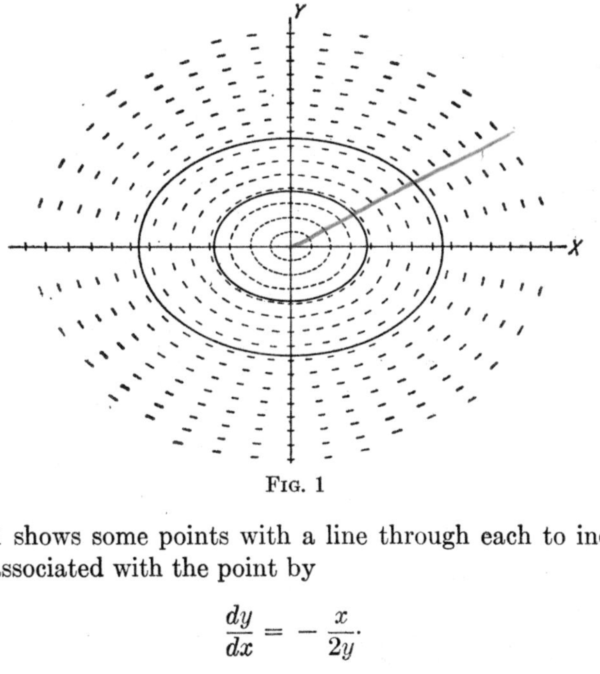

FIG. 1

Figure 1 shows some points with a line through each to indicate the direction associated with the point by

$$\frac{dy}{dx} = -\frac{x}{2y}. \tag{13}$$

The isoclines of (13) are defined by

$$-x/2y = m, \qquad \text{or} \qquad x = -2my, \tag{14}$$

and this represents all straight lines through (0,0). Thus, for $m = 0$, every point on $x = -2(0)y = 0$ has zero as associated slope and every point on $x = -2(1)y$ has 1 as associated slope. Note in Fig. 1 that any set of points associated with the same direction lie on a line through the origin.

Since any solution of (13) satisfies it, any corresponding curve must have at each of its points the slope dy/dx defined by (13); that is, the tangent line to the curve at any point on it has the direction associated with this point by (13). Testing shows that

$$x^2 + 2y^2 = c \tag{15}$$

satisfies (13) and therefore represents solutions of it. Figure 1 shows some ellipses representing solutions of (13). Since c in (15) may be any constant, (15) represents a family of ellipses. Any point $P(x_0,y_0)$ in the plane, except (0,0), will lie on the ellipse represented by equation (15) with $c = x_0^2 + 2y_0^2$, and through each point, except (0,0), will pass one and only one of these ellipses. The two arbitrary constants in the solution $x^2 + 2y^2 = x_0^2 + 2y_0^2$ are really equivalent to only one since all solutions could be obtained by taking $x_0 = 0$ and assigning values to y_0. The small ellipse is associated with the value $c = 1$ and the large one with $c = 4$.

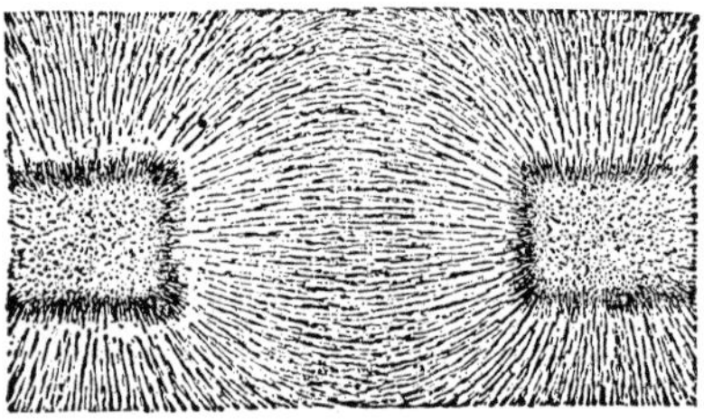

FIG. 2

Figure 2, showing the distribution of iron filings under the influence of a magnet, exhibits the same type of relationship. The iron filings serve as direction lines, and their distribution is such that the curves to which they belong are suggested. A map indicating the directions of ocean currents and winds by means of barbed lines suggests the same situation.

EXERCISES

1. By testing show that $y = \frac{1}{4}x^2 + c$ is a solution of $dy/dx = \frac{1}{2}x$. Find c for the curve through: (*a*) (0,0); (*b*) (0, −2); (*c*) $(0,y_0)$.

2. Write equations of the isoclines of $dy/dx = \frac{1}{2}x$. Draw short lines to indicate directions associated with points on the lines $x = 0$, $x = \pm 1$, $x = \pm 2$, $x = \pm 3$. Draw on the same graph solution curves of $dy/dx = \frac{1}{2}x$ through points (0,0), (0,1), (0,2), and (0, −1).

3. Verify that $y = x + c$ is a solution of $dy/dx = 1$. Why is any straight line inclined 45 deg to the X-axis an isocline? Are the lines represented by the solution the isoclines? Discuss the isoclines and solutions associated with $dy/dx = 2$.

4. Verify that $y = 2\sqrt{x} + c$ is a solution of $dy/dx = 1/\sqrt{x}$. Show that the isoclines are represented by $x = m^2$. Draw the isoclines for $m = 0$, $m = 1$, $m = \sqrt{2}$, $m = \sqrt{3}$, and $m = 2$, and indicate on each line by short strokes the associated directions. Sketch part of the solutions $y = 2\sqrt{x}$, $y = 2\sqrt{x} + 1$, and $y = 2\sqrt{x} + 2$. Why does no curve representing a solution extend to the left of the X-axis?

5. Check that $y = x^2 + cx$ is a solution of $x(dy/dx) - y = x^2$. Write the solution having a graph through: (*a*) (1,2); (*b*) (−1,3); (*c*) (1,0); (*d*) (3,5); (*e*) (2, −2).

5. Existence theorems

The existence theorems stated without proof in this section will be assumed throughout the text. For simplicity of statement, the conditions given here are unnecessarily restrictive. More general theorems are stated in §95.

The relation indicated geometrically in §4 illustrates a case covered by the following theorem:

THEOREM I. *A differential equation*

$$\frac{dy}{dx} = f(x,y) \tag{16}$$

has, in a region S, a unique solution $y = \varphi(x)$ satisfied by (x_0,y_0) provided that (x_0,y_0) is an interior point of S and that $f(x,y)$ and $\partial f(x,y)/\partial y$ are real, single-valued, and continuous in S.

Here x_0 and y_0 appear as two arbitrary constants. They are equivalent to only one for the reason suggested in §4. Theorem I indicates that through each point inside a region S of the xy-plane passes a unique curve whose equation satisfies (16) provided that $f(x,y)$ and $\partial f(x,y)/\partial y$ are real, single-valued, and continuous in S. For example, through every point (x_0,y_0), $y_0 \neq 0$, of the plane of Fig. 1, §4, passes a unique ellipse whose equation satisfies (13).

THEOREM II. *The system of differential equations*

$$\frac{d^2y}{dx^2} = f(x,y,z), \qquad \frac{dy}{dx} = z \tag{17}$$

has a unique solution

$$y = \varphi(x), \qquad z = \psi(x)$$

satisfied by the values $y = y_0$, $z = z_0$, when $x = x_0$, provided that only values of x, y, and z within the respective intervals

$$|x - p| \leqq a, \qquad |y - p| \leqq b, \qquad |z - r| \leqq c \tag{18}$$

are considered and that f, $\partial f/\partial y$, and $\partial f/\partial z$ are real, single-valued, and continuous in the region defined by (18).

Here again the arbitrary constants y_0 and z_0 at x_0 are equivalent to only two. Theorem II indicates that, under its restrictions, a unique curve passes through point $P(x_0,y_0)$ tangent to a line through P of slope z_0 and has an equation satisfying (17). A theorem analogous to Theorem II states that, *under certain conditions,* an nth-order equation has a unique solution satisfying the conditions*

$$y = a_1, \quad \frac{dy}{dx} = a_2, \quad \frac{d^2y}{dx^2} = a_3, \quad \ldots, \quad \frac{d^{n-1}y}{dx^n} = a_n \quad \text{when } x = x_0. \tag{19}$$

* See Theorem II, §§5 and 95.

Note that one arbitrary constant is involved in the general solution of a first-order equation, two for a second-order equation, and n constants, the a's of (19), for an nth-order equation.

A differential equation may have a so-called singular solution that represents an envelope of solution curves, and the restrictive conditions of the theorems are not all satisfied at its points. Singular solutions will be considered in Chap. 5.

6. General solution. Particular solution

A solution of a differential equation which defines all, or nearly all, of its solutions is called its **general solution.** For most of the types considered in this book, *it contains a number of arbitrary constants equal to the number expressing the order of the differential equation.* The student may observe that this relation held true for the equations and their solutions in §3. Also, the process of §7 will verify the relation. *A* **particular solution** *of a differential equation is any solution less comprehensive than the general solution.* For example, the general solution of $(d^2y/dx^2) + 4y = 0$ is $y = A \sin 2x + B \cos 2x$; particular solutions are $y = 3 \sin 2x$, $y = m \cos 2x$, and $y = A(\sin 2x + \cos 2x)$. The singular solution mentioned in §5 is a particular solution; it may or may not be obtainable by replacing arbitrary constants in the general solution by particular numbers. For example, the general solution of $y^2[1 + (dy/dx)^2] = 1$ is $(x - c)^2 + y^2 = 1$, and its singular solutions are $y = 1$ and $y = -1$. Note that particular solutions $y = 1$ and $y = -1$ satisfy $y^2[1 + (dy/dx)^2] = 1$, but they are not special cases of $(x - c)^2 + y^2 = 1$.

Again consider $d^2y/dx^2 = 12x$. Let $y' = dy/dx$ and the equation becomes

$$\frac{dy'}{dx} = 12x. \tag{a}$$

Obtain from this by integration

$$y' = 6x^2 + c_1.$$

Now replace y' by dy/dx, and integrate again to obtain

$$y = 2x^3 + c_1x + c_2. \tag{b}$$

Equation (*b*) is the general solution of the given differential equation. Note that it contains two arbitrary constants c_1 and c_2 and that 2 is the order of the given differential equation. If c_1 and c_2 in (*b*) are replaced by 1 and 0, respectively, the particular solution $y = 2x^3 + x$ is obtained.

7. Finding differential equation from general solution

Two problems arise: first, given a differential equation, to find a solution and the general solution if possible; second, given the general solution, or primitive, to find the differential equation.

Often, the general solution cannot be found in finite form. Consequently, much of our work will consist in dealing with important special cases. A very simple case is considered in §8. General methods by means of infinite series and approximation methods will be considered in Chaps. 12 and 13.

To solve the converse problem, namely, that of *finding the differential equation when the general solution is given: differentiate the general solution, differentiate the derived equation, differentiate the second derived equation, etc., until the number of derived equations is equal to the number of independent arbitrary constants in the general solution; finally eliminate the constants from the general solution and the derived equations.* A few examples will illustrate the process.

Example 1. Find the differential equation whose general solution is $y = c \cos x$.

Solution. For convenience, we shall use primes to indicate derivatives with respect to x. From the given general solution, obtain

$$y = c \cos x, \qquad \frac{dy}{dx} = y' = -c \sin x. \tag{a}$$

Equate the values of c from the two equations in (a) to get

$$\frac{y}{\cos x} = \frac{-y'}{\sin x}, \qquad \text{or} \qquad \mathbf{y' \cos x + y \sin x = 0.}^* \tag{b}$$

Also, using determinants to eliminate c from (a), we obtain

$$\begin{vmatrix} y & \cos x \\ y' & -\sin x \end{vmatrix} = \mathbf{0.}$$

Example 2. Find the differential equation whose general solution is $y = c_1e^{2x} + c_2e^{-x} + x$.

Solution. The general solution and the first two derived equations are

$$y = c_1e^{2x} + c_2e^{-x} + x, \tag{a}$$

$$\frac{dy}{dx} = y' = 2c_1e^{2x} - c_2e^{-x} + 1, \tag{b}$$

$$\frac{d^2y}{dx^2} = y'' = 4c_1e^{2x} + c_2e^{-x}. \tag{c}$$

Eliminating c_2 from (a) and (b) and then from (b) and (c), we get

$$y' + y = 3c_1e^{2x} + x + 1, \qquad y'' + y' = 6c_1e^{2x} + 1. \tag{d}$$

* Throughout the text, answers to examples appear in boldface type.

Multiplying the first equation of (*d*) by 2, subtracting the result from the second, and simplifying slightly, we get*

$$\mathbf{y'' - y' - 2y = -2x - 1.}$$

Also by determinants we obtain from (*a*), (*b*), and (*c*)

$$\begin{vmatrix} y - x & e^{2x} & e^{-x} \\ y' - 1 & 2e^{2x} & -e^{-x} \\ y'' & 4e^{2x} & e^{-x} \end{vmatrix} = e^{2x}e^{-x} \begin{vmatrix} y - x & 1 & 1 \\ y' - 1 & 2 & -1 \\ y'' & 4 & 1 \end{vmatrix} = 0.$$

Example 3. Find the differential equation of the system of ellipses having their axes along the X-axis and the Y-axis.

Solution. The equation of the system may be written

$$\frac{x^2}{a^2} = 1 - \frac{y^2}{b^2}, \qquad (a)$$

where a and b are arbitrary constants. By two differentiations we obtain from (*a*)

$$\frac{2x}{a^2} = -\frac{2y}{b^2}\,y', \qquad (b)$$

$$\frac{2}{a^2} = -\frac{2yy'' + 2y'^2}{b^2}. \qquad (c)$$

Dividing (*b*) by (*c*) member by member and simplifying, we get

$$\mathbf{x(yy'' + y'^2) = yy'.}$$

EXERCISES

Find the differential equations having as general solutions:

1. $y = x^3 + c$.
2. $y = cx^2$.
3. $y = 3 - cx$.
4. $y = cx + 2c$.
5. $y = ce^x$.
6. $y = cx^2 + cx$.
7. $y = cx + c^2$.
8. $y = c_1x^2 + c_2$.
9. $y = c_1x^2 + c_2x$.
10. $y = c_1e^x + c_2e^{-x}$.
11. $y = c_1 \sin 2x + c_2 \cos 2x$.
12. $y = \sin x + c_1 \sin 2x + c_2 \cos 2x$.
13. $y = c_1x^2 + c_2x + c_3$.
★**14.**† $y = x \sin (x + c)$.

Find the differential equation of each system of curves:

15. All lines through the origin.
16. All circles with centers (0,0).

* Observe that three equations, one given and two derived, were used in eliminating two arbitrary constants and that this led to a second-order differential equation having as solution the given equation in two arbitrary constants. Similarly, for an equation in n arbitrary constants, we would expect to differentiate n times, eliminate the n constants, and thus find an nth-order differential equation having the given equation in n constants as solutions.

† A solid star ★ indicates a difficult problem or a complicated solution.

17. All straight lines.
★**18.** All circles through points (0,0) and (2,0) (see Fig. 3).
★**19.** All circles of radius 1 and centers on line $x = y$ (see Fig. 4).

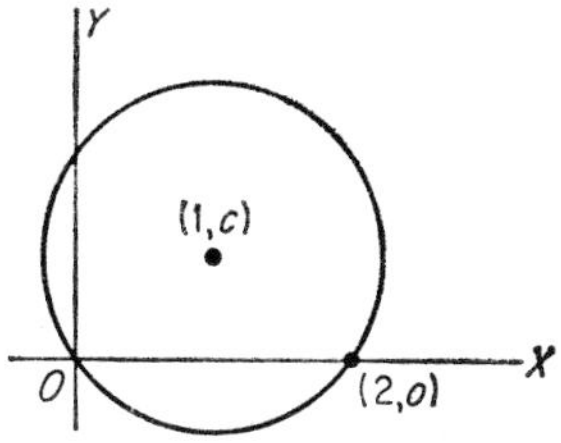

FIG. 3

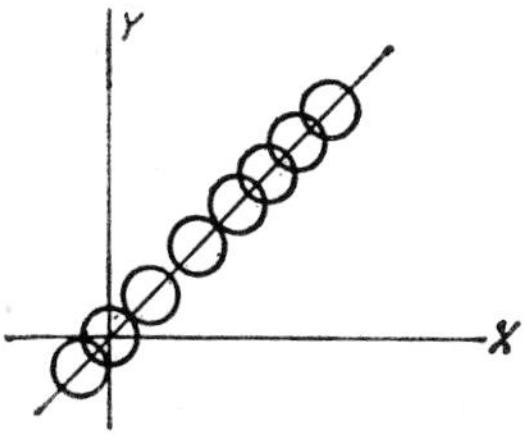

FIG. 4

8. Variables separable

In the differential equation

$$M(x,y) + N(x,y)\frac{dy}{dx} = 0, \tag{20}$$

each part has a definite numerical interpretation. However, for convenience and suggestive quality, (20) is often written in the differential form

$$M(x,y)\,dx + N(x,y)\,dy = 0. \tag{21}$$

The suggestiveness of (21) is exemplified below in (23).

To illustrate the type of problem which calls for the general solution of a given differential equation, we shall consider a type of the first order and first degree, which can easily be reduced to the form

$$f_1(x)\,dx + f_2(y)\,dy = 0, \tag{22}$$

where $f_1(x)$ is a function of x alone and $f_2(y)$ is a function of y alone. This type is referred to as **variables separable.** Direct integration of equation (22) gives the general solution

$$\int f_1(x)\,dx + \int f_2(y)\,dy = c, \tag{23}$$

where c is an arbitrary constant. It is evident that equation (22) would result from differentiating equation (23), even if we should write any function of c instead of c. Hence, we may use $\ln c$, $\tan^{-1} c$, or any other function of c instead of c, in order to obtain the simplest form of a solution.

Example 1. Find the equation of the curves for which

$$xy\,dy - \frac{1 + y^2}{1 + x^2}\,dx = 0. \tag{a}$$

Also, find the solution of (a) having a graph containing point $(1,-3)$.

Solution. Division of (*a*) by $x(1 + y^2)$ gives

$$\frac{y\,dy}{1 + y^2} - \frac{dx}{x(1 + x^2)} = 0. \tag{b}$$

By integration we obtain from (*b*)

$$\int \frac{y\,dy}{1 + y^2} - \int \frac{dx}{x(1 + x^2)} = \text{constant},$$

or

$$\frac{1}{2}\ln(1 + y^2) - \frac{1}{2}\ln\frac{x^2}{1 + x^2} = \frac{1}{2}\ln c. \tag{c}$$

Canceling $\frac{1}{2}$ and using the laws of logarithms, we get

$$\ln\frac{(1 + y^2)(1 + x^2)}{x^2} = \ln c. \tag{d}$$

Two numbers that have the same logarithm are equal. Hence,

$$\frac{(1 + y^2)(1 + x^2)}{x^2} = c, \qquad \text{or} \qquad (\mathbf{1} + \mathbf{y}^2)(\mathbf{1} + \mathbf{x}^2) = \mathbf{cx}^2. \tag{e}$$

To find the equation of the curve through $(1, -3)$, substitute 1 for x and -3 for y in (*e*) to obtain $(1 + 9)(1 + 1) = c(1)^2$, or $c = 20$. Now replace c in (*e*) by 20 to obtain

$$(\mathbf{1} + \mathbf{y}^2)(\mathbf{1} + \mathbf{x}^2) = \mathbf{20x}^2.$$

Example 2. Find the general solution of $a[x(dy/dx) + 2y] = xy(dy/dx)$, and then find a particular solution in which $y = a$ when $x = 2a$.

Solution. Clearing of fractions and grouping the terms containing dx and those containing dy, we get

$$2ay\,dx + (ax - xy)\,dy = 0, \tag{a}$$

or

$$2ay\,dx + x(a - y)\,dy = 0. \tag{b}$$

Dividing through by xy and integrating, we obtain

$$2a\int\frac{dx}{x} + a\int\frac{dy}{y} - \int dy = \text{constant},$$

or

$$2a\ln x + a\ln y - y = a\ln c. \tag{c}$$

Dividing by a, replacing $2\ln x$ by $\ln x^2$, and combining the logarithmic terms, we get

$$\ln\frac{x^2y}{c} = \frac{y}{a}.$$

Remembering that $e^{\ln N} = N$, we obtain

$$e^{\ln x^2y/c} = e^{y/a}, \qquad \text{or} \qquad \mathbf{x}^2\mathbf{y} = \mathbf{c}\mathbf{e}^{y/a}. \tag{d}$$

To find c so that $y = a$ when $x = 2a$, substitute $2a$ for x and a for y in (*d*), and solve for c to obtain

$$4a^3 = ce^{a/a}, \qquad \text{or} \qquad c = 4a^3e^{-1}.$$

Substitute this value of c in (d) to obtain the required particular solution

$$\mathbf{x^2y = 4a^3e^{-1}e^{y/a}}.$$

EXERCISES

Find the general solution of each differential equation:

1. $x\,dx + y\,dy = 0$.
2. $dx + dy = 0$.
3. $x^2\,dx + y^2\,dy = 0$.
4. $x\,dy + y\,dx = 0$.
5. $\rho\,d\theta + \theta\,d\rho = 0$.
6. $2x(1 + y^2)\,dx - y(1 + 2x^2)\,dy = 0$.
7. $\dfrac{d\rho}{d\theta} = \rho$.
8. $x\,dy + y\,dx = 3\,dx$.
9. $x\,dy + \sqrt{1 + y^2}\,dx = 0$.
10. $\dfrac{dS}{dt} = 15 - 16S$.
11. $L\dfrac{di}{dt} + Ri = 0$, L and R constants.
12. $e^x e^y\,dx - e^{-2y}\,dy = 0$.
13. $x\,dy + y\,dx = y^2\,dy$.
14. $x\,dy - y\,dx = x^3\,dy$.
15. $\dfrac{dy}{dx} - 2y = y^2$.
16. $\sqrt{1 - y^2}\,dx = \sqrt{1 - x^2}\,dy$.

Find the particular solution of each differential equation satisfied by the indicated values of the variables:

17. $x\,dy + y\,dx = 0$; $y = \frac{1}{3}$ when $x = -\frac{1}{2}$.
18. $\theta\dfrac{dr}{d\theta} - r = 0$; $\theta = 1$ when $r = 3$.
19. $e^x\,dy + e^y\,dx = 0$; $y = 0$ when $x = 0$.
20. $d\rho = \rho\cot\theta\,d\theta$; $\rho = 2$ when $\theta = \frac{1}{2}\pi$.
21. $2y\,dx + x^2\,dy = -dx$; $y = \frac{7}{2}$ when $x = 1/\ln 2$.
22. $4\,dy + y\,dx = x^2\,dy$; $x = 4$ when $y = -1$.
23. $x^3\,dy + xy\,dx = x^2\,dy + 2y\,dx$; $y = e$ when $x = 2$, where e (= 2.7183 nearly) is the base of natural logarithms.

24. Find y if $\int_a^x y\,dx = k(y^3 - b^3)$. *Hint:* $(d/dx)\int_a^x y\,dx = y$ if y is a continuous function of x. Therefore, equate the derivatives of the members of the given equation to obtain $y\,dx = 3ky^2\,dy$, and note that, when $x = a$, the integral is zero and $y = b$.

Solve problem 24, and then find y in terms of x from:

25. $\int_a^x y\,dx = k(y - b)$.
26. $\int_a^x y\,dx = k(y^2 - b^2)$.
27. $\int_a^x y^2\,dx = k(y - b)$.

9. Review exercises

In the following exercises derivatives with respect to x are denoted by primes.

EXERCISES

Give order and degree of each differential equation:

1. $x(y')^3 + y' = 7xy$.
2. $x^2 + yy' + (y')^{\frac{3}{2}} = 0$.
3. $\sqrt{y'} = 3(y'')^{\frac{2}{3}}$.
4. $y'' = [1 + (y')^2]^{\frac{1}{3}}$.

Prove that each equation is a solution of the differential equation written opposite it:

5. $y = c^2 + cx^{-1}$, $\qquad y + xy' = x^4(y')^2$.
6. $x^2 + y^2 = cx$, $\qquad 2xyy' = y^2 - x^2$.
7. $c(x^2 + y^2 - x^2y^2) = 1$, $\qquad (x - y^2x)\,dx + (1 - x^2)y\,dy = 0$.
8. $e^{\cos x}(1 - \cos y) = c$, $\qquad \sin y\, y' + \sin x \cos y = \sin x$.

Find the differential equations having the following general solutions:

9. $y = cx + c^3$.
10. $y = ce^{5x}$.
11. $y = c_1e^{3x} + c_2e^{-5x}$.
12. $y = x^2 + c_1e^x + c_2e^{-x}$.
13. $(x - c_1)^2 + y^2 = c_2^2$.
14. $(x - c_1)^2 + c_2y = c_3$.

Find the differential equation of each system of curves:

15. All circles with centers on the X-axis and radius 1.
16. All circles with centers on the y-axis.
17. All tangents to $x^2 = 4y$. Also, prove that $x^2 = 4y$ is a solution of your answer. *Hint:* From $x^2 = 4y$, $y' = \frac{1}{2}x$. Hence, the slope of the tangent through $(2c,c^2)$ is c.
18. All normals to $y^2 = x$.

Solve the following differential equations, and determine constants of integration where initial conditions are indicated:

19. $x\,dy - y\,dx = 0$; $y = 5$ when $x = 3$.
20. $2\,dx - 3\,dy = 0$; $y = -4$ when $x = 0$.
21. $2x\,dy + y\,dx = 0$; $x = 3$ when $y = 1$.
22. $2x\,dy + dx = dy$; $x = 3$ when $y = 0$.
23. $(x + 1)\,dy + (y - 1)\,dx = 0$; $y = 3$ when $x = 0$.
24. $(x - 2)\,dx + 2(y + 3)\,dy = 0$.
25. $a(dy/dx) + ay = y - x(dy/dx)$.
26. $x^2\,dy + y^2\,dx = 0$; $y = 1$ when $x = 1$.
27. $(dy/dx) - y = y^2$; $x = \ln \frac{1}{2}$ when $y = 1$.
28. $xy\,dy + (1 + y^2)\,dx = 0$; $y = 4$ when $x = 1$.
29. $3e^x \tan y\,dx + (1 + e^x)\sec^2 y\,dy = 0$; $y = \frac{1}{4}\pi$ when $x = \ln 2$.

Review problem 24, §8, and then find y in terms of x from:

30. $\int_a^x y^2\,dx = k(y^2 - b^2)$.
31. $\int_a^x x^2y\,dx = x^3(y - b)$.

32. $\int_a^x x^6y^2\,dx = x^7(y^2 - b^2)$.

33. (*a*) Solve the differential equation $y' = \sqrt{y}$. (*b*) Write the equation of the isoclines. (*c*) Draw short lines having $\sqrt{y}$ as slopes for a number of points between $x = -4$ and $x = 4$ on each of the isoclines $y = 0$, $y = 1$, $y = 2$, $y = 3$, and $y = 4$. (*d*) Sketch on the graph of part (*c*) curves representing solutions of $y' = \sqrt{y}$ through (0,0), (1,0), (2,0), (−1,0), (−2,0) respectively. (*e*) Why does no solution curve pass below the X-axis?

34. (*a*) Solve the equation $y' = 1/y$. (*b*) Write the equation of the isoclines. (*c*) Draw short lines having $1/y$ as slope for a number of points between $x = -3$ and $x = 3$ on the isoclines $y = \frac{1}{10}$, $y = \pm 1$, $y = \pm 2$, $y = \pm 3$. (*d*) Sketch on the graph of part (*c*) curves representing solutions of $y' = 1/y$ through (1,1), (−1,1), (1,2), (−1,2), (1,0.5), respectively. (*e*) Is $y' = 1/y$ satisfied at any point on the X-axis?

CHAPTER 2

APPLICATIONS

10. Geometric applications using rectangular coordinates

A great number of geometric problems can be solved by using the process of expressing a geometric relation in the form of a differential equation and solving it. Take, for example, the problem of finding the equation of the curve through (3, −4) having at each point (x,y) on it a slope of $2y/x$. Since dy/dx represents the slope of the curve, we have

$$\frac{dy}{dx} = \frac{2y}{x}. \tag{1}$$

Integrating equation (1), obtain

$$\ln y = 2 \ln x + \ln c = \ln cx^2; \tag{2}$$

hence,

$$y = cx^2. \tag{3}$$

Since (3, −4) lies on the curve, substitute 3 for x and −4 for y in (3) to obtain

$$-4 = 9c, \qquad \text{or} \qquad c = \frac{-4}{9}. \tag{4}$$

Therefore, the required equation is

$$y = \frac{-4}{9} x^2,$$

or

$$\mathbf{4x^2 + 9y = 0.} \tag{5}$$

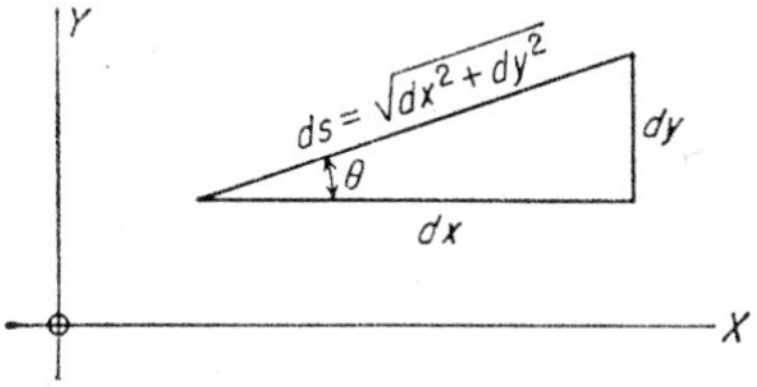

Fig. 1

Some important geometric relations are easily recalled by means of figures. Thus, from Fig. 1 read

$$ds = \sqrt{dx^2 + dy^2} = \sqrt{1 + \left(\frac{dy}{dx}\right)^2}\, dx = \sqrt{1 + \left(\frac{dx}{dy}\right)^2}\, dy, \tag{6}$$

$$\tan \theta = \text{slope} = \frac{dy}{dx}, \qquad \sin \theta = \frac{dy}{ds}, \qquad \cos \theta = \frac{dx}{ds}, \qquad \text{etc.} \tag{7}$$

Example. Find the equation of a curve if the part of each of its tangent lines from the point of contact to the intersection with the X-axis is bisected by the Y-axis.

Solution. To solve a problem of this kind, the student should *first draw a figure representing the curve with any point (x,y) on it and showing the essential relations involved in the problem; then try to find the value of the slope of the required curve or of some expression containing the slope, form an equation, and integrate it.*

Figure 2 relates to the problem under consideration. From it we see that $AO = OD = x$ and that the slope of the tangent at P is $y/2x$. Hence,

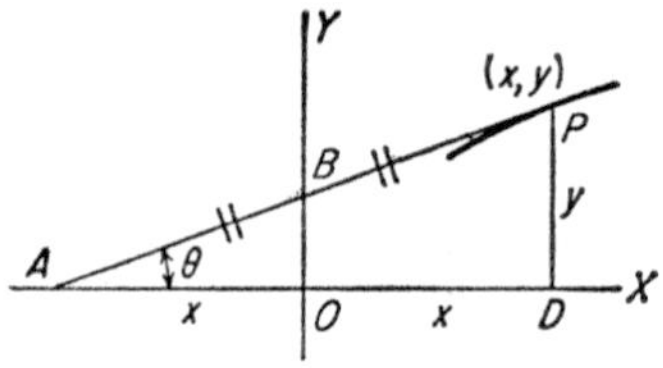

FIG. 2

$$\frac{dy}{dx} = \frac{y}{2x}.$$

The solution of this equation is

$$\mathbf{y^2 = cx.}$$

11. Orthogonal trajectories

A curve C in a plane with a system S of curves is an **orthogonal trajectory** *of S if every point of C is a point where C meets a curve of S at right angles and if every intersection of C with a curve of S is at right angles.* For example, lines parallel to the X-axis are orthogonal trajectories of the system of lines parallel to the Y-axis, and the lines through a point are orthogonal trajectories of the system of circles having that point as center. A system, such as all circles through the origin, may have no orthogonal trajectories.

Example. Find the equation of the orthogonal trajectories of the system of curves

$$y^2 = cx^3. \qquad (a)$$

Also, find the equation of the particular orthogonal trajectory through the point (2,4).

Solution. Differentiating (a) and solving the result for dy/dx, obtain

$$\frac{dy}{dx} = \frac{3x^2c}{2y}. \qquad (b)$$

The slope dy/dx from (b) at (x,y) depends upon c, and therefore upon a curve through (x,y). To get a value depending only on x and y, replace c of (b) by y^2/x^3 from (a). This gives

$$\frac{dy}{dx} = \frac{3x^2}{2y}\frac{y^2}{x^3} = \frac{3y}{2x}. \qquad (c)$$

Now, if a curve is to intersect a member of the system at right angles in (x,y), this curve must have the negative reciprocal, namely, $-2x/3y$, as the slope of its tangent at (x,y). Hence,

$$\left(\frac{dy}{dx}\right)_{\text{orthog traject}} = -\frac{2x}{3y}. \qquad (d)$$

The solution of (d) is

$$2x^2 + 3y^2 = c. \qquad (e)$$

This represents a family of ellipses. To find c for the particular curve

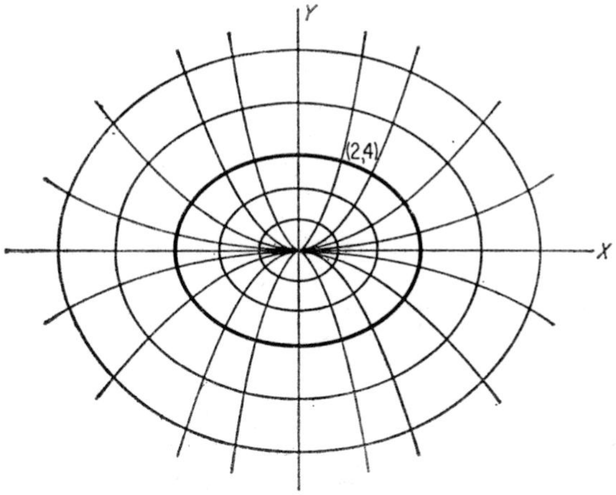

FIG. 3

through (2,4), substitute 2 for x and 4 for y in (e), and obtain $c = 56$. Hence,

$$2x^2 + 3y^2 = 56.$$

A brief consideration of Fig. 3 will serve to clarify essential relations.

EXERCISES

1. Find the equation of the system of curves and the equation of the particular curve that passes through point (3,4) if the slope of the tangent at any point (x,y) is:

(a) $2x - 2$. (b) $\dfrac{1 - x}{1 + y}$. (c) $\dfrac{y - 1}{1 - x}$.

2. Prove that a curve having a constant slope is a straight line.

3. Find an expression $u(x)$ which has a derivative with respect to x that is: (a) equal to $u(x)$; (b) 6 times $u(x)$; (c) 4 less than $u(x)$.

4. Find the orthogonal trajectories of the system of circles $x^2 + y^2 = c$. Sketch two of these circles and any two orthogonal trajectories.

Find the equations of the orthogonal trajectories of the systems of curves numbered 5 to 7:

5. The hyperbolas $y^2 = x^2 + c$. **6.** The parabolas $x^2 = 2cy$.
7. The cubics $x^2 = 4cy^3$.

8. In the solution of the example, the constant c in (b) was replaced by y^2/x^3 to obtain (c). Why was this necessary?

9. Find the most general kind of curve such that the normal at any point of it coincides in direction with the line connecting this point to the origin. Use Fig. 4.

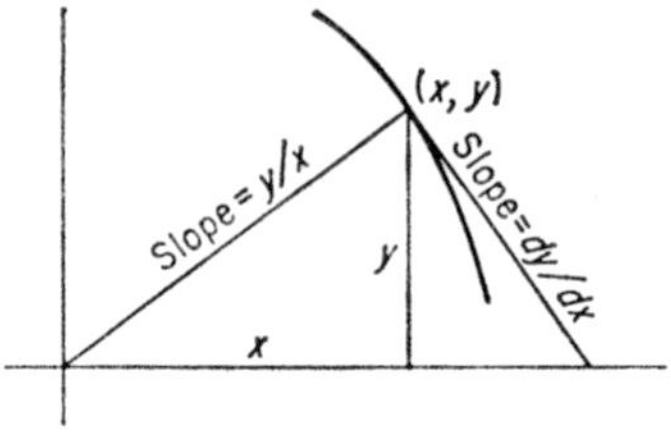

FIG. 4

10. The part of the normal to a curve, at any point (x,y) on the curve, between (x,y) and the point where the normal meets the Y-axis is bisected by the X-axis. Find the equation of the curve.

11. For a certain curve the point of contact of each tangent to it bisects the part of the tangent terminating on the coordinate axes. Find the equation of the curve.

12. Find the equation of the curve so drawn that every point on it is equidistant from the origin and the intersection of the X-axis with the normal to the curve at the point.

13. The area bounded by a curve, the X-axis, a fixed positive ordinate, and a variable ordinate is proportional to the difference between the ordinates. Find the equation of the curve.

14. Figure 5 represents a curve C with $P(x,y)$ any point on it. The tangent and the normal of curve C at P cut the X-axis in A and α and the Y-axis in B and β, respectively. Point $(x,0)$ is E, and θ is the angle that AP makes with the X-axis. Consider all line segments as directed so that $OE = -EO$, $A\alpha = -\alpha A$, etc. Verify that $\tan\theta = dy/dx$, $OE = x$, $E\alpha/y = \tan\theta$, and $E\alpha = y\, dy/dx$. Show that $AE = y\, dx/dy$, $OA = x - y\, dx/dy$, and $O\beta = y + x\, dx/dy$.

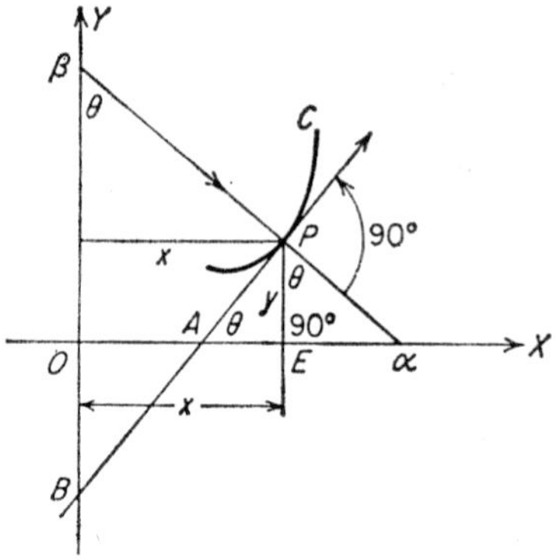

FIG. 5

Read problem 14, and then find the equation of curve C in Fig. 5 if:

15. AE is a constant k.

16. Area of triangle $PE\alpha$ is a constant k.

17. P bisects $\alpha\beta$. Note that $OE = E\alpha$; therefore, $x = y\, dy/dx$.

18. A bisects BP. Note that $OA = AE$.

19. B bisects AP. Note that $AB = BP$; therefore, $-OA = OE$.

20. β is between α and P and is twice as far from α as from P. Note that $\alpha\beta = 2\beta P$, or $2OE = \alpha O = -O\alpha$.

21. B is between A and P and twice as far from P as from A.

22. $AP/PB = 2a$, a constant.

12. Geometric applications using polar coordinates

A basic formula relating to curves in polar coordinates ρ and θ is

$$\tan\psi = \frac{\rho\, d\theta}{d\rho}, \tag{8}$$

where, as indicated in Fig. 6, ψ represents the angle between the tangent to the curve at (ρ,θ) and the radius vector to (ρ,θ). This formula enables us to obtain the equations of many curves having interesting

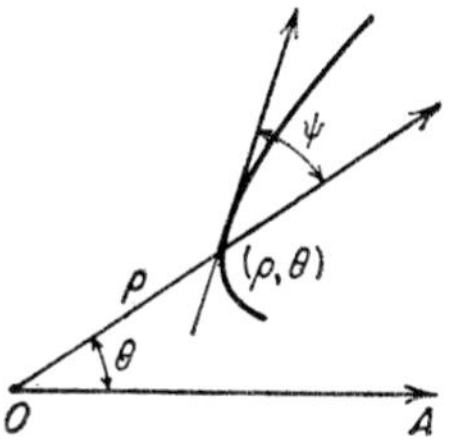

FIG. 6

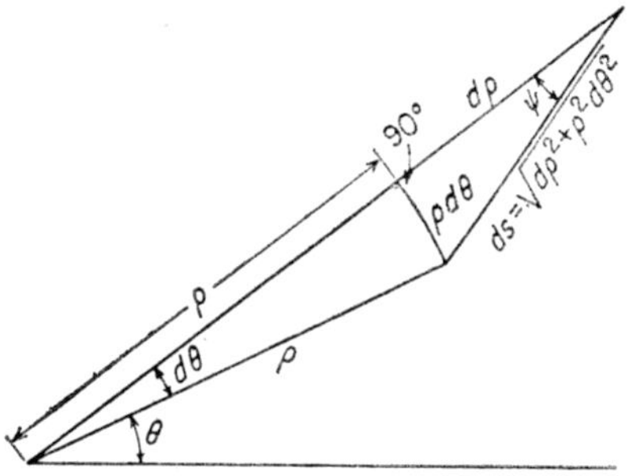

FIG. 7

geometric properties. Figure 7 suggests formula (8) and also the following formulas:

$$ds = \sqrt{d\rho^2 + \rho^2\,d\theta^2} = \sqrt{\left(\frac{d\rho}{d\theta}\right)^2 + \rho^2}\,d\theta, \tag{9}$$

$$\cos\psi = \frac{d\rho}{ds}, \qquad \sin\psi = \frac{\rho\,d\theta}{ds}. \tag{10}$$

Example. Find the equation of the orthogonal trajectories of the circles $\rho = c\cos\theta$.

Solution. If ψ_c represents the angle ψ of formula (8) for the given curve at a point and ψ_0 that for a perpendicular curve through the same point, then

$$\psi_0 = \psi_c \pm 90^\circ,$$
$$\tan\psi_0 = -\cot\psi_c = -\frac{1}{\tan\psi_c}. \tag{11}$$

From (8), for circles $\rho = c\cos\theta$,

$$\tan\psi_c = \frac{\rho\,d\theta}{d\rho} = \frac{\rho}{d\rho/d\theta} = \frac{c\cos\theta}{-c\sin\theta}.$$

Therefore, from (11), $\tan\psi_0 = \sin\theta/\cos\theta$. Hence, using (8) for the orthogonal trajectory, obtain

$$\left(\frac{\rho\,d\theta}{d\rho}\right)_{\text{orthog traject}} = \tan\theta.$$

The solution of this equation is

$$\ln\rho = \ln\sin\theta + \ln c_1,$$

or

$$\rho = c\sin\theta.$$

Figure 8 represents two systems of circles, the original set with centers on the X-axis and the orthogonal trajectories with centers on the Y-axis.

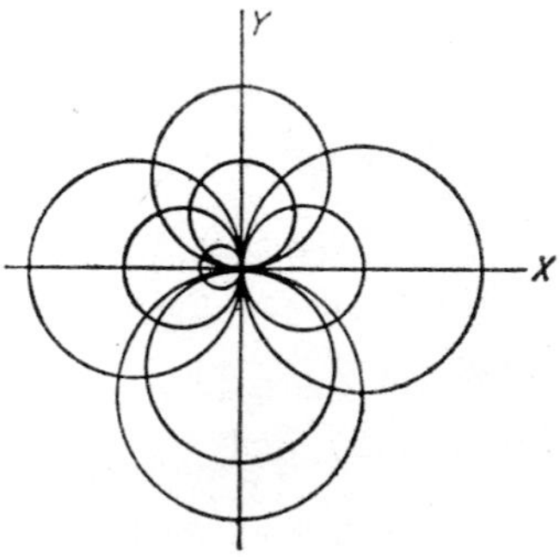

FIG. 8

PROBLEMS

Find the equations of the orthogonal trajectories of the systems of curves defined by the equations numbered 1 to 6:

1. $\rho = c \sin \theta$.
2. $\rho = c(\sin \theta - \cos \theta)$.
3. $\rho = c \sin 2\theta,\ \rho \neq 0$.
4. $\rho = c \cos^2 \theta$.
5. $\rho = c \sin^n \theta$.
6. $\rho = c/(1 + \cos \theta),\ c > 0$.*

7. Find the equation of the curve through point ($\rho = a$, $\theta = 0$) and cutting all lines through the pole at a constant angle α. *Hint:* $\tan \psi = \tan \alpha$.

8. Find the equation of the curve for which the angle between the radius vector to any point on it and the tangent to it at this same point is equal to: (*a*) n times the vectorial angle of the point; (*b*) one-third of the angle between the tangent line and the polar axis. *Hint to* (*b*): Use $\psi = \frac{1}{3}(\psi + \theta)$ and $180° - \psi = \frac{1}{3}(\psi + \theta)$.

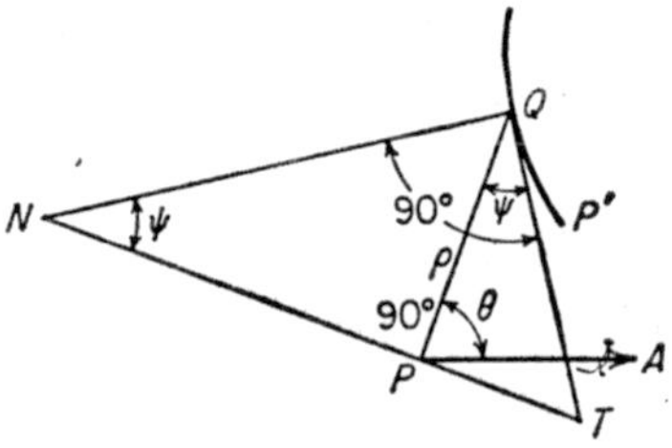

FIG. 9

9. A perpendicular at the pole P to the radius vector of any point Q on a certain curve meets the tangent at Q in point T and the normal at Q in point N (see Fig. 9). Find the equation of the curve: (*a*) if $PN = a$, a constant; (*b*) if $PT = a$.

10.† Find the equation of orthogonal trajectories of

$$\rho = c\theta, \qquad \rho > 0, \qquad 0 < \theta < 2\pi.$$

13. Use of limits

In many cases it is convenient to use limits instead of determining the constant of integration and other constants. Integrating the differential equation

$$f_1(x)\,dx + f_2(y)\,dy = 0, \tag{12}$$

we obtain

$$F_1(x) + F_2(y) = c, \tag{13}$$

where we get $F_1(x)$ and $F_2(y)$ by integrating $f_1(x)\,dx$ and $f_2(y)\,dy$, respectively. Suppose then that (a,b) and (l,m) are pairs of values satisfying (13) for some value of c. Then,

$$F_1(a) + F_2(b) = c,$$
$$F_1(l) + F_2(m) = c.$$
$$F_1(x) - F_1(a) + F_2(y) - F_2(b) = 0, \tag{14}$$
$$F_1(l) - F_1(a) + F_2(m) - F_2(b) = 0. \tag{15}$$

* If c should represent any number, the system would have two curves through every point, one for the positive value of c and one for the negative value, and no system of orthogonal trajectories for it would exist.

† The system of curves $\rho = c\theta$ is rather complex. Let $P(\rho_1, \theta_1 + k2\pi)$, k any integer, represent any fixed point in the plane. Since P satisfies $\rho = [\rho_1/(\theta_1 + k2\pi)]\theta$, k any integer, we see that infinitely many curves of the system $\rho = c\theta$ pass through P. The restrictions of problem 10 specify a part of the general system for which orthogonal trajectories exist.

Equations (14) and (15) may be written in the respective forms

$$\int_a^x f_1(x)\,dx + \int_b^y f_2(y)\,dy = 0, \qquad \int_a^l f_1(x)\,dx + \int_b^m f_2(y)\,dy = 0. \quad (16)$$

For example, given that $5x^4\,dx + k2y\,dy = 0$, $y = 5$ when $x = 0$ and $y = 10$ when $x = 2$, we get, from (16),

$$[x^5]_0^2 + [ky^2]_5^{10} = 0, \qquad [x^5]_0^x + [ky^2]_5^y = 0,$$
$$32 + k75 = 0, \qquad x^5 - \tfrac{32}{75}(y^2 - 25) = 0.$$

In summary, *if* (a,b) *and* (l,m) *represent corresponding value pairs for* x *and* y *of a solution of* (12), *then either form of* (16) *may be used in deducing a desired result.*

EXERCISES

1. If $2x\,dx + 2y\,dy = 0$, use the first equation of (16) to find a nonintegral relation between x and y such that $y = 3$ when $x = 2$.

2. Given $3x^2\,dx + k2y\,dy = 0$, $y = 5$ when $x = 0$ and $y = 3$ when $x = 2$, use the second equation of (16) to find k and then the first to find a nondifferential relation between x and y.

3. Given $y\,dx + k\,dy = 0$, $y = e^2$ when $x = 2$ and $y = e^3$ when $x = 5$, use (16) to find k and a nondifferential equation in x and y.

14. Physical applications

Most situations in nature are so complicated that they cannot be dealt with exactly by mathematics. The regular procedure is to apply mathematics to an ideal situation having only important features of the actual one. The results are approximations having a practical importance which depends upon the closeness of approximation as verified by reasoning and experiment. Consider, for example, the procedure for the flight of a projectile. The forces of gravity and air resistance acting upon a large projectile rotating while moving forward are very complicated. If we assume that gravity is a constant vertical force and neglect both air resistance and rotary motion, a simple solution is easily obtained; but it is practically worthless. If, as a better approximation, we assume that air resistance is proportional to velocity and acts opposite to the direction of motion, and if we get a good factor of proportionality based on experiment, the solution will give a better approximation to the actual motion and may be useful for some purposes. Finally, if a group of mathematicians, physicists, and technicians are supplied with powerful computing machines and a proving ground permitting extensive experimentation, they can get results accurate enough for any practical purpose. They would investigate all forces involved, devise a theory, and then apply methods in the development of which differential equations would play a prominent role.

In this treatment, the laws obtained by observation, experimentation, and reasoning are given. The student is required to express them in mathematical symbols, solve the resulting differential equations, and interpret the solutions.

15. Compound-interest-law problems

Quantities which vary at a rate proportional to their size are said to obey the *compound-interest law,* or *snowball law.* Instances of such quantities are frequent in science. The following example has reference to such a quantity:

Example. Radium decomposes at a rate proportional to the amount present.* If of 100 mg set aside now there will be left 96 mg 100 years hence, find how much will be left t centuries from the time when the radium was set aside, how long a time will elapse before one-tenth of the radium has disappeared, and the amount left after 30.3 centuries.

Solution. Let q be the number of milligrams of radium left after t centuries. Then, since dq/dt is the rate of increase,

$$\frac{dq}{dt} = kq, \qquad \text{or} \qquad \frac{dq}{q} = k\,dt. \tag{a}$$

We have as pairs of corresponding values

q	100	96	90	Q
t	0	1	T	30.3

(b)

From (a) and (b), obtain

$$\int_{100}^{q} \frac{dq}{q} = k\int_0^t dt, \qquad \int_{100}^{96} \frac{dq}{q} = k\int_0^1 dt,$$
$$\int_{100}^{90} \frac{dq}{q} = k\int_0^T dt, \qquad \int_{100}^{Q} \frac{dq}{q} = k\int_0^{30.3} dt. \tag{c}$$

From the first equation of (c), obtain

$$\ln q - \ln 100 = kt, \qquad \text{or} \qquad q = 100e^{kt}. \tag{d}$$

Since $q = 96$ when $t = 1$, obtain, from (d),

$$96 = 100e^k. \tag{e}$$

Replacing e^k in (d) by its value from (e), obtain

$$q = 100(0.96)^t. \tag{f}$$

* Radium does not disintegrate continuously as here indicated; very small particles radiate so that decrease of quantity takes place atom by atom, that is, discontinuously. However, the results obtained by the method of the example are reliable when fairly large amounts of radium are considered. If the method were applied to a single atom of radium, the result would be meaningless.

Now using the Keuffel and Esser log-log duplex slide rule (any log-log slide rule may be used),

Set index of scale C opposite 0.96 on scale LL01.
Opposite 0.9 on LL02, read 2.58 ($= T$) on C.
Opposite 303 on C read 0.290 ($= Q/100$) on LL03.

Hence, T = **2.58 centuries,** Q = **29.0 mg.**

Instead of using the slide rule, we could solve the last three equations of (c), after supplying the logarithms, to obtain

$$k = -0.041, \qquad T = 2.58, \qquad Q = 29.0.$$

PROBLEMS

1. Assume that a body cools according to Newton's law $d\theta/dt = -k\theta$, where t is the time and θ is the difference between the temperature T of the body and that of the surrounding air. Find the temperature T at time t of a boiler of water cooling in air at 0°C if the water was initially boiling at 100°C and the temperature dropped 10° during the first 20 min. Also, find the time for the temperature of the water to drop from 90 to 80°C and the temperature of the water after 90 min.

2. Replace 0°C for the temperature of the air in problem 1 by 20°C, and solve the resulting problem.

3. The half-life of a radioactive substance is the time required for one-half the atoms in a sample to decay. The isotopes U^{238}, U^{235}, and U^{234} of uranium have half-lives of 4.5×10^9 years, 8.8×10^8 years, and 2.7×10^5 years, respectively. Each decays at a rate proportional to the amount present. Find for each a formula expressing the amount left after t years from an initial 1-g amount.

4. In a chemical transformation, substance A changes into another substance at a rate proportional to the amount of A unchanged. If initially there was 40 g of A and 1 hr later 12 g, when will 90 per cent of A be transformed?

5. When the electromotive force (emf) is removed from a circuit containing inductance and resistance but no capacitors, the rate of decrease of current is proportional to the current. If the initial current is 30 amp and it dies down to 11 amp in 0.01 sec, find the current in terms of the time.

6. Assume that the rate of change of air pressure with altitude (distance above the earth) is proportional to the air pressure.* If the air pressure on the ground is 14.7 lb/in.², and if at an altitude of 10,000 ft it is 10.1 lb/in.², find air pressure in terms of altitude, and find the air pressure at an altitude of 15,000 ft.

7. When an amount A of money is invested at r per cent compounded continuously, $dA/dt = \frac{1}{100} rA$. Find the amount of one dollar invested at 6 per cent compounded continuously at the end of: (a) 1 year; (b) 10 years.

8. What time is required for an amount of money compounded continuously at 6 per cent to double itself?

9. A man has a certain sum of money drawing interest at the rate of 6 per cent per year compounded continuously. Assuming that he draws out the money continuously at the rate of 10 dollars per day (3,650 dollars per year) and exhausts the sum in

* The rate of change of pressure depends on air pressure, temperature of the air, and other conditions. Hence, a formula neglecting all conditions except air pressure will give only rough approximations.

20 years, find the original sum. *Hint:* If A is the amount of money at time t years, then $\Delta A = (0.06A - 3{,}650 + \epsilon)\,\Delta t$, where $\epsilon \to 0$ when $\Delta t \to 0$.

10. How much money should a man invest now at 5 per cent per annum compounded continuously so that he can draw out 2,000 dollars per year approximately at a uniform rate and just exhaust his credit at the end of 20 years?

16. Acceleration. Velocity. Distance

If a particle of mass m moves in a straight line with acceleration a under the influence of several applied forces having resultant F, then, in accordance with Newton's laws of motion, we have

$$F = ma = \frac{W}{g}\,a, \tag{17}$$

where F is force in pounds (lb), a is acceleration in feet per second per second (ft/sec²), W is weight in pounds measured by spring balance, and g is the acceleration of gravity in feet per second per second measured at the point on the earth where W is measured. Correspondingly velocity is measured in feet per second (ft/sec). Other units may be used. Thus, in the centimeter-gram-second (cgs) system, $F = ma$, where F is in dynes, m in grams, and a in centimeters per second per second (cm/sec²).

Using the notation t, s, v, and a for *time, distance, velocity*, and *acceleration*, respectively, we have from calculus

$$\mathbf{v} = \frac{\mathbf{ds}}{\mathbf{dt}}, \qquad \mathbf{a} = \frac{\mathbf{dv}}{\mathbf{dt}} = \frac{\mathbf{v\,dv}}{\mathbf{ds}}. \tag{18}$$

Since $g = 32.2$ ft/sec² nearly, we may write (17) in the form

$$\mathbf{F\ (lb)} = \frac{\mathbf{W\ (lb)}}{\mathbf{32.2}}\frac{\mathbf{dv}}{\mathbf{dt}} = \frac{\mathbf{W}}{\mathbf{32.2}}\frac{\mathbf{v\,dv}}{\mathbf{ds}}. \tag{19}$$

Example. A coasting party weighing 1,000 lb coasts down a 5-deg incline. The component of gravitational force parallel to the direction of motion is 1,000 sin 5° lb = 87.2 lb. If the force of friction opposing the motion is 40 lb and the air resistance in pounds is numerically equal to 1.5 times the speed in feet per second,* find an expression for the speed after t sec from rest, the speed after 10 sec from rest, and the limiting speed.

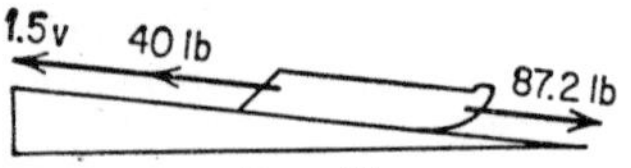

FIG. 10

Solution. If downhill is chosen as the positive direction, we see from Fig. 10 that $F = 87.2 - 40 - 1.5v$. Therefore, the equation of motion

* The problem of finding the resistance of a fluid on a body moving through it is very complicated. It depends on speed, shape of the body, and properties of the fluid. Any such simple expression as $1.5v$ can represent it reasonably well for only a short period of time in most cases.

from (19) is

$$47.2 - 1.5v = \frac{1{,}000}{32.2}\frac{dv}{dt}. \qquad (a)$$

The initial conditions may be written

v	0	v_{10}
t	0	10

(b)

Separating the variables in (a) and integrating, we obtain

$$\int_0^{v_{10}} \frac{-1.5\,dv}{47.2 - 1.5v} = -\int_0^{10} 0.0483\,dt,$$
$$\int_0^{v} \frac{-1.5\,dv}{47.2 - 1.5v} = -0.0483 \int_0^{t} dt. \qquad (c)$$

From the first part of (c),

$$[\ln (47.2 - 1.5v)]_0^{v_{10}} = \ln \frac{47.2 - 1.5v_{10}}{47.2} = -0.483.$$

Then $\dfrac{47.2 - 1.5v_{10}}{47.2} = e^{-0.483} = 0.617,$ and $v_{10} = \mathbf{12.1\ ft/sec.}$ (d)

From the second part of (c),

$$\ln \frac{47.2 - 1.5v}{47.2} = -0.0483t, \quad \text{or} \quad \frac{47.2 - 1.5v}{47.2} = e^{-0.0483t}. \qquad (e)$$

Solving (e) for v, we obtain

$$\mathbf{v = 31.5(1 - e^{-0.0483t})}. \qquad (f)$$

From (f), it appears that, as t increases without limit, $e^{-0.0483t}$ approaches zero as a limit and v approaches **31.5 ft/sec.**

This last result could have been found from the fact that, as v approaches a limiting value, the rate of change of v, or dv/dt, approaches zero. Hence, from equation (a), $47.2 - 1.5v$ approaches zero, and v approaches 31.5 ft/sec.

PROBLEMS

1. A body moves in a straight line with a constant acceleration of $a = 10$ ft/sec². If speed $v = 5$ ft/sec when $t = 0$ sec, replace a in $a = 10$ by dv/dt, and show that $v = 10t + 5$. Also, replace a by $v\,dv/ds$, and show that $v^2 = 25 + 20s$.

2. Using the equation $a = v\,dv/ds$ for rectilinear motion, prove that, if a is constant, $v^2 = v_0^2 + 2as$, where $v = v_0$ when $s = 0$. Also, prove that, if a is constant and $v = v_0$ when $t = 0$, then $v = v_0 + at$.

3. If distance is expressed in feet and time in seconds, then a and $-0.3v^2$ for a certain rectilinear motion are expressed by the same number; that is, $a = -0.3v^2$.* If $v = 20$ ft/sec when $t = 0$, find v in terms of t, and find v when $t = 10$ sec. Also, using $s = 0$ when $v = 20$ ft/sec and $v\, dv/ds$ for a, find v in terms of s.

4. A boat with its load weighs 322 lb (see Fig. 11). If the force exerted upon the boat by the motor in the direction of motion is equivalent to a constant force of 15

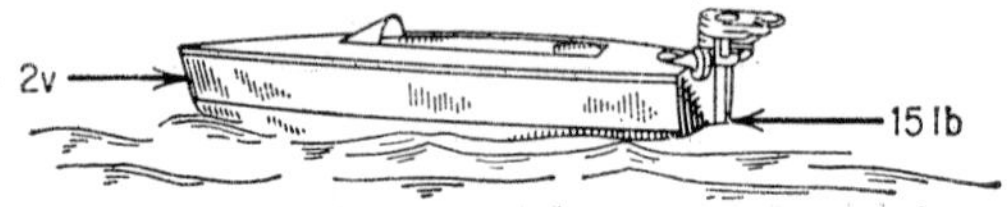

FIG. 11

lb, if the resistance (in pounds) to motion is equal numerically to twice the speed (in feet per second), that is, $2v$ lb, and if the boat starts from rest, find the speed: (*a*) after t sec; (*b*) after 10 sec; (*c*) when $t = \infty$, that is, the limiting speed.

5. Work problem 4 under the assumption that the boat is a scow so built that the resistance in pounds is four times the velocity in feet per second.

6. Figure 12 represents a uniform ball E having the weight and radius of the earth pulling a w-lb body toward it with a force inversely proportional to the square of the distance s from the center of E. By applying Newton's law of motion, we obtain the equation

$$\frac{w}{32.2}\,a = \frac{w}{32.2}\,\frac{v\,dv}{ds} = -\frac{wR^2}{s^2}$$

where $R = 4{,}000 \times 5{,}280$ ft, s is in feet, and t in seconds. Find the velocity attained by the body in falling from rest at a distance of $4R$ from the center of E to its surface. What velocity would correspond to a fall from an infinite distance?

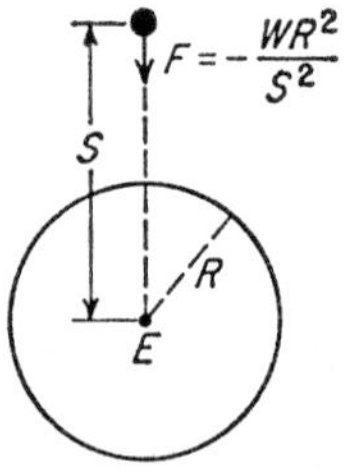

FIG. 12

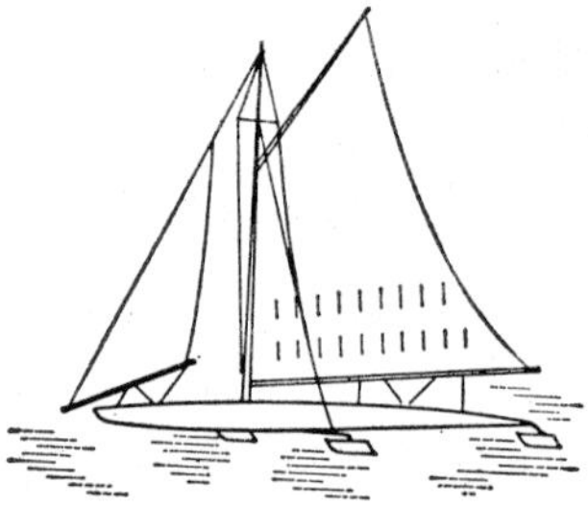

FIG. 13

7. An iceboat (see Fig. 13) with load weighs 322 lb. It is propelled by a force of $2(v_0 - v)$ lb when moving at a speed of v ft/sec in a v_0 ft/sec tail wind. There is a constant resistance to motion of 10 lb. Using (19) find its speed v at time t sec from rest in a 40 ft/sec wind. Also, find distance s in terms of t. Find its speed after 10 sec from rest and the distance covered during the first 10 sec.

★**8.** The traction resistance of a 3,220-lb car is 60 lb, and the air resistance is $0.08v^2$, where v represents speed in feet per second. For convenience, let $(0.08H^2 + 60)$ lb be a constant force applied to the car by means of the engine. Using (19) and assum-

* This equation appears to be incorrect dimensionally; for if L represents distance and T time, a has dimensions LT^{-2} and v^2 the dimensions L^2T^{-2}. To obtain balance, we assign to the constant 0.3 the dimension of L^{-1}. In general, we shall assume that the constants in our equations are such that the equations are dimensionally correct.

ing that $v = 0$ when $t = 0$, show that $\ln [(H + v)/(H - v)] = (H/625)t$. Show that H ft/sec is the limiting speed. Show that the time to change speeds from 44 to 88 ft/sec when $H = 140$ is about 3.69 sec. Derive a formula connecting distance s and velocity v, and use it with $H = 140$ to find the distance covered while the velocity changes from 44 to 88 ft/sec.

★9. A 64.4-lb weight on a spring attached to a ceiling moves up and down under the action of its weight and a restoring force $f = 50s$ lb (see Fig. 14), where s is the number of feet that the spring is stretched. Using the equation $F = ma$, show that $2a = 64.4 - 50s$. If velocity $v = 0$ when $s = 0$, show that v in feet per second is given by $v = \pm\sqrt{64.4s - 25s^2}$. Replace v in the equation by ds/dt, and show that $s = 1.288 + 1.288 \sin(\pm 5t + \frac{3}{2}\pi) = 1.288(1 - \cos 5t)$, provided that $s = 0$ when $t = 0$. Show that s varies from 0 to 2.576 ft and back to zero again periodically, the period being $\frac{2}{5}\pi$ sec.

10. A force that increases uniformly at the rate of 6 lb/sec from a value of 0 lb when $t = 0$ acts on a 32.2-lb body initially at rest. Find v in terms of t, then replace v by ds/dt, and integrate again to find s in terms of t. Also, find s in terms of v.

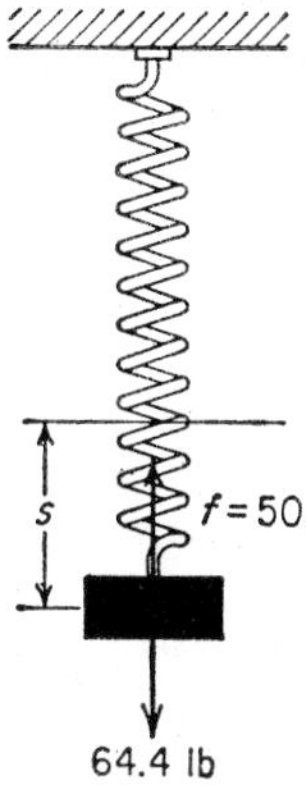

FIG. 14

17. Other rate problems

The idea of rate is basic in a great variety of problems. Three more types will be considered in this section.

Consider the flow of heat through a wall of area A which receives no heat except at its faces. Assume that the temperature T at any point in the wall distant x from a face is a function $T(x)$ of x. Experiment verifies that for such a wall heat flows from points at one temperature to points at lower temperature and that the rate of flow, Q units/sec, is proportional to dT/dx. Hence, we have

$$\mathbf{Q = -kA\, dT/dx,} \tag{20}$$

where k, the *conductivity*, is a constant found by experiment. The values used here for k apply for distance measured in centimeters, area A in square centimeters, T in degrees centigrade, and Q in calories per second.

Consider the heat loss per day through a barn wall made of cement, $k = 0.0022$, 3 m (meters) high, 10 m long, and 25 cm thick if the inner temperature is kept at 10°C and the outer temperature is −10°C. Using (20), we get

$$Q = -0.0022(300)(1{,}000)\, dT/dx. \tag{21}$$

The initial conditions are

T	10°C	−10°C
x	0	25 cm

Using these conditions, we get from (21) $Q = 528$ cal/sec. Hence, the loss per day is

$$528 \times 24 \times 3{,}600 = 46 \times 10^6 \text{ cal.}$$

A second problem relates to the flow of a fluid through an orifice. The velocity of a substance falling through h ft from rest is $\sqrt{2gh}$ ft/sec. When water is forced by its own weight to issue from a small orifice h units below the surface of the water (see Fig. 15), we may think of the water as issuing in a jet of cross-sectional area 0.6 the area of the orifice and velocity $\sqrt{2gh}$ ft/sec. Hence, if Q ft³ is the volume of water in a tank, we get

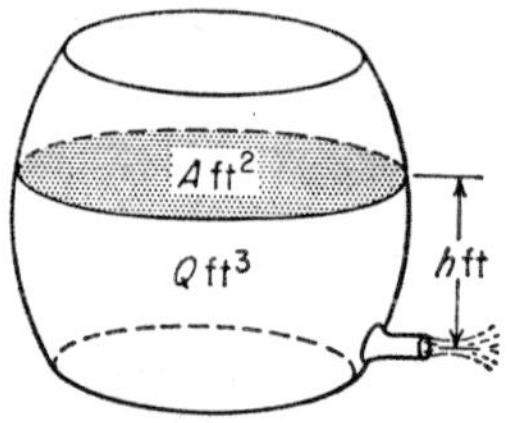

Fig. 15

$$\mathbf{dQ/dt = -0.6b\sqrt{2gh},} \tag{22}$$

where b ft² is the area of the orifice.

To find the time required to empty a cylindrical can, axis vertical, initially full of water, radius $\frac{1}{2}$ ft, height 2 ft, through an orifice $\frac{1}{3}$ in. in diameter in its bottom, apply (22) to obtain

$$d[\pi(\tfrac{1}{2})^2 h]/dt = -0.6\pi(\tfrac{1}{72})^2\sqrt{2(32)h}.$$

The conditions are $h = 2$ when $t = 0$ and $h = 0$ when $t = T$. The solution is $T = 764$ sec nearly, or 12 min 44 sec.

The following example illustrates a third application:

Example. A tank contains initially 100 gal of brine holding 150 lb of dissolved salt in solution. Salt water containing 1 lb of salt per gallon enters the tank at the rate of 2 gal/min, and the brine flows out at the same rate. If the mixture is kept uniform by stirring, find the amount of salt in the tank at the end of 1 hr.

Solution. If Q represents the amount of salt in the tank at the end of t min, we have

$$\frac{\mathbf{dQ}}{\mathbf{dt}} = \textbf{rate of gain} - \textbf{rate of loss.} \tag{23}$$

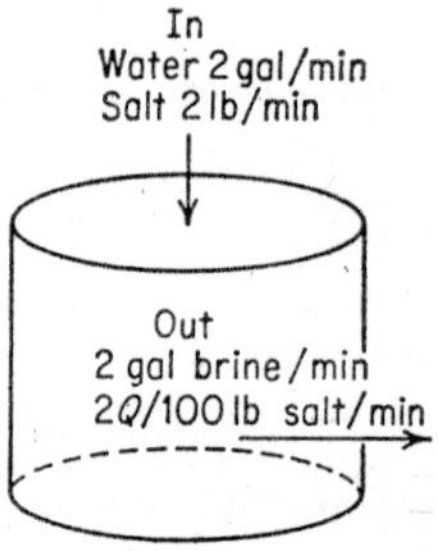

Fig. 16

Evidently the rate of gain is 2 lb/min, and as each gallon of brine in the tank contains $Q/100$ lb of salt, the rate of loss is $2Q/100$ lb/min. Figure 16 indicates the situation. Hence, the equation is

$$\frac{dQ}{dt} = 2 - \frac{2Q}{100}, \quad \text{or} \quad \frac{dQ}{Q - 100} = \frac{-2\,dt}{100}. \tag{a}$$

$\frac{200 - 2Q}{100} = \frac{2}{100}(100 - Q)$

Corresponding values of Q and t are

Q	150	Q_{60}
t	0	60

(b)

Solving equation (a) under conditions (b), we get Q_{60} = **115.1 lb.**

PROBLEMS

1. Use (20) with $k = 0.00023$ to find the number of calories per day passing through the wall of an ice house having area 10^7 cm², thickness 30.5 cm, inside temperature 0°C, and outside temperature 21.1°C.

2. Find the heat lost per hour through 1 m² of furnace wall if the wall is 45.7 cm thick, if k for the masonry is 0.0024, and if the faces of the wall are kept at 1000°C and 120°C, respectively.

3. Use (22) to find the time to empty a cylindrical tank 2 ft in diameter and 3 ft high through a hole 2 in. in diameter in the bottom of the tank. Initially the tank is full of water and its axis is: (a) vertical; (b) horizontal.

4. Use (22) properly modified to find the time required to fill a cubical tank of edge 3 ft if there is a round hole 1 in. in diameter in the bottom of the tank and if water is poured into the tank at π ft³/min.

5. Into a 100-gal tank initially filled with fresh water flows 3 gal/min of salt water containing 2 lb of salt per gallon. The solution, kept uniform by stirring, flows out at the same rate. (a) How many pounds of salt will there be in the tank at the end of 1 hr 40 min? (b) What is the upper limit for the number of pounds of salt in the tank if the process keeps up indefinitely? (c) How much time will elapse while the quantity of salt in the tank is changing from 100 to 150 lb?

6. Into a tank containing 300 lb of salt dissolved in 100 gal of water, pure water is poured at the rate of 3 gal/min, and the solution, kept well stirred, pours out at 2 gal/min. Find the amount of salt in the tank at the end of 1 hr.

7. A 100-gal tank initially filled with fresh water has a mixture of salt and insoluble material in its bottom. If the salt dissolves at a rate per minute equal to one-third of the difference between the concentration (number of pounds of salt per gallon) of the brine and the concentration of a saturated solution (3 lb/gal), and if the concentration is kept uniform by stirring, find the number of pounds of salt dissolved in 1 hr.

8. If a spherical drop of liquid evaporates at a rate proportional to its area, if initially its radius r is $\frac{1}{20}$ in. and in 15 minutes r is $\frac{1}{40}$ in., find r in terms of t.

9. If Q represents the amount of light falling on a sheet of water Δx thick, the amount ΔQ absorbed is given by $\Delta Q = (kQ + E)\,\Delta x$ and $E \to 0$ as $\Delta x \to 0$. If two-thirds of the light falling on a surface is absorbed in penetrating 15 ft of water, what part will be absorbed in penetrating 60 ft of water?

10. A room 30 by 30 by 10 ft contains air at 100°F. A fan blows 900 ft³/min of air at 65°F into the room, and the room air, assumed uniform in temperature, leaves at the same rate. How much time will elapse before the room temperature is 70°F?

11. Air containing 30 per cent oxygen passes slowly into a 3-gal flask initially filled with pure oxygen, and the mixture of air and oxygen, assumed uniform, passes out at the same rate. How much oxygen will the flask contain after 6 gal of air has passed into it?

18. Miscellaneous problems

The following brief outline may be helpful in beginning the solution of a problem based on a differential equation for which the variables are separable (§8).

Geometry:

$$\frac{dy}{dx} = \tan\theta \qquad \text{and Figs. 1, §10, and 5, §11.}$$

$$\frac{\rho\, d\theta}{d\rho} = \tan\psi \qquad \text{and Figs. 6 and 7, §12.}$$

Rate of change of a quantity Q proportional to Q:

$$\frac{dQ}{dt} = kQ, \qquad \text{§15.}$$

Motion caused by forces:

$$F = ma = \frac{w}{g}a, \qquad a = \frac{dv}{dt} = \frac{v\,dv}{ds}, \qquad \text{§16.}$$

Use formulas (20) and (22), §17, for heat loss and flow of liquids through an orifice, respectively.

Rate of change of a quantity Q increasing because of some factors and decreasing because of others:

$$\frac{dQ}{dt} = \text{rate of gain} - \text{rate of loss}, \qquad \text{§17.}$$

PROBLEMS

1. Find the equation of a curve through $(3, -2)$ and having at point (x,y) on it the slope $(y - 1)/(1 - x)$.

Find the equation of the orthogonal trajectories of each system of curves:

2. The quintics $y = cx^5$.
3. The probability curve $y = ce^{-x^2}$.
4. The spirals $\rho = c\theta^2$, $\rho > 0$, $0 < \theta < 2\pi$.

5. The charge of electricity on a body leaks away at a rate proportional to the charge, and half of it leaks away in 10 min. What part of the charge will remain after 50 min?

6. When a gas expands without gain or loss of heat, the rate of change of pressure with volume varies directly as the pressure and inversely as the volume. Find the law connecting pressure and volume in this case.

Find the equations of the curves having the properties 7 to 11:

7. Angle between the radius vector and tangent equals the angle between the radius vector and initial line. *Hint:* Use $\psi = \theta$ and $\psi = 180° - \theta$; therefore,

$$\tan\psi = \pm\tan\theta.$$

8. Perpendicular from the pole to tangent is constant.

9. Tangent is equally inclined to the radius vector and to the initial line. *Hint:* $\theta = 180° - 2\psi$, or $\psi = 90° - \frac{1}{2}\theta$.

10. Radius vector is equally inclined to the normal and to the initial line.

★**11.** Area bounded by the radius vector, the tangent, and the initial line is proportional to ρ^2. *Hint:* To find the intercept of the tangent on the initial line, apply the law of sines to the triangle bounded by the tangent, the radius vector, and the initial line.

12. Find the amount of money accumulated in 3,650 days from a continuous investment at the rate of 10 dollars per day if interest is at $\frac{4}{365}$ per cent per day compounded continuously. *Hint:* If Q dollars is the amount at time t, $dQ/dt = ?$

★**13.** A man invests money approximately continuously at 1,000 dollars per year for 25 years and then draws the money out at the rate of 3,000 dollars per year. If interest is at 5 per cent per annum compounded continuously, approximately how many years will he draw money?

14. A freighter of 42,000 tons displacement (1 ton = 2,000 lb) starts from rest. Assuming that the resistance in pounds to motion is $7{,}000v$, where v is the speed in feet per second, and that the force exerted on the ship by the propellers is 120,000 lb, find (*a*) the speed at any time; (*b*) the limiting speed; (*c*) the time taken to speed up to nine-tenths of the limiting speed.

★**15.** A room 30 by 30 by 10 ft receives 900 ft³/min of fresh air, 0.04 per cent CO_2. If the CO_2 content rises from 0.04 per cent CO_2 to 0.12 per cent CO_2 in $\frac{1}{2}$ hr after the crowd enters the room, what CO_2 content is to be expected 3 hr after the crowd enters? Assume that the crowd breathes CO_2 into the air at a constant rate.

16. A man and a parachute are falling (see Fig. 17) with a speed of 173 ft/sec when the parachute opens and the speed is reduced so as to approach the limiting value of 15 ft/sec by air resistance proportional to the square of the speed. Show that

$$t = \frac{15}{2g} \ln \left[\frac{79}{94} \cdot \left(\frac{v + 15}{v - 15}\right)\right].$$

Hint: When the speed is close to the limiting speed, the velocity is almost constant and the acceleration nearly zero.

17. Assuming that a man weighing w lb falls from rest, that the resistance of the air is proportional to his speed v, and that his limiting speed is 173 ft/sec, find an expression for his speed at any time, and find his speed at the end of the eleventh second.

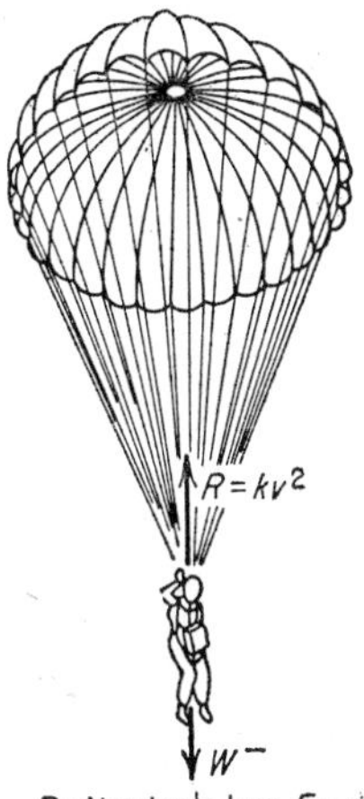

By Newton's law $F = ma$,
$W - kv^2 = \frac{W}{g}\frac{dv}{dt}$

FIG. 17

★**18.** Equation (20), §17, applies to a protected cylindrical hot-water or steam pipe under the conditions of problem 17 if x represents the distance from the axis of the pipe and A the lateral area of a cylinder of radius x and length equal to the length of the pipe considered, that is, if $A = 2\pi xl$.

Two steam pipes of 20 cm diameter, protected with coverings 10 cm thick of concrete ($k = 0.0022$) and magnesia ($k = 0.00017$), respectively, are run underneath the soil. If the outer surfaces are at 30°C and the pipes themselves are at 160°C, compute the losses per hour per meter length of pipe in the two cases. Also, find the heat lost per hour per meter length of pipe from one of those pipes if it is protected with a covering 5 cm thick of magnesia and, over this, a covering of concrete 5 cm thick.

19. A cubical tank of edge 4 ft is full of water which runs out a vertical slit $\frac{1}{8}$ in. wide and extending from the top to the bottom of the tank. If the quantity of water per second issuing from a small part of the slit of area a situated at distance x from the surface of the water is $0.6a\sqrt{2gx}$, find the time for the surface of the water to fall 3 ft. *Hint:* First, find the number of cubic feet per minute of water issuing from the slit when the water is h ft deep.

20. A hemisphere having radius 1 ft and base up is full of water which runs out through a hole 1 in. in diameter in its bottom. How long will it take the water to run out? Use (22), §17, and Fig. 18.

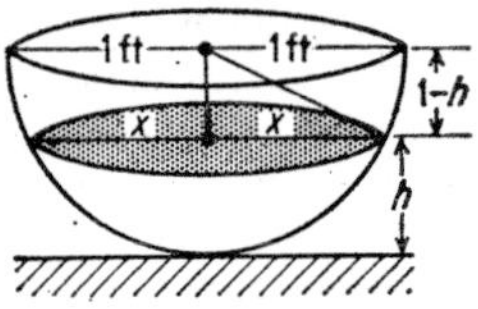

FIG. 18

★21. A tank 10 by 10 by 10 ft contains 500 ft³ of water and 500 ft³ of air at a pressure of 3,000 lb/ft². How long will it take the water to pass out through an orifice of area 1 in.² in the bottom of the tank? Neglect the pressure due to gravity, and assume that the discharge takes place in a vacuum. Use the modification of formula (22), §17, $dQ/dt = -0.6b\sqrt{2gp/\delta}$, where δ represents density (62.5 lb/ft³ for water) and p lb/ft² represents pressure. Assume that $pv = c$, a constant, for air.

★22. A certain uniform rubber band of natural length x in. is stretched kxF in. by a force of F lb. How much will l in. of the string stretch under its own weight of w lb when suspended from one end?

CHAPTER 3

DIFFERENTIAL EQUATIONS OF THE FIRST ORDER AND THE FIRST DEGREE

19. Simple substitutions

Many problems may be reduced to the case of *variables separable* by simple substitutions. Thus, to solve

$$(x + y - 3)\,dx + (x + y + 4)\,dy = 0, \tag{a}$$

let us try the substitution

$$z = x + y. \tag{b}$$

Then,

$$dz = dx + dy. \tag{c}$$

The next step is to eliminate either y or x from (a) by using (b) and (c). From (b), $y = z - x$; and from (c), $dy = dz - dx$. Substituting these values in (a), we obtain

$$(z - 3)\,dx + (z + 4)(dz - dx) = 0,$$

or

$$-7\,dx + (z + 4)\,dz = 0.$$

Here the variables are separated, and, solving, we find

$$14x - z^2 - 8z = -c.$$

Replacing z by its equal $x + y$, we find

$$14x - (x + y)^2 - 8(x + y) = -c,$$

or

$$\mathbf{x^2 + 2xy + y^2 - 6x + 8y = c.}$$

If the form of an equation indicates that two expressions play a prominent role, it may be well to introduce two new variables. Thus, in considering the equation

$$x(x + y)(dx + dy) = \frac{y}{x}(x\,dy - y\,dx), \tag{d}$$

we note that $x + y$ and y/x stand out. This suggests the substitution

$$z = x + y, \qquad w = \frac{y}{x}. \tag{e}$$

Taking differentials of equations (*e*), and also solving (*e*) for x in terms of z and w, obtain

$$dz = dx + dy, \qquad dw = \frac{x\,dy - y\,dx}{x^2}, \qquad x = \frac{z}{1+w}. \tag{f}$$

Substituting from (*e*) and (*f*) in (*d*), obtain

$$zx\,dz = x^2 w\,dw,$$

and from this

$$z\,dz = \frac{zw\,dw}{1+w}. \tag{g}$$

The solution of (*g*) is

$$z = w - \ln(1+w) + c. \tag{h}$$

Replacing w and z in (*h*) by their values from (*e*), obtain

$$x + y = \frac{y}{x} - \ln\left(1 + \frac{y}{x}\right) + c. \tag{i}$$

To solve a differential equation by substitution: (*a*) *write the substitution equations;* (*b*) *differentiate the substitution equations;* (*c*) *eliminate all but two of the unknowns from the given differential equation and the results of* (*a*) *and* (*b*); (*d*) *solve the result from* (*c*); (*e*) *replace the new variables in terms of the old in the result of* (*d*).

No general rule for finding effective substitution equations can be given; however, the form of the differential equation may be suggestive. Any outstanding expression may be made the basis of a substitution. Occasionally, substitutions effective for certain types will be given.

EXERCISES

Solve the following differential equations, and determine the constants of integration when initial conditions are given:

1. $2(x - y)\,dx + dy = 0$; let $z = x - y$.
2. $2\,dx + (2x + 3y)\,dy = 0$.
3. $(x + y)\,dx + (x + y - 2)\,dy = 0$; let $z = x + y$.
4. $(2x + y + 6)\,dx + (2x + y)\,dy = 0$.
5. $(x - 2y + 5)\,dx - [2(x - 2y) + 9]\,dy = 0$.
6. $(2x + y)^2\,dx - 2\,dy = 0$.
7. $xy(x\,dy + y\,dx) = 6y^3\,dy$; let $z = xy$; when $y = 1$, $x = 2$.
8. $x^2(x\,dx + y\,dy) = (x^2 + y^2)^2\,dx$; let $z = x^2 + y^2$; when $x = 1$, $y = 2$.
9. $(st + 1)t\,ds + (2st - 1)s\,dt = 0$; let $z = st$.
10. $(x^2 + y^2)\,dx + 2xy\,dy = 0$; let $y = vx$; when $x = 2$, $y = 1$.
11. $(x^3 + y^3)\,dx + 3xy^2\,dy = 0$; let $y = vx$; when $x = 1$, $y = 1$.
12. $3\theta \dfrac{d\rho}{d\theta} + 3\rho = \rho^4\theta^4 e^\theta$; let $z = \rho\theta$.
13. $dx + dy = (x + y)(1 + y/x)^2(x\,dy - y\,dx)$; let $z = x + y$, $w = y/x$.
14. $(x^2 + y^2)(x\,dy + y\,dx) - xy(x\,dx + y\,dy) = 0$; let $z = x^2 + y^2$, $w = xy$.

20. Homogeneous equations

A homogeneous expression of the nth degree in x and y is an expression such that, if x and y are replaced by tx and ty, the result will be the original expression multiplied by t^n, or, analytically expressed,

$$\mathbf{f(tx,ty) = t^n f(x,y).} \tag{1}$$

Thus $x^2 + y^2$ is homogeneous in x and y, for $(tx)^2 + (ty)^2 = t^2(x^2 + y^2)$. In fact, *any polynomial all terms of which are of the same degree in x and y is homogeneous.* For example, $ax^2 + bxy + cy^2$ is homogeneous in x and y, since $a(tx)^2 + b(tx)(ty) + c(ty)^2 = t^2(ax^2 + bxy + cy^2)$.

Note that any function of y/x is homogeneous of degree 0; for evidently

$$\varphi\left(\frac{ty}{tx}\right) = t^0\varphi\left(\frac{y}{x}\right). \tag{2}$$

For example, $(y/x)^2 + \ln(3y/x)$ is homogeneous, as may be seen by applying (1).

A useful relation is obtained by letting $t = 1/x$ in the definition expressed by (1). This gives for a homogeneous expression of the nth degree

$$\begin{aligned} \frac{1}{x^n} f(x,y) &= f\left(\frac{x}{x}, \frac{y}{x}\right) = \varphi\left(\frac{y}{x}\right), \\ f(x,y) &= x^n f\left(1, \frac{y}{x}\right) = x^n\varphi\left(\frac{y}{x}\right). \end{aligned} \tag{3}$$

A differential equation

$$M\,dx + N\,dy = 0 \tag{4}$$

is homogeneous in x **and** y *if M and N are homogeneous functions of the same degree in x and y.*

Since, in accord with (2), y/x plays an important role in a homogeneous expression, we would expect that the substitution $y/x = v$, or

$$\mathbf{y = vx, \qquad dy = v\,dx + x\,dv,} \tag{5}$$

might be effective in solving a homogeneous equation. We shall prove that *the substitution* (5) *in a homogeneous equation of the first order and first degree leads to an equation of the type variables separable.* Let n be the degree of the homogeneous differential equation (4), and write, in accordance with (3),

$$M\,dx + N\,dy = x^n\varphi_1\left(\frac{y}{x}\right)dx + x^n\varphi_2\left(\frac{y}{x}\right)dy = 0. \tag{6}$$

Now make the substitution (5) in (6) to get

$$x^n\varphi_1(v)\,dx + x^n\varphi_2(v)(v\,dx + x\,dv) = 0. \tag{7}$$

Dividing (7) by x^n and collecting the terms involving dx and those involving dv, we have

$$[\varphi_1(v) + v\varphi_2(v)]\,dx + x\varphi_2(v)\,dv = 0,$$

or

$$\frac{dx}{x} + \frac{\varphi_2(v)\,dv}{\varphi_1(v) + v\varphi_2(v)} = 0, \tag{8}$$

and the variables are separated.

The substitution

$$\mathbf{x = vy, \qquad dx = v\,dy + y\,dv} \tag{9}$$

may be used in place of (5). In solving $M\,dx + N\,dy = 0$, an advantage is sometimes gained by using (5) when N is simpler than M and (9) when M is simpler than N.

Example. Solve $(x^2 + y^2)\,dx - 2xy\,dy = 0$.

Solution. Since the equation is homogeneous, write

$$y = vx, \qquad dy = v\,dx + x\,dv.$$

Substituting these values for y and dy in the given equation, we get

$$(x^2 + v^2x^2)\,dx - 2vx^2(v\,dx + x\,dv) = 0.$$

Collecting coefficients of dx and dv, we obtain

$$(x^2 + v^2x^2 - 2v^2x^2)\,dx - 2vx^3\,dv = 0,$$

or

$$x^2(1 - v^2)\,dx - 2vx^3\,dv = 0.$$

Division by $x^3(1 - v^2)$ gives

$$\frac{dx}{x} - \frac{2v\,dv}{1 - v^2} = 0.$$

Integrating this, we obtain

$$\ln x + \ln(1 - v^2) = \ln c, \qquad \text{or} \qquad x(1 - v^2) = c.$$

Replacing v by its equal y/x, we have

$$x\left(1 - \frac{y^2}{x^2}\right) = c, \qquad \text{or} \qquad \mathbf{x^2 - y^2 = cx.}$$

EXERCISES

1. Show that each expression is homogeneous:

(a) $8x^2 + 8xy - 10y^2$.

(b) $x^3 + y^3 - 3x^2y$.

(c) $x^n + 3x^{n-k}y^k + y^n$.

(d) $x^2 \sin\frac{y}{x} + y^2 \cos\frac{y}{x} + xy \ln\frac{x + y}{x - y}$.

Solve the following differential equations, and determine constants of integration when initial conditions are given:

2. $(2x - 3y)\,dx - (2y + 3x)\,dy = 0.$ **3.** $(3x + 2y)\,dx + 2x\,dy = 0.$

4. $y\,dx + (2x + 3y)\,dy = 0.$ **5.** $(6x^2 - 7y^2)\,dx - 14xy\,dy = 0.$

6. $(3\theta + 2\rho)\,d\theta + (2\theta - 4\rho)\,d\rho = 0.$

7. $xy^2\,dy - (x^3 + y^3)\,dx = 0$; $y = 0$ when $x = 1$.

8. $(2xy + y^2)\,dx - 2x^2\,dy = 0$; $y = e$ when $x = e$.

9. $y(x^2 + xy - 2y^2)\,dx + x(3y^2 - xy - x^2)\,dy = 0.$

10. $x\,dy - y\,dx = \sqrt{x^2 + y^2}\,dx.$ **11.** $\left(x + y \sin \frac{y}{x}\right) dx - x \sin \frac{y}{x}\,dy = 0.$

12. Show that a straight line through the origin intersects at a constant angle all integral curves of a homogeneous differential equation.

13. Find the orthogonal trajectories of the circles $x^2 + y^2 + 2cx = 0$.

14. Show that an equation of the type $\varphi(y)\,dy + x^n\varphi(x/y)(x\,dy - y\,dx) = 0$ can be transformed by the substitution $x = vy$ to one of the type *variables separable.*

21. Equations of the form $(ax + by + c)\,dx + (\alpha x + \beta y + \gamma)\,dy = 0$

To solve this type of equation, make the substitution

$$x = x' + h, \qquad y = y' + k, \qquad dx = dx', \qquad dy = dy', \tag{10}$$

to obtain

$$(ax' + by' + ah + bk + c)\,dx' + (\alpha x' + \beta y' + \alpha h + \beta k + \gamma)\,dy' = 0. \tag{11}$$

If we now choose h and k so that

$$ah + bk + c = 0, \qquad \alpha h + \beta k + \gamma = 0, \tag{12}$$

equation (11) in x' and y' becomes homogeneous. We then apply the method for solving homogeneous equations and replace, in the resulting solution, the new variables in terms of the old.

The method just described breaks down if $a/b = \alpha/\beta$. In this case, the substitution $z = ax + by$, or $z = \alpha x + \beta y$, will give rise to an equation in which the variables are separable.

Example. Solve $(2x - 3y + 4)\,dx + (3x - 2y + 1)\,dy = 0$.

Solution. Substituting $x = x' + h$, $y = y' + k$ in the given equation, we obtain

$$(2x' - 3y' + 2h - 3k + 4)\,dx' + (3x' - 2y' + 3h - 2k + 1)\,dy' = 0. \tag{a}$$

Let $2h - 3k + 4 = 0$ and $3h - 2k + 1 = 0$. Then $h = 1$ and $k = 2$, and equation (a) reduces to

$$(2x' - 3y')\,dx' + (3x' - 2y')\,dy' = 0. \tag{b}$$

Solving this homogeneous equation and simplifying, we get

$$(y' + x')^5 = c(y' - x'). \tag{c}$$

Since $x = x' + h = x' + 1$, $y = y' + k = y' + 2$, we have

$$x' = x - 1, \qquad y' = y - 2. \tag{d}$$

Substituting the values of x' and y' from (*d*) in (*c*), we obtain

$$\mathbf{(x + y - 3)^5 = c(y - x - 1).}$$

EXERCISES

Solve the following differential equations:

1. $(x - 2y + 4)\,dx + (2x - y + 2)\,dy = 0.$
2. $(2x + 3y - 1)\,dx - 4(x + 1)\,dy = 0.$
3. $(2x + 3y)\,dx + (y + 2)\,dy = 0.$
4. $(2x + y)\,dx - (4x + 2y - 1)\,dy = 0.$ *Hint:* Let $z = 2x + y$.
5. $(2x - 3y + 2)\,dx + 3(4x - 6y - 1)\,dy = 0.$
6. $(4x + 3y - 7)\,dx + (3x - 7y + 4)\,dy = 0.$
7. $(2x - 2y)\,dx + (y - 1)\,dy = 0.$

22. Exact differentials

The formula for the total differential of a function $f(x,y)$ is

$$df(x,y) = \frac{\partial f}{\partial x}\,dx + \frac{\partial f}{\partial y}\,dy. \tag{13}$$

The right member of (13) *is called an* **exact differential,** *the right member equated to zero is called an* **exact differential equation,** *and* $f(x,y)$ *is called an* **integral** *of the exact differential and, also, of the exact differential equation.* For example,

$$d(x^2 + 8x^2y - 10y^3) = (2x + 16xy)\,dx + (8x^2 - 30y^2)\,dy \tag{14}$$

is an exact differential,

$$(2x + 16xy)\,dx + (8x^2 - 30y^2)\,dy = 0 \tag{15}$$

is an exact differential equation, and $x^2 + 8x^2y - 10y^3 + c$ is an integral of (14).

Example. Find an integral of the exact differential

$$(6xy^2 - 3x^2)\,dx + (6x^2y + 3y^2 - 7)\,dy. \tag{a}$$

Solution. Let $f(x,y)$ be the required integral. Then comparison of (*a*) and (13) shows that

$$\frac{\partial f}{\partial x} = 6xy^2 - 3x^2, \qquad \frac{\partial f}{\partial y} = 6x^2y + 3y^2 - 7. \tag{b}$$

Integrating the first expression with respect to x (treating y as constant) and the second with respect to y, and equating the two values of f thus obtained, we get

$$f(x,y) = 3x^2y^2 - x^3 + \varphi(y) = 3x^2y^2 + y^3 - 7y + \psi(x), \qquad (c)$$

where $\varphi(y)$ and $\psi(x)$ are to be found. Inspection of (c) shows that we must have

$$\varphi(y) = y^3 - 7y + g, \qquad \psi(x) = -x^3 + g, \qquad (d)$$

where g is a constant. Hence,

$$\mathbf{f(x,y) = 3x^2y^2 - x^3 + y^3 - 7y + g.} \qquad (e)$$

EXERCISES

Find the total differential of each expression:

1. $x^2 + y^2$.
2. y/x.
3. $\ln (x^3y^3)$.
4. x^4y^5.
5. x^my^n.
6. $\tan^{-1} (y/x)$.
7. ye^{mx}.
8. $y^{-n}e^{mx}$.

Form an exact differential equation from each expression by equating its total derivative to zero:

9. $x^3y - 3y^2$.
10. y^2e^{ax}.
11. y^3/x^3.

12. If M represents the coefficient of dx and N that of dy in each of the answers to problems 9 to 11, show that $\partial M/\partial y = \partial N/\partial x$ in each case.

Using the method of the example, find an integral of each of the following exact differentials:

13. $(2xy + 4x + 3)\, dx + (x^2 + 2y - 5)\, dy$.
14. $(2x - y + 2)\, dx - (x - 1/y)\, dy$.
15. $(1/x)\, dy - (y/x^2)\, dx$.
16. $(\sin x + y)\, dx + (x - 2 \cos y)\, dy$.
17. $[(1/y^2) - y/x^2]\, dx + [(1/x) - (2x/y^3) - 2]\, dy$.
18. $x^{-3}y^{-2}\, dx + (x^{-2}y^{-3} + 2y)\, dy$.
19. Show that, if $u(x,y)$ and $v(x,y)$ are two integrals of $M(x,y)\, dx + N(x,y)\, dy$, then $u - v = c$, a constant. *Hint:* Show that $du - dv = 0$.

23. Exact differential equations

Assume in §§23 to 25 that the discussion applies to a rectangular region R defined by such inequalities as $|x - p| \leqq a$, $|y - q| \leqq b$, $a > 0$, $b > 0$ and that M, N, $\partial M/\partial x$, $\partial M/\partial y$, $\partial N/\partial x$, and $\partial N/\partial y$ are single-valued and continuous in the region R.

From (13), §22, it appears that an equation

$$M(x,y)\, dx + N(x,y)\, dy = 0 \qquad (16)$$

is exact if there exists a function $f(x,y)$ such that

$$M = \frac{\partial f}{\partial x}, \qquad N = \frac{\partial f}{\partial y}. \qquad (17)$$

From (17), we get

$$\frac{\partial M}{\partial y} = \frac{\partial^2 f}{\partial y\, \partial x}, \qquad \frac{\partial N}{\partial x} = \frac{\partial^2 f}{\partial x\, \partial y}. \tag{18}$$

Since $\partial^2 f/\partial x\, \partial y = \partial^2 f/\partial y\, \partial x$, we get from (18)

$$\boldsymbol{\frac{\partial M}{\partial y} = \frac{\partial N}{\partial x}.} \tag{19}$$

Hence, *if* (16) *is an exact differential equation,* (19) *holds.*

Conversely if (19) *holds,* (16) *is an exact differential equation.* To prove this, we shall show that, if (19) holds, and if fixed point (a,b) and any point (x,y) are in the region R, then (17) is satisfied by

$$f(x,y) = \int_a^x M(x,y)\, dx + \int_b^y N(a,y)\, dy, \tag{20}$$

where y in the first integral of (20) is considered as constant for the integration. We know from calculus that, for any function $\varphi(x,c)$ fulfilling the conditions assumed for M and N,

$$\frac{\partial}{\partial x}\int_a^x \varphi(x,c)\, dx = \varphi(x,c), \qquad \frac{\partial}{\partial c}\int_a^x \varphi(x,c)\, dx = \int_a^x \frac{\partial \varphi(x,c)}{\partial c}\, dx. \tag{21}$$

Therefore, from (19), (20), and (21) we get

$$\frac{\partial f}{\partial x} = M(x,y) + \frac{\partial}{\partial x}\int_b^y N(a,y)\, dy = M(x,y),$$

$$\frac{\partial f}{\partial y} = \int_a^x \frac{\partial M(x,y)}{\partial y}\, dx + \frac{\partial}{\partial y}\int_b^y N(a,y)\, dy = \int_a^x \frac{\partial N(x,y)}{\partial x}\, dx + N(a,y)$$

$$= N(x,y) - N(a,y) + N(a,y) = N(x,y).$$

This completes the proof.

By a similar proof we can show that, when (19) holds, $dF(x,y) = M\, dx + N\, dy$, where

$$F(x,y) = \int_b^y N(x,y)\, dy + \int_a^x N(x,b)\, dx, \tag{22}$$

where x is considered as constant in the first integral.

We now see that, when (19) holds, $f(x,y)$ from (20) satisfies (17) and, accordingly, that

$$\mathbf{f(x,y)} = \int_a^x \mathbf{M(x,y)\, dx} + \int_b^y \mathbf{N(a,y)\, dy = c} \tag{23}$$

satisfies (16) since $d[f(x,y)] = dc = 0$ from (23).

To solve a differential equation $M\, dx + N\, dy = 0$, for which $\partial M/\partial y = \partial N/\partial x$, substitute in (23). Note that *any particular numbers for a and b, provided that (a,b) is inside R, may be used and additive constants arising in the integration may be discarded.*

If M and N are polynomials for which $\partial M/\partial y = \partial N/\partial x$, use $a = 0$, $b = 0$, since polynomials and their derivatives are continuous everywhere and R may be considered as the whole plane.

Example 1. Solve $(6x^2 + 4xy + y^2)\,dx + (2x^2 + 2xy - 3y^2)\,dy = 0$.

Solution. Here $M = 6x^2 + 4xy + y^2$, and $N = 2x^2 + 2xy - 3y^2$, and we get

$$\frac{\partial M}{\partial y} = \frac{\partial N}{\partial x} = 4x + 2y.$$

Now, using (23) with $a = 0$, $b = 0$, we get

$$\int_0^x (6x^2 + 4xy + y^2)\,dx + \int_0^y [2(0)^2 + 2(0)y - 3y^2]\,dy = c,$$
$$\mathbf{2x^3 + 2x^2y + y^2x - y^3 = c.}$$

Example 2. Solve $(3x^2 + 2y \sin 2x)\,dx + (2 \sin^2 x + 3y^2)\,dy = 0$.

Solution. Here we have $M = 3x^2 + 2y \sin 2x$, $N = 2 \sin^2 x + 3y^2$, and $\partial M/\partial y = \partial N/\partial x = 2 \sin 2x$. Also, M and N are continuous everywhere. Therefore, use (23) with $a = 0$, $b = 0$, to get

$$\int_0^x (3x^2 + 2y \sin 2x)\,dx + \int_0^y (2 \cdot 0^2 + 3y^2)\,dy = 0,$$
$$x^3 - y \cos 2x - (0^3 - y \cos 0) + y^3 = c,$$
$$\mathbf{x^3 - y \cos 2x + y + y^3 = c.}$$

Example 3. Solve $(3x^2 + 2y/x)\,dx + (2 \ln 3x + 3/y)\,dy = 0$.

Solution. Here R may be taken as any one of the four quadrants exclusive of the coordinate axes. In R, $\partial M/\partial y = \partial N/\partial x = 2/x$. Taking $a = 1$, $b = 1$ in (23), we get as the required solution

$$\int_1^x (3x^2 + 2y/x)\,dx + \int_1^y (2 \ln 3 + 3/y)\,dy = c,$$
$$x^3 + 2y \ln |x| + 2y \ln 3 + 3 \ln |y| = c_1,$$
$$\mathbf{x^3 + 2y \ln |3x| + 3 \ln |y| = c.}$$

EXERCISES

Test the differential equations numbered 1 to 19 for exactness by using (19), and solve:

1. $(4x - 2y + 5)\,dx + (2y - 2x)\,dy = 0$.
2. $(3x^2 + 3xy^2)\,dx + (3x^2y - 3y^2 + 2y)\,dy = 0$.
3. $(a^2 - 2xy - y^2)\,dx - (x + y)^2\,dy = 0$.
4. $(2ax + by + g)\,dx + (2ey + bx + h)\,dy = 0$.
5. $\dfrac{1}{y}\,dx - \dfrac{x}{y^2}\,dy = 0$.
6. $\dfrac{y\,dx - x\,dy}{x^2} = 0$.
7. $\dfrac{y}{x}\,dy - \left(\dfrac{y^2}{2x^2} + x\right)dx = 0$.
8. $(x - 1)^{-1}y\,dx + [\ln (2x - 2) + 1/y]\,dy = 0$.
9. $(x + 3)^{-1} \cos y\,dx - \left[\sin y \ln (5x + 15) - \dfrac{1}{y}\right] dy = 0$.

10. $\rho^2 \sec 2\theta \tan 2\theta \, d\theta + \rho(\sec 2\theta + 2) \, d\rho = 0.$

11. $(\sin 2\theta - 2\rho \cos 2\theta) \, d\rho + (2\rho \cos 2\theta + 2\rho^2 \sin 2\theta) \, d\theta = 0.$

12. $(2x/y) \, dy + (2 \ln 5y + 1/x) \, dx = 0.$ 13. $e^{2x}(dy + 2y \, dx) = x^2 \, dx.$

14. $e^{x^2}(dy + 2xy \, dx) = 3x^2 \, dx.$ 15. $\dfrac{x \, dy - y \, dx}{y^2} = x^3 \, dx.$

16. $\dfrac{dx}{\sqrt{x^2 + y^2}} + \left(\dfrac{1}{y} - \dfrac{x}{y\sqrt{x^2 + y^2}}\right) dy = 0.$

17. $\dfrac{y^2 - 2x^2}{xy^2 - x^3} \, dx + \dfrac{2y^2 - x^2}{y^3 - x^2y} \, dy = 0.$ 18. $y^3 \sin 2x \, dx - 3y^2 \cos^2 x \, dy = 0.$

19. $\dfrac{3y^2 \, dx}{x^2 + 3x} + \left(2y \ln \dfrac{5x}{x + 3} + 3 \sin y\right) dy = 0.$

24. Integrating factors

If, when a differential equation is multiplied through by an expression, the result is an exact differential equation, the expression is called an **integrating factor** of the equation.

Integrating factors of many differential equations may be found by recognizing certain groups as differentials of known expressions. From $d(y/x) = (x \, dy - y \, dx)/x^2$, it appears that $1/x^2$ is an integrating factor of $x \, dy - y \, dx + f(x) \, dx = 0$, for

$$\frac{x \, dy - y \, dx}{x^2} + \frac{f(x) \, dx}{x^2} = 0$$

is an exact differential equation and its solution is

$$\frac{y}{x} + \int \frac{f(x)}{x^2} \, dx = c.$$

Similarly, $1/y^2$ is an integrating factor of

$$x \, dy - y \, dx + f(y) \, dy = 0,$$

and its solution is

$$-\frac{x}{y} + \int \frac{f(y) \, dy}{y^2} = c.$$

The form $(x \, dy - y \, dx)/(ax^2 + bxy + cy^2)$ is an exact differential,* as may be proved by applying test (19) or by writing

$$\frac{(x \, dy - y \, dx)/x^2}{(ax^2 + bxy + cy^2)/x^2} = \frac{d(y/x)}{a + b(y/x) + c(y/x)^2}. \tag{24}$$

* If $F'(u)$ represents an integrable function, then $F'(y/x)(x \, dy - y \, dx)/x^2$ is an exact differential; for if $u = y/x$,

$$F'(y/x)(x \, dy - y \, dx)/x^2 = F'(u) \, du = dF(u).$$

Since a, b, and c are any numbers, it appears from (24) that an exact differential is obtained by dividing $x\,dy - y\,dx$ by x^2, y^2, xy, $x^2 + y^2$, $x^2 - y^2$, or any other expression having the form $ax^2 + bxy + cy^2$. To integrate the equation

$$x\,dy - y\,dx = x^2y^3\,dx, \tag{25}$$

we derive from it

$$\frac{x}{y}\,\frac{x\,dy - y\,dx}{y^2} = x^3\,dx,$$

$$-\textstyle\int (x/y)\,d(x/y) = \int x^3\,dx, \quad -(x/y)^2/2 = \frac{1}{4}x^4 + \frac{1}{4}c.$$

Also, we could have multiplied both members of (25) by $(x/y)(1/y^2)$ and could have integrated the resulting exact differential equation.

Observe that $d(x^py^q) = px^{p-1}y^q\,dx + qx^py^{q-1}\,dy$, or

$$\mathbf{d(x^py^q) = x^{p-1}y^{q-1}(py\,dx + qx\,dy),} \tag{26}$$

shows that $py\,dx + qx\,dy$ suggests $x^{p-1}y^{q-1}$ as an integrating factor. For example,

$$\begin{aligned} 3y\,dx + 5x\,dy &\quad \text{suggests} \quad x^{3-1}y^{5-1}(3y\,dx + 5x\,dy) = d(x^3y^5), \\ 3y\,dx - 5x\,dy &\quad \text{suggests} \quad x^{3-1}y^{-5-1}(3y\,dx - 5x\,dy) = d(x^3y^{-5}), \\ \tfrac{1}{2}y\,dx - \tfrac{2}{3}x\,dy &\quad \text{suggests} \quad x^{-\frac{1}{2}}y^{-\frac{5}{3}}(\tfrac{1}{2}y\,dx - \tfrac{2}{3}x\,dy) = d(x^{\frac{1}{2}}y^{-\frac{2}{3}}). \end{aligned} \tag{27}$$

Also, it is important to note that these simple differential forms, suggesting expressions playing a prominent role, indicate substitutions. In each line of Table 1 is listed, for convenience of reference, an expression of the form $M\,dx + N\,dy$, a corresponding integrating factor u, and an integral $\int u(M\,dx + n\,dy)$ of the exact differential.

TABLE 1

	$M\,dx + N\,dy$	Integrating factor u	$\int u(M\,dx + N\,dy)$
I	$py\,dx + qx\,dy$	$x^{p-1}y^{q-1}$	x^py^q
I(*a*)	$y\,dx - x\,dy$	$\begin{cases} 1/x^2,\ 1/y^2,\ 1/(xy) \\ 1/(ax^2 + bxy + cy^2) \end{cases}$	$-y/x$, x/y, etc.
I(*b*)	$y\,dx + x\,dy$	1	xy
II	$px\,dx + qy\,dy$	1	$\frac{1}{2}(px^2 + qy^2)$

Also, see §§25 and 26 for other integrating factors. Observe that *the substitution of v equated to an expression in the third column is suggested by the presence in a differential equation of the corresponding expression in the first column.*

The following examples will illustrate methods using integrating factors and substitutions in solving differential equations:

Example 1. Solve $x\,dx + y\,dy = 3\sqrt{x^2 + y^2}\,y^2\,dy$.

Solution. $1/\sqrt{x^2 + y^2}$ is observed to be an integrating factor. Multiplying the equation through by this, we get

$$\frac{x\,dx + y\,dy}{\sqrt{x^2 + y^2}} = 3y^2\,dy.$$

As this equation is exact, we can solve it as such or we may write it

$$(x^2 + y^2)^{-\frac{1}{2}} \cdot \tfrac{1}{2}d(x^2 + y^2) = 3y^2\,dy$$

and integrate this to get

$$\mathbf{(x^2 + y^2)^{\frac{1}{2}} = y^3 + c.}$$

Also, the substitution $u = x^2 + y^2$, suggested by $x\,dx + y\,dy$, could have been used.

Example 2. Solve $(x^3y^2 + x)\,dy + (x^2y^3 - y)\,dx = 0$.

Solution. The equation may be written

$$x\,dy - y\,dx + (xy)^2(x\,dy + y\,dx) = 0.$$

Here $1/(xy)$ is an integrating factor, and the solution is

$$\mathbf{\ln (y/x) + \tfrac{1}{2}(xy)^2 = c.}$$

Also, we could have used the substitution $u = y/x$, $v = xy$ suggested by $y\,dx - x\,dy$ and $x\,dy + y\,dx$.

Example 3. Solve $4y\,dx + x\,dy = xy^2\,dx$. (*a*)

Solution. The substitution suggested by (26) with $p = 4$, $q = 1$ or line I of Table 1 is

$$u = x^4y, \qquad y = ux^{-4}, \qquad dy = x^{-4}\,du - 4x^{-5}u\,dx. \tag{b}$$

Replacing y and dy in (*a*) by their values from (*b*), we get

$$4ux^{-4}\,dx + x(x^{-4}\,du - 4x^{-5}u\,dx) = xu^2x^{-8}\,dx. \tag{c}$$

The solution of this equation, found by the method of separating the variables, is

$$3u^{-1} = x^{-3} + c. \tag{d}$$

In this, replace u by x^4y, its value from (*b*), and simplify slightly to obtain the solution of (*a*),

$$\mathbf{3 = (x + cx^4)y.}$$

EXERCISES

Solve by using integrating factors:

1. $x\,dy + y\,dx = 3x^2\,dx$.
2. $x\,dy + y\,dx = xy^3\,dx$. Use the integrating factor $1/(xy)^3$.

3. $x\,dy - y\,dx = (xy)y^2\,dy.$

4. $x\,dy - y\,dx = (x^2 - 3)\,dx.$

5. $x\,dy - y\,dx = (y^2 - 3)\,dy.$

6. $x\,dy - y\,dx = (x^2 + xy - 2y^2)\,dx.$

7. $x\,dy - y\,dx = y^3(x^2 + y^2)\,dy.$

8. $y\,dx - x\,dy = (x^2 + y^2)^2(x\,dx + y\,dy).$

9. $y\,dx + x\,dy = \sqrt{x^2 + y^2}\,(x\,dx + y\,dy).$

10. $x\,dy - y\,dx = \sqrt{4x^2 + 9y^2}\,(4x\,dx + 9y\,dy).$

Hint: $\dfrac{x\,dy - y\,dx}{4x^2 + 9y^2} = \dfrac{d(y/x)}{4 + 9(y/x)^2} = \dfrac{1}{6}\,d\tan^{-1}\dfrac{3y}{2x}.$

11. $x\,dy - y\,dx = x\,dx + y\,dy.$

Use Table 1 to solve the equations numbered 12 to 19 by substitutions:

12. $2y\,dx + 3x\,dy = 3x^{-1}\,dy.$ Use $p = 2,\ q = 3.$

13. $3y\,dx + 4x\,dy = 5x^2y^{-3}\,dx.$

14. $4x\,dy - 3y\,dx = y^{-3}x\,dx.$

15. $x\,dy - 2y\,dx = (xy)^3y\,dy.$

16. $y\,dx + 2x\,dy = x^3y\,dx.$

17. $2y\,dx - x\,dy = xy^3\,dy.$

18. $x\,dy + 2y\,dx = x^3y^3\,dy.$

19. $3y\,dx - 2x\,dy = x^4y^2\,dx.$

Solve the following differential equations:

20. $x\,dy - 3y\,dx = x^4y^{-1}\,dx.$

21. $x\,dx + y\,dy = (x^2 + y^2)^3(x\,dy - y\,dx).$

22. $x\,dy - y\,dx = (x^2 - 3axy + 2a^2y^2)(x\,dx + y\,dy).$

23. $y\,dx - 2x\,dy = xy^5\,dy.$

24. $x\,dy - y\,dx = (2x^2 + 3y^2)^3(2x\,dx + 3y\,dy).$

25. If the differential equation $M\,dx + N\,dy = 0$ is homogeneous, then

$$1/(xM + yN)$$

is an integrating factor. Use this fact to solve the equations:

(*a*) $(y^2 - xy)\,dx + x^2\,dy = 0.$ (*b*) $(x^3 - y^3)\,dx + xy^2\,dy = 0.$

★26. Prove that x^k is an integrating factor of $M\,dx + N\,dy = 0$ when $(\partial M/\partial y) - (\partial N/\partial x) = Nk/x.$ Use this fact to solve:

(*a*) $(y^4 + x^3)\,dx + 8xy^3\,dy = 0.$ (*b*) $(5x^3 + 3xy + 2y^2)\,dx + (x^2 + 2xy)\,dy = 0.$

25. Linear differential equation

A differential equation of any order is said to be **linear** *when it is of the first degree in the dependent variable and its derivatives.* Linear differential equations are extremely important because of their wide range of application. In the next chapter we shall find many applications of them, and in Chaps. 6 to 8, dealing with general linear equations, we shall meet with a wide range of problems solved by using them.

A differential equation of any order is said to be linear when it is of the first degree in the dependent variable and its derivatives. It follows that a general type of differential equation of the first order and linear in y is

$$\frac{dy}{dx} + Py = Q, \tag{28}$$

where P and Q are functions of x only.

To find an integrating factor of (28), let us solve

$$\frac{dy}{dx} + Py = 0, \qquad \text{or} \qquad \frac{dy}{y} = -P\,dx.$$

Here the variables are separated, and the solution is

$$ye^{\int P\,dx} = c. \tag{29}$$

The differential of the left-hand member of (29) is $e^{\int P\,dx}(dy + Py\,dx)$. It appears then that, if (28) is multiplied by $e^{\int P\,dx}\,dx$, the left-hand member will be an exact differential and the right-hand member will contain x only. Hence, multiplying (28) by $e^{\int P\,dx}\,dx$, we obtain the exact equation

$$e^{\int P\,dx}(dy + Py\,dx) = Qe^{\int P\,dx}\,dx. \tag{30}$$

The solution of (30), and therefore of (28), is

$$\mathbf{ye^{\int P\,dx} = \int Qe^{\int P\,dx}\,dx + c.} \tag{31}$$

Hence, *to solve an equation having the form* (28), *either substitute in form* (31), *or multiply by* $e^{\int P\,dx}$ *and integrate the result as an exact differential equation.*

As an exercise the student may show that the solution of an equation, linear in x, is given by

$$dx/dy + G(y)x = H(y), \tag{32}$$

$$xe^{\int G(y)\,dy} = \int e^{\int G(y)\,dy}H(y)\,dy + c. \tag{33}$$

Example 1. Solve $x(dy/dx) + 2y = x^3$.

Solution. Division by x gives

$$\frac{dy}{dx} + \frac{2}{x}y = x^2.$$

This has the form (28), and

$$Q = x^2, \qquad P = \frac{2}{x}, \qquad e^{\int P\,dx} = e^{2\int dx/x} = e^{\ln x^2} = x^2.$$

Substituting these values in (31), we obtain

$$yx^2 = \int x^2x^2\,dx + \frac{c}{5} = \frac{x^5}{5} + \frac{c}{5},$$

or

$$\mathbf{5yx^2 = x^5 + c.}$$

Alternate method. Multiply the given equation through by dx/x to obtain

$$dy + (2/x)y\,dx = x^2\,dx. \tag{a}$$

In accord with the italicized statement, $e^{\int P\,dx} = e^{\int (2/x)\,dx} = x^2$ is an integrating factor of (a). Multiplying (a) through by x^2, we get

$$x^2\,dy + 2xy\,dx = x^4\,dx. \qquad (b)$$

This is an exact differential equation, and its solution is

$$x^2y = \tfrac{1}{5}x^5 + c. \qquad (c)$$

Example 2. Solve $dx/dy - 2xy = 2e^{y^2}y$.

Solution. Substituting $-2y$ for G and $2ye^{y^2}$ for H in (33), we obtain the required solution

$$xe^{\int -2y\,dy} = \int e^{\int -2y\,dy} 2ye^{y^2}\,dy + c,$$

or

$$xe^{-y^2} = y^2 + c.$$

Also, we could have multiplied (a) through by the integrating factor $e^{\int -2y\,dy} = e^{-y^2}$ and then have solved the resulting exact differential equation.

EXERCISES

After attempting to write each of the following equations in one of the standard forms (28) or (32), state whether it is linear in x, linear in y, or nonlinear:

1. $\dfrac{dy}{dx} + 3x^2y = x^3$.

2. $3x\,dy + 4y\,dx = x^4\,dx$.

3. $y\,dx = y^2x\,dy + 7\,dx$.

4. $y\,dx + x\,dy - x^4y^4\,dx = 0$.

5. $dx = y\,dy - xy^3\,dy$.

6. $x\,dx + y\,dy = x^2y^{-1}\,dy$.

Solve each of the following differential equations, and, when initial conditions are indicated, find the particular solution satisfied by them:

7. $\dfrac{dy}{dx} + \dfrac{1}{x}y = x^3 - 3$.

8. $\dfrac{dy}{dx} + \dfrac{2}{x}y = x^2 + 2$.

9. $x\dfrac{dy}{dx} - 2y = x^2 + x$; $y = 1$ when $x = 1$.

10. $\dfrac{dx}{dy} + \dfrac{3}{y}x = 2y$.

11. $y\dfrac{dx}{dy} - 2x = 3y^2 - 2$; $y = 1$ when $x = 1$.

12. $x^2\dfrac{dy}{dx} - 2xy = x^4 + 3$; $y = 2$ when $x = 1$.

13. $x^2\,dy - \sin 2x\,dx + 3xy\,dx = 0$.

14. $y\,dx - 4x\,dy = y^6\,dy$; $x = 4$ when $y = 1$.

15. $dy(1 + 2x \cot y) = dx$.

16. $(x + 2y)\,dx + dy = 0$; $y = -1$ when $x = 0$.

17. $dx - xy\,dy = ye^{y^2}\,dy$; $y = 0$ when $x = 5$.

18. $t\,ds = (3t + 1)s\,dt + t^3e^{3t}\,dt$.

19. $dt + 2st\,ds = se^{-s^2}\,ds$.

20. $(y + 2x)\,dy + dx = 0$; $x = -1$ when $y = 0$.

21. $(a + xy)\,dx = (1 + x^2)\,dy$; $y = 2a$ when $x = 0$.

22. $(\sin 2\theta - 2\rho \cos \theta)\, d\theta = 2\, d\rho$.

23. $f(x)\, dy + 2yf'(x)\, dx = f(x)f'(x)\, dx$.

24. $[f(y)]^2 \dfrac{dx}{dy} + 3f(y)f'(y)x = f'(y)$.

26. Equations reducible to linear form

The equation

$$\frac{dy}{dx} + Py = Qy^n, \tag{34}$$

where P and Q are functions of x only, is named **Bernoulli's equation,** after James Bernoulli, who studied it in 1695.

From §25, or by differentiation, we can show that

$$e^{\int P\,dx}(dy + Py\,dx) = d(ye^{\int P\,dx}). \tag{35}$$

This suggests for solving (34) the substitution

$$v = ye^{\int P\,dx}, \qquad \text{or} \qquad y = ve^{-\int P\,dx}. \tag{36}$$

The substitution (36) in (34) produces an equation of the type *variables separable,* and from this the required solution* is formed. Similarly, to solve the equation

$$dx + x[G(y)\,dy] = H(y)x^n\,dy, \tag{37}$$

make the substitution

$$v = xe^{\int G\,dy}, \qquad \text{or} \qquad x = ve^{-\int G\,dy}, \tag{38}$$

solve the resulting equation in v and y, and in the result replace v by its value $xe^{\int G\,dy}$ from (38). Two examples will illustrate the method of solution.

Example 1. Solve $dy + 2xy\,dx = xe^{-x^2}y^3\,dx$. (*a*)

Solution. In accord with (36) make the substitution

$$v = ye^{\int 2x\,dx} = ye^{x^2}, \qquad \text{or} \qquad y = ve^{-x^2}. \tag{b}$$

Replacing y in (*a*) by ve^{-x^2} from (*b*), we get

$$e^{-x^2}\,dv - 2xe^{-x^2}v\,dx + 2xve^{-x^2}\,dx = xe^{-x^2}v^3e^{-3x^2}\,dx. \tag{c}$$

Simplifying (*c*) and multiplying through by $v^{-3}e^{x^2}$, we get

$$v^{-3}\,dv = xe^{-3x^2}\,dx. \tag{d}$$

Solving this equation, replacing v in the result by ye^{x^2} from (*b*), and simplifying, we get

$$-\tfrac{1}{2}v^{-2} = -\tfrac{1}{6}e^{-3x^2} - \tfrac{1}{6}c,$$
$$3y^{-2} = e^{-x^2} + ce^{2x^2}.$$

* This same substitution furnishes a solution of an equation of the type $(dy/dx) + Py = Qf(ye^{\int P\,dx})$.

Example 2. Solve $dx - \dfrac{2}{y}\, x\, dy = x^4\, dy.$ $\quad (a)$

Solution. In accordance with (38), make the substitution

$$v = xe^{-\int (2/y)\, dy} = xy^{-2}, \qquad \text{or} \qquad x = vy^2, \tag{b}$$

to obtain

$$y^2\, dv + 2yv\, dy - (2/y)vy^2\, dy = v^4y^8\, dy. \tag{c}$$

Now solve this equation in v and y, replace v in the result by xy^{-2} from (b), and simplify to get

$$v^{-4}\, dv = y^6\, dy,$$

$$-\tfrac{1}{3}(xy^{-2})^{-3} = \tfrac{1}{7}y^7 - \frac{c}{21}, \tag{d}$$

$$\mathbf{7x^{-3} = cy^{-6} - 3y.} \tag{e}$$

EXERCISES

Use the substitution (36) in solving:

1. $dy + (1/x)y\, dx = 3x^2y^2\, dx.$

2. $dy + y\, dx = 2xy^2e^x\, dx.$

3. $2\dfrac{dy}{dx} - \dfrac{y}{x} = 5x^3y^3.$

4. $3\dfrac{dy}{dx} + \dfrac{3}{x}y = 2x^4y^4.$

Use the substitution (38) in solving:

5. $dx + (2/y)x\, dy = 2x^2y^2\, dy.$

6. $dx - 2xy\, dy = 6x^3y^2e^{-2y^2}\, dy.$

Solve each of the following differential equations, and determine the constant of integration when initial conditions are given:

7. $(dy/dx) + [1/(x-2)]y = 5(x-2)\sqrt{y}.$
8. $3\, dy - y\, dx = 3y^3e^{\frac{4}{3}x}\, dx.$
9. $(12e^{2x}y^2 - y)\, dx = dy;\ y = 1$ when $x = 0.$
10. $3y^2(dy/dx) + [y^3/(x+1)] - 8(x+1) = 0;\ y = 0$ when $x = 0.$
11. $(x+1)\, dy = y[y(x+1)\ln(x+1) - 1]\, dx;\ y = e^{-1}$ when $x = e - 1.$
12. $x\, dy - 2y\, dx = \frac{1}{3}x^8y^{-2}[3(yx^{-2})^2 + 2yx^{-2}]\, dx.$
13. $dy - y\sin x\, dx = y\ln(ye^{\cos x})\, dx.$
14. $dx + x\cot y\, dy = [x\sin y\cos y/(x^2\sin^2 y + 1)]\, dy.$

27. Simultaneous equations

Two differential equations in three variables often arise in applications. Only pairs of equations that can be solved by means of the theory already developed will be considered at this time. Two equations,

$$\begin{aligned} A_1\, dx + A_2\, dy + A_3\, dt &= 0,\\ B_1\, dx + B_2\, dy + B_3\, dt &= 0, \end{aligned} \tag{39}$$

where the A's and B's represent functions of x, y, and t, have solutions consisting of two relations of the form

$$f_1(x,y,t,c_1,c_2) = 0, \qquad f_2(x,y,t,c_1,c_2) = 0. \tag{40}$$

One relation is generally found by eliminating one of the variables from the given equations and solving the resulting equation in two unknowns by methods already considered. When one relation has been found, it may be used with the given differential equations to find others. Of course, if an equation contains all three variables but separated so that no term contains more than one variable or, more generally, if an equation is exact, it may be integrated directly to obtain one of the required equations. Thus, from $2x\,dx + 2y\,dy + 2t\,dt = 0$, obtain $x^2 + y^2 + t^2 = c$.

Example 1. Solve

$$\frac{dx}{dt} + y = x, \qquad \frac{dy}{dt} = 3y. \tag{a}$$

Solution. Since there are only two variables in the second equation, we solve it to obtain

$$y = c_1e^{3t}. \tag{b}$$

Substituting y from (b) in the first of (a), we obtain

$$\frac{dx}{dt} + c_1e^{3t} = x. \tag{c}$$

Since (c) is a linear equation in two variables, we solve it by a method of §25 to find

$$xe^{-t} = -\tfrac{1}{2}c_1e^{2t} + c_2. \tag{d}$$

Rewriting equations (b) and (d) slightly simplified, we have

$$\mathbf{y = c_1e^{3t}}, \qquad \mathbf{x = -\tfrac{1}{2}c_1e^{3t} + c_2e^{t}}.$$

Example 2. Solve

$$\frac{dx}{dt} + t\frac{dy}{dt} = 2t, \qquad t\frac{dx}{dt} - \frac{dy}{dt} = -x. \tag{a}$$

Solution. To eliminate y, multiply the second equation of (a) by t, add the result to the first, and obtain

$$(1 + t^2)\frac{dx}{dt} = -tx + 2t. \tag{b}$$

Equation (b) may be solved by separating the variables. The solution is

$$\ln (x - 2) = \ln [c_1(1 + t^2)^{-\frac{1}{2}}],$$

or

$$\mathbf{x = 2 + c_1(1 + t^2)^{-\frac{1}{2}}}. \tag{c}$$

Substituting x from (c) in the first of (a), we get

$$-c_1t(1 + t^2)^{-\frac{3}{2}} + t\frac{dy}{dt} = 2t. \tag{d}$$

Separating the variables in (*d*) and integrating, we find

$$y = 2t + \frac{c_1 t}{\sqrt{1 + t^2}} + c_2. \tag{e}$$

Equations (*c*) and (*e*) constitute the solution.

EXERCISES

Solve the following differential equations:

1. $\dfrac{dx}{dt} - 2t = 0,\ \dfrac{dy}{dt} - x + t^2 = 0.$

2. $\dfrac{dy}{dt} + y = e^{-t},\ \dfrac{dx}{dt} + y = te^{-t}.$

3. $\dfrac{dx}{dt} = 1{,}000,\ \dfrac{dy}{dt} = 0.5\dfrac{dx}{dt} - 16t.$

4. $\dfrac{d\rho}{dt} + \rho = e^t,\ \dfrac{d\theta}{dt} = \rho.$

5. $(t - 1)\dfrac{dx}{dt} + \dfrac{dy}{dt} = 6t^2,\ \dfrac{dx}{dt} - \dfrac{dy}{dt} = x.$

6. $x\,dt + t\,dx = 2t\,dt,\ \dfrac{dx}{dt} + \dfrac{dy}{dt} = x - t.$

7. $(x^2 + t^2)\,dt - xt\,dx = 0,\ t\dfrac{dy}{dt} = x^2t + y.$

8. $t\dfrac{dx}{dt} + \dfrac{dy}{dt} = 4(t^2 + 1)e^t,\ \dfrac{dx}{dt} - t\dfrac{dy}{dt} = 4(t^2 + 1)e^{2t}.$

9. $\dfrac{d\rho}{\rho} = \dfrac{d\theta}{\rho + \theta + t} = \dfrac{dt}{t}.$

10. $dx + ay\,dt = 0,\ dy - ax\,dt = 0.$

28. Summary

In solving a differential equation of the form $M\,dx + N\,dy = 0$, the student will often find it helpful to proceed, until a method of solution is found, as follows:

1. Consider whether the equation comes under the case of:
   - *a.* Variables separable (§8).
   - *b.* M and N homogeneous and of the same degree (§20).
   - *c.* Linear equation (§25).
   - *d.* Reducible to linear equation (§26).
   - *e.* Exact differential equation (§23).
   - *f.* M and N linear but not homogeneous (§21).
2. Search for an integrating factor (§24).
3. Make a substitution and consider the result under headings 1 and 2, §§19, 24, 25, 26.

At present, we have studied a few important special types of the differential equation having the form $M\,dx + N\,dy = 0$. It may be of interest to consider what remains to be done with this form. The result of multiplying this equation by $\mu(x,y)$ will be exact, provided that $\partial(\mu M)/\partial y = \partial(\mu N)/\partial x$. In Chap. 14, §122, we shall learn how to solve this partial differential equation for μ in terms of x and y. Not only will this furnish a general method of attack, but also it will enable us to make up types of equations that are readily solvable. In Chap. 13, some methods of approximating a particular solution of a differential equation are explained. Also, in Chap. 12 the method of integration in infinite series is considered. This method may be applied to solve a great variety of differential equations.

EXERCISES

Solve each of the following differential equations, and determine the constant of integration when initial conditions are given:

1. $x^2\,dy + y^2\,dx = x^2y\,dy - xy^2\,dx.$

2. $(x^2 + 3)\dfrac{dy}{dx} + 2xy + 5x^2 = 0.$

3. $(5x^2 + y^2)\,dx + 2x^2\,dy = 0.$

4. $(y + x)^2\dfrac{dy}{dx} = 2(y + x)^2 - 3.$

5. $\cos x\,dy + 3y\sin x\,dx - 2\cos^2 x\,dx = 0.$

6. $(xy^2 + y)\,dx - x\,dy = 0.$

7. $(3x^2 + 2xy)\,dx + (x^2 + \cos y)\,dy = 0;\ y = \dfrac{\pi}{2}$ when $x = 0.$

8. $y^2 + x^2\dfrac{dy}{dx} = xy\dfrac{dy}{dx};\ y = 1$ when $x = 1.$

9. $y\,dx + x\,dy = xy(dx + dy).$

10. $x^2\,dy^2 - y^4\,dx^2 = 0.$

11. $x\,dy + y\,dx = x^4y^8\,dy.$

12. $dy - 4xy\,dx = x^3y^2\,dx.$

13. $dx + 2yx\,dy = x^2y\,dy.$

14. $[(y + x)/x]\,dx + (\ln 3x + 2y)\,dy = 0.$

15. $3y\,dx + 5x\,dy = xy^3\,dy.$

16. $(2x^2 + y^2 - 3)(x\,dy + y\,dx) = (xy)^3(4x\,dx + 2y\,dy).$

17. $xy\left(\dfrac{dy}{dx}\right)^2 - (2x^2 + y^2)\dfrac{dy}{dx} + 2xy = 0.$ *Hint:* Solve for $\dfrac{dy}{dx}.$

18. $2x^3y\,dx + x^2y^2\,dy = y\,dx + x^2\,dy;\ y = 1$ when $x = 1.$

19. $(xy + 1)(x\,dy - y\,dx) = y^2(x\,dy + y\,dx);\ y = 2$ when $x = 1.$

20. $y^2\,dx + y\,dy = 2\cos x\,dx;\ y = 0$ when $x = \dfrac{\pi}{2}.$

21. $x\,dy = (xy^2 - 3y)\,dx;\ y = 2$ when $x = 2.$

22. $(2x + 3y - 1)\,dx = (5 - 2x - 3y)\,dy.$

23. $(x^2y + y^3)\,dx - 2x^3\,dy = 0;\ y = 3$ when $x = 2.$

24. $(x^3 - x)\dfrac{dy}{dx} = (x^2 + 1)y + 12x(x^2 - 1)^3;\ y = 9$ when $x = 2.$

25. $[6x(x + 2y) + a^2]\,dy + (12xy + 6y^2 + b^2)\,dx = 0.$

26. $\left(\dfrac{1}{x} + \dfrac{2y}{x^2 - 1}\right)dx + \left(\ln\dfrac{x - 1}{x + 1} + \dfrac{1}{y}\right)dy = 0.$

27. $(x + y - 3)\,dx + (x + y + 5)\,dy = 0;\ y = 0$ when $x = 1.$

28. $(5x + 4y + 4)\,dx + (4x + 3y + 1)\,dy = 0.$

29. $4(x^2 - y)^3(2x\,dx - dy) = 3(x^2 - y^2)^{-\frac{1}{2}}(x\,dx - y\,dy).$

30. $(x^2 - y^2)(x\,dy + y\,dx) = 2xy(x\,dy - y\,dx).$

31. $(4x - 3y)^2\,dy = 2(4x - 3y)\,dy + 4\,dx.$

32. $\dfrac{dy}{dx} - xy = xy^2 - 2xy^3;\ y = 2$ when $x = 0.$

33. $(3x^2 + 4y^2 - 5)x\,dx = (6 - 3x^2 - 4y^2)y\,dy$; let $u = x^2$, $v = y^2$.

34. $\cos x \dfrac{dy}{dx} + \sin x = 1 - y$.

35. $2x^3y^2\,dx + 2x^2y^3\,dy = x\,dy + y\,dx$; $y = -1$ when $x = 1$.

36. $(x - y^2)\,dx + 2xy\,dy = 0$; $y = -2$ when $x = 1$.

37. $x(x + y)\,dx + y(y\,dx - x\,dy) = 0$; $y = 2$ when $x = 2$.

38. $(x - 2y)\,dx + (2x - y - 3)\,dy = 0$; $y = -1$ when $x = -1$.

39. $(y^2 + 4xy + 3x^2)\,dx + (x^2 - y^2)\,dy = 0$.

40. $(\rho + \sin\theta\cos\theta)\,d\theta + (\theta - \rho^2)\,d\rho = 0$.

41. $x^2(x + y)^2(dx + dy) = m(x\,dy - y\,dx)$.

42. $(x + y)^2(x\,dy - y\,dx) + [y^2 - 2x^2(x + y)^2](dx + dy) = 0$; let $v = x + y$, $w = \dfrac{y}{x}$.

43. $(x^2 + y^2)(x\,dy + y\,dx) + 2xy(x - y)(dx - dy) = 0$.

44. Transform $\varphi(x^my^n)y\,dx + \psi(x^my^n)x\,dy = 0$ to the type variables separable by the substitution $z = x^my^n$. Solve $(2 + 4x^2\sqrt{y})y\,dx + x^3\sqrt{y}\,dy = 0$.

45. The equation $(3xy^2 + 7x^3)\,dx + (4x^2y + 3\sqrt{xy})\,dy = 0$ has an integrating factor of the form x^k. Determine k, and solve the equation.

46. In the equation $(P + Rx^{k+1})\,dy = (Q + Ryx^k)\,dx$, P, Q, and R are homogeneous functions of x and y, P and Q are of the same degree, and k is a constant. Transform the given equation to the type considered in §26 by the substitution $y = vx$. Solve

$$[x^2 + y^2 + (y + 2x)x^{-1}]\,dy = [2(x^2 + y^2) + (y + 2x)x^{-2}y]\,dx.$$

47. $\dfrac{dx}{dt} - 3x = e^{3t}$, $dx - dy + x\,dt = 0$.

48. $dx - dy = dt$, $x\,dt + y\,dx = 0$.

49. $x\,dy + y\,dx = 2t\,dt$, $(xy + t^2)(dx + dy) = 4t\,dt$.

50. $\left(\dfrac{dx}{dt}\right)^2 + \left(\dfrac{dy}{dt}\right)^2 = 25$, $y\dfrac{dy}{dx} = 1$.

51. $\dfrac{dx}{dt} = \dfrac{2}{2y + x}$, $\dfrac{dy}{dt} = \dfrac{6x - 1}{2y + x}$.

52. $xy\,dt + xt\,dy + yt\,dx = 0$, $(x + y)\,dt + (x + t)\,dy + (y + t)\,dx = 0$.

CHAPTER 4

APPLICATIONS INVOLVING DIFFERENTIAL EQUATIONS OF THE FIRST ORDER

29. Miscellaneous elementary applications

The solutions of the following problems involve various types of first-order differential equations. Inasmuch as no new knowledge or new methods are needed in finding and solving the appropriate differential equations, no introductory illustrative examples will be given.

EXERCISES

Find the equation of a curve if:

1. It passes through $(3,-2)$ and its slope at any point (x,y) on it is $(x^2+y^2)/(y^3-2xy)$.

2. Its slope at any point (x,y) on it is $\frac{1}{3}\sqrt{2x+3y}$.

3. $\overline{ON} = \overline{OP}$, where O is the origin, P is any point (x,y) on the curve, and N is the point where the normal at P meets the X-axis.

4. The area bounded by the curve, any two ordinates, and the X-axis is equal to the average of these two ordinates multiplied by the distance between them.

5. The radius vector, length ρ, of a moving point (ρ,θ) sweeps out an area proportional to ρ^n as θ changes from zero to any angle θ in the range $0 \leqq \theta \leqq 2\pi$.

6. The intercept on the X-axis of the tangent at any point on the curve divided by the square of the ordinate of the point is constant.

7. The intercept on the X-axis of the normal at any point on the curve divided by the nth power of the radius vector to the point is constant. Use rectangular coordinates.

8. The abscissa x of the point of contact of the tangent and a perpendicular from the origin to the tangent have equal lengths. Note that the distance from $(0,0)$ to the tangent at (x,y) on the curve is given by $(y - x\,dy/dx)/\sqrt{1+(dy/dx)^2}$.

In connection with the theory of the rates of chemical reactions, formulas of the following type are used:

$$\frac{dx}{dt} = k(a_1 - x)^{p_1}(a_2 - x)^{p_2} \cdots (a_n - x)^{p_n}, \qquad (a)$$

where x is the amount of substance transformed and k, a_1, a_2, . . . , a_n and p_1, p_2, . . . , p_n are constants. Find t in terms of x, and also the limiting values of x as t increases without bound if:

9. $\dfrac{dx}{dt} = k(2 - x)(4 - x)$; $x = 0$ when $t = 0$, $x = \frac{3}{2}$ when $t = 10$.

10. $\dfrac{dx}{dt} = k(3 - x)^2(4 - x)$; $x = 0$ when $t = 0$, $x = 2$ when $t = 5$.

11. $\dfrac{dx}{dt} = k(3 - x)(4 - x)(5 - x)$; $x = 0$ when $t = 0$, $x = 2$ when $t = 5$.

12. For a chemical reaction obeying the special case of formula (a),

$$\frac{dx}{dt} = k(a - x)(b - x)(c - x),$$

where $0 < a < b < c$ and $x = 0$ when $t = 0$, show that the amount x of substance transformed approaches a but is always less than a.

13. A tank contains initially 10 gal of brine with 15 lb of salt in solution. Brine containing 1 lb of salt per gallon enters the tank at 2 gal/min, and the brine, kept well stirred, flows out at 1 gal/min. Find the amount of salt in the tank at the end of 5 min.

14. A light situated at a point in a plane sends out beams in every direction. The beams in the plane meet a curve and are all reflected parallel to a fixed straight line in the plane. If the angle of incidence with the normal to the curve at the point of incidence is equal to the angle of reflection, find the equation of the curve. Solve by using polar coordinates and also by using rectangular coordinates (see Fig. 1). *Hint:* In Fig. 1, $\psi = 180° - \frac{1}{2}\theta$; also, $\varphi = \frac{1}{2}\theta$, and $\tan \varphi = dy/dx$.

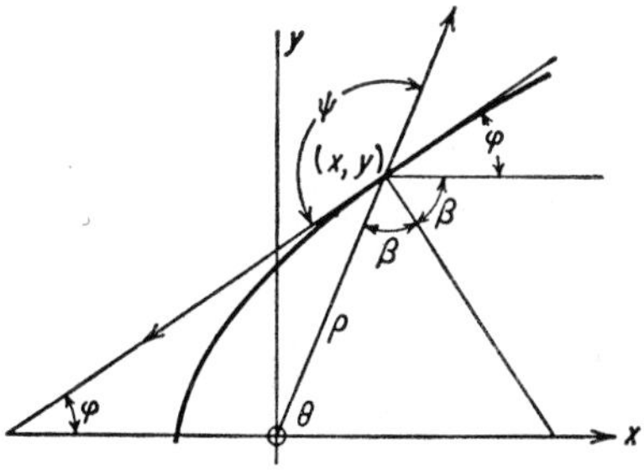

Fig. 1

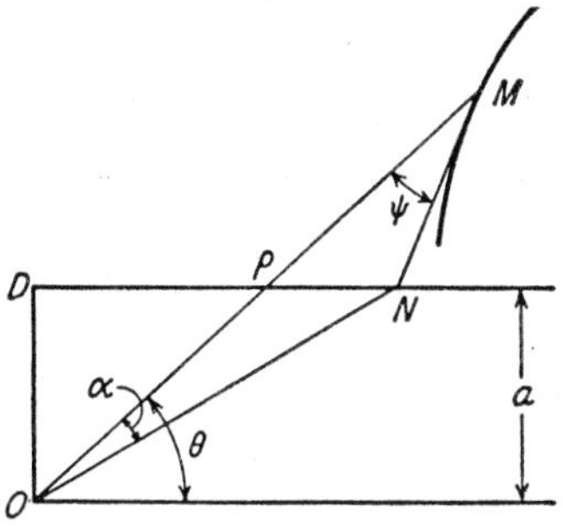

Fig. 2

15. Find the equation of the orthogonal trajectories (see §11) of all circles $x^2 + y^2 - 2my = 0$ tangent to the X-axis at the origin.

16. Given a point O and a straight line D, find a curve such that the portion of the tangent MN included between the point of contact M and the point of intersection N of the tangent and the line D subtends a constant angle at O (see Fig. 2). *Hint:* Use the law of sines to obtain

$$\frac{ON}{\sin \psi} = \frac{\rho}{\sin (\psi + \alpha)}.$$

Also, $ON = a \csc (\theta - \alpha)$.

17. If, in problem 16, the angle MON, instead of being constant, is equal to angle OMN, show that the differential equation of the curve is either $d\theta = 0$ or $(2a - \rho \sin \theta)\, d\rho + \rho^2 \cos \theta \, d\theta = 0$. Prove that $1/\rho^3$ is an integrating factor of this latter equation, and find its solution.

★18. One end of an inextensible string, of length l, is fastened to a weight which rests on a rough horizontal table. The other end is carried slowly along a straight line in the table. Find the path of the weight. Assume that the string is always tangent to the curve described by the weight.

30. Applications involving simultaneous equations

Let x, y, s, v, and t represent abscissa, ordinate, arc length, velocity, and time, respectively, for a point moving in a plane, and let dots denote derivatives with respect to the time. Then the quantities

$$v = \frac{ds}{dt} = \dot{s}, \qquad \dot{x} = \frac{dx}{dt}, \qquad \dot{y} = \frac{dy}{dt} \tag{1}$$

have the relations indicated in Fig. 3. From the triangle we read, for example,

$$\frac{dy}{dx} = \tan\theta, \qquad \dot{x} = v\cos\theta, \qquad \dot{y} = v\sin\theta, \tag{2}$$

$$|v| = \sqrt{\dot{x}^2 + \dot{y}^2}. \tag{3}$$

$\dot{x}$ is called the component of velocity along the X-axis and $\dot{y}$ the component along the Y-axis. A number of the problems in this section refer to plane motion.

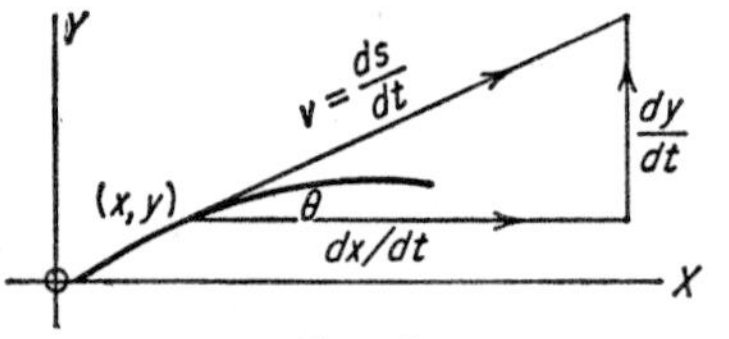

Fig. 3

Some problems will refer to substances in solution. In these, a pertinent equation will often be obtained by using the expression

Rate of change of substance in a region = rate of entrance − rate of exit. (4)

Example 1. A particle moves on the curve $y = \frac{2}{3}x^{\frac{3}{2}}$ with a constant velocity of $\frac{2}{3}$ unit/sec. Find x and y in terms of t if $\dot{x}$ is positive and $x = 0$ when $t = 1$.

Solution. Two equations for the motion are

$$y = \tfrac{2}{3}x^{\frac{3}{2}}, \qquad \dot{x}^2 + \dot{y}^2 = \tfrac{4}{9}. \tag{a}$$

Differentiating the first equation of (a) with respect to t and substituting $\dot{y}$ thus obtained in the second equation, we get

$$\dot{y} = \sqrt{x}\,\dot{x}, \qquad \dot{x}^2 + x\dot{x}^2 = \tfrac{4}{9}. \tag{b}$$

From the second equation of (b), we get

$$(1 + x)^{\frac{1}{2}}\,dx = \tfrac{2}{3}\,dt, \qquad \tfrac{2}{3}(1 + x)^{\frac{3}{2}} = \tfrac{2}{3}t + c.$$

Since $x = 0$ when $t = 1$, $c = 0$. Hence,

$$(1 + x)^{\frac{3}{2}} = t, \qquad \text{or} \qquad x = t^{\frac{2}{3}} - 1.$$

Since $y = \frac{2}{3}x^{\frac{3}{2}}$ from (a), we have

$$\mathbf{x = t^{\frac{2}{3}} - 1, \qquad y = \tfrac{2}{3}(t^{\frac{2}{3}} - 1)^{\frac{3}{2}}.}$$

Example 2. Initially tank I and tank II (see Fig. 4) each contain 100 gal of brine, tank I having 200 lb of salt and tank II 50 lb of salt in solution. Brine runs at 2 gal/min from tank I to tank II through one pipe and at 3 gal/min from tank II to tank I through another pipe. The brine is kept well stirred. How much salt will the second tank contain at the end of 50 min?

Solution. Let Q_1 and Q_2 represent the respective amounts of salt in tanks I and II at time t. Then, using (4), we get

$$\dot{Q}_1 = \frac{3Q_2}{100 - t} - \frac{2Q_1}{100 + t}, \qquad (a)$$

$$\dot{Q}_2 = \frac{2Q_1}{100 + t} - \frac{3Q_2}{100 - t}. \qquad (b)$$

Evidently, $\qquad Q_1 + Q_2 = 250 \qquad (c)$

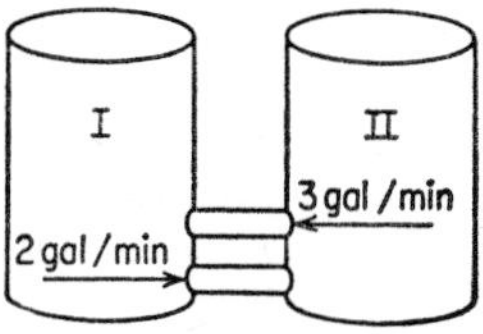

FIG. 4

at all times. Substituting Q_1 from (c) in (b), we get

$$\frac{dQ_2}{dt} = \frac{500 - 2Q_2}{100 + t} - \frac{3Q_2}{100 - t} = \frac{-(500 + t)Q_2}{100^2 - t^2} + \frac{500}{100 + t}.$$

The general solution of this linear equation is

$$Q_2 = \frac{500}{(100 + t)^2}[100(100 - t) - (100 - t)^2 + c(100 - t)^3]. \qquad (d)$$

Using the fact that $Q_2 = 50$ when $t = 0$, we get $c = 0.001$. Then, replacing t by 50, we get $(Q_2)_{t=50} = \mathbf{58\frac{1}{3}}$ lb.

Example 3. A rocket of original mass M g expels gas at the constant rate of k g/sec and at velocity c cm/sec relative to the rocket. Assuming no external forces acting on the rocket, derive a differential equation of its motion.

Solution. The **momentum** *of a moving body is the product of its mass and velocity.* One of Newton's laws of motion applied to a body moving in a straight line may be written

$$\textbf{Force} = \textbf{rate of change of momentum.} \qquad (a)^*$$

The mass of the rocket at time t sec is $(M - kt)$ g, and its momentum is $(M - kt)v$ g-cm/sec, where v represents the velocity of the rocket. The change of momentum of $M - kt$ during the Δt sec following time t is composed of two parts, one the momentum of the unburned material $(M - kt - k\,\Delta t)(v + \Delta v)$ and the other the momentum of the material burned during time Δt, or $k\,\Delta t(\bar{v} - c)$, where $\bar{v} = v + \epsilon\,\Delta t$, $|\epsilon| \leqq 1$ and $\epsilon \to 0$ as $\Delta t \to 0$. Hence, since $F = 0$, we have, change in momentum during the time Δt is zero, or

$$(M - kt - k\,\Delta t)(v + \Delta v) + k\,\Delta t(\bar{v} - c) - (M - kt)v = F\,\Delta t = 0. \qquad (b)$$

* This agrees with the law $F = ma = d(mv)/dt$.

Dividing (*b*) through by Δt and considering limits as $\Delta t \to 0$, we get

$$(\mathbf{M} - \mathbf{kt}) \frac{\mathbf{dv}}{\mathbf{dt}} = \mathbf{kc}. \tag{c}$$

PROBLEMS

1. A particle moves on parabola $y^2 = 4x$ with a velocity such that $\dot{x} = 2t + 2$ at all times. Find x and y in terms of t if the particle passes through (4,4) at time $t = 1$ with positive y-component.

2. A particle moves on the catenary $y = \cosh x$ with a velocity of constant magnitude 2 ft/sec. It passes through (0,1) at time $t = 0$. Show that $x = \sinh^{-1} (2t)$, $y = \sqrt{1 + 4t^2}$.

3. A particle moves on curve $y = x^2 - \frac{1}{8} \ln x$ with a velocity of constant magnitude 10. If it passes through (1,1) with positive x-component of velocity at time $t = 0$, show that $8x^2 + \ln x = 80t + 8$.

4. Under certain conditions the motion of a projectile is given approximately by the equations

$$\dot{x} + 0.032x = 1{,}600, \qquad \dot{y} + 0.032y = 1{,}600 - 32t.$$

If $x = 0$ and $y = 0$ when $t = 0$, find x and y in terms of t.

5. Brine from a first tank runs into a second tank at 2 gal/min, and brine from the second tank runs into the first at 1 gal/min. Initially, there are 10 gal of brine containing 20 lb of salt in the first tank and 10 gal of fresh water in the second tank. How much salt will the first tank contain after 5 min? Assume that the brine in each tank is kept uniform by stirring.

★6. Brine containing 2 lb of salt per gallon runs into a first tank at 2 gal/min, brine from the first tank runs into a second tank at 3 gal/min, and brine runs out of the second tank at 3 gal/min. Initially, the first tank contains 10 gal of brine with 30 lb of salt in solution and the second tank 10 gal of fresh water. Assuming uniform concentration in each tank, find the quantity of salt in the second tank at the end of 5 min.

7. In the chemical process called fractional precipitation, the equations

$$\frac{dx}{dt} = k_1(a - x)(c - z), \qquad \frac{dy}{dt} = k_2(b - y)(c - z)$$

apply. Given that $x = 0$ when $y = 0$, prove that

$$k_1 : k_2 = \ln \frac{a}{a - x} : \ln \frac{b}{b - y}.$$

8. A particle moves on a curve in the xy-plane. Its motion is defined by

$$\dot{y} = x^3y^2 - xy, \qquad \dot{x} = x^2$$

and the fact that it passes through $(1,-1)$ at time $t = 1$. Find the equation of its path, and find x and y in terms of t.

9. If, for the motion of a particle in the xy-plane, $\dot{x} = a \cos pt$, $\dot{y} = b \sin pt$, show that it moves in an ellipse of semiaxes a/p and b/p and that it moves round the ellipse once every $2\pi/p$ units of time. If (m,n) is the center of the ellipse, show that $(x - m)\dot{y} - (y - n)\dot{x}$ is constant for the motion.

10. The path of a particle moving in the xy-plane is the hyperbola $x^2 - y^2 = 25$, and the components $\dot{x}$ and $\dot{y}$ of its velocity satisfy $\dot{x} + \dot{y} = 1$. Find x and y in terms of t if $x = 5$ when $t = 5$.

11. A point moves in a plane curve through (1,1) so that its components $\dot{x}$ and $\dot{y}$ are given by

$$\dot{x} = -2x + 6y, \qquad \dot{y} = 2x + 2y.$$

Prove that it must move either on the line $x = y$ or on the line $x + 3y = 0$, and find x and y in terms of t for its motion on the line $x = y$. *Hint:* Divide the second equation by the first, member by member.

12. Using equation (*c*) of example 3 and the initial conditions $v = 0$ when $t = 0$, show that

$$v = -c \ln [(M - kt)/M].$$

Why is $t < M/k$? State the physical significance of this fact. Also, find the velocity of the rocket when 0.9 of its mass has been consumed.

13. If distance $x = 0$ when $t = 0$, derive from the equation of exercise 12

$$x = ct + (c/k)(M - kt) \ln [(M - kt)/M].$$

Find x for the rocket when 0.9 of its mass has been consumed.

14. To take account of the earth's pull, or gravity, for the rocket of example 3 directed upward, show that $g(kt - M)$ dynes should be added to the right member of equation (*c*). In this case, find v and x for the rocket at time t and at time $t = 0.9M/k$ if $v = 0$, $x = 0$, when $t = 0$.

31. Applications to the flow of electricity

We may think of electricity as a substance which flows through conductors such as wires. *One unit of electricity is the* **coulomb.** Just as we speak of gallons of water, we speak of coulombs of electricity. The rate of flow of electricity is called **current.** If I coulombs of electricity per second are passing a point in a conductor, the current in the conductor is I amp.

For the circuit indicated in Fig. 5, the following equations hold:

$$L\frac{di}{dt} + Ri + \frac{q}{C} = \epsilon, \qquad i = \frac{dq}{dt}, \qquad (5)$$

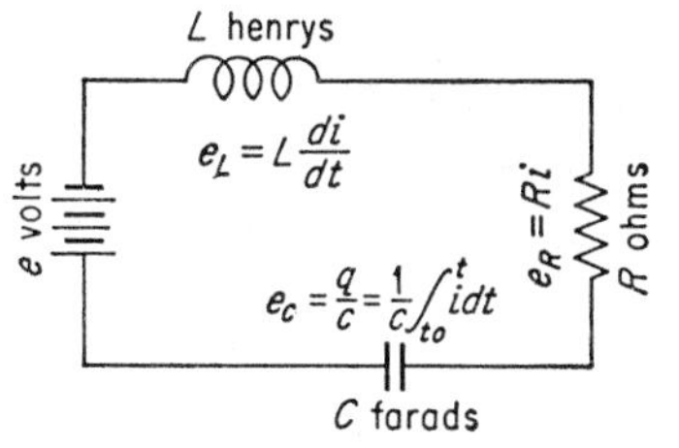

FIG. 5

where ϵ represents emf, i represents current, q represents the charge, or quantity of electricity, on the capacitor, and L, R, and C are constants. *Electromotive force* ϵ is analogous to *force, inductance* L to *mass* or *inertia, resistance* R to *friction*, and *capacitance* C to the size of a *storage tank.*

If there is no capacitor in a circuit, the corresponding equation (5) does not contain the term q/C and no consideration of q enters the discussion.

A set of units in common use are *quantity* q in *coulombs, current* i in *amperes, emf* ϵ in *volts, inductance* L in *henrys, resistance* R in *ohms*, and *capacitance* C in *farads.*

Example. Discuss the charging of a large capacitor, or battery, in a circuit containing a constant emf E, a resistance R, and no inductance.

Solution. Setting $L = 0$ and $i = dq/dt$ in the first of equations (5), obtain

$$R\frac{dq}{dt} + \frac{q}{C} = E. \qquad (a)$$

The initial condition may be taken as $q = 0$ when $t = 0$. The solution of (*a*) subject to this condition is

$$q = CE(1 - e^{-t/(RC)}). \qquad (b)$$

From the second equation of (5),

$$i = \frac{dq}{dt} = \frac{E}{R}e^{-t/(RC)}. \qquad (c)$$

The upper limit of the charge is found from (*b*) to be CE. When $t = RC$, $q = CE(1 - e^{-1}) = 0.632CE$, and when $t = 2RC$, $q = CE(1 - e^{-2}) = 0.865CE$. The initial current is E/R when $t = 0$, and it dies away as t increases.

EXERCISES

1. Discuss the *discharge of a capacitor* through a resistance R by solving (5) with $L = 0$, $\epsilon = 0$, subject to initial conditions $q = q_0$ when $t = 0$, and by finding q when $t = \infty$, $t = CR$, and $t = 2CR$. Also, find t when $q = 0.01q_0$.

2. Discuss the *decay of a current* of initial value I_0 in a circuit containing neither emf nor capacitor, after solving $L\,di/dt + Ri = 0$ and finding the value of i when $t = L/R$, $2L/R$, and ∞.

3. Discuss the growth of current of zero initial value in a circuit containing no capacitor, a resistance R, an inductance L, and emf (*a*) E; (*b*) $E \sin \omega t$.

4. By setting $L = 0$ and $\epsilon = E \sin \omega t$ in (5), show that the corresponding current i approaches $EC\omega/(1 + R^2C^2\omega^2)(\cos \omega t + RC\omega \sin \omega t)$ as t increases without bound.

5. By solving (5) for q and i in terms of t with $L = 0$, $R = 10$ ohms, $C = 250 \times 10^{-6}$ farad, and $\epsilon = 110 \sin 300t$, show that q rapidly approaches $11(4 \sin 300t - 3 \cos 300t)/2{,}500$ and that i rapidly approaches $1.32(4 \cos 300t + 3 \sin 300t)$.

6. If there is no capacitor in a circuit of the type shown in Fig. 5 and if $L = 0.1$ henry, $R = 10$ ohms, and $\epsilon = 100 \sin 200t$, show that the current i is given (nearly) by $i = 2 \sin 200t - 4 \cos 200t$ after a very short time.

7. Use equations (5) with $R = 0$ and $\epsilon = 0$ to find i and q for the discharge of a capacitor through an inductance L. Assume as initial conditions $q = q_0$, $i = 0$, when $t = 0$. *Hint:* To solve $L(d^2q/dt^2) + (q/C) = 0$, first let

$$i = \frac{dq}{dt} \quad \text{and} \quad \frac{d^2q}{dt^2} = \frac{di}{dq}\frac{dq}{dt} = \frac{i\,di}{dq}.$$

After solving for i, replace i by dq/dt, and solve for q.

32. Air pressure

To obtain an expression for air pressure at height h above the earth, consider a vertical column of air (see Fig. 6) having a small square cross section of area A and extending from the ground upward indefinitely. An element of this column bounded above and below by two horizontal planes at heights h ft and $h + \Delta h$ ft, respectively, from the ground is subjected to an upward force on its lower side of p lb/in.², to a downward force on its upper side of $p + \Delta p$ lb/in.², to the weight of the element, and to horizontal forces. Since the element is in equilibrium, the vertical forces balance. Equating the algebraic sum of the vertical forces to zero, we have

$$pA - (p + \Delta p)A - \bar{\rho}A\,\Delta h = 0, \qquad (6)$$

where $\bar{\rho}$ represents the average density of the element of air. Canceling A, dividing by Δh, and finding the limit approached as Δh approaches zero, we obtain

$$dp + \rho\,dh = 0. \qquad (7)$$

If the air obeys Boyle's law for perfect gases,

$$\rho = kp.^* \qquad (8)$$

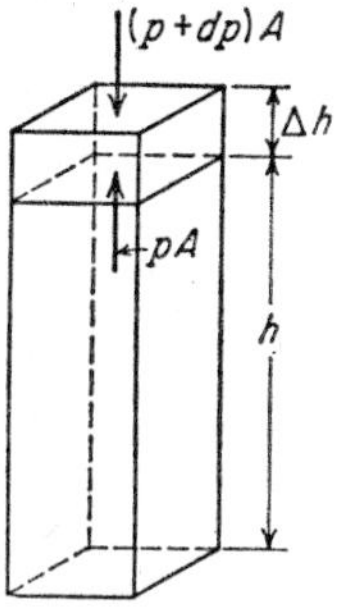

FIG. 6

Solving (7) and (8) as simultaneous equations, we obtain

$$p = ce^{-kh}, \qquad \rho = kce^{-kh}.$$

PROBLEMS

1. Assuming that the atmosphere obeys Boyle's law, find the air pressure at a height of 70,000 ft. Assume that the pressure at the surface of the earth is 14.7 lb/in.² and that it is 10.08 lb/in.² at an altitude of 10,000 ft.

2. Find air pressure at an altitude h if air obeys the adiabatic law $p = k\rho^{1.4}$. Show that in this case the pressure would become zero at a finite height. Find this height in terms of k and the pressure p_0 at the surface of the earth.

3. Compute the theoretical height of an atmosphere which obeys the adiabatic law $p = k\rho^{1.4}$, assuming that pressure at height zero is 14.7 lb/in.² and pressure at a height of 10,000 ft is 10.08 lb/in.²

33. Applications involving forces and velocities

The applications of this section deal with forces acting in a plane and with velocities of particles moving in a plane.

A force may be represented by a directed line segment or vector. Thus, vector PQ in Fig. 7, f units long, represents a force of *magnitude* f units of force and having a direction from P to Q. If PQ makes an angle θ with the directed X-axis, the signed numbers

$$X = f\cos\theta, \qquad Y = f\sin\theta \qquad (9)$$

* A good approximation to air pressure is not to be expected by assuming Boyle's law or the law of adiabatic expansion because the density of a gas depends on its temperature and many other factors.

are called, respectively, the **x-component** and the **y-component** of the force. X may be considered as a force having the direction of the X-axis or the opposite direction according as X is positive or negative, and a similar statement applies to Y. Note that a force is defined in magnitude and direction by its two components X and Y referred to a given system of axes. We shall denote a force with components X and Y by $[X,Y]$ and, in agreement with experiment, define the sum of two forces by

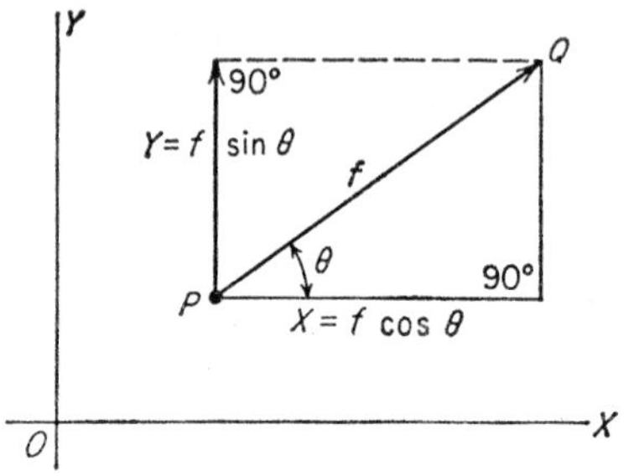

FIG. 7

$$[\mathbf{X}_1,\mathbf{Y}_1] + [\mathbf{X}_2,\mathbf{Y}_2] = [\mathbf{X}_1 + \mathbf{X}_2,\ \mathbf{Y}_1 + \mathbf{Y}_2]. \quad \mathbf{(10)}$$

Observe that, if the magnitude of the force of Fig. 7 were taken as cf, the components would be $X = cf \cos \theta$, $Y = cf \sin \theta$, and

$$\mathbf{c}[\mathbf{X},\mathbf{Y}] = [\mathbf{cX},\mathbf{cY}]. \quad \mathbf{(11)}$$

By means of (10) and (11), we can easily derive

$$a[X_1,Y_1] + b[X_2,Y_2] = [aX_1 + bX_2,\ aY_1 + bY_2]. \quad (12)$$

Let $X(x,y)$ and $Y(x,y)$ represent functions of x and y, and let $[X(x,y), Y(x,y)]$ represent a force acting at point (x,y). Then, the corresponding set of forces, one for each point (x,y) in a region, is called a field of force. Figure 8 represents the field of force $[0,-w]$. This is approximately the field of force, or weight, in a small part of a vertical plane near the surface of the earth.

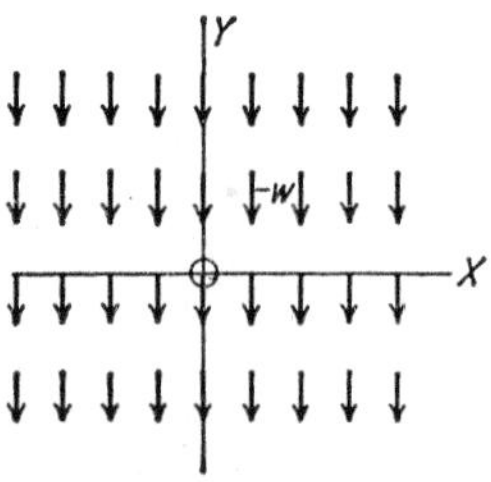

FIG. 8

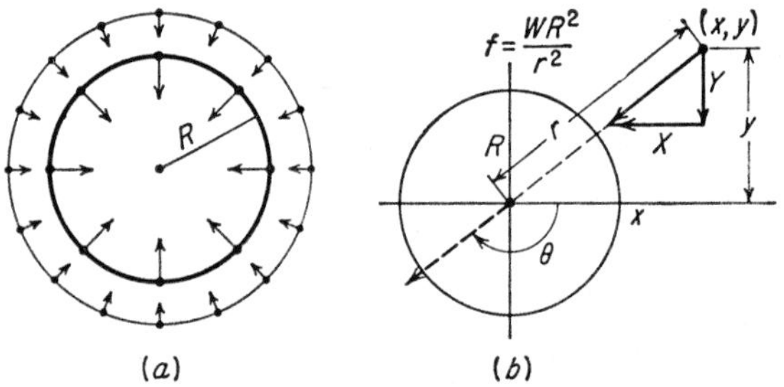

FIG. 9

Figure 9a indicates approximately the field of force of gravity, or earth pull, in a plane through the center of the earth. Figure 9b shows a representative force acting at point (x,y) and having magnitude $f = wR^2/r^2$, where R is the radius of the earth and $r = \sqrt{x^2 + y^2}$. Note that $\cos\theta = -x/r$, $\sin\theta = -y/r$; hence, the field is represented by

$$\left[-\frac{wR^2}{r^2}\frac{x}{r}, -\frac{wR^2}{r^2}\frac{y}{r}\right]. \tag{13}$$

Figure 10 represents the field of force defined by $[y, -x]$. The magnitude of the force is $\sqrt{x^2 + y^2}$ units.

A **line of force** *is a curve in the field of force which has at each of its points a tangent line having the same slope as the vector representing the*

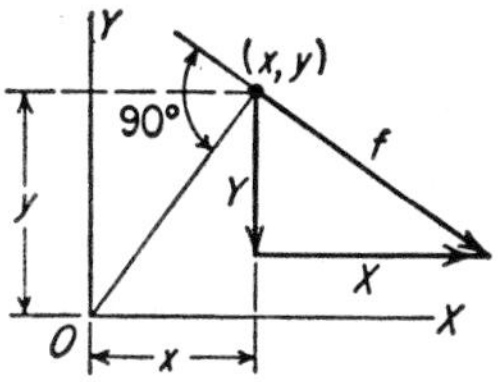

FIG. 10

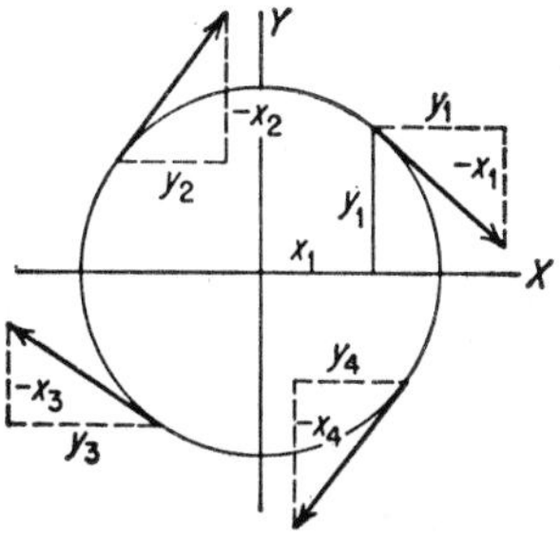

FIG. 11

force through the point. From Fig. 7, we see that the lines of force of field $[X,Y]$ satisfy the differential equation

$$\tan\theta = \frac{dy}{dx} = \frac{Y}{X}, \qquad \text{or} \qquad Y\,dx - X\,dy = 0. \tag{14}$$

The lines of force for the field of Fig. 9 are defined by

$$\frac{dy}{dx} = \frac{-(wR^2/r^2)y}{-(wR^2/r^2)x} = y/x, \qquad \text{or} \qquad y = cx;$$

this represents all lines through the origin.

The lines of force for the field $[y, -x]$ satisfy

$$\frac{dy}{dx} = \frac{-x}{y} \qquad \text{or} \qquad x^2 + y^2 = c.$$

Figure 11 indicates one line of force and some associated forces.

The energy a body has because of its position in a field of force is called its **potential.** Thus, a weight on a platform has potential energy because energy was expended in lifting it up to the platform. It is shown in books on physics that the equation of the curves in a field of force $[X(x,y), Y(x,y)]$ along which potential due to the field is constant is

$$X\,dx + Y\,dy = 0. \tag{15}$$

Comparing $dy/dx = -X/Y$ from (15) for equipotential curves with $dy/dx = Y/X$ for lines of force, we see that *the equipotential curves are the orthogonal trajectories of the lines of force.* The equipotential curves of the field of Fig. 9, from (13) and (15), are defined by

$$X\,dx + Y\,dy = (-wR^2/r^3)(x\,dx + y\,dy) = 0, \qquad \text{or} \qquad x^2 + y^2 = c.$$

Figure 12 shows the equipotential circles $x^2 + y^2 = c$ cutting the lines of force $y = cx$ at right angles.

Applying (15) to the field $[0,-w]$ of Fig. 8, we get $y = c$ as the equipotential curves. Also, the student may apply (14) and (15) to the field $[y,-x]$ of Fig. 11 to find circles with (0,0) as center as lines of force and lines through the origin as equipotential curves. A velocity has magnitude and direction and therefore, like force, can be represented by a vector $[u,v]$. To each point in a region, we can associate a velocity by $[u(x,y),\, v(x,y)]$ and thus define a **velocity field.** The **stream lines** corresponding to **lines of force** are defined by

$$\frac{\mathbf{dy}}{\mathbf{dx}} = \frac{\mathbf{v}}{\mathbf{u}}, \qquad \text{or} \qquad \mathbf{v\,dx - u\,dy = 0}, \tag{16}$$

and the velocity equipotential curves are defined by

$$\mathbf{u\,dx + v\,dy = 0.} \tag{17}$$

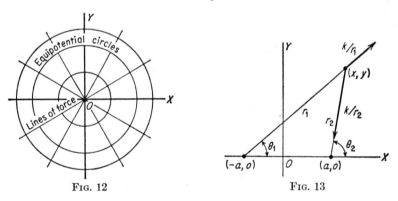

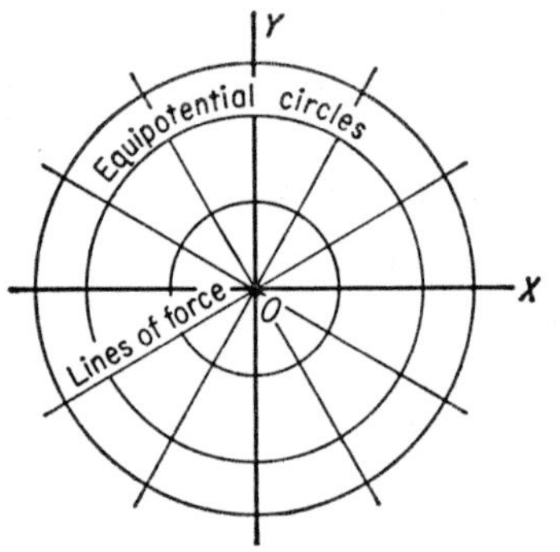

Fig. 12

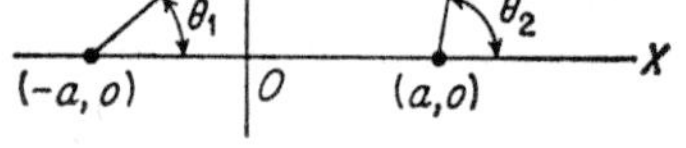

Fig. 13

Example. For the field of force indicated in Fig. 13, find the equations of the lines of force and of the equipotential curves.

Solution. The components of the forces at (x,y) are

$$X_1 = \frac{k}{r_1}\cos\theta_1, \quad Y_1 = \frac{k}{r_1}\sin\theta_1, \quad X_2 = \frac{-k}{r_2}\cos\theta_2, \quad Y_2 = \frac{-k}{r_2}\sin\theta_2. \tag{a}$$

Using formula (10) and values of $\cos\theta_1$, $\cos\theta_2$, $\sin\theta_1$, $\sin\theta_2$, we get for the field

$$\left[\frac{k}{r_1}\cdot\frac{x+a}{r_1} - \frac{k}{r_2}\cdot\frac{x-a}{r_2}, \quad \frac{k}{r_1}\cdot\frac{y}{r_1} - \frac{k}{r_2}\cdot\frac{y}{r_2}\right]. \tag{b}$$

Noting that $r_1 = \sqrt{(x+a)^2 + y^2}$, $r_2 = \sqrt{(x-a)^2 + y^2}$, writing equation (14) for force (*b*), dividing through by $-k$, and rearranging, we get

$$\frac{(x+a)\,dy - y\,dx}{(x+a)^2 + y^2} - \frac{(x-a)\,dy - y\,dx}{(x-a)^2 + y^2} = 0. \qquad (c)$$

Each of the two differentials in (*c*) is exact, and, solving (*c*), we get

$$\tan^{-1}[y/(x+a)] - \tan^{-1}[y/(x-a)] = \tan^{-1} c_1. \qquad (d)$$

Equating the tangents of the members of (*d*) and transforming the result, we get

$$\mathbf{x^2 + (y - c)^2 = a^2 + c^2} \qquad (e)$$

as the equation of the lines of force.

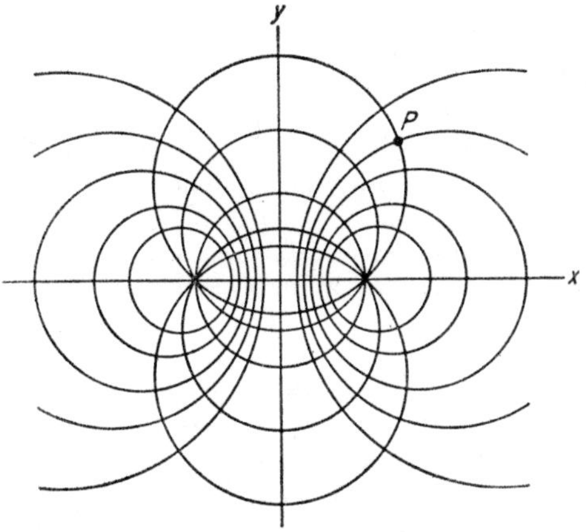

FIG. 14

To get the equations of the equipotential curves, use X and Y from (*b*) in (15), and rearrange the result to obtain

$$\frac{k}{2}\left[\frac{2(x+a)\,dx + 2y\,dy}{(x+a)^2 + y^2} - \frac{2(x-a)\,dx + 2y\,dy}{(x-a)^2 + y^2}\right] = 0. \qquad (f)$$

Here each fraction is an exact differential, and the solution of (*f*) is

$$\ln \frac{(x+a)^2 + y^2}{(x-a)^2 + y^2} = \ln c_1. \qquad (g)$$

Removing the logarithms from (*g*) and simplifying, we get as the equation of the equipotential curves

$$\mathbf{x^2 + y^2 + a^2 + cx = 0}, \qquad (h)$$

where $c = 2a(1 + c_1)/(1 - c_1)$. Observe that points $(a,0)$ and $(-a,0)$ lie on circles (*e*) and that circles (*e*) are the orthogonal trajectories of (*h*). Figure 14 shows a few curves of each family.

EXERCISES

Using differential equations (14) and (15), find the equations of the equipotential curves and of the lines of force for the fields numbered 1 to 6:

1. $[2x,2y]$.

2. $[2x,-2y]$.

3. $[2y,2x]$.

4. $[2xy,\ x^2 - y^2]$.

5. $\left[\dfrac{-y}{x^2+y^2},\ 2 + \dfrac{x}{x^2+y^2}\right]$.

6. $[x^2 + y^2,\ 2xy]$.

7. Figure 15 represents the constant field of force $[10,-32]$. Find the equations of its equipotential lines and of its lines of force. Draw a few curves of each family.

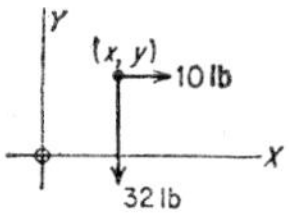

FIG. 15

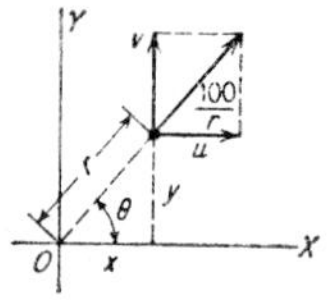

FIG. 16

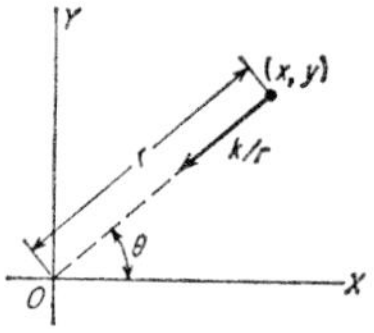

FIG. 17

8. If the velocity field for a thin sheet of water flowing in a plane is defined by Fig. 16, find the equations of the streamlines and of the velocity equipotential curves for the flow. *Hint:* $u = (100/r)\cos\theta = 100x/(x^2+y^2)$.

9. The gravitational field of force for a particle inside the earth obeys approximately the law suggested by Fig. 17. Write a bracket representation of the field, and find the corresponding equations of the equipotential curves and of the lines of force.

10. If $z = x + iy$, $i^2 = -1$, and $f(z) = \varphi(x,y) + i\psi(x,y)$, where φ and ψ are real functions having continuous partial derivatives of the first and second orders, and if $f(z)$ is a differentiable function of z, it can be shown that

$$\frac{\partial\varphi}{\partial x} = \frac{\partial\psi}{\partial y}, \qquad \frac{\partial\varphi}{\partial y} = -\frac{\partial\psi}{\partial x}.^{*} \tag{I}$$

(*a*) Prove that

$$\frac{\partial^2\varphi}{\partial x^2} + \frac{\partial^2\varphi}{\partial y^2} = 0, \qquad \frac{\partial^2\psi}{\partial x^2} + \frac{\partial^2\psi}{\partial y^2} = 0.^{\dagger}$$

(*b*) Show that the differential equations for the velocity equipotential curves and for the streamlines of the two velocity fields

$$[\psi(x,y),\ \varphi(x,y)] \quad \text{and} \quad [-\varphi(x,y),\ \psi(x,y)]$$

are exact.

11. From exercise 10, it appears that a velocity field derived from $z^2 = (x+iy)^2 = x^2 - y^2 + 2xyi$ is represented by $[2xy,\ x^2 - y^2]$. (*a*) Derive a bracket representation of a velocity field from $z^3 = (x+iy)^3$. (*b*) Find the equations of the equipotential curves and of the streamlines for each of the velocity fields.

12. Using the method of exercise 11, write bracket representations of velocity fields and find the equations of their velocity equipotential curves and of their streamlines from:

(*a*) $\dfrac{1}{z} = \dfrac{1}{x+iy} = \dfrac{x-iy}{x^2+y^2}$. (*b*) $2 + \dfrac{3}{z}$. (*c*) $\dfrac{1}{z^2}$.

* These are the celebrated Cauchy-Riemann equations.

† These equations, called Laplace's equations, are of basic importance in many theories of modern physics. To prove them, use (I) and the fact that $\partial^2\varphi/(\partial x\,\partial y) = \partial^2\varphi/(\partial y\,\partial x)$.

13. Figure 18 represents a field of force due to electrical charges, an attraction at $(a,0)$ and a repulsion at $(-a,0)$. Check that the field of force is defined by

$$\left[\frac{k(x+a)}{r_1^3} - \frac{k(x-a)}{r_2^3}, \quad \frac{ky}{r_1^3} - \frac{ky}{r_2^3}\right].$$

Find the equations of the equipotential curves and of the lines of force. The illustrative example is suggestive. The equation of the lines of force formed from the given vector has y as an integrating factor.

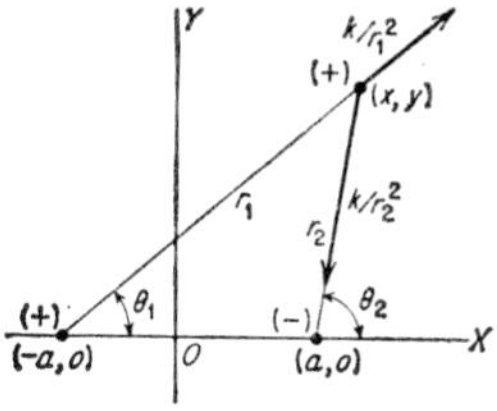

FIG. 18

★14. If r_1 and r_2 are defined by Fig. 18, state an integrating factor for

$$\frac{(x+a)\,dy - y\,dx}{r_1^n} - \frac{(x-a)\,dy - y\,dx}{r_2^n} = 0.$$

34. Review problems

The following argument brings out many instructive features and leads to another application of the linear equation.

Figure 19 represents a chain wrapped partially around a cylinder with horizontal axis; PQ represents a small element of the chain, which we assume to be on the point of slipping in the direction from P to Q. T at P and $T + \Delta T$ at Q represent tensions in the chain. The normal reaction of cylinder on PQ is represented by the components $\Delta N(1 + \mathcal{E}_1)$ along OP and $\mathcal{E}_2\,\Delta N$ along the tangent to the cylinder at P. Similarly, friction is represented by components $\mu(\Delta N + \mathcal{E}_3)$ and $\mu\mathcal{E}_4\,\Delta N$. The

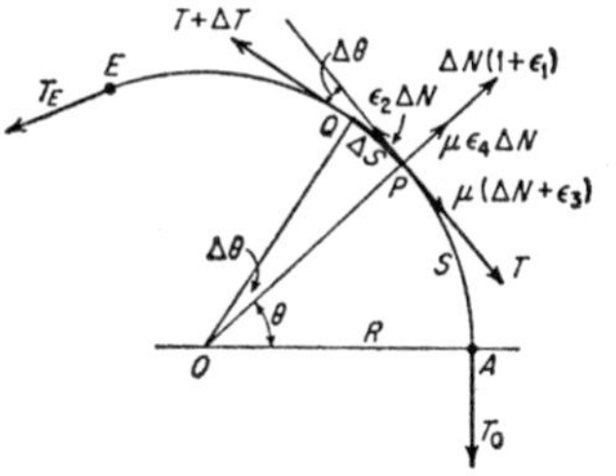

FIG. 19

$\mathcal{E}$'s $\to 0$ as $\Delta\theta \to 0$. The nature of these infinitesimal components constitutes an assumption, but it appears justifiable as soon as we consider PQ to be very small. The remaining notation on the figure is self-explanatory. Resolving forces along the line OP and along the tangent at P, we get

$$\Delta N(1 + \mathcal{E}_1) + \mu\mathcal{E}_4\,\Delta N - (T + \Delta T)\sin\Delta\theta = 0, \tag{18}$$
$$(T + \Delta T)\cos\Delta\theta - T + \mathcal{E}_2\,\Delta N - \mu(\Delta N + \mathcal{E}_3) = 0. \tag{19}$$

Note that second-order infinitesimals vanish as $\Delta\theta \to 0$; thus, $\lim\limits_{\Delta\theta\to 0} \mathcal{E}_1(\Delta N/$

$\Delta\theta) = 0 \cdot dN/d\theta = 0$. Also,

$$T\,\frac{\cos\Delta\theta - 1}{\Delta\theta} = -T_2\left(\frac{\sin\frac{1}{2}\Delta\theta}{\Delta\theta}\right)2\sin\tfrac{1}{2}\Delta\theta \to 0$$

as $\Delta\theta \to 0$. Hence, dividing (18) and (19) through by $\Delta\theta$ and taking limits as $\Delta\theta \to 0$, we get

$$\frac{dN}{d\theta} - T = 0, \qquad \frac{dT}{d\theta} - \mu\frac{dN}{d\theta} = 0. \tag{20}$$

From (20), we get

$$\frac{dT}{d\theta} = \mu T, \qquad \text{or} \qquad T = ce^{\mu\theta} \tag{21}$$

Inspection of Fig. 19 shows that $T = T_0$ when $\theta = 0$. Hence, from (21), $T_0 = ce^{\mu 0} = c$, and (21) becomes

$$T = T_0 e^{\mu\theta}. \tag{22}$$

If $T_0 = 100$ lb, $\mu = 0.3$, and the chain is wrapped halfway round the cylinder so that $\theta = \pi$, we get from (22)

$$T_E = 100e^{0.3\pi}\text{ lb} = 256.6\text{ lb}$$

EXERCISES

1. The slope of a certain curve at each of its points (x,y) is given by

$$(3ax^2 + 2bxy - ey^2)/(3fy^2 + 2exy - bx^2),$$

and it passes through $(m,0)$; find its equation.

2. Find in polar coordinates the equation of a curve passing through (5,2) if $\tan\psi$ (§12) at each point (ρ,θ) on the curve is given by $\tan\psi = \rho\theta/(\rho + \theta^3)$.

3. Find the equation of a curve for which the ordinate y of the point of contact of each tangent and the length of the perpendicular to the tangent from the origin are equal. First show that the distance from (0,0) to the tangent is $[(y - x\,dy/dx)]/\sqrt{1 + (dy/dx)^2}$.

4. Find the equation of the orthogonal trajectories (§12) of the system of circles $\rho = c(\cos\theta + 6\sin\theta)$.

5. A tank initially contains salt in the pores of inert material and 10 gal of fresh water. The salt dissolves at a rate per minute of two times the difference between 3 lb/gal and the concentration of the brine. Two gallons of fresh water per minute enter the tank. How much salt will dissolve in the first 10 min?

6. In problem 5, assume, in addition to the given conditions, that 1 gal/min of the brine runs out, and then find how much salt dissolves in the first 10 min and how much of the dissolved salt is still in the tank after 10 min.

7. *Prove that if $\rho^2\,d\theta/dt = bc$, $d\rho/dt = (c/\rho)\sqrt{b\rho - b^2}$ for a moving particle, and if $\rho = b$ when $\theta = 0$, then the particle moves on the parabola $\rho = 2b/(1 + \cos\theta)$.

* The motion of problem 7 is like that of a comet, and the motion of problem 8 is like that of a planet.

8. Find ρ in terms of θ if $\rho^2\,d\theta/dt = 15$, $d\rho/dt = \frac{4}{9}\sin\theta\,\rho^2\,d\theta/dt$, and $\rho = 1$ when $\theta = 0$. Show that the time for the particle to go round its curve (an ellipse) is 2π time units. Assume that $\int_0^{2\pi} d\theta/(5 + 4\cos\theta)^2 = \frac{10}{27}\pi$.

9. If the acceleration a ft/sec² of a body moving in a straight line is equal numerically to $-s$ ft, where s is the signed distance from a point on the line and $s = 0$, velocity $v = 1$ ft/sec when $t = 0$, find v in terms of s and s in terms of t. *Hint:* $a = v\,dv/ds$, $v = ds/dt$.

10. The motion of a weight hung from a ceiling by a spring is vertical and $a = 16(4 - s)$, where a ft/sec² is acceleration and s is the number of feet the spring is stretched. Also, $s = 0$, $v = 0$ when $t = 0$. Use $a = v\,dv/ds$ to find v in terms of s and then $v = ds/dt$ to find s in terms of t. Show that $0 \leq s \leq 4$ and that the time for a complete motion down and back is $\frac{1}{2}\pi$ sec.

11. A circuit has a resistance of 10 ohms, a capacitor of capacity 2×10^{-4} farad, and a battery of 100 volts. Find an expression for the quantity q of electricity on the capacitor at time t if initially $q = 0$ when $t = 0$. What are the approximate values of q and i after a few seconds?

12. In problem 11, replace the emf by $100 \sin 377t$, and solve the resulting problem. Assume that $\sqrt{500^2 + 377^2} = 626$.

★**13.** Find a nondifferential equation connecting i and q if $4L^2\,di/dt + 4LRi + R^2q = 0$, $i = dq/dt$. *Hint:* $di/dt = (di/dq)(dq/dt) = i\,di/dq$.

14. Find the theoretical height of an atmosphere on a planet for which $p = k\rho^2$, where p lb/ft² is pressure, ρ lb/ft³ is density, and k is a constant. Assume that, when height h is zero, $p = 2{,}210$ lb/ft² and, at $h = 10{,}000$ ft, $p = 1{,}452$ lb/ft².

15. Assume that the chain of Fig. 19 weighs ρ lb/ft. Hence, in Fig. 19 force $\rho R\,\Delta\theta$ acts vertically on element PQ. Assume that OA is horizontal, and, by resolving forces along and perpendicular to the tangent at P and taking limits, as $\Delta\theta \to 0$, derive

$$\frac{dT}{d\theta} - \mu T = \rho R(\cos\theta + \mu \sin\theta).$$

Find the general solution of this equation.

16. (*a*) Using the solution of problem 15, show that $l(1 + \mu^2) = 2\mu R(1 + e^{\pi\mu})$ if $T = 0$ when $\theta = 0$ and $T = \rho l$ when $\theta = \pi$. (*b*) Show that, if the chain extends only from $\theta = \frac{1}{2}\pi$ to $\theta = \pi$ and is about to slip, then $e^{\pi\mu/2}(1 - \mu^2) = 2\mu$. (*c*) If the chain extends only from $\theta = \frac{1}{4}\pi$ to $\theta = \pi$ and is about to slip, find the relation that μ must satisfy.

Find the equations of the lines of force and of the equipotential curves for the following fields defined by:

17. $[2x, -3y]$.

18. $[1/xy, 2 - 8x^2y^2]$.

19. $\left[\frac{x}{\sqrt{x^2 + y^2}} - 10x, \frac{y}{\sqrt{x^2 + y^2}} - 4\right]$.

20. $\left[\frac{y}{\sqrt{x^2 + y^2}}, \frac{-x}{\sqrt{x^2 + y^2}} + 1\right]$.

21. $[Y,X]$, where $X + iY = x + iy - 2/(x + iy)$.

★**22.** If $z = x + iy$, $i^2 = -1$, then $df(z)/dz$ and $\int f(z)\,dz$ are found by the same method as if z were real. Show that if $X + iY = f(z)$ then the lines of force and the equipotential curves of $[Y,X]$ are given by $\text{Re} \int f(z)\,dz = c_1$, $\text{Im} \int f(z)\,dz = ic_2$, where Re and Im mean *real part of* and *imaginary part of*. Check this for $f(z) = z^2$. *Hint:* From $[\text{Re}\,(-i)f(z), \text{Re}\,f(z)]$, we get

$$\text{Re}\,[\int -if(z)\,dy - f(z)\,dx] = \text{Re} \int -f(z)(dx + i\,dy) = \text{Re} \int -f(z)\,dz.$$

CHAPTER 5

FIRST-ORDER EQUATIONS OF DEGREE HIGHER THAN THE FIRST

35. Foreword

This chapter relates mainly to three types of differential equations of the first order and degree higher than the first. Since certain special solutions, called *singular solutions*, involve envelopes of families of curves, a little theory of envelopes will be reviewed and used.

36. Equations solvable for dy/dx

This section deals with a type of first-order differential equation which can be resolved into factors linear in dy/dx. The notation

$$p = \frac{dy}{dx} \tag{1}$$

will be used throughout this chapter. An equation which can be reduced to the form

$$(p - A_1)(p - A_2) \cdots (p - A_n) = 0, \tag{2}$$

where the $A_1, A_2, \ldots, A_n$ are functions of x and y, may be solved by equating each factor to zero and integrating the resulting equations. The solutions thus obtained

$$\varphi_1(x,y,c_1) = 0, \qquad \varphi_2(x,y,c_2) = 0, \qquad \ldots, \qquad \varphi_n(x,y,c_n) = 0 \tag{3}$$

may be regarded as the result required, or we may use

$$\varphi_1(x,y,c) \cdot \varphi_2(x,y,c) \cdots \varphi_n(x,y,c) = 0 \tag{4}$$

as the general solution; for (4) represents all curves defined by (3) and no others.

Take, for example,

$$(p - 1)(p - \tfrac{1}{2}x) = 0. \tag{5}$$

Equating each factor to zero and solving the resulting equations, we get the solutions

$$y = x + c_1, \qquad y = \tfrac{1}{4}x^2 + c_2. \tag{6}$$

Either of the equations (6) satisfies (5), as does also

$$(y - x + c)(y - \tfrac{1}{4}x^2 + c) = 0. \tag{7}$$

Figure 1 relates to (5) and (6). Each short stroke has a slope defined by $p - 1 = 0$, and the lines suggested by these strokes represent the solution $y = x + c_1$. Similarly, each long stroke has a direction associated

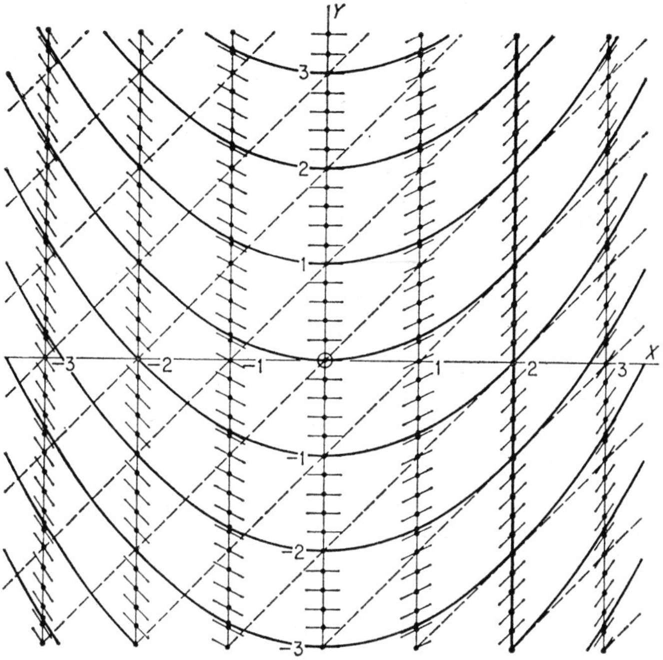

FIG. 1

to its mid-point (x,y) by $p - x = 0$, and each solution parabola $y = \frac{1}{2}x^2 + c$ has at each point P on it a tangent line containing the long stroke associated with P. Observe that every point in the plane, except those on line $x = 2$, has two associated directions. Accordingly, through each point in the plane passes a solution straight line and a solution parabola; for points on line $x = 2$, the line is tangent to the parabola.

EXERCISES

Solve the following equations:

1. $9p^2 - x^4 = 0,\ p = \dfrac{dy}{dx}.$

2. $(p - 3x^2)(p - xy)(p - y^2) = 0.$

3. $4p^2 = 25x.$

4. $p^2 - 4y^2 = 0.$

5. $y^2(a^2 + p^2) = 1.$

6. $8ap^3 = 27y.$

7. $2x^2p^2 + 5xyp + 2y^2 = 0.$

8. $p^2 + apy = x^2 + axy.$

9. $xp^2 - 2yp - x = 0.$

10. $(x + 2y)p^3 + 3(x + y)p^2 + (y + 2x)p = 0.$

11. $(a^2 - x^2)p^3 + bx(a^2 - x^2)p^2 - p - bx = 0.$

12. If, from the equation $x^2p^2 + 5xyp + 6y^2 = 0$, we form a new equation by replacing p by $-1/p$, what will be the relation between the systems of curves represented by the solutions of the two equations?

13. Denote by P any point on a curve C, by T the point where the tangent to C at P meets the Y-axis, and by N the point where the normal to C at P meets the X-axis. Find the equation of C if: (a) $PT = k$, a constant; (b) $PN = k$.

37. Envelopes

Since the equations of envelopes appear as particular solutions of differential equations, a brief review of the pertinent facts of envelopes is in order.

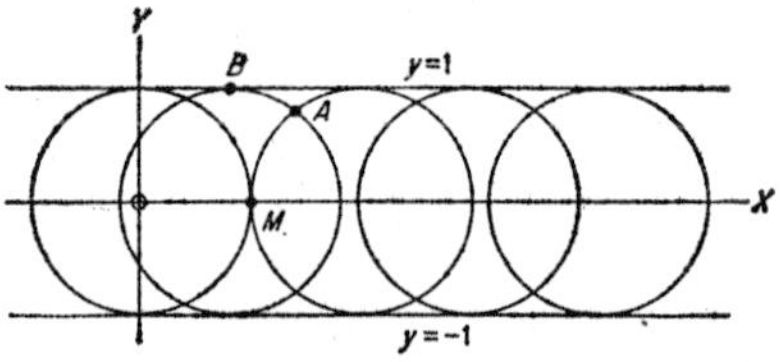

FIG. 2

Any curve which is tangent to an infinite number of members of a singly infinite family of curves and which is tangent at each of its points to at least one of these curves is a part or the whole of the **envelope** *of the family.*

For example (see Fig. 2), the envelope of the circles

$$(x - c)^2 + y^2 = 1 \tag{8}$$

consists of the lines

$$y = \pm 1.$$

Consider the system of straight lines defined by

$$y - cx + c^2 = 0. \tag{9}$$

To each point in the plane, (9) usually associates two values of c, namely,

$$c = (x \pm \sqrt{x^2 - 4y})/2. \tag{10}$$

Hence, two lines of system (9) usually pass through a point. From (10), we see that to each point on the graph of $x^2 - 4y = 0$ only one value of c will be associated. Hence, only one line of system (9) will pass through a point on $x^2 - 4y = 0$. The slope of the line (9) is $dy/dx = c$, and the slope of $x^2 - 4y = 0$ is $dy/dx = \frac{1}{2}x$. Since, by (10), $c = \frac{1}{2}x$ when $x^2 - 4y = 0$, we see that each of the lines of system (9) is tangent to $x^2 - 4y = 0$. Figure 3 represents the curve $x^2 - 4y = 0$ as the envelope of the system of lines (9).

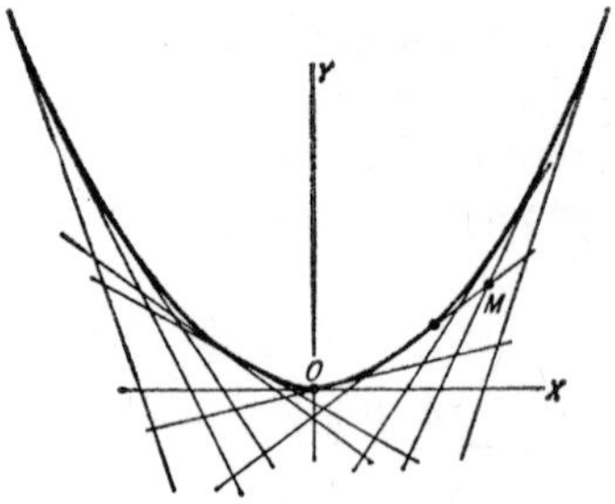

FIG. 3

Note that, when $x^2 - 4y < 0$, the values of p from (10) are imaginary. Hence, no lines of system (9) go through points inside the parabola of Fig. 3.

A general system of curves is represented by

$$f(x,y,c) = 0. \tag{11}$$

For convenience, denote partial derivatives by subscripts. Thus

$$\frac{\partial f(x,y,c)}{\partial x} = f_x(x,y,c), \qquad \frac{\partial^2 f(x,y,c)}{\partial c^2} = f_{cc}(x,y,c), \qquad \text{etc.} \tag{12}$$

Assume that f and its partial derivatives of the first and second orders are continuous in all regions involved. Then, for fixed values of x and y such that $f_{cc}(x,y,c) \neq 0$, c will be a double root* of $f(x,y,c) = 0$ if and only if

$$\mathbf{f(x,y,c) = 0, \qquad f_c(x,y,c) = 0.} \tag{14}$$

We shall show that (14) is satisfied by any envelope of $f(x,y,c) = 0$. The coordinates of intersection of an envelope of (11) with one of its curves is determined by a value of c; that is, values of x and y for points on an envelope may be written in the form

$$x = \varphi(c), \qquad y = \psi(c). \tag{15}$$

Since x and y from (15) satisfy (11), $f(\varphi,\psi,c) = 0$ identically and

$$f(\varphi,\psi,c) = 0, \qquad f_x\frac{dx}{dc} + f_y\frac{dy}{dc} + f_c = 0. \tag{16}$$

The slope of (11) is given by $dy/dx = -f_x/f_y$ and the slope of (15) by $dy/dx = (d\psi/dc)/(d\varphi/dc)$; these two slopes are equal at a point on (15), and therefore

$$-\frac{f_x}{f_y} = \frac{d\psi/dc}{d\varphi/dc} \qquad \text{or} \qquad f_x\frac{d\varphi}{dc} + f_y\frac{d\psi}{dc} = 0. \tag{17}$$

From (17) and (16), we easily deduce (14) and conclude that *any envelope of* (11) *must satisfy* (14).

The slopes in (17) would be undefined if, at points of (14), $d\varphi/dc$ and $d\psi/dc$ were both zero or if f_x and f_y were both zero. Hence, we assume that for points on (14)

$$f_x^2 + f_y^2 \neq 0, \qquad (d\varphi/dc)^2 + (d\psi/dc)^2 \neq 0. \tag{18}$$

* If, in an interval $c - d \leqq m \leqq c + d$, $f'(m) \neq 0$ and $f(m)$, $f'(m)$, and $f''(m)$ are continuous, then Taylor's formula from calculus states that to each value m in the interval there is associated a value ξ depending on m and lying between $c - d$ and $c + d$ such that

$$f(m) = f(c) + f'(c)(m - c) + \tfrac{1}{2}f''(\xi)(m - c)^2. \tag{13}$$

Hence, under the conditions mentioned, c is a double root of $f(m) = 0$ if and only if $f(c) = 0$ and $f'(c) = 0$.

A curve along which $f_x = 0$ and $f_y = 0$ is a locus of singular points, that is, cusps, nodes, and isolated points. The equation of this locus satisfies (14) but is generally not part of the envelope.

Also, any curve defined by equations of the form (15) which satisfy (14) and (18) must be an envelope of (11); for (16) holds for such a curve, and, from (16) and (14), we easily deduce (17).

The result of eliminating c from (14) is called the **c-discriminant** of $f(x,y,c) = 0$. *To find the envelope of a system in the form* (11), *find the c-discriminant of the given equation. All parts of it for which* (18) *holds will belong to the envelope. Investigate all other parts.*

Equation (14) applied for $f = y - cx + c^2 = 0$ from (9) gives

$$y - cx + c^2 = 0, \qquad -x + 2c = 0.$$

Elimination of c from these gives the equation of the envelope of f, namely,

$$y - (\tfrac{1}{2}x)x + (\tfrac{1}{2}x)^2 = 0, \qquad \text{or} \qquad 4y - x^2 = 0.$$

Also, (14) applied to f from (8) gives the equation of the envelope of (8), namely,

$$(x - c)^2 + y^2 = 1, \qquad 2(x - c)(-1) = 0, \qquad \text{or} \qquad y = \pm 1.$$

There may be no envelope. For example, the system of parallel lines

$$5x + 6y - c = 0$$

evidently has no envelope. For it $\partial f/\partial c = -1$, and -1 cannot be zero.

Example. Find the equation of the envelope of

$$f = y^2 - (x - c)(x - 2c)^2 = 0. \tag{a}$$

Solution. Applying (14), we obtain

$$y^2 - (x - c)(x - 2c)^2 = 0, \qquad (x - 2c)^2 + 4(x - c)(x - 2c) = 0,$$

or

$$y^2 - (x - c)(x - 2c)^2 = 0, \qquad (x - 2c)(5x - 6c) = 0. \tag{b}$$

One part of (*b*) is $x = 2c$, $y = 0$. Note that

$$\begin{aligned} f_{x(x=2c)} &= [-(x - 2c)^2 - 2(x - c)(x - 2c)]_{x=2c} = 0, \\ (f_y)_{y=0} &= (2y)_{y=0} = 0. \end{aligned} \tag{c}$$

Figure 4 shows the graph of $y = 0$, $x = 2c$ as a locus of singular points (nodes and isolated points) of (*a*), not part of its envelope.

The second part of (*b*) is

$$y^2 - (x - c)(x - 2c)^2 = 0, \qquad 5x - 6c = 0. \tag{d}$$

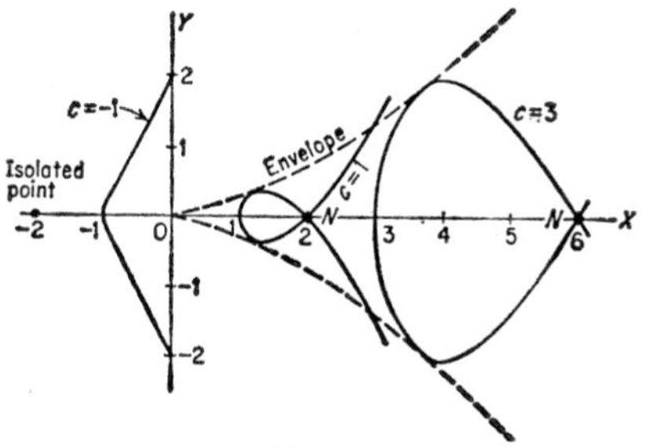

FIG. 4

Eliminating c from (d), we obtain the envelope of (a),

$$y^2 - \tfrac{2}{27}x^3 = 0. \tag{e}$$

The dashed curve of Fig. 4 represents this equation.

EXERCISES

1. Use (14) to show that the envelope of the circles $x^2 + (y - 10c)^2 = 20c^2$ is $x = \pm\frac{1}{2}y$, and check that Fig. 5 represents the system of circles and its envelope.

Use (14) to find the equations of the envelope of:

2. $c^2 + cx + y^2 = 0.$

3. $xc^2 + 2cy - x = 1.$

4. $c^3 - 3cy = x.$

5. $x^2 + (y - c)^2 = 1.$

6. Show that the system of curves $x^2 + 2y^3 = c$ has no envelope.

7. Show that the c-discriminant of $x^2 - y^2 + c(x + y - 2) = 0$ consists of the point $(1,1)$.

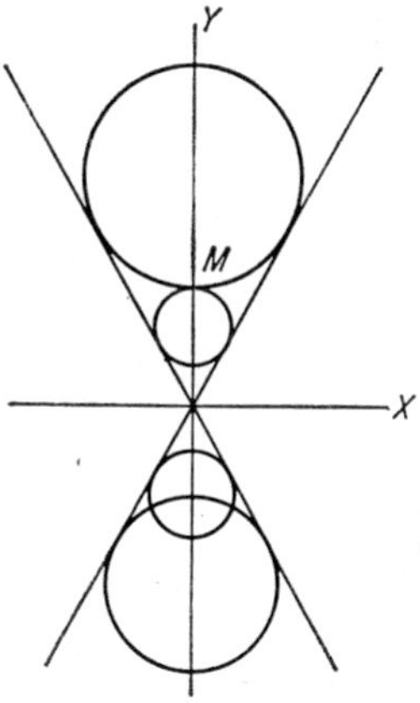

FIG. 5

38. Envelope from differential equation

Represent a general differential equation and its general solution by

$$\varphi(x,y,p) = 0, \qquad f(x,y,c) = 0. \tag{19}$$

To each value c_0 of c satisfying $f(x_0,y_0,c) = 0$, there is associated a value p_0 of p satisfying $\varphi(x_0,y_0,p) = 0$ and p_0 is the slope of $f(x,y,c_0) = 0$ at (x_0,y_0).

If c_0 is a double root of $f(x_0,y_0,c) = 0$, then there is a double root p_0 of $\varphi(x_0,y_0,p) = 0$ which is the slope of the tangent to $f(x,y,c) = 0$ at (x_0,y_0). From §37, the envelope of $f(x,y,c) = 0$ is a locus of points (x,y) at each of which $f(x,y,c) = 0$ has a double root. Therefore, the envelope of $f(x,y,c) = 0$ is a locus of points (x,y) for each of which $\varphi(x,y,p)$ has a double root, and, in accordance with the footnote on page 73,

$$\varphi(x,y,p) = 0, \qquad \varphi_p(x,y,p) = 0 \tag{20}$$

contain the envelope of $f(x,y,c) = 0$.

The result of eliminating p from (20) is called the **p-discriminant** of $\varphi(x,y,p) = 0$. The name **tac-locus** is given to a locus of points at which two curves of a system have the same tangent. In Fig. 2, $y = 0$ and in Fig. 5, $x = 0$ are tac-loci of points such as M. Since, at a point on the tac-locus of $f(x,y,c) = 0$, two values of p associated to the point by $\varphi(x,y,p) = 0$ are equal, the coordinates of the point must satisfy the p-discriminant of $\varphi(x,y,p) = 0$. *Hence, the p-discriminant of* $\varphi(x,y,p) = 0$ *must contain the equation of any tac-locus* $f(x,y,c) = 0$ *may have.* A like argument shows that *the p-discriminant of* $\varphi(x,y,p) = 0$ *contains the equation of any locus of cusps that* $f(x,y,c) = 0$ *may have.* The equation of a tac-locus or a locus of cusps does not generally satisfy the corresponding differential equation. *The equation of the envelope of* $f(x,y,c) = 0$ *satisfies* $\varphi(x,y,p) = 0$ *and is called the singular solution of* $\varphi(x,y,p) = 0$.

To find the equation of the envelope of the general solution of a differential equation $\varphi(x,y,p) = 0$, *find the p-discriminant of* $\varphi(x,y,p) = 0$; *the part of it which satisfies* $\varphi(x,y,p) = 0$ *represents the required envelope.*

Example 1. Find the singular solution of

$$4y = 8px + 8x^2 + p^2. \tag{a}$$

Solution. In this case, we get from (20)

$$4y = 8px + 8x^2 + p^2, \qquad 8x + 2p = 0. \tag{b}$$

Replace p in the first equation by $-4x$ from the second, and simplify to get

$$\mathbf{y + 2x^2 = 0.} \tag{c}$$

Testing $y = -2x^2$, $p = -4x$ in (a), we get

$$4(-2x^2) = 8(-4x)x + 8x^2 + (-4x)^2, \qquad \text{or} \qquad -8x^2 = -8x^2.$$

Since $y + 2x^2 = 0$ satisfies (a), it is a solution of (a), and, being also the p-discriminant of (a), it represents the envelope of the general solution of (a).

Example 2. Find the singular solution of

$$4(1 - p)^2 = 9(x + y)(1 + p)^2. \tag{a}$$

Solution. The derivative of (a) with respect to p is

$$-8(1 - p) = 18(x + y)(1 + p). \tag{b}$$

Replacing $(1 - p)/(1 + p)$ of (a) by its value $-9(x + y)/4$ from (b) and simplifying, we get

$$(x + y)(9x + 9y - 4) = 0. \qquad (c)$$

Neither $x + y = 0$ nor $9x + 9y - 4 = 0$ satisfies (a), and therefore the general solution of (a), which is

$$(x + y)^3 = (x - y + c)^2, \qquad (d)$$

has no envelope. Figure 6 represents the solution (d). For (d), $x + y = 0$ is a locus of cusps. $9x + 9y - 4 = 0$ is an extraneous factor introduced by the process of elimination. Note that (a) does not have equal roots for p when $9(x + y) = 4$.

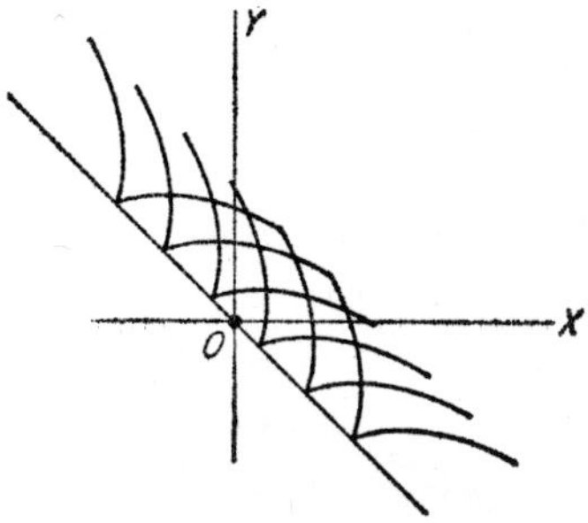

FIG. 6

EXERCISES

1. Show that the p-discriminant of $y = x^3p^2 - 2xp$, obtained by using (20) with $\psi = y - x^3p^2 + 2xp$, is $y = -x^{-1}$. Prove that $y = -x^{-1}$ satisfies $y = x^3p^2 - 2xp$ and is therefore a singular solution of it.

2. Show that the p-discriminant of $y = 2px + p^2$ is $y + x^2 = 0$. Show that this does not satisfy the differential equation, and conclude that $y = 2px + p^2$ has no singular solution.

3. The differential equation of the circles $(x - c)^2 + y^2 = 1$ (see Fig. 2) is $y^2(1 + p^2) = 1$. Show that the p-discriminant represents the envelope $y = \pm 1$ and also the tac-locus $y = 0$. Does $y = 0$ satisfy the differential equation?

4. Find the p-discriminant of $y = 2px - yp^2$. Is the p-discriminant a singular solution of $y = 2px - yp^2$?

5. Differentiate partially with respect to p

$$(p^2 + 1)(2y - x)^2 = (x + py)^2 \qquad (a)$$

to obtain

$$2p(2y - x)^2 = 2(x + py)y. \qquad (b)$$

Replace $(2y - x)^2$ in (a) by its values from (b), and simplify to obtain $y = px$; then eliminate p between $y = px$ and (a) to obtain the singular solution $y(3y - 4x) = 0$. Prove that this singular solution satisfies (a). Also, replace $x + py$ in (a) by its value from (b), thus showing that $2y - x = 0$ is part of the p-discriminant. Prove that $2y - x = 0$ does not satisfy (a). It defines a tac-locus. The solution of (a) is

$$(x - 2c)^2 + (y - c)^2 = c^2. \qquad (c)$$

Show that the c-discriminant, representing the envelope of (c), is $y(3y - 4x) = 0$. Plot the c-discriminant, the tac-locus, and a few of the circles (c).

Find the singular solutions of:

6. $2y = p^2 + 4px + 2x^2$.

7. $y = 2px + 3p^2$.

8. $y = p^2$.

9. $4yx^6 = px^7 + 4p^2$.

39. Equations solvable for y

When a first-order differential equation is solvable for y, it may be written in the form

$$y = f(x,p). \tag{21}$$

Taking the total derivative of this equation with respect to x, we get

$$\frac{dy}{dx} = p = \frac{\partial f}{\partial x} + \frac{\partial f}{\partial p}\frac{dp}{dx}. \tag{22}$$

This equation, since y does not appear in it, may be solved as an equation in x and p to get

$$\psi(x,p,c) = 0. \tag{23}$$

Equations (21) and (23) may be thought of as the parametric equations (p being the parameter) of a system of curves and therefore as the general solution of (21).

The result of eliminating p between equations (21) and (23) gives the general solution as an equation in x, y, and an arbitrary constant. If one suspects that the eliminant contains, as it may, extraneous factors that do not represent solutions, one should check by substitution in the differential equation.

Any singular solution may be found by using the p-discriminant as indicated in §37.

Example 1. Solve

$$y = \tfrac{9}{2}xp^{-1} + \tfrac{1}{2}px. \tag{a}$$

Solution. Differentiating (a) with respect to x, obtain

$$p = (-\tfrac{9}{2}xp^{-2} + \tfrac{1}{2}x)\frac{dp}{dx} + \tfrac{9}{2}p^{-1} + \tfrac{1}{2}p, \tag{b}$$

or, rearranged,

$$(-\tfrac{9}{2}p^{-2} + \tfrac{1}{2})x\frac{dp}{dx} - p(-\tfrac{9}{2}p^{-2} + \tfrac{1}{2}) = 0. \tag{c}$$

Equation (c) will be satisfied if either of the equations

$$x\frac{dp}{dx} - p = 0, \qquad -\tfrac{9}{2}p^{-2} + \tfrac{1}{2} = 0 \tag{d}$$

holds true. From the first of (d), obtain

$$x = cp. \tag{e}$$

Parametric equations of the solution, obtained by solving (a) and (e) for x and y in terms of p, are

$$\mathbf{x} = \mathbf{cp}, \qquad \mathbf{y} = \tfrac{9}{2}\mathbf{c} + \tfrac{1}{2}\mathbf{cp}^2. \tag{f}$$

To get the solution in terms of x and y, eliminate p from (f). Replacing p in the second equation of (f) by its value from the first and simplifying, obtain

$$\mathbf{2cy = 9c^2 + x^2}. \qquad (g)$$

The **singular solution** is obtained by eliminating p between (a) and the second equation of (d) and simplifying. This gives

$$\mathbf{y = \pm 3x}. \qquad (h)$$

Check by trial that $y = 3x$ and $y = -3x$ both satisfy (a). Also observe that for no value of c does (g) give (h).

Example 2. Solve the equation*

$$y = px - \tfrac{4}{27}p^3. \qquad (a)$$

Solution. Differentiation of (a) with respect to x gives

$$p = p + (x - \tfrac{4}{9}p^2)\frac{dp}{dx}, \qquad \text{or} \qquad (x - \tfrac{4}{9}p^2)\frac{dp}{dx} = 0. \qquad (b)$$

Equating dp/dx to zero and solving it, we get

$$p = c. \qquad (c)$$

Substitution of c for p in (a) gives the general solution

$$\mathbf{y = cx - \tfrac{4}{27}c^3}. \qquad (d)$$

To get the singular solution, eliminate p from

$$y = px - \tfrac{4}{27}p^3 \qquad \text{and} \qquad x - \tfrac{4}{9}p^2 = 0, \qquad (e)$$

to obtain

$$\mathbf{y^2 = x^3}. \qquad (f)$$

By testing we find that this satisfies (a) and is therefore its singular solution. Also (f) is the envelope of (a) by §37 and the lines (a) are the tangents of the semicubical parabola (f).

EXERCISES

Find the general solution and the singular solution of:

1. $2y = p^2 + 4px + 2x^2$.

2. $2yp = 3x + xp^2$.

3. $y = 5px + 5x^2 + p^2$.

4. $p^2x^4 = y + px$.

For each equation find a solution in parametric form, and use the p-discriminant to show that there is no singular solution:

5. $y = -px + p^2$.

6. $y = 2xp - 3p^2$.

* The equation of the example is a special case of the famous Clairaut's equation

$$y = px + f(p).$$

Alexis Claude Clairaut (1713–1765) was the first man to differentiate a differential equation, as we have done in this section, in order to solve it. The solution is $y = cx + f(c)$, and the p-discriminant always gives a singular solution.

7. Find the general solution of $y = (p + p^{-1})x + p^2$.

★**8.** Show that the general solution of Clairaut's equation $y = px + f(p)$ is $y = cx + f(c)$. Find the complete solution of $y = px + p^3$.

9. Show by the method of this section that the general solution of $y = px \ln x + \varphi(px)$ is $y = c \ln x + \varphi(c)$. Show that the singular solution of $y = px \ln x + p^2x^2$ is $4y = -(\ln x)^2$.

10. Show that the general solution of $y = px + 2x^2 + f(p + 4x)$ is $y = cx - 2x^2 + f(c)$. Find the singular solution when $f(p + 4x) = (p + 4x)^4$.

★**11.** Find the general solution of $y = (px + x^2) \ln x - \frac{1}{2}x^2 + \varphi(px + x^2)$. Also, find the singular solution when $\varphi(px + x^2) = (px + x^2)^2$.

40. Equations solvable for x

An equation of the first order when written in the form

$$x = \varphi(y,p) \tag{24}$$

can be solved by differentiating with respect to y, replacing dx/dy by $1/p$, and proceeding as in §39. Also, it may be solved by differentiating (24) with respect to y, replacing dx/dy by q and p by $1/q$, and then proceeding as in §39.

A first-order differential equation which is solvable for x may be written in the form

$$x = f(y,p). \tag{25}$$

Taking the total derivative of this equation with respect to y, we get

$$\frac{dx}{dy} = \frac{1}{p} = \frac{\partial f}{\partial y} + \frac{\partial f}{\partial p}\frac{dp}{dy}. \tag{26}$$

This equation may be solved as an equation in y and p to obtain

$$\psi(y,p,c) = 0. \tag{27}$$

Equations (25) and (27) may be considered as the general solution in parametric form, or we may eliminate p between (25) and (27) to obtain the solution as a relation between x, y, and a constant of integration.

Example. Solve

$$y = 2px + y^2p^3. \tag{a}$$

Solution. Solving for x, we get

$$x = \frac{y}{2p} - \frac{y^2p^2}{2}. \tag{b}$$

The derivative of (b) with respect to y is

$$\frac{dx}{dy} = \frac{1}{p} = \frac{1}{2p} - yp^2 - \left(\frac{y}{2p^2} + y^2p\right)\frac{dp}{dy}, \tag{c}$$

or, simplified,

$$\frac{1}{2p} + yp^2 = -\frac{y}{p}\left(\frac{1}{2p} + yp^2\right)\frac{dp}{dy}. \tag{d}$$

Dividing out $(1/2p) + yp^2$ and integrating, we obtain

$$py = c, \qquad \text{or} \qquad y = \frac{c}{p}. \tag{e}$$

Substituting y from (e) in (b), we get

$$x = \frac{c}{2p^2} - \frac{c^2}{2}. \tag{f}$$

Equations (e) and (f) give, in parametric form, the general solution required. Eliminating p between (e) and (f), we find the solution in rectangular form to be

$$x = \frac{y^2}{2c} - \frac{c^2}{2}, \qquad \text{or} \qquad \mathbf{y^2 = 2cx + c^3.}$$

Equation (d) is satisfied if $(1/2p) + yp^2 = 0$. Eliminating p between this equation and (a), we obtain the singular solution,

$$\mathbf{27y^4 = -32x^3.}$$

EXERCISES

1. Use the method of this section to find the general solution of $px = 1 + 4p^3e^{2y}$. Also, find the singular solution.

Solve the following equations completely:

2. $x = y + \ln p$.

3. $4px - 2y = p^3y^2$.

4. $xp^2 - 2yp + x + 2y = 0$.

5. $2px = 2 \tan y + p^3 \cos^2 y$.

Find the solution of the following equations in parametric form:

6. $x = y + p^2$.

7. $p^2x = 2yp - 3$.

Find the general solution of:

8. $3px = y + 3p\varphi(py^2)$.

9. $px = 1 + p\varphi(pe^y)$.

10. Find a singular solution of the equation in problem 9, assuming that $\varphi(u) = \frac{1}{3}u^3$.

41. Review problems

Let p represent dy/dx.

The solution of an equation $f(x,y,p) = 0$ (see §36) which can be factored is obtained by equating each factor to zero and solving the resulting equations.

The solution of an equation which can be solved for y in terms of x and p is obtained by the method of §39. Use the method of §40 to solve an equation which can be solved for x in terms of y and p.

If $f(x,y,p) = 0$ represents a differential equation and $\varphi(x,y,c) = 0$ its general solution, the p-discriminant, §38, of $f(x,y,p) = 0$ is obtained by eliminating p from

$$f(x,y,p) = 0, \qquad f_p(x,y,p) = 0, \tag{28}$$

and the c-discriminant, §37, by eliminating c from

$$\varphi(x,y,c) = 0, \qquad \varphi_c(x,y,c) = 0. \tag{29}$$

Both the p-discriminant and the c-discriminant contain any singular solution that $f(x,y,p) = 0$ may have. Only parts of the p-discriminant or the c-discriminant which satisfy $f(x,y,p) = 0$ constitute solutions of $f(x,y,p) = 0$ and represent envelopes of $\varphi(x,y,c) = 0$.

EXERCISES

Find the solutions, general and singular, of the following equations:

1. $(p - 3y)(p - 4x) = 0$.

2. $(p - y)[p^2 + (1 - 2x)p - 2x] = 0$.

3. $y = px + p^2$.

4. $x = y/p + p^2$.

5. $y = px + 3x^2 + \frac{1}{2}(p + 6x)^2$.

6. $y = 2px + y^2p^3$.

7. $4y - 4px \ln x = p^2x^2$.

8. $3px - 3 = p^3e^{2y}$.

Find the general solution of:

9. $3px = y + 3p\varphi(py^2)$.

10. $y = p \tan x \ln (\sin x) + \varphi(p \tan x)$.

11. Find the general solution and the particular solution of $y^2(1 + p^2) = x + yp$. Figure 7 represents the solution. What curves in Fig. 7 are represented by the general solution and what curve by the singular solution?

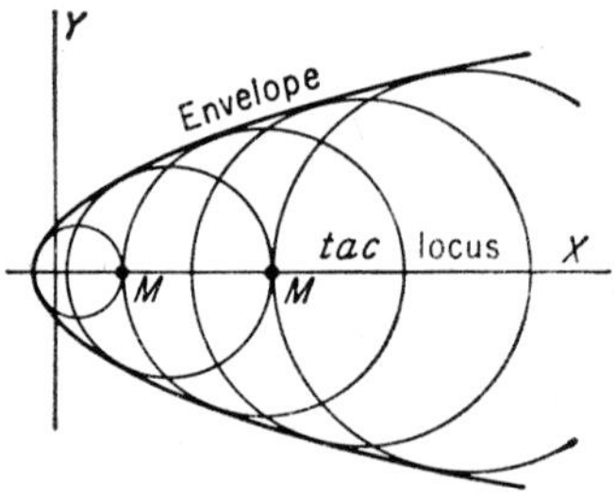

FIG. 7

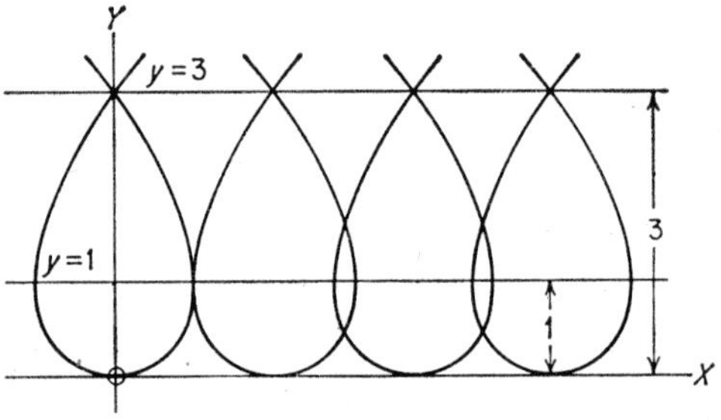

FIG. 8

12. Find the general solution of $f(x,y,p) = 4y - 9(y - 1)^2p^2 = 0$ and also the singular solution. What line in Fig. 8 is defined by the singular solution? The line $y = 1$ satisfies $f_p = 0$. Name this locus relative to the system of solution curves. The c-discriminant is satisfied by the line $x = c$, $y = 3$; name this locus.

13. Find the equation of the curve to which the lines defined by $y = px + 2p^4$ are tangents.

14. Find the differential equation of the tangents and also the equation of the envelope of the normals for: (*a*) $y^2 = x$; (*b*) $y^2 = 2x + 2$. *Hint:* For $y^2 = x$ at (m^2,m), slope $p = 1/(2y)$; therefore, $m = 1/(2p)$. Use this relation in $y - m = p(x - m^2)$ to eliminate m. For the normals, $y - m = (-1/p)(x - m^2)$.

15. The evolute of a curve is the envelope of its normals. Find the equation of the evolute of $2x^2y = 1$. *Hint:* See hint to problem 14.

CHAPTER 6

LINEAR DIFFERENTIAL EQUATIONS WITH CONSTANT COEFFICIENTS

42. Operators

The operators discussed below furnish a convenient notation and also timesaving methods of solving differential equations.

An **operator** is a symbol indicating an operation to be performed. We define the operator D to mean *take the derivative with respect to x of*, and generally $D, D^2, \ldots, D^k$ indicate that

$$Du \equiv \frac{du}{dx}, \qquad D^2u \equiv \frac{d^2u}{dx^2}, \quad \ldots, \qquad D^ku \equiv \frac{d^ku}{dx^k}, \qquad D^0u \equiv 1u \equiv u, \quad (1)$$

where u is a function of x. Also, we denote by $f(x)D^k$ an operator such that

$$f(x)D^ku = f(x)\frac{d^ku}{dx^k}. \qquad (2)$$

Thus, $$4xD^2x^3 = 4x(d^2x^3/dx^2) = 4x \cdot 6x = 24x^2.$$

Two operators are said to be **equal** if they produce equal results when applied to any function of x, $u(x)$.

Any symbol having the form of a polynomial in D, such as $2D^2 + xD + 5$, will represent an operator defined by (1) and the following definitions of sum and product:

$$\begin{aligned}(aD^k + bD^r)u &= aD^ku + bD^ru,\\ aD^k \cdot bD^ru &= aD^k(bD^ru),\end{aligned} \qquad (3)$$

where u is a function of x. Thus

$$(3D + 5)u = 3Du + 5u = \frac{3du}{dx} + 5u,$$

and

$$\begin{aligned}[(2D^2) + (3D + 5)]u &= 2D^2u + (3D + 5)u\\ &= 2\frac{d^2u}{dx^2} + 3\frac{du}{dx} + 5u.\end{aligned}$$

Note in the product formula that the operator adjacent to u was applied first. Illustrations of (3) are

$$[(D^4 + 2D^3) + (3D + 5)]u = (D^4 + 2D^3)u + (3D + 5)u$$
$$= \frac{d^4u}{dx^4} + 2\frac{d^3u}{dx^3} + 3\frac{du}{dx} + 5u,$$
$$(D + 2)D(x^2 + 3x) = (D + 2)(2x + 3) = 2 + 4x + 6 = 8 + 4x.$$

The elementary operators aD^k, where a is a constant, obey the fundamental laws of algebra; for we see by calculus and definitions (1) to (3) that for a, b, and c constants

$$\begin{aligned} (aD^m + bD^n)u &= (bD^n + aD^m)u, \\ (aD^m) \cdot (bD^n)u &= (bD^m) \cdot (aD^n)u, \\ [aD^m + (bD^n + cD^r)]u &= [(aD^m + bD^n) + cD^r]u, \\ aD^m(bD^n \cdot cD^r)u &= (aD^m \cdot bD^n)cD^ru, \\ aD^m(bD^n + cD^r)u &= aD^m \cdot bD^nu + aD^m \cdot cD^ru. \end{aligned} \tag{4}$$

By applying definitions (1), (3), and laws (4), we can build up complicated operators just as we build up complicated expressions in algebra. In particular, we can build the polynomial operators

$$\mathbf{a_0D^n + a_1D^{n-1} + \cdots + a_n}, \tag{5}$$

where $a_0, a_1, \ldots, a_n$ are constants, and they will indicate that

$$\mathbf{(a_0D^n + a_1D^{n-1} + \cdots + a_n)u = a_0\frac{d^nu}{dx^n} + a_1\frac{d^{n-1}u}{dx^{n-1}} + \cdots + a_nu.} \tag{6}$$

Because the operators aD^k, a constant, obey the fundamental laws (4) *of algebra, we may obtain from given polynomial operators other equal operators by multiplication, factorization, and introduction or removal of parentheses, just as though the operators were algebraic expressions. Notice particularly that the order of terms in a sum or of factors in a product is immaterial.*

Illustrations of operators and operations follow:

$$\begin{aligned} a^2D^2 + 2aD - 3 &= (aD + 3)(aD - 1), \\ (2D^2 + 5D + 6)x^3 &= 12x + 15x^2 + 6x^3, \\ (D - a)(D - b)y &= [D^2 - (a + b)D + ab]y. \end{aligned}$$

The following examples illustrate a use of operators in solving differential equations:

Example 1. Solve

$$(D^2 - 5D + 6)y = 6. \tag{a}$$

Solution. The given equation may be written

$$(D - 2)[(D - 3)y] = 6. \tag{b}$$

In this, let

$$(D - 3)y = z, \qquad (c)$$

and obtain

$$(D - 2)z = 6, \qquad \text{or} \qquad \frac{dz}{dx} - 2z = 6. \qquad (d)$$

The solution of (d), found by using the method of §25, is $z = -3 + ce^{2x}$. Replacing z in (c) by this value $-3 + ce^{2x}$, we get

$$(D - 3)y = -3 + ce^{2x}, \qquad \text{or} \qquad \frac{dy}{dx} - 3y = -3 + ce^{2x}. \qquad (e)$$

The solution of (e) by the method of §25 is

$$\mathbf{y = 1 + c_1e^{2x} + c_2e^{3x}}, \qquad (f)$$

where c_1 replaces $-c$.

Example 2. Solve

$$(D - a)(D - a)(D - a)y = 0. \qquad (a)$$

Solution. In (a), let

$$(D - a)(D - a)y = z, \qquad (b)$$

and solve the result, $(D - a)z = 0$, to get

$$z = c_1e^{ax}. \qquad (c)$$

Replacing z in (b) by the value c_1e^{ax} from (c), we get

$$(D - a)(D - a)y = ce^{ax}. \qquad (d)$$

In (d), make the substitution

$$(D - a)y = w, \qquad (e)$$

to get $(D - a)w = ce^{ax}$. The solution of this is

$$w = (cx + c_2)e^{ax}. \qquad (f)$$

Replace w in (e) by its value from (f), and solve the result for y to obtain

$$y = (c_1x^2 + c_2x + c_3)e^{ax},$$

where $c_1 = \frac{1}{2}c$.

Example 3. Solve $(D - 2)(D + 3)y = 1 - 6x$, and determine the constants of integration so that $y = 7$ and $Dy = 0$ when $x = 0$.

Solution. Solving the given differential equation by the method used in the solutions of examples 1 and 2, we get

$$y = x + c_1e^{2x} + c_2e^{-3x}. \qquad (a)$$

From (a), we get by differentiation

$$Dy = 1 + 2c_1e^{2x} - 3c_2e^{-3x}. \qquad (b)$$

Replacing x by 0, y by 7, and Dy by 0 in (a) and (b), we get

$$\begin{aligned} 7 &= c_1 + c_2, \\ 0 &= 2c_1 - 3c_2 + 1. \end{aligned} \tag{c}$$

The solution of (c) for c_1 and c_2 is $c_1 = 4$, $c_2 = 3$. Substituting these values of c_1 and c_2 in (a), we get

$$\mathbf{y = x + 4e^{2x} + 3e^{-3x}}.$$

EXERCISES

Perform the operations indicated in the following exercises:

1. Dx^2. **2.** $(D + 1)(8x^2)$. **3.** $(D - 2)x^3$.
4. D^2x^4. **5.** D^3e^{3x}. **6.** $(D - 3)e^{5x}$.
7. $(D^2 - a^2) \sin ax$. **8.** $(D^2 + a^2) \cos ax$. **9.** $(D - a)e^{ax}$.
10. $(D + 1)[(D + 2)(5e^{-x})]$. **11.** $(D + 1)(D + 1)(xe^{-x})$. **12.** $(D - 1)(x \cos x)$.

13. $(D + 1)^2(D + 2)(x^2e^{-x})$. **14.** $(D^2 + 4D + 4)(x^2e^{-2x})$.
15. $(D^3 + D^2 - 12)e^{2x}$.

Solve the following differential equations by the methods used in the solutions of examples 1 and 2:

16. $(D - 2)Dy = 0$. **17.** $(D - 2)(D + 2)y = 0$. **18.** $D(D - 2)y = 6x$.
19. $(D - 3)(D + 4)y = 12$. **20.** $D(D - 3)y = e^x$. **21.** $(D^2 - 4)y = e^{3x}$.

22. $(D + 3)D^2y = e^{-x}$. *Hint:* Let $z = D^2y$, solve for z, in the result replace z by DDy, then substitute w for Dy, solve for w, replace w in the result by Dy, and solve for y.

23. $(D - 1)(D - 2)(D - 3)y = 0$. **24.** $(D - 1)(D + 2)y = e^x$.
25. $D^2y = 12x^2$. **26.** $(D - 2)^2y = 2e^{2x}$.

Review the solution of example 3, and then find the particular solution of each equation satisfying the indicated conditions:

27. $D(D + 3)y = 0$; $y = 5$, $Dy = -9$ when $x = 0$.
28. $(D^2 - 4)y = 0$; $y = 1$, $Dy = -10$ when $x = 0$.
29. $(D - 1)^2y = 2e^x$; $y = 3$, $Dy = 0$ when $x = 0$.

43. Linear independence of functions

Two functions* $f(x)$ and $g(x)$ are **linearly independent** if no two constants c_1 and c_2, not both zero, exist for which in $a \leq x \leq b$

$$c_1f(x) + c_2g(x) \equiv 0. \tag{7}$$

Evidently, x and x^2 are linearly independent; for if c_1 and c_2 are not both zero, $c_1x + c_2x^2$ cannot be identically zero. On the other hand, $10x$ and

* Assume that none of the functions $f(x)$, $g(x)$, $h(x)$, $Y_i(x)$, $i = 1, \ldots, n$, is the zero function $\alpha(x) \equiv 0$ and that all of them and their derivatives involved are continuous and single-valued in an interval $a \leq x \leq b$.

$150x$ are linearly dependent for $15(10x) - 1(150)x \equiv 0$. If $c_1f(x) + c_2g(x) \equiv 0$, then $c_1f'(x) + c_2g'(x) \equiv 0$. From this and (7) we get

$$c_1/c_2 = -g(x)/f(x) = -g'(x)/f'(x) \tag{8}$$

or

$$\begin{vmatrix} f(x) & g(x) \\ f'(x) & g'(x) \end{vmatrix} \equiv 0 \qquad a \leq x \leq b. \tag{9}$$

Hence (9) must hold if $f(x)$ and $g(x)$ are linearly dependent. If (9) does not hold, the functions are independent in $a \leq x \leq b$.

Three functions $f(x)$, $g(x)$, $h(x)$ are linearly independent if no three constants a, b, and c, not all zero, exist such that

$$af(x) + bg(x) + ch(x) \equiv 0. \tag{10}$$

Thus, x, x^2, x^3 are linearly independent, for $c_1x + c_2x^2 + c_3x^3$ cannot be identically zero unless $c_1 = 0$, $c_2 = 0$, $c_3 = 0$. On the other hand, $x^2 + x$, x^2, $3x^2 + 2x$ are dependent since $2(x^2 + x) + 1x^2 - 1(3x^2 + 2x) = 0$. Reasoning as before, we could deduce that if $f(x)$, $g(x)$, and $h(x)$ are linearly dependent in $a \leq x \leq b$, then

$$\begin{vmatrix} f(x) & g(x) & h(x) \\ f'(x) & g'(x) & h'(x) \\ f''(x) & g''(x) & h''(x) \end{vmatrix} \equiv 0, \; a \leq x \leq b. \tag{11}$$

Otherwise f, g, and h are linearly independent in $a \leq x \leq b$. By similar reasoning we could show that if functions $Y_i(x)$, $i = 1, 2, \ldots, n$, are linearly dependent, (12) below holds; if (12) does not hold they are linearly independent.

$$\begin{vmatrix} Y_1 & Y_2 & \cdots & Y_n \\ Y_1' & Y_2' & \cdots & Y_n' \\ \cdots & \cdots & \cdots & \cdots \\ Y_1^{(n-1)} & Y_2^{(n-1)} & \cdots & Y_n^{(n-1)} \end{vmatrix} \equiv 0. \tag{12}$$

Determinants (9), (11), and (12) are called **wronskians.**

EXERCISES

1. Show that x^2 and $11x^2$ are linearly dependent.

2. Applying (9), show that $x + 5$ and $x + 6$ are linearly independent.

3. Show that ax and bx, a and b constants, are linearly dependent.

4. Show directly that x^2, x, $3x^2 + 3x$ are linearly dependent.

5. Show by using (11) that $\sin x$, $\cos x$, and $2x$ are linearly independent.

6. Write the condition for the linear independence of four functions $p(x)$, $q(x)$, $r(x)$, and $s(x)$, and use it to show that x^3, x^2, x, and 8 are linearly independent.

44. Linear differential equation

A **linear differential equation** *contains the dependent variable and all its derivatives to the first degree only.* Its general form is

$$L(D)y = (a_0D^n + a_1D^{n-1} + \cdots + a_{n-1}D + a_n)y = X, \qquad (13)$$

where the a's and X are functions of x. If $X = 0$, the equation is said to be **homogeneous,** since each term is of the first degree in y and its derivatives.

A very important theorem relating to the operator $L(D)$ may be expressed by writing

$$\mathbf{L(D)(y_1 + y_2 + \cdots + y_m) = L(D)y_1 + L(D)y_2 + \cdots + L(D)y_m}, \qquad \mathbf{(14)}$$

where $y_1, y_2, \ldots, y_m$ represent functions of x. To prove (14), observe that

$$D^k(y_1 + y_2 + \cdots + y_m) = D^ky_1 + D^ky_2 + \cdots + D^ky_m, \qquad (15)$$

multiply both members of this by a_0 with $k = n$, by a_1 with $k = n - 1, \ldots,$ by a_n with $k = 0$, in succession, and add the results to obtain (14).

Equation (15) is the basis of an interesting property. If we think of $L(D)y$ as a force producing the displacement y, then (14) expresses that several forces $L(D)y_1, L(D)y_2, \ldots$ producing respective displacements $y_1, y_2, \ldots$ produce, when acting in combination, the displacement $y_1 + y_2 + \cdots$. This relation is often referred to as **superposition.** As an example, consider a beam projecting horizontally from a wall acted upon by its weight and a load hung on its end. Its total deflection y is $y_1 + y_2$, where y_1 is the deflection produced by its weight when acting alone and y_2 is the deflection produced by the load at its end. In the applications of linear differential equations, numerous illustrations of superposition are found.

If $Y(x)$ is a solution of (13) with $X = 0$, so is $cY(x)$; for

$$L(D)[Y(x)] = 0, \qquad D^k[cY(x)] = cD^k[Y(x)], \qquad k = 0, 1, \ldots n, \qquad (16)$$

and therefore

$$L(D)[cY(x)] = cL(D)[Y(x)] = c \cdot 0 = 0. \qquad (17)$$

If $Y_1(x), Y_2(x), \ldots, Y_n(x)$ are solutions of (13) with $X = 0$, then, in accord with (17), $y_1(x) = c_1Y_1(x)$, $y_2(x) = c_2Y_2(x), \ldots, y_n(x) = c_mY_m(x)$ are solutions. For these functions, the right member of (14), and therefore its left member, is zero; that is, $c_1Y_1(x) + c_2Y_2(x) + \cdots + c_mY_m(x)$ is a solution. Hence, the following theorem is true:

THEOREM. *If* $\mathbf{y} = \mathbf{Y}_1(\mathbf{x})$, $\mathbf{y} = \mathbf{Y}_2(\mathbf{x})$, . . . , $\mathbf{y} = \mathbf{Y}_n(\mathbf{x})$ *are solutions of a linear homogeneous equation, then*

$$\mathbf{y} = \mathbf{c}_1\mathbf{Y}_1(\mathbf{x}) + \mathbf{c}_2\mathbf{Y}_2(\mathbf{x}) + \cdots + \mathbf{c}_n\mathbf{Y}_n(\mathbf{x}) \tag{18}$$

is also a solution.

In accordance with a general existence theorem,* an equation having the form (13) with $X = 0$ and with a_i/a_0, $i = 1, \ldots, n$, continuous and single-valued will have n linearly independent solutions $Y_i(x)$, $i = 1, \ldots, n$, each possessing continuous derivatives of order 1 to $n - 1$. Therefore, it will have a solution of the form (18), where the functions $Y_i(x)$, $i = 1, \ldots, n$, satisfy (12), §43. The n arbitrary constants $c_1, c_2, \ldots, c_n$ are used to find a particular solution satisfying given initial conditions such as

$$y = a_0, \qquad Dy = a_1, \qquad \ldots, \qquad D^{n-1}y = a_{n-1}, \qquad \text{when } x = x_0. \tag{19}$$

45. Homogeneous linear differential equation with constant coefficients

We shall first find a method of solving equations of the type

$$(a_0D^n + a_1D^{n-1} + \cdots + a_{n-1}D + a_n)y = 0, \tag{20}$$

where the a's are constants.

A very special case of equation (20) is $Dy + ay = 0$, and its solution is $y = ce^{-ax}$. This suggests that a function of the form

$$y = ce^{mx} \tag{21}$$

might be a solution of (20). Substituting $y = ce^{mx}$, $dy/dx = cme^{mx}$, . . . , $d^ky/dx^k = cm^ke^{mx}$ in (20), we obtain

$$ce^{mx}(a_0m^n + a_1m^{n-1} + \cdots + a_{n-1}m + a_n) = 0.$$

This equation will be satisfied if m is a root of the equation

$$\mathbf{a}_0\mathbf{m}^n + \mathbf{a}_1\mathbf{m}^{n-1} + \cdots + \mathbf{a}_{n-1}\mathbf{m} + \mathbf{a}_n = \mathbf{0}. \tag{22}$$

Equation (22) is referred to as the **auxiliary equation.** Evidently, if $r_1, r_2, \ldots, r_n$ are the roots of (22), the equations

$$y = c_1e^{r_1x}, \qquad y = c_2e^{r_2x}, \qquad \ldots, \qquad y = c_ne^{r_nx} \tag{23}$$

are all solutions of (20). Therefore, in accordance with the theorem of §44,

$$\mathbf{y} = \mathbf{c}_1\mathbf{e}^{r_1x} + \mathbf{c}_2\mathbf{e}^{r_2x} + \cdots + \mathbf{c}_n\mathbf{e}^{r_nx} \tag{24}$$

is a solution of (20). Since (24) contains n arbitrary constants, it is the general solution of (20) provided that no two of the roots of (22) are equal.

* See Theorem II, §95.

Example. Solve

$$\frac{d^3y}{dx^3} + 2\frac{d^2y}{dx^2} - 3\frac{dy}{dx} = 0. \tag{a}$$

Solution. The auxiliary equation (22) in this case is

$$m^3 + 2m^2 - 3m = 0. \tag{b}$$

The roots of (*b*) are 1, −3, 0. Hence the solution of (*a*), in accordance with (24), is

$$\mathbf{y = c_1e^x + c_2e^{-3x} + c_3.}$$

EXERCISES

Solve the following differential equations:

1. $(D^2 - 3D + 2)y = 0.$
2. $(D^2 + 4D - 5)y = 0.$
3. $(D^2 + 4D + 3)y = 0.$
4. $D^2y + 3y = 5Dy.$
5. $(4D^3 - 5D)y = 0.$
6. $D^3y = Dy.$
7. $D^2y = k^2y.$
8. $(D^3 - 3D^2 - D + 3)y = 0.$
9. $(D^3 - 7D + 6)y = 0.$
10. $(D^4 - D^3 - 7D^2 + 3D)y = 0.$

46. Auxiliary equation has repeated roots

Let $r_1, r_2, \ldots, r_n$ be the roots of the auxiliary equation, and for convenience let us write

$$\begin{aligned} f(m) &= a_0m^n + a_1m^{n-1} + \cdots + a_{n-1}m + a_n \\ &= a_0(m - r_1)(m - r_2) \cdots (m - r_n). \end{aligned} \tag{25}$$

Equation (20) may then be written

$$a_0(D - r_1)(D - r_2) \cdots (D - r_n)y = f(D)y = 0. \tag{26}$$

If $f(m) = 0$ has a double root r, then by §45 the solution of (26) contains the two terms $c_1e^{rx} + c_2e^{rx}$; but since this may be written $(c_1 + c_2)e^{rx} =$ (constant) e^{rx}, only one arbitrary constant is involved. In this case, the solution, got by using (24) of §45, involves fewer than n independent arbitrary constants and consequently is not the general solution.

In example 2, §42, we derived the expression $y = (c_1 + c_2x + c_3x^2)e^{ax}$ as the solution of $(D - a)^3y = 0$. This suggests that *the part of a solution corresponding to a p-fold multiple root a of the auxiliary equation is*

$$\mathbf{(c_1 + c_2x + c_3x^2 + \cdots + c_px^{p-1})e^{ax}.} \tag{27}$$

Observe that

$$(D - a)(x^me^{ax}) = mx^{m-1}e^{ax} + ax^me^{ax} - ax^me^{ax} = mx^{m-1}e^{ax}.$$

Therefore, the result of operating on (27) by $D - a$ would give a result like (27) but with the degree of the polynomial reduced by 1. Hence,

$\varphi(D)(D - a)^p$ operating on (27) gives zero, and expression (27) satisfies $\varphi(D)(D - a)^p y = 0$. Also, an expression like (27) applies for any other multiple root. For example, the roots of the auxiliary equation of

$$(D - 2)^3(D + 3)^2(D - 4)y = 0 \tag{28}$$

are 2, 2, 2, -3, -3, and 4, and the general solution of (28) is

$$y = (c_1 + c_2x + c_3x^2)e^{2x} + (c_4 + c_5x)e^{-3x} + c_6e^{4x}.$$

Example. Find the general solution of $(D^5 - 2D^4 + D^3)y = 0$.

Solution. The auxiliary equation is $m^5 - 2m^4 + m^3 = 0$, and its roots are 0, 0, 0, 1, 1. Hence, in accordance with (27) the general solution is

$$y = c_0 + c_1x + c_2x^2 + e^x(c_3 + c_4x).$$

47. Constants of integration from initial conditions

To determine the constants of integration from the general solution of a differential equation, replace the variables in the solution and the derivatives of the solution by given corresponding values, and solve the resulting equations for the required constants.

Example. Find the particular solution of $(D^3 - 6D^2 + 9D)y = 0$ which satisfies the initial conditions $y = 0$, $Dy = 2$, $D^2y = -6$ when $x = 0$.

Solution. The auxiliary equation is $m^3 - 6m^2 + 9m = 0$, its roots are 0, 3, 3, and the general solution of the given equation is

$$y = c_1 + e^{3x}(c_2 + c_3x). \tag{a}$$

By differentiation, we obtain from (*a*)

$$\begin{aligned} Dy &= e^{3x}(3c_2 + c_3 + 3c_3x), \\ D^2y &= e^{3x}(9c_2 + 6c_3 + 9c_3x). \end{aligned} \tag{b}$$

Substitution of the initial conditions in (*a*) and (*b*) gives

$$\begin{aligned} 0 &= c_1 + e^0(c_2 + c_3 \cdot 0) = c_1 + c_2, \\ 2 &= 3c_2 + c_3, \qquad -6 = 9c_2 + 6c_3. \end{aligned} \tag{c}$$

Solving these equations for c_1, c_2, and c_3, we get

$$c_1 = -2, \qquad c_2 = 2, \qquad c_3 = -4.$$

The required particular solution, obtained by substituting these values of the c's in (*a*), is

$$\mathbf{y = -2 + e^{3x}(2 - 4x).}$$

EXERCISES

For each of the following equations, find the general solution and, for each of exercises 11 to 16, the particular solution satisfying the given initial conditions:

1. $(D^2 - 6D + 9)y = 0$.
2. $(D^2 + 4D + 4)y = 0$.
3. $(D^3 - D^2)y = 0$.
4. $(D^5 - 4D^3)y = 0$.
5. $(D^3 - 2D^2 + D)y = 0$.
6. $D^3y = 0$.
7. $(D^3 - D^2 - D + 1)y = 0$.
8. $(D^3 - 3D^2 + 3D - 1)y = 0$.
9. $(D^6 - 8D^4 + 16D^2)y = 0$.
10. $(D^5 - 12D^3 + 16D^2)y = 0$.

11. $(D^2 - 2D + 1)y = 0$; $y = 5$, $Dy = -9$ when $x = 0$.
12. $(D^2 + 2D + 1)y = 0$; $y = 1$, $Dy = -1$ when $x = 0$.
13. $(D^2)(D - 1)y = 0$; $y = 2$, $Dy = 3$, $D^2y = 2$ when $x = 0$.
14. $(D^3 + D^2)y = 0$; $y = 4$, $Dy = -2$, $D^2y = 4$ when $x = 0$.
15. $(D^3 - 4D^2 + 4D)y = 0$; $y = 1$, $Dy = 2$, $D^2y = 8$ when $x = 0$.
16. $(D^3 - D^2 - D + 1)y = 0$; $y = 0$, $Dy = 0$, $D^2y = 4$ when $x = 0$.

48. Auxiliary equation has imaginary roots

In the theory of complex numbers* $a + ib$, where $i^2 = -1$ and a and b are real, it is shown that the ordinary processes of algebra and also differentiation and integration apply as well to functions of complex variables as to functions of real variables. Hence, the solutions of differential equations based on real variables may be considered the solutions based on complex variables. For example, the solution $y = x^2 + c$ of $dy/dx = 2x$ may be thought of as

$$y_1 + iy_2 = (x_1 + ix_2)^2 + c_1 + ic_2.$$

Evidently, the real solution is obtained from this by setting $y_2 = 0$, $x_2 = 0$, and $c_2 = 0$.

We shall assume that complex exponents obey the ordinary laws of exponents and that

$$e^{i\theta} = \cos\theta + i\sin\theta, \tag{29}$$

where, for our present purposes, θ is assumed to be a real number.†

The part of the solution of (20), §45, corresponding to a pair of complex roots $a \pm ib$ of the auxiliary equation, may, in accordance with (24), §45, be written

$$Ae^{(a+ib)x} + Be^{(a-ib)x}, \tag{32}$$

where A, B, and x are considered as complex numbers. Transforming

* Most texts on college algebra give an elementary treatment of complex numbers. For a comprehensive treatment, read any book on the theory of functions of a complex variable.

† It is interesting to replace θ by $-\theta$ in (29) and obtain

$$e^{-i\theta} = \cos\theta - i\sin\theta \tag{30}$$

and solve this with (29) for $\cos\theta$ and $\sin\theta$ to obtain

$$\cos\theta = (e^{i\theta} + e^{-i\theta})/2 \qquad \sin\theta = (e^{i\theta} - e^{-i\theta})/(2i). \tag{31}$$

All the identities connecting the trigonometric functions can be deduced from (31). Also, generalized formulas are deduced from (31) and used in higher mathematics and its applications.

this by (29), we get

$$A e^{ax} e^{ibx} + B e^{ax} e^{-ibx}, \tag{33}$$

$$e^{ax}[A(\cos bx + i \sin bx) + B(\cos bx - i \sin bx)], \tag{34}$$
$$e^{ax}[(A + B) \cos bx + (A - B)i \sin bx].$$

To get the real part of the solution from (34), think of x as real, take $A + B = c_1$, $(A - B)i = c_2$, and obtain

$$e^{ax}(c_1 \cos bx + c_2 \sin bx). \tag{35}$$

To get a useful alternative form of (35), multiply and divide (34) by $\sqrt{c_1^2 + c_2^2} = c$, and in the result take

$$c_1 = c \sin \alpha, \quad c_2 = c \cos \alpha, \quad c_1/c_2 = \tan \alpha \tag{36}$$

and obtain $\quad c_1 = \frac{c}{2}(1+i) \quad c_2 = \frac{c}{2}(1-i)$

$$c e^{ax}[\sin \alpha \cos bx + \cos \alpha \sin b(x)], \tag{37}$$
$$c e^{ax} \sin (bx + \alpha), \tag{38}$$

where c and α are arbitrary constants. *The part of the general solution of an equation in the form (20), §45, corresponding to a pair of complex roots $a \pm ib$ of the auxiliary equation is generally written in form (35) or (38).*

In the case of a double pair of complex roots, the corresponding terms of the general solution are

$$e^{ax}[(A_0 + A_1 x) \cos bx + (B_0 + B_1 x) \sin bx],^* \tag{39}$$

or $\qquad e^{ax}[c_0 \sin (bx + \alpha_0) + c_1 x \sin (bx + \alpha_1)], \tag{40}$

and a similar extension applies for a p-fold multiple pair of complex roots.

Example. Solve $(D^3 - 3D^2 + 9D + 13)y = 0$.

Solution. The roots of the auxiliary equation are $-1, 2 \pm 3i$. Hence, the general solution is

$$y = c_1 e^{-x} + e^{2x}(c_2 \sin 3x + c_3 \cos 3x),$$

or $\qquad y = c_1 e^{-x} + c e^{2x} \sin (3x + \alpha).$

EXERCISES

Solve the following equations, and determine the constants of integration where initial conditions are given:

1. $(D^2 - 2D + 2)y = 0$.   2. $D(D^2 - 4D + 5)y = 0$.
3. $(D - 2)(D^2 + 2D + 10)y = 0$.   4. $(D^2 + 4)y = 0$.
5. $(D^4 + 8D^2 + 16)y = 0$.   6. $(D^4 + D^2)y = 0$.
7. $(D^6 + 6D^4 + 9D^2)y = 0$.   8. $(D^3 + a^3)y = 0$.

* This may be proved by substituting expression (39) or (40) for y in

$$[(D - a)^2 + b^2]^2 y = 0.$$

9. $(D^2 + 1)y = 0$; $y = 1$, $Dy = -1$ when $x = \pi$.
10. $(D^2 + 9)y = 0$; $y = 2$, $Dy = 0$ when $x = \pi/6$.
11. $(D^2 + 2D + 2)y = 0$; $y = 0$, $Dy = 1$ when $x = 0$.
12. $(D^3 - 2D^2 + 2D)y = 0$; $y = 1$, $Dy = 1$, $D^2y = 2$ when $x = 0$.
13. $(D^3 - 2D + 4)y = 0$; $y = -2$, $Dy = 8$, $D^2y = 0$ when $x = 0$.
14. $(D^2 + 4)y = 0$; $y = 4$, $Dy = 0$ when $x = 1$. *Hint:* Write the solution in the form $y = c_1 \sin 2(x - 1) + c_2 \cos 2(x - 1)$.

49. Right-hand member not zero

To solve the equation

$$(a_0D^n + a_1D^{n-1} + \cdots + a_{n-1}D + a_n)y = X, \tag{41}$$

where the a's are constants and X is a function of x, we shall write

$$y = y_c + y_p, \tag{42}$$

where $y = y_c$ is the general solution of (41) with X replaced by zero and $y = y_p$ is a particular solution of (41). Equation (42) is a solution of (41) involving n independent arbitrary constants and hence is the general solution. y_c is referred to as the **complementary function** and is found as in §§45 to 48. y_p may be found by various methods, one of which, the **method of undetermined coefficients,** is illustrated below. This method applies when the right-hand member consists of terms from which only a finite number of terms can be got by differentiation. Many of the equations arising in practice may be solved by this method.

Consider the equation

$$(D^2 + 3D + 2)y = 40e^{3x}. \tag{a}$$

The solution of $(D^2 + 3D + 2)y = 0$ is

$$y_c = c_1e^{-x} + c_2e^{-2x}. \tag{b}$$

Assume that the solution y_p of (a) has the form

$$y_p = Ae^{3x}. \tag{c}$$

Substitution of this in (a) gives

$$(D^2 + 3D + 2)(Ae^{3x}) = (9 + 9 + 2)Ae^{3x} = 40e^{3x}. \tag{d}$$

Hence, $20A = 40$, and $A = 2$. Therefore, from (c) $y_p = 2e^{3x}$, and the general solution of (a) is

$$\mathbf{y = y_c + y_p = c_1e^{-x} + c_2e^{-2x} + 2e^{3x}}. \tag{e}$$

As another problem, consider

$$(D^2 + 3D + 2)y = 8x + 14. \tag{f}$$

y_c is the same as before. Assume for y_p

$$y_p = Ax + B. \tag{g}$$

Substituting this value of y_p for y in (f), we get

$$(D^2 + 3D + 2)(Ax + B) = 0 + 3A + 2Ax + 2B = 8x + 14, \quad (h)$$

or

$$2Ax + (3A + 2B) = 8x + 14.$$

Since (h) is to hold identically, the coefficients of like terms must be equal; that is,

$$2A = 8, \qquad 3A + 2B = 14. \quad (i)$$

From these, we get $A = 4$, $B = 1$. Therefore, from (g) $y_p = 4x + 1$, and the general solution of (f) is

$$y = y_c + y_p = c_1e^{-x} + c_2e^{-2x} + 4x + 1. \quad (j)$$

If the right-hand member of (f) had been $40e^{3x} + 8x + 14$, we would have found two y_p's, one for $40e^{3x}$ and one for $8x + 14$, just as above and then would have used the sum of these y_p's as the y_p of the solution.

What form should the trial y_p assume? Table 1 shows a few expressions and their corresponding trial forms.

TABLE 1

Part of right-hand member	*Corresponding trial y_p*
e^{5x}	Ae^{5x}
sin $2x$, cos $2x$, or both	$A \sin 2x + B \cos 2x$
xe^{2x}	$Axe^{2x} + Be^{2x}$
20	A
Polynomial of degree 3	$A_0x^3 + A_1x^2 + A_2x + A_3$

Like terms are terms that differ only in their constant factor; thus, $8x$, $-247x$, and $(B + C)x$ are like terms. Note from Table 1 that *each y_p consists of the unlike terms in the corresponding part of the right-hand member and in successive derivatives of that part.*

EXERCISES

Solve the following equations, and determine the constants of integration where initial conditions are given:

1. $(D^2 - 4)y = 12$. *Hint:* Let $y_p = A$.

2. $(D^2 + 2D - 3)y = 42e^{4x}$.

3. $(D^2 + D - 2)y = 3 - 6x$.

4. $(D^2 - D - 2)y = 6e^x$.

5. $(D^2 + 1)y = 3 + 6e^x$.

6. $(D + 2)^2y = x + 8e^{2x}$.

7. $(D^2 + D)y = 6 \sin 2x$.

8. $(D^3 - D^2)y = 2 \cos x$.

9. $(D^2 + 1)y = 10e^x \sin x$.

10. $(D^2 - 1)y = 2x^2$. Let $y_p = Ax^2 + Bx + C$.

11. $(D^2 - 9)y = 18 \cos 3x + 9$; $y = -1$, $Dy = 3$ when $x = 0$.

12. $(D^2 + D - 6)y = 2 - 12x$; $y = 3$, $Dy = -7$ when $x = 0$.

13. $(D^2 + D)y = e^x$; $y = 3$, $Dy = 0$ when $x = \ln 2$.

★14. $(D^2 + 4D + 3)y = 8xe^x - 6$; $y = -\frac{11}{4}$, $Dy = \frac{1}{4}$ when $x = 0$.

★15. $(D^3 - 4D)y = 6e^{-x} - 3e^x$; $y = 7$, $Dy = 9$, $D^2y = 19$ when $x = \ln 2$.

50. Special case when the right-hand member is not zero

It may happen that a term in the trial solution of $f(D)y = X$, found in accordance with the method of §49, is like a term in the complementary function. Such a term will give zero when substituted in the left-hand member $f(D)y$ because it is a solution of $f(D)y = 0$; hence, it cannot function to give a term like itself. For example, consider the equation

$$(D^2 + 4)y = \sin 2x. \tag{43}$$

Here $y_c = c_1 \sin 2x + c_2 \cos 2x$. Letting $y_p = A \sin 2x + B \cos 2x$, and substituting in (43), we get the impossible equation $0 \equiv \sin 2x$. The process for multiple roots suggests that a factor x be introduced. Hence, we use

$$y_p = x(A \sin 2x + B \cos 2x). \tag{44}$$

Substituting this value of y_p in (43), we obtain after slight simplification

$$4A \cos 2x - 4B \sin 2x = \sin 2x.$$

Hence, $4A = 0, \quad -4B = 1, \quad \text{or} \quad A = 0, \quad B = -\tfrac{1}{4}$,

and the solution of (43) is

$$\mathbf{y = y_c + y_p = c_1 \sin 2x + c_2 \cos 2x - \tfrac{1}{4}x \cos 2x.} \tag{45}$$

As another example, consider

$$(D^2 - 2D + 1)y = xe^x + 5. \tag{46}$$

The complementary function is

$$y_c = (c_1 + c_2x)e^x. \tag{47}$$

Divide the task of finding y_p into two parts: that of finding the particular solution relating to xe^x, and that relating to 5. For the part xe^x, we write

$$y_{p_1} = x^2(A + Bx)e^x. \tag{48}$$

The part $(A + Bx)e^x$ was written in accordance with §49, and the factor x^2 was supplied to make y_{p_1} unlike the complementary function. Substituting y_{p_1} from (48) in the left-hand member of (46) and equating the result to xe^x, we obtain after simplification

$$e^x(6Bx + 2A) = xe^x.$$

Equating the coefficients of like terms, we get $B = \frac{1}{6}$, $A = 0$, and $y_{p_1} = \frac{1}{6}x^3e^x$. The particular solution of (46) relating to 5, found by the regular procedure of §49, is $y_{p_2} = 5$. Hence, the solution of (46) is

$$y = y_c + y_{p_1} + y_{p_2} = (c_1 + c_2x)e^x + \tfrac{1}{6}x^3e^x + 5.$$

Observe that, in forming a trial y_p for any term in the right-hand member, it is first formed by the method of §49 and then multiplied by x^n, where n is the least integer that will make each term of the trial y_p unlike any term in the complementary function.

EXERCISES

Solve the following differential equations:

1. $(D^2 + D)y = 4x$. *Hint:* Take $y_p = x(Ax + B)$.
2. $(D^2 - 1)y = 5e^x$. *Hint:* Take $y_p = Axe^x$.

Find a particular solution of each of the following differential equations:

3. $(D^2 + D)y = e^{-x}$.
4. $(D^2 + 1)y = \sin x$.
5. $(D^2 - 1)y = e^{-x}$.
6. $(D^2 + 4D + 3)y = 3x + e^{-x}$.
7. $(D^2 - 2D + 1)y = e^x + 3$.
8. $(D^2 + 4)y = \cos 2x$.
9. $(D^2 + 2D)y = 8x + e^{-2x}$.
10. $(D^3 + 4D)y = 8 \cos 2x + 4$.
★11. $(D^3 - 2D^2 + 5D)y = 10 + 15 \cos 2x$.
★12. $(D^2 - 2D + 2)y = e^x \sin x$.

51. A basic theorem relating to operators

THEOREM. *If $\varphi(y)$ represents a polynomial, then*

$$\boldsymbol{\varphi(D)(e^{ax}X) = e^{ax}\varphi(D + a)X,} \tag{49}$$

where X is any function of x possessing all the derivatives indicated in (49).

Proof. First we shall use mathematical induction in proving that

$$D^n(e^{ax}X) = e^{ax}(D + a)^n X. \tag{50}$$

When $n = 0$, each member of (50) is equal to $e^{ax}X$. Hence, (50) is true when $n = 0$. Let k be any nonnegative integer for which (50) holds. Then,

$$D^k(e^{ax}X) = e^{ax}(D + a)^k X,$$

and, differentiating this, obtain

$$\begin{aligned} D^{k+1}(e^{ax}X) &= D[e^{ax}(D + a)^k X] = e^{ax}D(D + a)^k X + ae^{ax}(D + a)^k X \\ &= e^{ax}(D + a)^{k+1}X. \end{aligned}$$

That is, if (50) holds when $n = k$, it holds when $n = k + 1$. Therefore, by complete induction, (50) is true when $n = 0$ or a positive integer. Consequently, (49) holds, because each term in the left-hand member equals the corresponding term in the right-hand member.

As an illustration of (49), consider that

$$(D^2 - 4)(e^{2x}x^2) = e^{2x}[(D + 2)^2 - 4]x^2 = e^{2x}(D^2 + 4D)x^2 = e^{2x}(2 + 8x).$$

Some special cases of (49) are useful.

If in (49) we let $\varphi(D) = \psi(D - a)$ and interchange members, we get

$$e^{ax}\psi(D)X = \psi(D - a)(e^{ax}X). \tag{51}$$

Evidently, $KD^n(e^{ax}) = Ka^ne^{ax}$, and since a polynomial $\varphi(D)$ is a sum of such terms as KD^n, we have

$$\boldsymbol{\varphi(\mathrm{D})(\mathrm{e}^{ax}) = \mathrm{e}^{ax}\varphi(\mathrm{a}).} \tag{52}$$

Thus

$$(D^5 + 5D^2 + 2)e^{-x} = [(-1)^5 + 5(-1)^2 + 2]e^{-x} = 6e^{-x}.$$

Example. Solve

$$(D + 2)^3y = xe^{-2x}. \tag{a}$$

Solution. Multiply both members by e^{2x}, use (51) with $\psi(D) = (D + 2)^3$, and obtain

$$e^{2x}(D + 2)^3y = D^3(ye^{2x}) = x. \tag{b}$$

Obviously, a particular solution of (*b*) is $ye^{2x} = x^4/24$. Hence, the general solution is

$$\mathbf{y = y_c + y_p = (c_1 + c_2x + c_3x^2 + \tfrac{1}{24}x^4)e^{-2x}.} \tag{c}$$

EXERCISES

Use (52) to carry out indicated operations:

1. $(D - a)^5(e^{ax})$.
2. $(D + a)^5e^{ax}$.
3. $(D^3 + D^2 + 4)e^{-2x}$.
4. $(D - 1)(D - 2)(D - 3)e^{-3x}$.

Use (49) to carry out indicated operations:

5. $(D - a)^5(x^5e^{ax})$.
6. $(D + 1)^5(D - 3)^3(x^2e^{3x})$.
7. $(D - 2)^4(e^{2x} \sin x)$.
8. $(D + 1)^n(e^{-x}x^{n-1})$.

9. Show that $y = X_{n-1}e^{ax}$ satisfies $(D - a)^ny = 0$ if X_{n-1} is a polynomial of degree $n - 1$ in x.

10. To solve $(D + a)^2y = xe^{-ax}$, multiply through by e^{ax}, use (51) with $\psi(D) = (D + a)^2$, and solve the result for $Y = ye^{ax}$.

Use the method of exercise **10** and of the illustrative example to solve the following equations:

11. $(D + 2)^3y = xe^{-2x}$.
12. $(D^2 + 2D)y = e^{-2x} \sin x$.
★**13.** $(D + 1)^2Dy = 12e^{-x}$.
14. $[(D + 2)^2 + 4]y = e^{-2x} \sin x$.

52. Methods using symbolic operators

In this section, $f(D)$, $\varphi(D)$, and $\psi(D)$ refer to polynomial operators and X refers to a function of x possessing all derivatives and integrals involved.

A solution of the differential equation $\varphi(D)y = X$ is represented by

$\varphi^{-1}(D)X$ and also by $[1/\varphi(D)]X$. We write

$$\varphi^{-1}(D)X \cong y(x) \qquad \textit{provided} \qquad \varphi(D)y = X. \tag{53}$$

The symbol $\cong$ *is read* **is equivalent to.** Operator $\varphi^{-1}(D)$ is called the operator **inverse** to $\varphi(D)$. Note that $\varphi^{-1}(D)X$ is any solution of $\varphi(D)y = X$, but generally we desire a simple one to use as a particular solution y_p. Also, note from (53) that

$$\varphi(\mathbf{D})\varphi^{-1}(\mathbf{D})\mathbf{X} = \mathbf{X}, \tag{54}$$

and if $\quad \varphi^{-1}(D)\varphi(D)X \cong X_1, \quad$ *then* $\quad \varphi(D)X = \varphi(D)X_1. \qquad (55)$

To find explicit forms of such expressions as $D^{-1}(6x - 6x^2)$ and $(D - 2)^{-1}(6x - 6x^2)$, we may solve the corresponding differential equations. Thus, for $D^{-1}(6x - 6x^2)$ we write

$$Dy = 6x - 6x^2, \qquad y \cong 3x^2 - 2x^3, \qquad D^{-1}(6x - 6x^2) \cong 3x^2 - 2x^3. \tag{56}$$

Also, we have

$$(D - 2)y = 6x - 6x^2, \qquad y = 3x^2, \qquad (D - 2)^{-1}(6x - 6x^2) \cong 3x^2.$$

The formulas, developed below, will furnish short methods of dealing with inverse operators.

Since *the order of factors in* $\varphi(D)$ *is immaterial, the same thing is true in* $1/\varphi(D)$ by (53). Also, we have

$$\frac{1}{\varphi(D)\psi(D)}[\varphi(D) + \psi(D)]X \cong \left[\frac{1}{\varphi(D)} + \frac{1}{\psi(D)}\right]X \cong \frac{1}{\varphi(D)}X + \frac{1}{\psi(D)}X; \tag{57}$$

for operating on each of the three expressions by $\varphi(D)\psi(D)$, we get in each case $[\varphi(D) + \psi(D)]X$. For example, using (57), we get

$$\frac{1}{D(D-2)}(6x - 6x^2) \cong \frac{1}{2}\left[\frac{1}{D-2} - \frac{1}{D}\right](6x - 6x^2)$$
$$\cong \tfrac{1}{2}(3x^2 - 3x^2 + 2x^3) = x^3. \tag{58}$$

Again we have

$$\frac{\mathbf{1}}{\varphi(\mathbf{D})}(\mathbf{X}e^{ax}) \cong e^{ax}\frac{\mathbf{1}}{\varphi(\mathbf{D} + \mathbf{a})}\mathbf{X}. \tag{59}$$

For, applying $\varphi(D)$ to both members and taking into account (54) and (49), §51, we get

$$\varphi(D)\left[\frac{1}{\varphi(D)}(Xe^{ax})\right] = Xe^{ax},$$

$$\varphi(D)\left[e^{ax}\frac{X}{\varphi(D+a)}\right] = e^{ax}\varphi(D + a)\frac{X}{\varphi(D+a)} = Xe^{ax},$$

or Xe^{ax} in both cases. An illustration of the use of (59) follows:

$$\frac{x^2e^{ax}}{D-a} \cong e^{ax}\left(\frac{1}{D}x^2\right) \cong \tfrac{1}{3}x^3e^{ax},$$

and $y_p = \frac{1}{3}x^3e^{ax}$ is a particular solution of $(D-a)y = x^2e^{ax}$.

Since $(D^2)^n \sin ax = (-a^2)^n \sin ax$ and $(D^2)^n \cos ax = (-a^2)^n \cos ax$, we see that for a polynomial operator having the form $\varphi(D^2)$

$$\varphi(D^2) \sin ax = \varphi(-a^2) \sin ax, \qquad \varphi(D^2) \cos ax = \varphi(-a^2) \cos ax. \tag{60}$$

Also,

$$\frac{1}{\varphi(D^2)} \sin ax \cong \frac{1}{\varphi(-a^2)} \sin ax, \qquad \frac{1}{\varphi(D^2)} \cos ax \cong \frac{1}{\varphi(-a^2)} \cos ax; \tag{61}$$

for, in each case, $\varphi(D^2)$ applied to the left-hand side equals $\varphi(D^2)$ applied to the right-hand side. As an example of the use of (61), we see from (61) that a particular solution of $(D^4 - 5D^2 + 4)y = \sin 3x$ is

$$y_p \cong \frac{1}{D^4 - 5D^2 + 4} \sin 3x \cong \frac{\sin 3x}{(-9)^2 - 5(-9) + 4} \cong \tfrac{1}{130} \sin 3x.$$

Another set of useful formulas is

$$\frac{1}{D}X \cong \int X\,dx, \qquad \frac{1}{D^2}X \cong \int\left(\int X\,dx\right)dx, \qquad \ldots . \tag{62}$$

For example, to solve the equation $(D^5 + D^4 - 6D^3)y = x^2$, we can find the complementary solution in the ordinary way and then, in finding a particular solution, operate on both members by $1/D^3$ and obtain

$$(D^2 + D - 6)y \cong \frac{1}{D^3}x^2 \cong \tfrac{1}{60}x^5. \tag{63}$$

If X is a polynomial of degree n, the following formula applies to find a particular solution of $(D + a)y = X$:

$$\frac{1}{D+a}X \cong \frac{(1/a)X}{1 + D/a} \cong \frac{1}{a}\left[1 - \frac{D}{a} + \frac{D^2}{a^2} + \cdots + (-1)^n\frac{D^n}{a^n}\right]X; \tag{64}$$

for, operating on the last member and using (57) extended for n functions, we get

$$(D+a)\left\{\frac{1}{a}\left[1 - \frac{D}{a} + \cdots + (-1)^n\frac{D^n}{a^n}\right]X\right\}$$
$$= \left[1 + (-1)^n\left(\frac{D}{a}\right)^{n+1}\right]X,$$

and since $D^{n+1}X = 0$, this is equal to X. As an example, let us find

$\int x^4e^{2x}\,dx$. We have by (59) and (64)

$$\int x^4e^{2x}\,dx \cong \frac{1}{D}(x^4e^{2x}) \cong e^{2x}\frac{1}{D+2}x^4 \cong \tfrac{1}{2}e^{2x}\frac{1}{1+D/2}x^4$$
$$\cong \tfrac{1}{2}e^{2x}\left(1-\frac{D}{2}+\frac{D^2}{4}-\frac{D^3}{8}+\frac{D^4}{16}\right)x^4$$
$$\cong \tfrac{1}{2}e^{2x}\,(x^4-2x^3+3x^2-3x+\tfrac{3}{2}).$$

A method of carrying out the indicated operation $[1/\varphi(D)](a_0x^n + a_1x^n + \cdots + a_n)$ consists in operating on the polynomial in x by the part of the quotient $1/\varphi(D)$ containing terms of degree n or less. Thus,

$$\frac{1}{2+2D^2+D^4}x^4 \cong (\tfrac{1}{2}-\tfrac{1}{2}D^2+\tfrac{1}{4}D^4+\cdots)x^4 = \tfrac{1}{2}x^4-6x^2+6.$$

The first step in solving an equation $\varphi(D)y = X$ is to write it in the form $y = \varphi^{-1}(D)X$. Note that the four formulas, written in boldface, (59), (61), (62), and (64), are the basis of short cuts in carrying out operations. Use (59) to move a power of e to a position preceding the operator. Thus $1/(D+1)(e^{2x}\sin 3x) = e^{2x}[1/(D+3)]\sin 3x$. Use (61) to operate on $\sin ax$ or $\cos ax$. Thus,

$$\frac{1}{D+3}\sin 3x = \frac{D-3}{D^2-9}\sin 3x = \frac{3\cos 3x - 3\sin 3x}{-18}.$$

Use (62) to quickly dispose of factors having the form $1/D^n$. Thus,

$$[1/(D^3+D^2)]x^2 = [1/(D+1)](1/D^2)x^2 = [1/(D+1)]\tfrac{1}{12}x^4.$$

Use (64) to operate on a polynomial; thus,

$$\frac{1}{D+2}4x^2 = \frac{1}{2}\frac{1}{1+D/2}4x^2 = \frac{1}{2}\left(1-\frac{D}{2}+\frac{D^2}{4}\right)4x^2 = 2x^2-2x+1.$$

Example 1. Find a particular solution of

$$(D-2)^3(D-1)y = 6(x^2+2x)e^{2x}.$$

Solution. Using (59), (64), and (62) in order, we get

$$y \cong \frac{1}{(D-2)^3(D-1)}(6x^2+12x)e^{2x} \cong e^{2x}\frac{6x^2+12x}{D^3(D+1)}$$
$$= e^{2x}\frac{1}{D^3}(6x^2+12x-12x-12+12) = \tfrac{1}{10}\mathbf{x^5e^{2x}}.$$

Example 2. Find a particular solution of $(D^2+1)y = e^x \sin x$.

Solution. Using (59) first and then (61), obtain

$$y \cong \frac{1}{D^2+1}(e^x \sin x) \cong e^x \frac{1}{(D+1)^2+1}\sin x$$
$$\cong e^x \frac{1}{D^2+2D+2}\sin x \cong e^x \frac{1}{-1+2D+2}\sin x^*$$
$$\cong e^x \frac{(2D-1)}{4D^2-1}\sin x\dagger \cong \frac{\mathbf{2\cos x - \sin x}}{\mathbf{-5}}\mathbf{e}^x.$$

Example 3. Find a particular solution of $(D-2)(D-1)y = 4x^3e^{2x}$.
Solution. Here,

$$y \cong \frac{4x^3e^{2x}}{(D-2)(D-1)} \cong e^{2x}\cdot\frac{4x^3}{D(D+1)} = e^{2x}\cdot\frac{x^4}{D+1}.$$

Now, using (64), obtain

$$\frac{1}{1+D}x^4 = (1 - D + D^2 - D^3 + D^4)x^4$$
$$= x^4 - 4x^3 + 12x^2 - 24x + 24.$$

Therefore, $\mathbf{y = e^{2x}(x^4 - 4x^3 + 12x^2 - 24x + 24)}$.

Example 4. Find a particular solution of $(D^3 + 4D)y = 4\sin 2x$.
Solution. By (62),

$$y \cong \frac{4\sin 2x}{(D^2+4)D} = \frac{-2\cos 2x}{D^2+4}.$$

Here, (61) fails because it involves zero as a divisor. Let Re mean *real part of*. Note that $\cos 2x = \text{Re } e^{i2x}$ from (29), §48. Hence, by (59), (62), and (64), we get

$$y \cong \frac{-2\cos 2x}{D^2+4} \cong \text{Re}\left(\frac{-2e^{i2x}}{D^2+4}\right) \cong \text{Re } e^{i2x}\frac{(-2)}{(D+2i)^2+4}$$
$$\cong \text{Re } e^{i2x}\frac{-2}{D^2+4iD} \cong \text{Re } e^{i2x}\frac{-2x}{D+4i}$$
$$\cong \text{Re }(\cos 2x + i\sin 2x)\left[\frac{1}{4i}\left(1-\frac{D}{4i}\right)(-2x)\right]$$
$$\cong \text{Re }[(\cos 2x + i\sin 2x)(\tfrac{1}{2}ix - \tfrac{1}{8})] \cong -\tfrac{1}{8}\cos 2x - \tfrac{1}{2}x\sin 2x.$$

* To see the justification for using (61) in a partial manner, consider the differential equation $(D^2 + 2D - 2)y = \sin x$, and think of finding a particular solution by letting $y_p = A\sin x + B\cos x$. Then, $D^2y_p = -1(A\sin x + B\cos x)$, and the D^2 part of the operator functions as though it were -1.

† Here we multiplied numerator and denominator of the operator by $2D - 1$. Since, from (54), $\alpha(D)[1/\alpha(D)\ 1/\psi(D)]X = [1/\psi(D)]X$, no error will arise in finding a solution of $\psi(D)y = X$ if the $1/\alpha(D)$ operation is performed first. Operation with $\alpha(D)$ before $1/\alpha(D)$ is justified when operation $1/\alpha(D)$ restores X completely. Note, for example, that $(1/D)(6x+2) \cong D(1/D^2)(6x+2) \cong D(x^3+x^2) = 3x^2+2x$. But $(1/D^2)D(6x+3) = (1/D^2)6 = 3x^2$. Now $3x^2+2x$ is a particular solution of $Dy = 6x+2$, but $3x^2$ is not.

Since $y = \cos 2x$ satisfies $(D^3 + 4D)y = 0$ it may be discarded. Hence, an answer is $\mathbf{y_p = -\frac{1}{2}x \sin 2x}$.

EXERCISES

In each case carry out the operations of the indicated formulas to find an equivalent expression not involving D:

1. $\dfrac{1}{D}x^3$; (62).

2. $\dfrac{1}{D^2}(8e^{2x})$; (62).

3. $\dfrac{1}{(D-1)^2}(xe^x)$; (59), (62).

4. $\dfrac{D}{D^2+4}\sin 3x$; (61).

5. $(D+1)^{-1}x^4$; (64).

6. $(D^2+4)^{-3}\cos 4x$; (61).

7. $[(D+3)D]^{-1}(3x^2)$; (62), (64).

8. $(D-1)^{-2}(e^{2x}\cos x)$; (59), (61).

Solve:

9. $(D-3)^2y = 48xe^{3x}$. Write $y = [1/(D-3)^2](48xe^{3x})$, and use (59) and (62).

10. $(D+1)^3y = 16(2x+3)^{-3}e^{-x}$.

11. $(D^2 - 2D - 3)y = 64xe^{3x}$.

12. $(D^4 + 2D^2 + 1)y = \sin 2x$. Write $[1/(D^2+1)^2]\sin 2x$, and use (61).

13. $(D^2+1)y = \sin 2x + \cos 3x$. Use (61) on each term of the right-hand member.

★14. $(D-1)^3y = e^x \cos x$.

★15. $(D^2+4)y = 9e^x \sin 2x$. Read example 2.

★16. $(D^2 - D + 2)y = 58e^x \cos 3x$.

17. $(D-1)^2y = e^x \sin x + e^{2x}\cos x$.

18. $(D^2+4)y = e^x \sin 2x$.

19. $(D^2 - 4D + 2)y = 8e^x \cos x$.

Use inverse operators changed to the form of partial fractions in solving the equations numbered 20 to 23:

20. $(D-1)(D-2)y = x^2e^{3x}$.

21. $(D^2-4)y = 27x^2e^{2x}$.

22. $(D+1)(D-3)y = 16xe^{3x}$.

23. $(D-3)(D+2)y = e^{2x}(2 + 6x - 4x^2)$.

24. Divide 1 by $2 + D + D^2$ to three terms, and operate with the result on $x^2 + 2x$, thus finding a solution of $(D^2 + D + 2)y = x^2 + 2x$.

Use the method of solving problem 24 to find a solution of:

25. $(2 + 4D - D^2)y = 4x^3$.

26. $(1 + 2D^2 + D^3)y = x^3 - 2x^2$.

Use the method of example 4 to solve the following equations:

27. $(D^2+1)y = 4\cos x$.

28. $(D^2+9)y = 36\sin 3x$.*

29. $(D^2+1)y = 16x\cos x$.

30. $(D^2+4)y = 64x\sin 2x + 32\cos 2x$.

31. Show that $[1/\varphi(D)]e^{ax} \cong e^{ax}/\varphi(a)$. Check that $(1/D^3)e^{ax} \cong e^{ax}/a^3 + b + cx + gx^2$. Also, check that $(1/D^n)e^{ax} \cong e^{ax}/a^n$.

32. Use the principle of exercise 31 to write a solution of $(3D^3 + 4D^2 + 1)y = e^{2x}$.

53. Variation of parameters

The methods used in §§49 to 52 generally fail to give a solution when the derivatives of the right-hand member X do not contain a finite num-

* $\sin 3x = \text{Re}\,(-ie^{i3x})$.

ber of terms. The method illustrated below, known as **variation of parameters,** is used to find the solution of general linear differential equations when the solution y_c of the corresponding homogeneous differential equation is known.

Consider the differential equation

$$(D^3 + D)y = \sec x. \tag{a}$$

The solution of $(D^3 + D)y = 0$ is

$$y = A \sin x + B \cos x + C. \tag{b}$$

Now we assume that (*b*) is the solution of (*a*), where A, B, C are functions of x to be determined. From (*b*),

$$D(y) = A \cos x - B \sin x + A' \sin x + B' \cos x + C', \tag{c}$$

where the primes denote derivatives with respect to x. A, B, and C, being three arbitrary functions, may be subjected to three conditions; hence, let us take

$$A' \sin x + B' \cos x + C' = 0. \tag{d}$$

Then, $D^2y = -A \sin x - B \cos x + A' \cos x - B' \sin x.$ (*e*)

Take $A' \cos x - B' \sin x = 0.$ (*f*)

Then, $D^3y = -A \cos x + B \sin x - A' \sin x - B' \cos x.$ (*g*)

Substituting y and its derivatives from (*b*), (*c*), (*e*), and (*g*) in (*a*) while taking account of (*d*) and (*f*), we get, after slight simplification,

$$-A' \sin x - B' \cos x = \sec x. \tag{h}$$

The solution of (*d*), (*f*), and (*h*) for A', B', and C' is

$$A' = -\tan x, \qquad B' = -1, \qquad C' = \sin x \tan x + \cos x = \sec x. \tag{i}$$

Solving (*i*) for A, B, and C, obtain

$$A = \ln \cos x + c_1, \quad B = -x + c_2, \quad C = \ln(\sec x + \tan x) + c_3. \tag{j}$$

Substituting the values of A, B, and C from (*j*) in (*b*), obtain the solution of (*a*),

$$y = (\ln \cos x + c_1) \sin x + (c_2 - x) \cos x + \ln(\sec x + \tan x) + c_3.$$

The following example considers a case in which the coefficients of D^2y, Dy, and y are not all constants:

Example. Solve

$$(x - 1)D^2y - xDy + y = (x - 1)^2. \tag{a}$$

Solution. By trial, we find that $y_1 = x$ and $y_2 = e^x$ are solutions of

$$(x - 1)D^2y - xDy + y = 0. \tag{b}$$

Check this. Therefore, by the theorem of §44,

$$y = Ax + Be^x \tag{c}$$

is the general solution of (*b*). Think of A and B as such functions of x that (*c*) is the general solution of (*a*). From (*c*),

$$Dy = A + Be^x + xA' + e^xB'. \tag{d}$$

Take

$$xA' + e^xB' = 0. \tag{e}$$

From (*d*), obtain

$$D^2y = Be^x + A' + e^xB'. \tag{f}$$

Replace y, Dy, and D^2y in (*a*) by their values from (*c*), (*d*), and (*f*), and simplify to get

$$(x - 1)(A' + e^xB') = (x - 1)^2. \tag{g}$$

Solve (*e*) and (*g*) for A' and B' to get

$$A' = -1, \qquad B' = xe^{-x}. \tag{h}$$

From (*h*), obtain

$$A = -x + c_1, \qquad B = -(x + 1)e^{-x} + c_2. \tag{i}$$

Replace A and B in (*c*) by their values from (*i*), and simplify slightly to obtain

$$\mathbf{y = c_1x + c_2e^x - x^2 - x - 1.} \tag{j}$$

The terms c_1x and $-x$ could be replaced by cx.

EXERCISES

1. To solve $(D^2 + 1)y = \tan x$, write

$$y = A \sin x + B \cos x, \tag{a}$$

find Dy, treating A, B, and x as variables, and take

$$A' \sin x + B' \cos x = 0. \tag{b}$$

Find D^2y and substitute Dy and D^2y in the given differential equation to obtain, after simplification,

$$A' \cos x - B' \sin x = \tan x. \tag{c}$$

Solve (*b*) and (*c*) for A' and B', integrate the results to find A and B, and then replace A and B in (*a*) by these values.

Solve exercise 1, and then solve the following differential equations by using the same methods:

2. $(D^2 + 1)y = \sec x$.

3. $(D^2 + 4)y = 4 \cot 2x$.

4. $(D^2 + 2D + 2)y = e^{-x} \sec x$.

5. $(D - 2)^2y = x^ne^{2x}$.

6. $(D + 2)^2y = x^{-2}e^{-2x}$.

7. $(D + 1)^2y = x^{-2}e^{-x} \ln x$.

8. $(D - 1)^3y = 18x^{-4}e^x \ln x$.

Solve each of the following equations after checking the two indicated solutions of the left-hand member equated to zero:

9. $(xD^2 - D)y = 4/x;\ y_1 = 1,\ y_2 = x^2.$
10. $[(x - 1)D^2 - xD + 1]y = (x - 1)^2/x;\ y_1 = x,\ y_2 = e^x.$
11. $(x^4D^2 + 2x^3D - 1)y = 16e^{3/x};\ y_1 = e^{1/x},\ y_2 = e^{-1/x}.$

54. Simultaneous differential equations

A solution of n simultaneous equations in $n + 1$ unknowns consists of n independent relations involving one or more of these unknowns but not their derivatives; if these n relations are solved for n of the unknown quantities in terms of the remaining one, and if the results are substituted in the given differential equations, identities must result. *The first object in solving such a system is so to combine the given equations and other equations derived from them as to obtain an equation in two unknowns.* This may be integrated to obtain one relation, and the result may be used to obtain other relations. In the process of eliminating variables, we often find that operators can be used to advantage. Using the facts relating to operators in §§42, 51, and 52, we shall find the process of elimination in the case of linear equations with constant coefficients to be very much like an analogous process of elimination used in algebra.

Example. Solve

$$\frac{dx}{dt} + \frac{dy}{dt} + y - x = e^{2t},\qquad \frac{d^2x}{dt^2} + \frac{dy}{dt} = 3e^{2t}. \tag{a}$$

Solution. Replacing d/dt by D, we may write the equations (a) in the form

$$(D - 1)x + (D + 1)y = e^{2t},\qquad D^2x + Dy = 3e^{2t}. \tag{b}$$

Operating on the first of equations (b) with D and on the second with $(D + 1)$, we obtain

$$(D^2 - D)x + D(D + 1)y = De^{2t} = 2e^{2t},\qquad (D^3 + D^2)x + (D + 1)Dy = D(3e^{2t}) + 3e^{2t} = 9e^{2t}. \tag{c}$$

Subtracting the first of equations (c) from the second, we get

$$(D^3 + D)x = 7e^{2t}. \tag{d}$$

The solution of this equation is

$$\mathbf{x = c_1 + c_2 \sin t + c_3 \cos t + \tfrac{7}{10}e^{2t}}. \tag{e}$$

Substituting the value of x from (e) in the second equation of (b) and integrating the resulting equation, we obtain

$$\mathbf{y = \tfrac{1}{10}e^{2t} - c_2 \cos t + c_3 \sin t + c_4}. \tag{f}$$

There may be too many constants of integration in the solution given by (*e*) and (*f*). It can be shown* that the number of constants of integration to be expected in the general solution of a system of simultaneous linear differential equations with constant coefficients is the same as the degree in D of the determinant of the equations. Thus, the determinant of (*b*) is

$$\begin{vmatrix} D-1 & D+1 \\ D^2 & D \end{vmatrix},$$

its degree is 3, and there should be only three constants of integration in the solution of (*a*).

The general procedure in finding any relation that may exist between the constants is to substitute the solution in one of the original equations, simplify as much as possible, and equate the coefficients of like terms in the two members of the result. Substituting the value of x from (*e*) and y from (*f*) in the first equation of (*b*), we obtain after simplification

$$c_4 - c_1 = 0, \qquad \text{or} \qquad c_4 = c_1.$$

It therefore appears that the solution is

$$\begin{aligned} x &= c_1 + c_2 \sin t + c_3 \cos t + \tfrac{7}{10}e^{2t}, \\ y &= c_1 + c_3 \sin t - c_2 \cos t + \tfrac{1}{10}e^{2t}. \end{aligned} \tag{g}$$

Remark. Extraneous constants of integration can often be avoided by deriving from the given set of equations an equation of low order to be used in finding the expression for an additional variable after the expressions for several variables have already been found. Thus, after finding (*e*) subtract the second equation of (*b*) from the first, solve the result for y, and get

$$y = -2e^{2t} + (D^2 - D + 1)x. \tag{h}$$

Now, substitute the right-hand member of (*e*) for x in (*h*), simplify, and get the second equation of (*g*).

EXERCISES

Solve the following systems of differential equations, where $D = d/dt$:

1. $x + Dy = 0,\ (D - 1)x + (D - 1)y = 2t.$
2. $(D - 1)x + Dy = 0,\ Dx + 2Dy = 4e^{2t}.$
3. $D^2x = y,\ D^2y = x + 1.$
4. $(D^2 - 3)x - 4y = 0,\ x + (D^2 + 1)y = 0.$
5. $(2D^2 - 4)y - Dx = 4t,\ (4D - 3)x + 2Dy = 0.$
6. $(D^2 - 1)x + 8Dy = 16e^t,\ Dx + 3(D^2 + 1)y = 0.$
7. Find the particular solution of the system

$$(D^2 - 3)x - 4y + 3 = 0, \qquad (D^2 + 1)y + x + 5 = 0,$$

for which $x = y = Dx = Dy = 0$ when $t = 0$.

* See E. L. Ince, "Ordinary Differential Equations," p. 150.

8. $Dx - 3y = 0$, $Dy + z = x$, $Dz + y = 0$.
9. $x + y + z = t$, $Dx + z = 0$, $2x - Dy = 0$.
10. $(D^2 - 1)x + 2(D + 1)y + (D + 1)z = e^t$, $(D + 1)^2x + 2(D + 1)y - (D + 1)z = 0$, $(D - 1)x - 2y - z = 0$.

55. Summary and review exercises

In this section, a linear differential equation with constant coefficients will be referred to as $L(D)y = X$. The general solution of $L(D)y = X$ is

$$y = y_c + y_p,$$

where y_c refers to the general solution of $L(D)y = 0$ and y_p is a particular solution of $L(D)y = X$.

To solve an equation of the type $L(D)y = 0$, find the roots of the auxiliary equation $L(m) = 0$, and then write the solution in accordance with (24), §45, (27), §46, and (35) and (38), §48.

The shortest methods of finding particular solutions of equations coming under the type $L(D)y = X$ are the operator methods based on equations (59), (61), (62), and (64) of §52. The method used in example 4 of §52 is especially powerful when equations (61) fail. The methods of §§49 and 50 are instructive but generally cumbersome.

When the kth derivative, $k = 1, 2, \ldots$, of the right member X has an endless set of variable parts, the method of variation of parameters, §53, should be used.

EXERCISES

Solve the following differential equations, and determine constants of integration when initial conditions are given:

1. $(D^2 + k^2)y = 0$.
2. $(D^4 - a^4)y = 0$.
3. $(D^2 - 4)y = 16$.
4. $(D^2 + 2D + 1)y = e^{-x}$.
5. $(D^3 - D^2)y = 0$.
6. $(D - 1)^3(D + 2)^2y = 0$.
7. $(D^2 + 2D + 3)y = 0$.
8. $D^2(D - 3)y = 54x$.
9. $(D^3 + D^2 - 2D)y = 8x$.
10. $(D^2 + 2D - 8)y = 16x - 12$.

11. $(D^2 - 4)y = 0$; $y = 3$, $Dy = 6$ when $x = 0$.
12. $D^2(D - 3)y = 6$; $y = 1$, $Dy = -1$, $D^2y = -2$ when $x = 1$.
13. $(D - 1)^2y = x^2 - 3x$; $y = 0$, $Dy = 2$ when $x = 0$.
14. $(D^2 - 1)y = \sin x$; $y = 1$, $Dy = -\frac{3}{2}$ when $x = 0$.
15. $(D^2 - 4)y = 25e^{3x}$; $y = 0$, $Dy = 5$ when $x = 0$.
16. $D(D^2 + 1)y = -6 \cos 2x$; $y = 1$, $Dy = -3$, $D^2y = 0$ when $x = \pi/2$.
★17. $(D - 1)(D^2 + 1)y = 5e^x \sin x$; $y = 0$, $Dy = -2$, $D^2y = -3$ when $x = 0$.
★18. $D^2(D + 1)y = 4xe^x$; $y = -4$, $Dy = -4$, $D^2y = 0$ when $x = 0$.
★19. $D(D - 1)(D + 1)y = 6 + 130 \cos 5x$; $y = 1$, $Dy = -12$, $D^2y = 1$ when $x = 0$.
★20. $(D^2 + 2D + 2)y = e^x(\cos 2x - 8 \sin 2x)$; $y = 0$, $Dy = 2$ when $x = 0$.

21. $(D^3 + 4D)y = 16 \sin 2x.$

22. $(D - 1)^2y = x^5e^x.$

23. $(D^2 - 4)y = 64xe^{2x}.$

24. $[(D - 1)^2 + 1]y = 24e^x \sin 3x.$

25. $(D^3 - 3D^2 + 4D - 2)y = e^x \sec x.$

26. $(D^2 - 2D + 2)y = e^x(\tan x + \cot x).$

27. $(2D^2 + D - 3)y = 15e^x + 20e^{-3x/2}.$

28. $D(D - 1)^2y = xe^x.$

29. $[(D - 1)^2 + 2]^2y = e^x \cos x.$

Use the method of example 4, §52, in solving the following equations:

30. $(D^2 + 9)y = 12 \cos 3x.$

31. $(D^2 + 9)y = 72x \cos 3x.$

32. $(D^2 - 2D + 2)y = 4e^x \sin x.$

33. $(D^2 + 4D + 5)y = 12e^{-2x} \cos x.$

Use variation of parameters in solving the following problems:

34. $(D^2 + 4)y = 8 \tan^2 2x.$

35. $(D^2 + 2D - 8)y = (6x^{-1} - x^{-2})e^{2x}.$

36. $(D^2 + 1)y = -x^{-2} \sin x + 2x^{-1} \cos x.$

37. $(D^2 + 1)y = 2 \sec^3 x.$

38. $(x^2D^2 - 3xD + 3)y = 16x^{-1}$; check that $y_1 = x$ and $y_2 = x^3$ both satisfy $(x^2D^2 - 3xD + 3)y = 0.$

39. $(xD^2 - D - 4x^3)y = 24x^3e^{2x^2}$; check that $y_1 = e^{x^2}$, $y_2 = e^{-x^2}$ both satisfy $(xD^2 - D - 4x^3)y = 0.$

Solve the following systems of equations, in which $D = d/dt$:

40. $(D - 7)x + y = 0,\ Dy + 3x - 5y = 0.$

41. $Dx + Dy + 3x = \sin t,\ Dx + y - x = \cos t.$

42. $Dx + Dy - x - y = 2e^t,\ Dx - Dz = 0,\ D(x + y + z) = e^t.$

CHAPTER 7

LAPLACE TRANSFORMS

56. Introduction

Oliver Heaviside, in an effort to solve ordinary linear differential equations with facility, devised a method of operational calculus which led to Laplace transforms. These have many uses. However, the one with which we are concerned relates to the solution of important types of differential equations. Since a desired particular solution is obtained directly by transforms, the method is especially useful in treating problems of electrical circuits and others requiring particular solutions. To obtain a thorough knowledge of transforms, the reader should study books dealing with transforms and their applications.*

57. Definition of a Laplace transform

Definition. *If $f(t)$ is defined for all values of t in the interval $t > 0$, and if p is a real number such that the integral $F(p)$ defined by*

$$\mathbf{F(p) = \int_0^\infty e^{-pt}\, f(t)\, dt} \tag{1}$$

converges for some finite value of p and all greater values, then $F(p)$ is called the **Laplace transform of** *$f(t)$.*

Observe the notation *f for a function and F for its transform.* Also, we shall use the notation based on (1),

$$\mathbf{T\{f(t)\} = F(p).} \tag{2}$$

An example will give some familiarity with the concept.

Example. Find the transform of (*a*) $f(t) = 1$; (*b*) $f(t) = t$; (*c*) $f(t) = e^{at}$, $p > a$.

Solution. Using (1), we have:

(*a*) $$F(p) = \int_0^\infty e^{-pt}1\, dt = \left[-\frac{1}{p}e^{-pt}\right]_0^\infty = \frac{\mathbf{1}}{\mathbf{p}}.$$

* Consult, for example, Ruel V. Churchill, "Operational Mathematics," 2d ed., McGraw-Hill Book Company, Inc., New York, 1958; Murray F. Gardner and John L. Barnes, "Transients in Linear Systems," John Wiley & Sons, Inc., New York, 1949; H. S. Carslaw and J. C. Jaeger, "Operational Methods in Applied Mathematics," Oxford University Press, New York, 1949.

(b) $$F(p) = \int_0^\infty e^{-pt}t\,dt = \left[-\frac{te^{-pt}}{p} - \frac{e^{-pt}}{p^2}\right]_0^\infty = \frac{1}{p^2}.$$

(c) $$F(p) = \int_0^\infty e^{-pt}e^{at}\,dt = \left[\frac{-e^{-(p-a)t}}{p-a}\right]_0^\infty = \frac{1}{p-a}.$$

EXERCISES

Use (1) to verify the following equations:

1. $T\{at\} = a/p^2$.
2. $T\{t^2\} = 2/p^3$.
3. $T\{t^3\} = \dfrac{3!}{p^4}$.
4. $T\{\sin kt\} = \dfrac{k}{p^2 + k^2}$.
5. $T\{\cos kt\} = \dfrac{p}{p^2 + k^2}$.
6. $T\{a + bt\} = \dfrac{a}{p} + \dfrac{b}{p^2}$.
7. $T\{\frac{1}{2}(e^{at} + e^{-at})\} = T\{\cosh at\} = \dfrac{p}{p^2 - a^2},\ p > |a|$.
8. $T\{\frac{1}{2}(e^{at} - e^{-at})\} = T\{\sinh at\} = \dfrac{a}{p^2 - a^2},\ p > |a|$.
9. $T\{te^{-at}\} = \dfrac{1}{(p+a)^2},\ p > -a$.
10. $T\{e^{-at}\sin kt\} = \dfrac{k}{(p+a)^2 + k^2},\ p > -a$.
11. $T\{e^{-at}\cos kt\} = \dfrac{p+a}{(p+a)^2 + k^2},\ p > -a$.

58. Some properties of Laplace transforms

DEFINITION I. *A function $f(t)$ is* **sectionally continuous** *on a finite closed interval if the interval consists of a finite set of subintervals in each of which $f(t)$ is continuous and approaches a finite limit as t approaches either end point from within the subinterval.*

DEFINITION II. *A function $f(t)$ is of* **exponential order as t tends to infinity** *if there exist numbers α, M, and L such that*

$$|f(t)| < Me^{\alpha t} \qquad \text{when } t \geqq L. \tag{3}$$

For example, t^3e^{at} describes a function in question, for

$$|t^3e^{at}| < e^{(a+1)t} \qquad \text{when } t > 5.$$

In fact, the product of e^{at} and any polynomial in t is easily shown to be of exponential order as t tends to infinity.

The transform (1), §57, *of a function $f(t)$ exists if $f(t)$ is sectionally continuous for all finite intervals in the domain $t \geqq 0$ and if $f(t)$ is of exponential order as t tends to infinity.* To see this, note first that $\int_0^m e^{-pt}f(t)\,dt$ exists if m is finite; for it is the sum of the integrals along the continuous parts of the curve. Therefore, considering (3), we see that, under the conditions mentioned, there is a number M such that

$$|e^{-pt}f(t)| < Me^{-(p-\alpha)t}, \qquad p > \alpha;$$

since $\int_0^\infty Me^{-(p-\alpha)t}\,dt$, $p > \alpha$, is $M/(p - \alpha)$,* the integral of the left-hand member exists and $\int_0^\infty e^{-pt}f(t)\,dt$, $p > \alpha$, converges absolutely.

In the material on transforms, we shall *assume without mention that all functions $f(t)$ considered for transformation are sectionally continuous in every finite interval in the domain $t \geqq 0$ and are of exponential order as t tends to infinity.*

The relation (2), §57, between $F(p)$ and $f(t)$ is also denoted by

$$\mathbf{T^{-1}\{F(p)\} = f(t),} \tag{4}$$

and $T^{-1}\{F(p)\}$ is called the inverse transform of $F(p)$. It can be shown that any two inverse transforms of a function $F(p)$ differ only at the ends of continuous sections of $f(t)$. Such differences may be disregarded for our purposes, and we shall think of the inverse of a function of p as unique.

The usual way of finding transforms and inverse transforms is by means of a table listing standard functions and their transforms. Table 1 on page 113 is sufficient for our purposes. Other transforms can be found by using general relations. Since transforms are integrals, they obey the same laws as regards sums and constant factors; therefore,

$$\mathbf{T\{af(t) + bg(t)\} = aT\{f(t)\} + bT\{g(t)\} = aF(p) + bG(p),} \tag{5}$$

and, from this and the uniqueness of inverse transforms, we get

$$\mathbf{T^{-1}\{aF(p) + bG(p)\} = aT^{-1}\{F(p)\} + bT^{-1}\{G(p)\} = af(t) + bg(t).} \tag{6}$$

Thus, using (5) and Table 1 with 3 for a, we get

$$T\{2 + 4e^{3t}\} = 2T\{1\} + 4T\{e^{3t}\} = 2/p + 4/(p - 3),$$

$$T\{4 \sin 3t - 5 \cos 3t\} = 4T\{\sin 3t\} - 5T\{\cos 3t\} = \frac{12}{p^2 + 9} - \frac{5p}{p^2 + 9}.$$

Similarly, using (6) and Table 1, we get

$$T^{-1}\left\{\frac{8p}{p^2 + 16} - \frac{6}{p^2 + 16}\right\} = 8T^{-1}\left\{\frac{p}{p^2 + 16}\right\} - \tfrac{6}{4}T^{-1}\left\{\frac{4}{p^2 + 16}\right\}$$
$$= 8 \cos 4t - \tfrac{3}{2} \sin 4t,$$

$$T^{-1}\left\{\frac{p}{(p^2 + 9)^2} + \frac{7}{(p^2 + 9)^2}\right\} = \frac{t}{6} \sin 3t + \frac{7}{54} (\sin 3t - 3t \cos 3t).$$

* Observe that limit $M/(p - \alpha) \to 0$ as $p \to \infty$ so that no such transform as $(p + 1)/p$ exists.

TABLE 1. LAPLACE TRANSFORMS

	$F(p)$	$f(t)$
1	$\frac{1}{p}$	1
2	$\frac{1}{p^2}$	t
3	$\frac{1}{p^n}, n = 1, 2, \ldots$	$\frac{t^{n-1}}{(n-1)!}$
4	$\frac{1}{p-a}, p > a$	e^{at}
5	$\frac{1}{(p-a)^n}, p > a$	$\frac{e^{at}t^{n-1}}{(n-1)!}$
6	$\frac{p}{p^2+a^2}$	$\cos at$
7	$\frac{a}{p^2+a^2}$	$\sin at$
8	$\frac{p-a}{(p-a)^2+b^2}$	$e^{at}\cos bt$
9	$\frac{1}{(p-a)^2+b^2}$	$\frac{1}{b}e^{at}\sin bt$
10	$\frac{p}{p^2-a^2}, p > \|a\|$	$\cosh at$
11	$\frac{a}{p^2-a^2}, p > \|a\|$	$\sinh at$
12	$\frac{1}{(p-a)(p-b)}, p > a$	$\frac{1}{a-b}(e^{at} - e^{bt}), a > b$
13	$\frac{p}{(p-a)(p-b)}, p > a$	$\frac{1}{a-b}(ae^{at} - be^{bt}), a > b$
14	$\frac{p}{(p^2+a^2)^2}$	$\frac{t}{2a}\sin at$
15	$\frac{p^2-a^2}{(p^2+a^2)^2}$	$t\cos at$
16	$\frac{1}{(p^2+a^2)^2}$	$\frac{1}{2a^3}(\sin at - at\cos at)$
17	$\frac{p}{(p^2+a^2)(p^2+b^2)}, a^2 \neq b^2$	$\frac{\cos at - \cos bt}{b^2-a^2}$
18	$\frac{1}{(p^2+a^2)(p^2+b^2)}, a^2 \neq b^2$	$\frac{a\sin bt - b\sin at}{ab(a^2-b^2)}$
19	$\frac{1}{p^2+b^2}\cdot\frac{1}{(p+\alpha)^2+a^2}$	$\frac{-2b\alpha\cos bt + N\sin bt}{b(N^2+4\alpha^2b^2)} + \frac{e^{-\alpha t}(2a\alpha\cos at + M\sin at)}{a(M^2+4\alpha^2a^2)}$
	where $M = \alpha^2 + b^2 - a^2$, $N = \alpha^2 + a^2 - b^2$	
20	$\frac{p}{p^2+b^2}\cdot\frac{1}{(p+\alpha)^2+a^2}$	$\frac{N\cos bt + 2b\alpha\sin bt}{4b^2\alpha^2+N^2} + \frac{e^{-\alpha t}(aP\cos at - \alpha Q\sin at)}{a(4a^2\alpha^2+M^2)}$
	where $M = \alpha^2 + b^2 - a^2$, $N = \alpha^2 + a^2 - b^2$, $P = b^2 - a^2 - \alpha^2$, $Q = b^2 + a^2 + \alpha^2$	

EXERCISES

Using Table 1, page 113, and (5) and (6), find in the form of direct expressions:

1. $T\{1 + t^3\}$.
2. $T\{\frac{1}{2} \sin 2t + \frac{1}{2} \cos 2t\}$.
3. $T\{5 \sinh 3t - 4 \cosh 3t\}$.
4. $T\{2e^{3t} \sin 2t - 3e^{3t} \cos 2t\}$.
5. $T\{e^{2t} \sin 4t - 3e^{2t} \cos 4t\}$.
6. $T\{e^{-2t} \sin 7t + e^{-2t} \cos 7t\}$.
7. $T^{-1}\left\{\frac{5}{p^7} + \frac{7}{p - a}\right\}$.
8. $T^{-1}\left\{\frac{3}{p - m} + \frac{4}{p + m}\right\}$.
9. $T^{-1}\left\{\frac{3}{p^2 + 9}\right\}$.
10. $T^{-1}\left\{\frac{p}{p^2 - 9}\right\}$.
11. $T^{-1}\left\{\frac{5 + 5p}{p^2 + 25}\right\}$.
12. $T^{-1}\left\{\frac{p}{(p - 2)^2 + 9}\right\}$.

59. Deriving transform relations from given ones

The processes considered in this section and §§60 and 61 are used for simplifying transforms, for indicating short cuts in working with transforms, for deriving transforms, and for various theoretical purposes.

If in (1), §57, we replace p by $p + a$, we get

$$F(p + a) = \int_0^\infty e^{-(p+a)t} f(t)\, dt = \int_0^\infty e^{-pt}[e^{-at} f(t)]\, dt.$$

From this, we see that

$$\mathbf{F(p + a) = T\{e^{-at} f(t)\}}. \qquad \textbf{(7)}$$

Observing that $f(t) = T^{-1}\{F(p)\}$, equating the inverse transforms of the members of (7), and multiplying the result through by e^{at}, we get

$$\mathbf{T^{-1}\{F(p)\} = e^{at} T^{-1}\{F(p + a)\}}. \qquad \textbf{(8)}$$

For example, from $T^{-1}\{1/p^2\} = t$ we get from (8)

$$T^{-1}\left\{\frac{1}{(p - a)^2}\right\} = e^{at} T^{-1}\left\{\frac{1}{(p + a - a)^2}\right\} = te^{at},$$

and from $T^{-1}\{k/(p^2 + k^2)\} = \sin kt$ we get

$$T^{-1}\left\{\frac{k}{(p + a)^2 + k^2}\right\} = e^{-at} T^{-1}\left\{\frac{k}{p^2 + k^2}\right\} = e^{-at} \sin kt.$$

Also, note that by using $(mp + n)/(p^2 + k^2) = T\{m \cos kt + (n/k) \sin kt\}$ and (7) we get

$$\frac{5p - 13}{(p - 3)^2 + 16} = \frac{5(p - 3) + 2}{(p - 3)^2 + 16} = T\{5e^{3t} \cos 4t + \tfrac{1}{2} e^{3t} \sin 4t\}.$$

Replace p by mp, where $m > 0$, in (1), §57, and then make the substitution $mt = \tau$ in the integral to get

$$\int_0^\infty e^{-p\tau}f\left(\frac{\tau}{m}\right)\frac{d\tau}{m} = F\{pm\}$$

or

$$\frac{\mathbf{1}}{\mathbf{m}}\mathbf{T}\left\{\mathbf{f}\left(\frac{\mathbf{t}}{\mathbf{m}}\right)\right\} = \mathbf{F}(\mathbf{mp}). \tag{9}$$

For example,

$$\frac{7p}{(7p)^2 + 16} = \tfrac{1}{7}T\{\cos \tfrac{4}{7}t\}, \qquad \frac{8}{(5p)^2 + 16} = \tfrac{2}{5}T\{\sin \tfrac{4}{5}t\},$$

$$\frac{14p + 10}{(7p + 2)^2 + 9} = \frac{2(7p + 2) + 6}{(7p + 2)^2 + 9} = \tfrac{1}{7}T\{e^{-2t/7}(2 \cos \tfrac{3}{7}t + 2 \sin \tfrac{3}{7}t)\}.$$

Equating the derivatives with respect to p of the sides of (1), §57, we get*

$$\frac{d}{dp}F(p) = \int_0^\infty -te^{-pt}f(t)\,dt = \int_0^\infty e^{-pt}[-tf(t)]\,dt$$

or

$$\frac{\mathbf{d}}{\mathbf{dp}}\mathbf{F}(\mathbf{p}) = \mathbf{T}\{-\mathbf{tf}(\mathbf{t})\}. \tag{10}$$

Thus, from $1/p = T\{1\}$ obtain

$$\frac{d}{dp}\left(\frac{1}{p}\right) = T\{-t \cdot 1\}, \qquad \text{or} \qquad -\frac{1}{p^2} = T\{-t\},$$

$$\frac{d}{dp}\left(-\frac{1}{p^2}\right) = T\{(-t)^2 \cdot 1\}, \qquad \text{or} \qquad \frac{2}{p^3} = T\{t^2\},$$

and so on. Also, from $a/(p^2 + a^2) = T\{\sin at\}$ obtain

$$\frac{d}{dp}\frac{a}{p^2 + a^2} = \frac{-2ap}{(p^2 + a^2)^2} = T\{(-t) \sin at\},$$

$$\frac{d}{dp}\frac{-2ap}{(p^2 + a^2)^2} = \frac{6ap^2 - 2a^3}{(p^2 + a^2)^3} = T\{(-t)^2 \sin at\}.$$

Applying (10) repeatedly, we get

$$\frac{\mathbf{d}^n}{\mathbf{dp}^n}\mathbf{F}(\mathbf{p}) = \mathbf{T}\{(-\mathbf{t})^n\mathbf{f}(\mathbf{t})\}. \tag{11}$$

Formulas (II), (III), (IV), and (V) of Table 2, page 116, express the results derived in this section.

* The conditions under which differentiation with respect to p under the integral sign is valid are satisfied provided that $f(t)$ fulfills the conditions prescribed in §57 for the existence of $T\{f(t)\}$. See R. Courant, "Differential and Integral Calculus," vol. II, p. 312, Interscience Publishers, Inc., New York.

TABLE 2. FORMULAS INVOLVING LAPLACE TRANSFORMS

(I)	$aF_1(p) + bF_2(p)$	$= T\{af_1(t) + bf_2(t)\}$
(II)	$F(p + a)$	$= T\{e^{-at}f(t)\}$
(III)	$T^{-1}\{F(p)\}$	$= e^{at}T^{-1}\{F(p + a)\}$
(IV)	$F(mp)$	$= T\left\{\frac{1}{m}f\left(\frac{t}{m}\right)\right\}, \; m > 0$
(V)	$\frac{d^k}{dp^k}F(p)$	$= T\{(-t)^k f(t)\}$
(VI)	$G(p) \cdot F(p)$	$= T\left\{\int_0^t g(t-\tau)\cdot f(\tau)\,d\tau\right\} = T\left\{\int_0^t f(t-\tau)\cdot g(\tau)\,d\tau\right\}$
(VII)	$\frac{1}{p}F(p)$	$= T\left\{\int_0^t f(\tau)\,d\tau\right\}$
(VIII)	$\frac{1}{p^2}F(p)$	$= T\left\{\int_0^t \int_0^\tau f(\theta)\,d\theta\,d\tau\right\}$
(IX)	$T\{f^{(n)}(t)\}$	$= p^nF(p) - p^{n-1}f(0) - p^{n-2}f'0 - \cdots - f^{(n-1)}(0)$

EXERCISES

Use (7) to derive by Table 1, page 113, formula:

1. 4 from 1. **2.** 5 from 3. **3.** 8 from 6. **4.** 9 from 7.

Apply (8) to show that:

5. $T^{-1}\left\{\frac{p+3}{(p+3)^2+1}\right\} = e^{-3t}T^{-1}\left\{\frac{p}{p^2+1}\right\}.$

6. $e^{-2t}T^{-1}\left\{\frac{p}{(p-2)^2+9}\right\} = T^{-1}\left\{\frac{p+2}{p^2+9}\right\}.$

Use (8) or (7) and 10, 11, and 14 from Table 1 to find in terms of t:

7. $T^{-1}\left\{\frac{p-m}{(p-m)^2-a^2}\right\}.$

8. $T^{-1}\left\{\frac{1}{(p-m)^2-a^2}\right\}.$

9. $T^{-1}\left\{\frac{p+m}{(p+m)^2+a^2}\right\}.$

Use (7) and Table 1 to express in terms of t:

10. $T^{-1}\left\{\frac{6!}{(p-2)^7}\right\}.$

11. $T^{-1}\left\{\frac{p-3}{(p-3)^2+16}\right\}.$

12. $T^{-1}\left\{\frac{21}{(p+5)^2+49}\right\}.$

13. $T^{-1}\left\{\frac{1}{[(p-3)^2+16]^2}\right\}.$

14. $T^{-1}\left\{\frac{(p-2)^2-16}{[(p-2)^2+16]^2}\right\}.$

15. $T^{-1}\left\{\frac{p+m}{(p+c)^2+a^2}\right\}.$

Apply (10) to 6 and 7 of Table 1 to show that:

16. $T^{-1}\left\{\frac{a^2-p^2}{(p^2+a^2)^2}\right\} = -t\cos at.$

17. $T^{-1}\left\{\frac{2ap}{(p^2+a^2)^2}\right\} = t\sin at.$

Apply (11) with $n = 2$ to 4, 7, and 11 of Table 1 to express in terms of p:

18. $T\{t^2e^{at}\}$. **19.** $T\{t^2 \sin at\}$. **20.** $T\{t^2 \sinh at\}$.

Apply (9) and Table 1 to verify that:

21. $\dfrac{5p}{(5p)^2 + 16} = \frac{1}{5}T\{\cos \frac{4}{5}t\}$. **22.** $\dfrac{3p - 2}{(3p - 2)^2 - 49} = \frac{1}{3}T\{e^{\frac{2}{3}t} \cosh \frac{7}{3}t\}$.

23. $\dfrac{20}{(2p + 3)^2 + 25} = \frac{1}{2}T\{e^{-\frac{3}{2}t}4 \sin \frac{5}{2}t\}$.

24. $T^{-1}\left\{\dfrac{p}{(3p)^2 + 16}\right\} = \frac{1}{9} \cos \frac{4}{3}t$.

Using (7) to (11) and Table 1, express in terms of t:

25. $T^{-1}\left\{\dfrac{b(p - a)}{(p - a)^2 + k^2}\right\}$. **26.** $T^{-1}\left\{\dfrac{5!}{(p - 5)^6}\right\}$.

27. $T^{-1}\left\{\dfrac{7}{(p + 3)^2 - 25}\right\}$. **28.** $T^{-1}\left\{\dfrac{2p + 14}{(p - 2)^2 + 36}\right\}$.

29. $T^{-1}\left\{\dfrac{d}{dp}\left[\dfrac{3p + 8}{(3p + 7)^2 + 1}\right]\right\}$. **30.** $T^{-1}\left\{\dfrac{d^3}{dp^3}\left[\dfrac{2p + 14}{(p - 2)^2 - 16}\right]\right\}$.

Express in terms of p:

31. $T\{\sin 3t\}$. **32.** $T\{e^{-2t} \sin 3t\}$. **33.** $T\{(-t)e^{-2t} \sin 3t\}$.

34. $T\left\{\dfrac{1}{3!}t^3\right\}$. **35.** $T\left\{\dfrac{1}{3!}t^3e^{5t}\right\}$. **36.** $T\left\{\dfrac{(-t)t^3e^{5t}}{3!}\right\}$.

37. $T\{\sinh t\}$. **38.** $T\{e^{-t} \sinh t\}$. **39.** $T\{(-t)^2e^{-t} \cosh t\}$.

40. $T\{e^{-4t} \cosh t\}$. **41.** $T\{(-t)e^{-4t} \cosh t\}$. **42.** $T\{(-t)^2e^{-4t} \cosh t\}$.

43. $T\{2(-t)^2e^{3t} - 4(-t) \sin 3t + 4(-t) \cos 3t\}$.

60. Inverse transforms of products

By the definition of a transform, we have

$$G(p) \cdot F(p) = \int_0^\infty e^{-px}g(x)\,dx \cdot \int_0^\infty e^{-py}f(y)\,dy$$
$$= \int_0^\infty \int_0^\infty e^{-p(x+y)}g(x)f(y)\,dx\,dy. \quad (12)$$

Reference to the triangles of Figs. 1 and 2 indicates that (12) may be written

$$G(p) \cdot F(p) = \lim_{a \to \infty} \int_0^a \int_0^{a-x} e^{-p(x+y)}g(x)f(y)\,dy\,dx. \quad (13)$$

Now, make the change of variables*

$$x = t - \tau, \qquad y = \tau \quad (14)$$

* *Ibid.*, vol. II, p. 253.

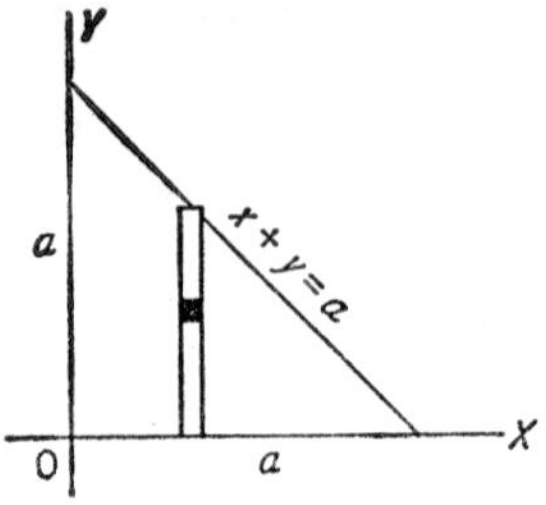

FIG. 1

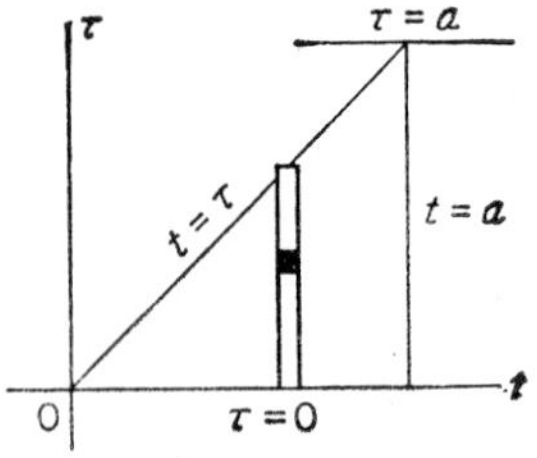

FIG. 2

in (13). Since, for (14)

$$\frac{\partial(x,y)}{\partial(t,\tau)} = \begin{vmatrix} \dfrac{\partial x}{\partial t} & \dfrac{\partial x}{\partial \tau} \\ \dfrac{\partial y}{\partial t} & \dfrac{\partial y}{\partial \tau} \end{vmatrix} = \begin{vmatrix} 1 & -1 \\ 0 & 1 \end{vmatrix} = 1,$$

integral (13) becomes

$$G(p) \cdot F(p) = \lim_{a \to \infty} \int_0^a e^{-pt} \left[\int_0^t g(t - \tau) f(\tau)\, d\tau \right] dt. \tag{15}$$

Figure 2 indicates the reason for the limits of integration in (15). From (15), we see that*

$$\mathbf{G(p) \cdot F(p) = T \left\{ \int_0^t g(t - \tau) f(\tau)\, d\tau \right\}}. \tag{16}$$

In the integral of (16), make the substitution $u = t - \tau$, $du = -d\tau$, and adjust the limits of integration to obtain

$$\int_0^t g(t - \tau) f(\tau)\, d\tau = \int_0^t f(t - u) g(u)\, du.$$

This equation, interpreted in the light of (16), shows that

$$T^{-1}\{G(p) \cdot F(p)\} = T^{-1}\{F(p) \cdot G(p)\}. \tag{17}$$

Hence, *change of order of factors of a transform does not change the inverse transform.*

Evidently, formula (16) could be used repeatedly. Thus,

$$H(p) \cdot G(p) \cdot F(p) = T \left\{ \int_0^t h(t - \tau) \left[\int_0^\tau g(\theta - \tau) \cdot f(\theta)\, d\theta \right] d\tau \right\}. \tag{18}$$

In (16), let $G(p) = 1/p$; then, $g(t) = 1$, and (15) becomes

$$\mathbf{\frac{1}{p} F(p) = T \left\{ \int_0^t f(\tau)\, d\tau \right\}}. \tag{19}$$

* Evidently, the right-hand member of equation (16) is zero when $t = 0$. Hence, $T^{-1}\{F(p) \cdot G(p)\} = 0$ when $t = 0$ and may be used as a check. Thus $T^{-1}\{[1/(p - 1)] \cdot [p/(p^2 + 4)]\} = \frac{1}{5}(e^t - \cos 2t) + \frac{2}{5} \sin 2t$, and this is zero when $t = 0$. Apply this check to 17, 18, 19, and 20 of Table 1.

Also, take $H(p) = G(p) = 1/p$ in (18) to get

$$\frac{1}{p^2}F(p) = T\left\{\int_0^t \left[\int_0^\tau f(\theta)\,d\theta\right] d\tau\right\}. \tag{20}$$

A few applications employing (16) and (19) to derive transform relations will give familiarity with the processes of using them.

Using $F(p) = a/(p^2 + a^2) = T\{\sin at\}$ in (19), we get

$$T^{-1}\{a/[p(p^2 + a^2)]\} = \int_0^t \sin a\tau\,d\tau = (1/a)(1 - \cos at),$$

and using $G(p) = 1/(p - b) = T\{e^{bt}\}$ and $F(p) = p/(p^2 + a^2) = T\{\cos at\}$ in (16), we get

$$T^{-1}\left\{\frac{1}{p - b}\,\frac{p}{p^2 + a^2}\right\} = \int_0^t e^{b(t-\tau)} \cos a\tau\,d\tau$$
$$= \frac{1}{a^2 + b^2}(a \sin at - b \cos at + be^{bt}).$$

Practically all the transforms considered will have the form $N(p)/M(p)$, where N and M represent polynomials in p with real coefficients, N is of lower degree than M, and M can be factored into linear and quadratic factors. Fractions of this type can be expressed as the sum of fractions having the form $(mp + n)/M_1(p)$, and the inverse transforms of such fractions can be found by means of Table 1, Table 2, and repeated application of (16). The following examples will illustrate procedures:

Example 1. (*a*) Express $(p^3 + 3p^2 - 3p - 7)/[(p^2 + 1)(p - 1)(p - 2)]$ in the form of fractions that have constant numerators. (*b*) Also, express in terms of t, $T^{-1}\{-12/[(p - 1)(p - 2)(p^2 + 1)]\}$.

Solution. (*a*)

$$\frac{p^3 + 3p^2 - 3p - 7}{(p^2 + 1)(p - 1)(p - 2)} = \frac{p(p^2 + 1) + 3(p^2 + 1) - 4p - 10}{(p^2 + 1)(p - 1)(p - 2)}$$
$$= \frac{p - 1 + 4}{(p - 1)(p - 2)} - \frac{4(p - 1) + 14}{(p^2 + 1)(p - 1)(p - 2)}$$
$$= \frac{1}{p - 2} + \frac{4}{(p - 1)(p - 2)} - \frac{4}{(p - 2)(p^2 + 1)} - \frac{14}{(p - 1)(p - 2)(p^2 + 1)}.$$

(*b*) By relations 12 and 6, Table 1, we have

$$T^{-1}\{-12/[(p - 1)(p - 2)]\} = -12(e^{2t} - e^t),$$
$$T^{-1}\{1/(p^2 + 1)\} = \sin t.$$

Hence, applying (16), we get

$$T^{-1}\{-12/[(p-1)(p-2)(p^2+1)]\} = \int_0^t (-12)(e^{2(t-\tau)} - e^{t-\tau}) \sin \tau \, d\tau$$
$$= -12e^{2t}\int_0^t e^{-2\tau} \sin \tau \, d\tau + 12e^t \int_0^t e^{-\tau} \sin \tau \, d\tau$$
$$= -\tfrac{6}{5} \sin t - \tfrac{18}{5} \cos t - \tfrac{12}{5} e^{2t} + 6e^t.$$

Example 2. Express in terms of t: $T^{-1}\{6/[(p-1)(p-2)^4]\}$.

Solution. $T^{-1}\{1/(p-1)\} = e^t$, $T^{-1}\{6/(p-2)^4\} = t^3e^{2t}$. Therefore, by (16) and the use of (59) and (64), §52,

$$T^{-1}\left\{\frac{1}{p-1} \cdot \frac{6}{(p-2)^4}\right\} = \int_0^t e^{t-\tau} \cdot e^{2\tau}\tau^3 \, d\tau = e^t \int_0^t e^{\tau}\tau^3 \, d\tau$$
$$= e^t \left[\frac{e^\tau \tau^3}{D}\right]_0^t = e^t \left[e^\tau \frac{\tau^3}{D+1}\right]_0^t = e^t e^\tau (1 - D + D^2 - D^3)\tau^3$$
$$= e^t[e^\tau(\tau^3 - 3\tau^2 + 6\tau - 6)]_0^t = e^{2t}(t^3 - 3t^2 + 6t - 6) + 6e^t.$$

The formulas of §§58, 59, and 60 are tabulated for convenient reference in Table 2, page 116.

EXERCISES

1. Using the fact that $T^{-1}\{1/p^2\} = t$, $T^{-1}\{1/(p-3)\} = e^{3t}$ in (16), find

$$T^{-1}\{(1/p^2) \cdot [1/(p-3)]\}.$$

Use Table 1 and (16) to find in terms of t:

2. $T^{-1}\left\{\frac{1}{p^3} \cdot \frac{64}{p-4}\right\}$.

3. $T^{-1}\left\{\frac{1}{(p-2)^2} \cdot \frac{1}{p-3}\right\}$.

4. $T^{-1}\left\{\frac{1}{p^2} \cdot \frac{2}{p^2+4}\right\}$.

5. $T^{-1}\left\{\frac{p+1}{p^2(p-3)}\right\}$.

6. $T^{-1}\left\{\frac{p^2+2p+3}{p^2(p^2+4)}\right\}$.

7. $T^{-1}\left\{\frac{1}{(p-1)(p-2)^4}\right\}$.

8. $T^{-1}\left\{\frac{p^3}{(p^2+1)^2}\right\}$. *Hint:* $\frac{p^3}{(p^2+1)^2} = \frac{p(p^2+1)-p}{(p^2+1)^2} = \frac{p}{p^2+1} - \frac{p}{(p^2+1)^2}$.

9. $T^{-1}\left\{\frac{p^3+p^2+4p}{(p^2+4)^2}\right\}$.

10. $T^{-1}\left\{\frac{3p^2+4p}{p^2(p^2+4)}\right\}$.

11. Read the solution of example 2, and then express, in terms of t,

$$T^{-1}\{1/[p(p-a)^n]\}.$$

★12. Express, in terms of t, $T^{-1}\{p^{-2}(p-a)^{-n}\}$.

Use 19 and 20, Table 1, to find in terms of t:

13. $T^{-1}\left\{\frac{8}{(p^2+1)[(p+2)^2+1]}\right\}$.

14. $T^{-1}\left\{\frac{p}{p^2+4} \cdot \frac{52}{(p-1)^2+9}\right\}$.

15. Use 19, Table 1, with $\alpha = 0$ to obtain 18, Table 1.

61. Transforms of derivatives

Using integration by parts and D for d/dt, we get

$$T\{Df(t)\} = \int_0^\infty e^{-pt}Df(t)\,dt = [e^{-pt}f(t)]_0^\infty + p\int_0^\infty e^{-pt}f(t)\,dt,$$
$$\text{or} \quad T\{Df(t)\} = pF(p) - f(0). \tag{21}$$

Applying (21) to $T\{D^2f(t)\}$, we get

$$T\{D^2f(t)\} = T\{[Df(t)]'\} = p[pF(p) - f(0)] - Df(0),$$
$$\text{or} \quad T\{D^2f(t)\} = p^2F(p) - pf(0) - Df(0). \tag{22}$$

Using (21) repeatedly, we finally obtain*

$$T\{D^nf(t)\} = p^nF(p) - p^{n-1}f(0) - p^{n-2}Df(0) - \cdots - D^{n-1}f(0). \tag{23}$$

The following solutions indicate the use made of formulas (21) to (23).

Example 1. Given that $T\{Dy\} = 1/(p-1)$ and that $y = 5$, when $t = 0$, find y.

Solution. Denoting $T(y)$ by Y and using (21), we get

$$T\{Dy\} = pY(p) - 5 = \frac{1}{p-1}, \qquad \text{or} \qquad Y = \frac{5}{p} + \frac{1}{p(p-1)}.$$

Therefore, using relations 1 and 12, Table 1, we get

$$y = T^{-1}\{Y\} = 5T^{-1}\left\{\frac{1}{p}\right\} + T^{-1}\left\{\frac{1}{p(p-1)}\right\} = 5 + (e^t - 1) = \mathbf{4 + e^t}.$$

Example 2. Find y in terms of t if $y = 2$, $Dy = 3$ when $x = 0$ and

$$T\{D^2y + Dy - 2y\} = 1/(p+2). \tag{a}$$

Solution. From equation (a), we get

$$T\{D^2y\} + T\{Dy\} - 2T\{y\} = 1/(p+2). \tag{b}$$

Denoting $T(y)$ by Y and using (22) and (21) on (b), we get

$$p^2Y - p\cdot 2 - 3 + pY - 2 - 2Y = 1/(p+2). \tag{c}$$

The solution of (c) for Y is

$$Y = \frac{1/(p+2) + 2p + 5}{p^2 + p - 2} = \frac{1}{(p+2)^2(p-1)} + \frac{2(p+2)+1}{(p+2)(p-1)}.$$

* Here $D^kf(t)$ means d^kf/dt^k, and $D^kf(0) = \lim_{t\to 0} D^kf(t)$, $t > 0$. Sufficient conditions for (23) are that $D^{n-1}f(t)$ be continuous in every finite interval $0 \leqq t \leqq T$ and that $f(t), Df(t), \ldots, D^nf(t)$ satisfy the usual conditions specified in §58.

Applying $y = T^{-1}\{Y\}$ and using Table 1 and (VI) in Table 2, we get

$$y = T^{-1}\left\{\frac{2}{p-1} + \frac{1}{(p-1)(p+2)} + \frac{1}{(p-1)(p+2)^2}\right\}$$
$$= 2e^t + \frac{1}{3}(e^t - e^{-2t}) + \int_0^t e^{t-\tau}\tau e^{-2\tau}\,d\tau = \tfrac{7}{3}e^t - \tfrac{1}{3}e^{-2t} + e^t\int_0^t \tau e^{-3\tau}\,d\tau,$$

or
$$y = -\tfrac{1}{3}te^{-2t} - \tfrac{4}{9}e^{-2t} + \tfrac{22}{9}e^t. \qquad (d)$$

The next section uses formulas (21) to (23) in solving differential equations.

EXERCISES

Find y in terms of t by using (21) to (23) and methods of finding inverse transforms:

1. $T\{D^2y\} = 1/(p-1)$, and $y = 2$, $Dy = 2$ when $t = 0$.
2. $T\{D^2y - 5Dy + 6y\} = 1/(p+2)$, and $y = 0$, $Dy = -2$ when $t = 0$.
3. $T\{D^3y + Dy\} = 3/p$, and $y = 0$, $Dy = 0$, $D^2y = 5$ when $t = 0$.

62. Solving differential equations by transforms

The following solutions will indicate the method of solving differential equations by transforms.

Example 1. Solve the equation $Dy + y = e^t$ subject to the condition $y = 3$ when $t = 0$.

Solution. From the given equation, we get

$$T\{Dy + y\} = T\{Dy\} + T\{y\} = T\{e^t\}. \qquad (a)$$

By means of Table 1, page 113, and (21), §61, we get

$$T\{e^t\} = 1/(p-1), \qquad T\{y\} = Y, \qquad T\{Dy\} = pY - 3. \qquad (b)$$

Use these values in (*a*) to obtain

$$pY - 3 + Y = 1/(p-1). \qquad (c)$$

The solution of (*c*) for Y is

$$Y = \frac{1/(p-1) + 3}{p+1} = \frac{1}{(p+1)(p-1)} + \frac{3}{p+1}. \qquad (d)$$

Now, using Table 1, we get

$$y = T^{-1}\{Y\} = T^{-1}\left\{\frac{1}{(p+1)(p-1)} + \frac{3}{p+1}\right\} = \frac{1}{2}(e^t - e^{-t}) + 3e^{-t}$$
$$= \tfrac{1}{2}e^t + \tfrac{5}{2}e^{-t}. \qquad (e)$$

By substitution we find that solution (*e*) satisfies the given equation, and evidently $y = 3$ when $t = 0$ from (*e*).

Example 2. Solve the equation

$$D^2y - 2Dy - 3y = 6e^t, \qquad \text{if } y = 1,\ Dy = 3 \text{ when } t = 0.$$

Solution. From the given differential equation, we get

$$T\{D^2y - 2Dy - 3y\} = T\{6e^t\} = 6/(p-1). \tag{a}$$

From (22) and (21), §61, and initial conditions $y(0) = 1$, $Dy(0) = 3$, we get

$$T\{D^2y\} = p^2Y - p - 3, \qquad T\{Dy\} = pY - 1. \tag{b}$$

Using (*b*) in (*a*), we obtain

$$p^2Y - p - 3 - 2pY + 2 - 3Y = 6/(p-1). \tag{c}$$

Solving (*c*) for Y, we get

$$\begin{aligned} Y &= \frac{6/(p-1) + p + 1}{p^2 - 2p - 3} = \frac{p^2 + 5}{(p-1)(p+1)(p-3)} \\ &= \frac{p^2 - 1 + 6}{(p-1)(p+1)(p-3)} = \frac{1}{p-3} + \frac{6}{(p-3)(p-1)(p+1)}. \end{aligned} \tag{d}$$

Hence, using Table 1 and (VI), Table 2, with $G(p) = 6/(p-3)$ and $F(p) = 1/[(p-1)(p+1)]$, we get from (*d*)

$$\begin{aligned} y &= T^{-1}\left\{\frac{1}{p-3}\right\} + T^{-1}\left\{\frac{6}{(p-1)(p+1)(p-3)}\right\} \\ &= e^{3t} + \int_0^t 6e^{3(t-\tau)}\tfrac{1}{2}(e^{\tau} - e^{-\tau})\, d\tau, \end{aligned}$$

$$y = e^{3t} + 3e^{3t}\int_0^t (e^{-2\tau} - e^{-4\tau})\, d\tau = \tfrac{7}{4}e^{3t} - \tfrac{3}{2}e^t + \tfrac{3}{4}e^{-t}. \tag{e}$$

A check shows that (*e*) satisfies the given equation and the initial conditions.

Example 3. Solve the integrodifferential equation

$$Dy + 2y - 3\int_0^t y\, dt = 5 + 5t; \qquad y = 2 \text{ when } t = 0. \tag{a}$$

Solution. By (VII), Table 2, $T\left\{\int_0^t y\, dt\right\} = (1/p)Y$. Therefore, equate the transforms of the members of (*a*) to obtain

$$pY - 2 + 2Y - \frac{3}{p}Y = \frac{5p + 5}{p^2}. \tag{b}$$

Solving (*b*) for Y and using inverse transforms, we get

$$y = T^{-1}\left\{\frac{5p+5}{p(p+3)(p-1)} + \frac{2p}{(p+3)(p-1)}\right\} = -\tfrac{5}{3} + 3e^t + \tfrac{2}{3}e^{-3t}.$$

EXERCISES

1. To find the solution of $D^2y + Dy = 2e^t$ for which $y = 5$, $Dy = -1$ when $t = 0$, show that

$$p^2Y - 5p + 1 + pY - 5 = 2/(p - 1).$$

Solve this for Y, and then use transforms to get $y = 2 + e^t + 2e^{-t}$.

Find by means of transforms the solution of each equation satisfying the indicated initial conditions:

2. $Dy - y = 2$; $y = 0$ when $t = 0$.
3. $(D^2 + 2D - 3)y = 0$; $y = 0$, $Dy = -8$ when $t = 0$.
4. $(D^2 + 4)y = 12$; $y = 6$, $Dy = -3$ when $t = 0$.
5. $(D^3 + 9D)y = 0$; $y = 0$, $Dy = 0$, $D^2y = 5$ when $t = 0$.
6. $(D^2 + 1)^2y = 0$; $y = 0$, $Dy = 0$, $D^2y = 0$, $D^3y = 5$ when $t = 0$.
7. $(D^2 + 9)y = 12\cos 3t$; $y = 2$, $Dy = 5$ when $t = 0$.
8. $(D^2 - 6D + 13)y = 26$; $y = 0$, $Dy = 2$ when $t = 0$. *Hint:* By (III) of Table 2,

$$T^{-1}\left\{\frac{26}{p(p^2 - 6p + 13)}\right\} = T^{-1}\left\{\frac{26}{p[(p - 3)^2 + 4]}\right\} = 13e^{3t}\,T^{-1}\left\{\frac{2}{(p + 3)(p^2 + 4)}\right\}.$$

Apply (VI) of Table 2.
9. $(D^3 - 6D^2 + 13D)y = 0$; $y = 1$, $Dy = -4$, $D^2y = 2$ when $t = 0$.
10. $(D^2 + 2D + 2)y = 2e^{-t}\cos t$; $y = 2$, $Dy = -2$ when $t = 0$.
11. $D^3(D - 1)y = 12$; $y = Dy = D^2y = D^3y = 0$ when $t = 0$.
12. $(D + 1)^2y = 6te^{-t}$; $y = 2$, $Dy = 5$ when $t = 0$.

Review example 3, and then solve:

13. $Dy + \int_0^t y\,dt = 1$; $y = 2$ when $t = 0$.

14. $Dy - y - 6\int_0^t y\,dt = 12e^{3t}$; $y = -3$ when $t = 0$.

★15. $D^2y + Dy - 4y - 4\int_0^t y\,dt = e^{2t}$; $y = 0$, $Dy = 2$ when $t = 0$.

16. $y + \int_0^t y\,dt = \sin 2t$.

17. Solve $(D^2 + 2D + 5)y = 52\sin 3t$; $y = 2$, $Dy = 0$ when $t = 0$. *Hint:* Use relation 19, Table 1.

63. Solving systems of differential equations

The general method of solving a system of differential equations by transforms is an extension of the method for solving a single differential equation. The following example will indicate the general procedure:

Example. Find that solution $x(t)$ and $y(t)$ of

$$\begin{aligned} Dx + x + Dy - y &= 2, \\ D^2x + Dx - Dy &= \cos t \end{aligned} \qquad (a)$$

for which $x = 0$, $Dx = 2$, $y = 1$ when $t = 0$.

Solution. Applying transforms to (*a*), we get

$$\begin{aligned} T\{Dx + Dy + x - y\} &= T\{2\} = \frac{2}{p}, \\ T\{D^2x + Dx - Dy\} &= T\{\cos t\} = p/(p^2 + 1). \end{aligned} \tag{b}$$

Since $T\{D^2x\} = p^2X - 2$, $T\{Dx\} = pX$, $T\{Dy\} = pY - 1$, (*b*) may be written

$$\begin{aligned} (p + 1)X + (p - 1)Y &= 1 + 2/p, \\ (p^2 + p)X - pY &= 1 + p/(p^2 + 1). \end{aligned} \tag{c}$$

Solving equations (*c*) for X and Y, we get

$$X = \frac{1}{p^2} + \frac{1}{p^2 + 1}, \qquad Y = \frac{p}{p^2 + 1} + \frac{1}{p^2}. \tag{d}$$

From (*d*),

$$x = T^{-1}\{X\} = \mathbf{t + \sin t}, \qquad y = T^{-1}\{Y\} = \mathbf{t + \cos t}. \tag{e}$$

The solution (*e*) satisfies (*a*) and the initial conditions.

EXERCISES

1. To solve the system of equations $x + Dy = 3$, $Dx - y = -2t$, where $x = 1$, $y = 0$ when $t = 0$, construct inverse transforms from them to get

$$X + pY = 3/p, \qquad pX - 1 - Y = -2/p^2.$$

Solve these for X and Y by algebraic procedures to get

$$X = 1/p, \qquad Y = (2p^2 + 2)/[p^2(p^2 + 1)].$$

From these obtain $x = 1$, $y = 2t$. Check this result.

Solve the following systems of equations:

2. $x - Dy = t - 2$.
$Dx + y = 1 + 2t$; $x = 0$, $y = 2$ when $t = 0$.

3. $Dx + D^2y = e^t$.
$2Dx - Dy = 2e^t - 1$; $x = 1$, $y = 0$, $Dy = 1$ when $t = 0$.

4. $D^2x + Dy = \cos t$.
$x - Dy = 3t + 2 - \cos t$; $x = 2$, $Dx = 3$, $y = 0$ when $t = 0$.

5. $D^2x + Dy = 2$.
$D^2x - D^2y = 0$; $x = 0$, $Dx = 2$, $y = -2$, $Dy = 2$ when $t = 0$.

6. $Dx + (D - 1)y = 2e^t + 1$.
$2D^2x - Dy = e^t$; $x = 2$, $Dx = 3$, $y = 3$ when $t = 0$.

7. $(D - 1)x + y = 2e^t$.
$3Dx - 3Dy = 3te^t$; $x = 0$, $y = 1$ when $t = 0$.

8. $D^2x - Dy = 0$.
$x + Dy = 1$; $x = 1$, $Dx = 1$, $y = 1$ when $t = 0$.

9. $D^2x - Dy = \cos t$.
$Dx + D^2y = -\sin t$; $x = 1$, $Dx = 0$, $y = 0$, $Dy = 1$ when $t = 0$.

+★**10.** The system of equations

$$mD^2x + HeDy = Ee, \qquad mD^2y - HeDx = 0$$

occurs in the investigation of finding ratio of charge to mass of an electron. Solve them assuming that m, e, E, H are constants and $x = y = Dx = Dy = 0$ when $t = 0$.

64. Resolving a fraction into partial fractions*

Inverse transforms of various functions of p may be obtained by expressing them in terms of partial fractions and then finding the sum of the inverse transforms of the fractions. To resolve the fraction $(7p - 1)/[(p - 3)(p + 2)(p - 1)]$ into fractions with simple denominators, we assume that numbers A, B, and C exist such that

$$\frac{7p - 1}{(p - 3)(p + 2)(p - 1)} = \frac{A}{p - 3} + \frac{B}{p + 2} + \frac{C}{p - 1}, \tag{a}$$

provided that p is any number except 3, -2, and 1. To find A, multiply (a) through by $p - 3$, the denominator associated with A, and let $p \to 3$ as a limit in the result to obtain

$$\frac{7 \cdot 3 - 1}{(3 + 2)(3 - 1)} = A + 0 + 0, \qquad \text{or} \qquad A = 2. \tag{b}$$

To find B, multiply (a) through by $p + 2$, and let $p \to -2$ as a limit in the result to obtain

$$\frac{7(-2) - 1}{(-2 - 3)(-2 - 1)} = 0 + B + 0, \qquad \text{or} \qquad B = -1. \tag{c}$$

By the same process, we find $C = -1$. Replacing A by 2, B by -1, and C by -1 in (a), we get

$$\frac{7p - 1}{(p - 3)(p + 2)(p - 1)} = \frac{2}{p - 3} + \frac{-1}{p + 2} + \frac{-1}{p - 1}. \tag{d}$$

Since the two sides are the same thing in different forms, their inverse transforms are equal, and since the inverse transform of a sum is the sum of the inverse transforms, we get from (d)

$$T^{-1}\left\{\frac{7p - 1}{(p - 3)(p + 2)(p - 1)}\right\} = 2e^{3t} - e^{-2t} - e^{t}. \tag{e}$$

Consider a fraction $N(p)/[(p - a_1)(p - a_2) \cdots (p - a_n)]$, where $N(p)$ is a polynomial† with real coefficients, with degree in p less than n,

* Elementary treatments of partial fractions may be found in most books on calculus.

† The fractions $N(p)/D(p)$ considered in this book are those in which N and D are polynomials in p with real coefficients and in which the degree in p of N is less than that of D. This will be assumed in §§64 to 67, with or without mention.

and with no two a's equal. Assume, from the theory of partial fractions, that constants A_i exist for which

$$\frac{N(p)}{(p-a_1)(p-a_2)\cdots(p-a_n)} = \frac{A_1}{p-a_1} + \frac{A_2}{p-a_2} + \cdots + \frac{A_n}{p-a_n}. \tag{24}$$

Multiplying both members by $p - a_i$ and letting $p \to a_i$ as a limit in the result, we get

$$\mathbf{A}_i = \mathbf{N}(\mathbf{a}_i)/\mathbf{M}_i(\mathbf{a}_i), \tag{25}$$

where M_i is the denominator with the factor $p - a_i$ deleted. Hence, we have the following rule:

RULE I. *To find the numerator A of the partial fraction $A/(p-a)$ of a fraction $N(p)/M(p)$ of type (24), delete $p - a$ from the denominator of N/M and substitute a for p in the result. Then, $T^{-1}\{A/(p-a)\} = Ae^{at}$.*

For example, applying rule I for each of the partial fractions of (a), we get

$$A = \frac{7(3)-1}{(3+2)(3-1)} = 2, \qquad B = \frac{7(-2)-1}{(-2-3)(-2-1)} = -1,$$
$$C = \frac{7\cdot 1-1}{(1-3)(1+2)} = -1.$$

Applying the rule for each partial fraction of (24) to find A_i ($i = 1, \ldots, n$) and then equating the inverse transforms of the two members, we get

$$\mathbf{T}^{-1}\left\{\frac{\mathbf{N}(\mathbf{p})}{(\mathbf{p}-\mathbf{a}_1)(\mathbf{p}-\mathbf{a}_2)\cdots(\mathbf{p}-\mathbf{a}_n)}\right\} = \sum_{j=1}^{n}\left[\frac{\mathbf{N}(\mathbf{a}_j)}{\mathbf{M}_j(\mathbf{a}_j)}\right]\mathbf{e}^{a_j t}, \tag{26}$$

where $$\sum_{j=1}^{n} F(a_j) = F(a_1) + F(a_2) + \cdots + F(a_n). \tag{27}$$

For example, by applying (26) we get

$$T^{-1}\left\{\frac{2D+3}{D(D+2)}\right\} = \frac{2\cdot 0+3}{0+2}e^{0t} + \frac{2(-2)+3}{-2}e^{-2t} = \tfrac{3}{2} + \tfrac{1}{2}e^{-2t},$$

$$T^{-1}\left\{\frac{mp+n}{(p-a)(p-b)}\right\} = \frac{ma+n}{a-b}e^{at} + \frac{mb+n}{b-a}e^{bt},$$

$$T^{-1}\left\{\frac{p^2+p+1}{p(p-1)(p+2)}\right\} = \frac{0+0+1}{(0-1)(0+2)}e^{0t} + \frac{1^2+1+1}{1(1+2)}e^{t}$$
$$+ \frac{(-2)^2+(-2)+1}{(-2)(-2-1)}e^{-2t} = -\tfrac{1}{2} + e^{t} + \tfrac{1}{2}e^{-2t}.$$

EXERCISES

1. Use rule I to find A and then to find B if $2p/[(p-1)(p-2)] = A/(p-1) + B/(p-2)$. Then write the inverse transform of $2p/[(p-1)(p-2)]$.

2. Use rule I to find A, B, and C if $(2p+3)/[p(p^2+3p+2)] = A/p + B/(p+1) + C/(p+2)$ and express $T^{-1}\{(2p+3)/[p(p^2+3p+2)]\}$ in terms of t.

Using rule I, express each inverse transform in terms of t:

3. $T^{-1}\left\{\dfrac{p+4}{p(p-5)}\right\}$.

4. $T^{-1}\left\{\dfrac{2p+3}{p^2-4}\right\}$.

5. $T^{-1}\left\{\dfrac{p^2+2}{p(p-1)(p-2)}\right\}$.

6. $T^{-1}\left\{\dfrac{p^2}{(p^2-4)(p+3)}\right\}$.

7. $T^{-1}\left\{\dfrac{2p-3}{p^3+4p^2+3p}\right\}$.

8. $T^{-1}\left\{\dfrac{p^2+1}{(p^2-1)(p^2-4)}\right\}$.

9. $T^{-1}\left\{\dfrac{p+1}{(p+2)(2p+3)}\right\}$. *Hint:* $\dfrac{p+1}{(p+2)(2p+3)} = \dfrac{\frac{1}{2}p+\frac{1}{2}}{(p+2)(p+\frac{3}{2})}$.

10. $T^{-1}\left\{\dfrac{2p^2-6p+6}{p(p-2)(2p+3)}\right\}$.

11. $T^{-1}\left\{\dfrac{ap+b}{(mp+n)(lp+r)}\right\}$.

Solve the following differential equations:

12. $D^2y - 4y = 10e^{3t}$; $y = 5$, $Dy = 0$ when $t = 0$.

13. $(D^2 + 2D - 3)y = -4e^{-t}$; $y = 3$, $Dy = -7$ when $t = 0$.

14. $(D^3 + 5D^2 + 4D)y = 20e^t$; $y = 1$, $Dy = 6$, $D^2y = -14$ when $t = 0$.

15. $Dy + 6y + 8\int_0^t y\,dt = 32t + 12$; $y = 2$ when $t = 0$.

16. $Dx + 3x + 2\int_0^t x\,dt = 6e^t + 6$; $x = 5$ when $t = 0$.

17. $Dy + y + x = 5e^t + 7$.
$D^2y + 2Dx = 4e^t$; $x = 4$, $y = 6$, $Dy = 2$ when $t = 0$.

18. $2D^2x + D^2y = 0$.
$Dx + x - Dy = 4 - 7e^{2t}$; $x = 3$, $Dx = -2$, $y = 2$, $Dy = 4$ when $t = 0$.

65. Fractions having repeated factors in the denominator

Consider the fraction $(2p+3)/[(p-1)^3(p-2)]$. According to the theory of partial fractions, numbers A, B, C, and E exist such that

$$\frac{2p+3}{(p-1)^3(p-2)} = \frac{A}{(p-1)^3} + \frac{B}{(p-1)^2} + \frac{C}{p-1} + \frac{E}{p-2}. \qquad (a)$$

Multiplying (a) through by $(p-1)^3$ and differentiating the resulting equation twice, we get

$$\frac{2p+3}{p-2} = A + B(p-1) + C(p-1)^2 + E\frac{(p-1)^3}{p-2}, \qquad (b)$$

$$\frac{-(2p+3)}{(p-2)^2} + \frac{2}{p-2} = B + 2C(p-1) + E\frac{(p-1)^2(2p-5)}{(p-2)^2}, \qquad (c)$$

$$\frac{2(2p+3)}{(p-2)^3} - \frac{4}{(p-2)^2} = 2C + E\frac{(p-1)(2p^2-10p+14)}{(p-2)^3}. \qquad (d)$$

Letting $p \to 1$ as a limit in (*b*), (*c*), and (*d*), we get

$$A = -5, \qquad B = -7, \qquad C = -7. \tag{e}$$

By rule I of §64 applied to (*a*), we get $E = (2 \cdot 2 + 3)/1 = 7$. Substituting -5 for A, -7 for B, -7 for C, and 7 for E in (*a*) and equating the inverse transforms of its members by means of 5, Table 1, page 113, we get

$$T^{-1}\left\{\frac{2p+3}{(p-1)^3(p-2)}\right\} = e^t\left(-\frac{5t^2}{2} - 7t - 7\right) + 7e^{2t}. \tag{f}$$

We shall use the symbol $[N/M]_r^{(s)}$ to mean the number obtained by substituting r for p in $d^s(N/M)/dp^s$. Consider the fraction $N(p)/[M(p)(p-r)^k]$, where $M(r) \neq 0$. Just as above, we assume that there exist constants $A_1, A_2, \ldots, A_k$ such that

$$\frac{N(p)/M(p)}{(p-r)^k} = \frac{A_1}{(p-r)^k} + \frac{A_2}{(p-r)^{k-1}} + \cdots + \frac{A_k}{p-r} + \varphi(p), \tag{28}$$

where $\varphi(p)$ and its derivatives are continuous in the neighborhood of r. Multiplying (28) through by $(p-r)^k$, differentiating the result $k-1$ times with respect to p, finding the values of the A's by considering limits of members of these equations as $p \to r$, and replacing the A's in (28) by these respective values, we get

$$\frac{N(p)/M(p)}{(p-r)^k} = \frac{(N/M)_r}{(p-r)^k} + \frac{[N/M]_r^{(1)}}{1!(p-r)^{k-1}} + \frac{[N/M]_r^{(2)}}{2!(p-r)^{k-2}} + \cdots + \frac{[N/M]_r^{(k-1)}}{(k-1)!(p-r)} + \varphi(p), \tag{29}$$

where $\varphi(p)$ and its derivatives are continuous at and near $p = r$. Observe that the fractions in the right-hand member of (29) could be obtained by writing the first k terms in the expansion of $N(p)/M(p)$ in powers of $p - r$ and dividing the result by $(p-r)^k$. Using transform 5, Table 1, page 113, on the fractions in the right-hand member of (29) we derive expression (30) below and justify the following rule:

RULE II. *To find the part of the inverse transform of* $N/[M \cdot (p-r)^k]$, $M(r) \neq 0$, *associated with* $(p-r)^k$, *use the expression*

$$\mathbf{e}^{rt}\left[\frac{(\mathbf{N}/\mathbf{M})_r}{\mathbf{1}}\frac{\mathbf{t}^{k-1}}{(\mathbf{k}-\mathbf{1})!} + \frac{[\mathbf{N}/\mathbf{M}]_r^{(1)}}{\mathbf{1}!}\frac{\mathbf{t}^{k-2}}{(\mathbf{k}-\mathbf{2})!} + \frac{[\mathbf{N}/\mathbf{M}]_r^{(2)}}{\mathbf{2}!}\frac{\mathbf{t}^{k-3}}{(\mathbf{k}-\mathbf{3})!} + \cdots + \frac{(\mathbf{N}/\mathbf{M})_r^{k-1}}{(\mathbf{k}-\mathbf{1})!}\frac{\mathbf{t}^0}{\mathbf{1}}\right] \tag{30}$$

where $(N/M)_r^{(s)}$ *means the number obtained by replacing* p *by* r *in*

$$\frac{d^s(N/M)}{dp^s}.$$

Example. Find, in terms of t, $T^{-1}\{(5p^2 + 22p)/[(p-1)(p+2)^4]\}$.

Solution. First use (29) with $N/M = (5p^2 + 22p)/(p - 1)$, or, making the division, $5p + 27 + 27/(p - 1)$. From this, we get

$$\frac{N}{M} = 5p + 27 + \frac{27}{p-1}, \qquad \left(\frac{N}{M}\right)^{(1)} = 5 - \frac{27}{(p-1)^2},$$
$$\left(\frac{N}{M}\right)^{(2)} = \frac{54}{(p-1)^3}, \qquad \left(\frac{N}{M}\right)^{(3)} = \frac{-162}{(p-1)^4}. \qquad (a)$$

Replacing p by -2 in (a), we get

$$(N/M)_{-2} = 8, \quad [N/M]_{-2}^{(1)} = 2, \quad [N/M]_{-2}^{(2)} = -2, \quad [N/M]_{-2}^{(3)} = -2. \qquad (b)$$

Using the values (b) in (30) with $k = 4$ and $r = -2$, we get

$$e^{-2t}\left(8\frac{t^3}{6} + 2\frac{t^2}{2} - \frac{2}{2}\cdot\frac{t}{1} - \frac{2}{6}\right) = e^{-2t}(\tfrac{4}{3}t^3 + t^2 - t - \tfrac{1}{3}). \qquad (c)$$

Using rule I, §64, we find the part of the inverse transform associated with the factor $p - 1$ to be $[(5p^2 + 22p)/(p+2)^4]_{p=1}e^t = \frac{1}{3}e^t$. Combining this with result (c), we obtain

$$T^{-1}\left\{\frac{5p^2 + 22p}{(p-1)(p+2)^4}\right\} = \mathbf{e}^{-2t}(\tfrac{4}{3}\mathbf{t}^3 + \mathbf{t}^2 - \mathbf{t} - \tfrac{1}{3}) + \tfrac{1}{3}\mathbf{e}^t. \qquad (d)$$

EXERCISES

1. Write (30) for the case when: (a) $k = 3$; (b) $k = 4$.

Using (26), §64, for the single factors of the denominator and (30) for repeated factors, find the inverse transform of each fraction:

2. $\dfrac{p^3 + p^2 + 2}{(p-1)^4}$. **3.** $\dfrac{4p^2 - 16}{p^3(p+2)^2}$. **4.** $\dfrac{8 + 10p^2 - 2p^3}{p(p-2)^5}$.

Find the solution of each equation subject to the indicated conditions, and check your answer:

5. $(D^2 - 2D + 1)y = e^{2t}$; $y = 1$, $Dy = 3$ when $t = 0$.
6. $(D^2 - 2D)y = 8$; $y = 3$, $Dy = -2$ when $t = 0$.
7. $(D^2 + D)y = te^{-t}$; $y = 2$, $Dy = -2$ when $t = 0$.
8. $(D^2 + 4D + 4)y = 6te^{-2t}$; $y = 0$, $Dy = 2$ when $t = 0$.
★9. $D(D-1)^2y = 2 + 12e^t$; $y = 0$, $Dy = 0$, $D^2y = 14$ when $t = 0$.
10. $Dx - 2y - x = -2te^{-t} + e^{-t} - 6t$.
$D^2x - Dy = te^{-t} - 2e^{-t} - 3$; $x = 0$, $Dx = 1$, $y = 0$, $Dy = 3$ when $t = 0$.

66. Partial fractions. Quadratic factors

Rule I, §64, still applies when some factors of the denominator involved contain imaginary constants. Consider the special form of (24), §64,

$$N(p)/\{M(p)\cdot[p - (a + ib)][p - (a - ib)]\},$$
$$i^2 = -1,\ M(a + ib) \neq 0. \qquad (31)$$

In accordance with rule I, §64, remove the factor $p - (a + ib)$ from the denominator of (31), and in the result replace p by $a + ib$ to get

$$\mathbf{N(a + ib)/[M(a + ib)(2ib)] = A + iB}, \tag{32}$$

where $A + iB$ symbolizes the left-hand member changed to standard complex form. The same procedure applied for the factor $p - (a - ib)$ gives

$$\mathbf{N(a - ib)/[M(a - ib)(-2ib)] = A - iB}, \tag{33}$$

for the second procedure is the same as the first with i replaced by $-i$. Now, using relation 4, Table 1, page 113, and the facts from §48 that $e^{(a+bi)t} = e^{at}e^{ibt}$ and $e^{i\theta} = \cos\theta + i\sin\theta$, we get

$$\begin{aligned} T^{-1}&\left\{\frac{A + iB}{p - (a + bi)} + \frac{A - iB}{p - (a - bi)}\right\} \\ &= (A + iB)e^{(a+ib)t} + (A - iB)e^{(a-ib)t} \\ &= e^{at}[(A + iB)(\cos bt + i\sin bt) + (A - iB)(\cos bt - i\sin bt)] \\ &= e^{at}(2A\cos bt - 2B\sin Bt + 0i). \end{aligned} \tag{34}$$

Just as in §48, we can show that

$$e^{at}(2A\cos bt - 2B\sin bt) = 2e^{at}\sqrt{A^2 + B^2}\sin(bt - \theta), \tag{35}$$

where $\cos\theta = A/\sqrt{A^2 + B^2}, \qquad \sin\theta = B/\sqrt{A^2 + B^2}.$ (36)

Accordingly, the following rule applies:

RULE III. *To find the part of* $T^{-1}\{N(p)/\{M(p)\cdot[p - (a + ib)][p - (a - ib)]\}\}$ *associated with the product* $[p - (a + ib)][p - (a - ib)]$, *compute A and B by using* (32) *and then write* $\mathbf{e^{at}(2A\cos bt - 2B\sin bt)}$ *or* $2e^{at}\sin(bt - \theta)$, *where θ is defined by* (36).

As an example, we find $T^{-1}\{(p^2 + 11)/[p(p^2 + 2p + 5)]\}$ in terms of t. Since $p^2 + 2p + 5 = (p + 1)^2 + 4 = (p + 1)^2 - 4i^2 = [p - (-1 + 2i)][p - (-1 - 2i)]$, we get from (32)

$$A + iB = \frac{(-1 + 2i)^2 + 11}{(-1 + 2i)(4i)} = \frac{2 - i}{-2 - i}\,\frac{-2 + i}{-2 + i} = -\tfrac{3}{5} + \tfrac{4}{5}i. \tag{37}$$

By rule I, §64, the part of the required inverse transform associated with the factor p of the denominator is $\frac{11}{5}e^{0t} = \frac{11}{5}$. Using this and rule III with $A = -\frac{3}{5}$, $B = \frac{4}{5}$ from (37), we get

$$T^{-1}\left\{\frac{p^2 + 11}{p(p^2 + 2p + 5)}\right\} = \frac{11}{5} + e^{-t}\left(-\frac{6}{5}\cos 2t - \frac{8}{5}\sin 2t\right).$$

For repeated quadratic factors of a denominator, consider

$$N(p)/\{M(p)[p - (a + ib)]^2[p - (a - ib)]^2\}, \qquad M(a + ib) \neq 0. \tag{38}$$

Applying the theory of §65 first for $[p - (a + ib)]^2$ and then for

$[p - (a - ib)]^2$, we find the associated partial fractions

$$\frac{A + iB}{[p - (a + ib)]^2} + \frac{A - iB}{[p - (a - ib)]^2} + \frac{\alpha + i\beta}{p - (a + ib)} + \frac{\alpha - i\beta}{p - (a - ib)}, \tag{39}$$

where A, B, α, and β are defined by

$$\begin{aligned} \frac{N(a + ib)/M(a + ib)}{(2ib)^2} &= A + iB, \\ \frac{d}{dp}\left\{\frac{N(p)/M(p)}{[p - (a - ib)]^2}\right\}_{p=a+bi} &= \alpha + i\beta. \end{aligned} \tag{40}$$

The part of the inverse transform of (38) *associated with the factor* $(p^2 - 2ap + a^2 + b^2)^2$, *found by manipulating the result of using* (40), (39), *and relation* 5 *with* $n = 2$ *from Table* 1, *page* 113, *is*

$$\mathbf{e^{at}[(2\alpha + 2At) \cos bt - (2\beta + 2Bt) \sin bt].} \tag{41}$$

A formula like (41) relating to a factor $(p^2 - 2ap + a^2 + b^2)^k$, based on an extension of (39) and (40), is easily developed.

Consider, for example, $(p^2 + 8)/[p(p^2 - 4p + 8)^2]$. For this case, $N = p^2 + 8$, $M = p$, $a + ib = 2 + 2i$, and, using (40), we find

$$A + iB = -\tfrac{1}{4} + 0i, \qquad \alpha + i\beta = -\tfrac{1}{16} - \tfrac{3}{16}i.$$

Hence, $A = -\frac{1}{4}$, $B = 0$, $\alpha = -\frac{1}{16}$, $\beta = -\frac{3}{16}$, $a = 2$, $b = 2$, and substitution of these values in (41) gives

$$e^{2t}[(-\tfrac{1}{8} - \tfrac{1}{2}t) \cos 2t + \tfrac{3}{8} \sin 2t]$$

as the part of $T^{-1}\{(p^2 + 8)/[p(p^2 - 4p + 8)^2]\}$ associated with the repeated quadratic factor.

EXERCISES

Use rule III and others to express in terms of t:

1. $T^{-1}\left\{\dfrac{p - 6}{p^2 - 4p + 8}\right\}$.

2. $T^{-1}\left\{\dfrac{1}{p^2 - 4ap + 8a^2}\right\}$.

3. $T^{-1}\left\{\dfrac{mp + n}{p^2 - 2ap + a^2 + b^2}\right\}$.

4. $T^{-1}\left\{\dfrac{p^2 + 2}{p(p^2 + 2p + 2)}\right\}$.

5. $T^{-1}\left\{\dfrac{p^2 + 2}{p(p + 1)(p^2 + 2p + 2)}\right\}$.

6. $T^{-1}\left\{\dfrac{p^2}{(p - 1)(p^2 - 2p + 5)}\right\}$.

Use (40) and (41) and others to express in terms of t:

★7. $T^{-1}\left\{\dfrac{p^2 + 3}{(p + 1)(p^2 + 2p + 2)^2}\right\}$.

8. $T^{-1}\left\{\dfrac{p^2 + 3}{(p^2 - 2p + 5)^2}\right\}$.

9. $T^{-1}\left\{\dfrac{p^2}{(p^2 + 1)^2}\right\}$.

10. The formula for the part of $T^{-1}\{[N(p)/M(p)]/(p^2 - 2ap + a^2 + b^2)^3\}$ associated with $(p^2 - 2ap + a^2 + b^2)^3$ is

$$2e^{at}[(A_1 + A_2t + \tfrac{1}{2}A_3t^2)\cos bt - (B_1 + B_2t + \tfrac{1}{2}B_3t^2)\sin bt].$$

Write symbols for the definitions of $A_1 + iB_1$, $A_2 + iB_2$, and $A_3 + iB_3$.

Solve the following differential equations:

11. $(D^2 + 1)y = 0$; $y = 0$, $Dy = 3$ when $t = 0$.
12. $(D^2 + 4)y = 4$; $y = 0$, $Dy = 4$ when $t = 0$.
13. $(D^2 - 4D + 8)y = e^{2t}$; $y = 2$, $Dy = -2$ when $t = 0$.
14. $(D^2 + 4)y = 12 \sin 2t$; $y = 0$, $Dy = 0$ when $t = 0$. *Hint:* By relation 7, Table 1, page 113, $T\{\sin 2t\} = 2/(p^2 + 4)$.
15. $(D^2 + 9)y = 6 \cos 3t$; $y = 1$, $Dy = 0$ when $t = 0$.
★16. $(D^2 + 6D + 13)y = 13e^{-3t} \sin 2t$; $y = 0$, $Dy = -2$ when $t = 0$.
17. $(D^2 + 4)y = 6(\sin t + \cos t)$; $y = 0$, $Dy = 1$ when $t = 0$.
18. Derive the relations 17 and 18 of Table 1, page 113.
19. Derive the relations 14 and 15 of Table 1, page 113, by the method of this section.
20. Derive the relations 19 and 20 of Table 1, page 113.
21. To find $T^{-1}\{1/\{[(p - 1)^2 + 4][(p + 1)^2 + 9]\}\}$ in terms of t, first use relation (III), Table 2, page 116, with $a = 1$, and then use relation 19, Table 1.

67. Review problems

In solving differential equations by transforms, it is necessary to use formula (IX), Table 2, page 116; the formula is discussed in §61. By using transform relations of Table 1, page 113, and the formulas of Table 2 [(VI) deserves special mention], the elementary problems of transforms can be solved.

Complicated transforms are handled expeditiously by partial fractions. For the real distinct factors of a transform use (26), §64; for repeated factors use rule II, §65; for quadratic factors $ap^2 + bp + c$, where $b^2 - 4ac < 0$, use rule III, §66, or for repeated quadratic factors use (40), (41), and their extensions.

EXERCISES

1. Use (1), §57, to find $T\{\sin kt\}$.
2. Find by (1), §57, $T\{1\}$; using this result and (VII), Table 2, develop the formula $T\{x^4\} = 4!/p^5$.
3. Use (VII), Table 2, and relation 7, Table 1, to get $T^{-1}\{1/[p(p^2 + a^2)]\}$ in terms of t.

Using Tables 1 and 2, find in terms of t:

4. $T^{-1}\left\{\dfrac{1}{p(p^2 + a^2)^2}\right\}$. **5.** $T^{-1}\left\{\dfrac{1}{(p - c)[(p - c)^2 + a^2]^2}\right\}$.

6. $T^{-1}\left\{\dfrac{1}{(p - c)^2[(p - c)^2 + a^2]^2}\right\}$.

Using Tables 1 and 2, find in terms of p:

7. $T\{(-t)^2 \cos kt\}$.

8. $T\left\{\int_0^t (-t) \cos kt\, dt\right\}$.

9. $T\left\{\int_0^t (t - \tau)^2 \sin k\tau\, d\tau\right\}$.

Solve the following differential equations:

10. $D^3y - Dy = 4t$; $y = 2$, $Dy = 2$, $D^2y = -2$ when $t = 0$.

11. $(D^2 - 2D + 10)y = 2 \cos 3t + 12 \sin 3t$; $y = 2$, $Dy = 6$ when $t = 0$.

12. $D^3y + Dy = 8t$; $y = 3$, $Dy = 0$, $D^2y = 5$ when $t = 0$.

13. $(D^2 + 4D + 13)y = 26$; $y = 2$, $Dy = -6$ when $t = 0$.

14. $(D^2 + 16)y = 32t - 24 \sin 4t$; $y = 0$, $Dy = 5$ when $t = 0$.

15. $(D^2 + 2D + 10)y = 12e^{-t} \cos 3t$, $y = 4$, $Dy = -4$ when $t = 0$.

16. $(D^2 + D)y = 6t^5$; $y = 0$, $Dy = 1$ when $t = 0$.

17. $D^2y + Dy - 9y - 9\int_0^t y\, dt = 8e^{-t} - 6$; $y = 5$, $Dy = 4$ when $t = 0$.

18. $Dy + 4\int_0^t y\, dt = -4 \sin 2t$; $y = -3$ when $t = 0$.

19. $x + Dy = 0$, $(D - 1)x + (D - 1)y = 2t$; $x = 1$, $y = -6$ when $t = 0$.

20. $(D^2 - 3)x - 4y = 0$, $x + (D^2 + 1)y = 0$; $x = 4$, $Dx = -4$, $y = 0$, $Dy = 2$ when $t = 0$.

CHAPTER 8

APPLICATIONS OF LINEAR EQUATIONS WITH CONSTANT COEFFICIENTS

68. Harmonic motion. Damping

For convenience of reference, we shall recall, at this point, a few facts concerning harmonic motion and damping.

If, as a particle moves in a straight line, its motion is defined by

$$y = c \sin (\omega t + \varphi) + a, \tag{1}$$

where a is a constant, y is the distance of the particle from a fixed point on the line, and t is the time, its motion is called **simple harmonic motion.** The number c, representing the greatest value of $y - a$, is called the **amplitude of the motion.** Because of the periodic nature of $\sin (\omega t + \varphi)$, it is clear that the motion consists of an endless repetition of the movement that takes place while the angle $\omega t + \varphi$ changes by 2π radians; hence, the motion is called **periodic.** The time T required for the angle $\omega t + \varphi$ to change by 2π radians is called the **period of the motion.** Therefore, we must have

$$\omega(t + T) + \varphi - (\omega t + \varphi) = 2\pi,$$

or

$$\textbf{Period T} = \frac{2\pi}{\omega}. \tag{2}$$

The number n of repetitions of the least complete motion, that is, the number of cycles per unit of time, is called the **frequency.** Hence,

$$\textbf{Frequency n} = \frac{1}{\mathrm{T}} = \frac{\omega}{2\pi}. \tag{3}$$

The angle φ is often referred to as the **angle of epoch,** and $\omega t + \varphi$ as the **phase.** Figure 1 represents the motion. The heavy part of the curve between A and B represents one period of the motion, the length c is the amplitude, and the distance from A to B represents the period $T = (2\pi - \varphi)/\omega - (-\varphi/\omega) = 2\pi/\omega$.

An equation having the form $y - a = c_1 \sin \omega t + c_2 \cos \omega t$ may be

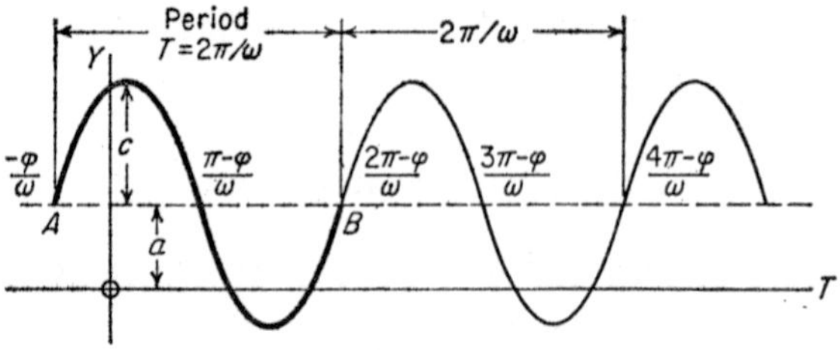

FIG. 1

written in the form (1). For

$$c_1 \sin \omega t + c_2 \cos \omega t = \sqrt{c_1^2 + c_2^2}\left(\frac{c_1 \sin \omega t}{\sqrt{c_1^2 + c_2^2}} + \frac{c_2 \cos \omega t}{\sqrt{c_1^2 + c_2^2}}\right),$$

and this, in view of Fig. 2, may be written

$$\sqrt{c_1^2 + c_2^2}\,(\sin \omega t \cos \varphi + \cos \omega t \sin \varphi) = \sqrt{c_1^2 + c_2^2}\,\sin (\omega t + \varphi). \quad (4)$$

Hence, it appears from Fig. 2 that

$$y - a = c_1 \sin \omega t + c_2 \cos \omega t = c \sin (\omega t + \varphi), \quad (5)$$

where $$c = \sqrt{c_1^2 + c_2^2}, \qquad \varphi = \tan^{-1} \frac{c_2}{c_1}. \quad (6)$$

A very important damped oscillatory motion is represented by

$$y = ce^{-at} \sin (\omega t + \varphi), \qquad a > 0.$$

Observe that the factor $\sin (\omega t + \varphi)$ describes an oscillatory kind of motion and that e^{-at} becomes smaller and smaller as t increases so that the oscillations become smaller and smaller in magnitude. Figure 3 represents the motion. Observe that the length of time for each wave is the same but that the heights of the waves become smaller and smaller with increasing t; that is, the motion is damped. *The factor e^{-at} is called the* **damping factor,** *a the* **damping constant,** *$2\pi/\omega$ the* **period of oscillation,** and *$\omega/2\pi$ the* **frequency** of y. For example, if

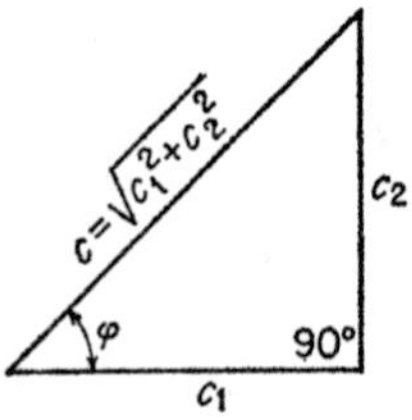

FIG. 2

$$y = 10e^{-0.02t} \sin \left(120\pi t - \frac{\pi}{2}\right),$$

the period is $2\pi/(120\pi) = \frac{1}{60}$, the frequency is 60 cycles, 0.02 is the damping constant, and $e^{-0.02t}$ is the damping factor. To find the time required by the damping factor to decrease one-half its value, we have $e^{-0.02t} = \frac{1}{2}$; hence, $\ln e^{-0.02t} = \ln \frac{1}{2}$, or $-0.02t = -\ln 2 = -0.6931$, and $t = 34.7$. This shows that the magnitude of the damping factor at the end of a 34.7-unit interval is one-half its magnitude at the beginning.

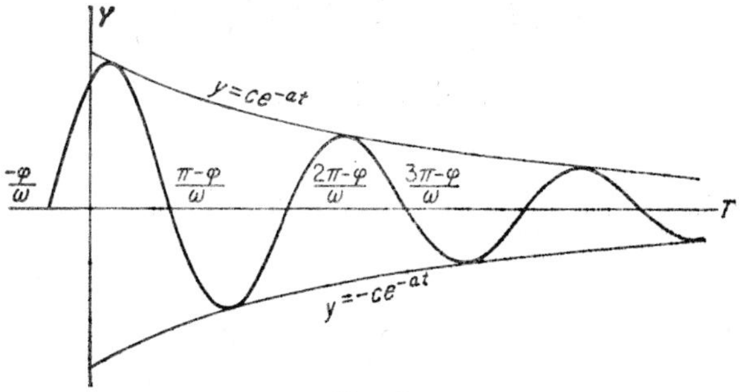

FIG. 3

EXERCISES

In the following exercises, assume distance in feet and time in seconds.

1. For a straight-line motion represented by $y = 5 \sin (12\pi t + \pi/6)$, find the amplitude, the period, the frequency, and two positive values of t for which $y = 0$.

2. For a straight-line motion represented by $y = 5 \sin 32t + 12 \cos 32t$, find the period, frequency, and amplitude, and show that the maximum value of dy/dt is 416.

3. The equation $(d^2y/dt^2) + 100y = 0$ represents a simple harmonic motion. Find the general solution of the equation, and determine the constants of integration if $y = 10$, $dy/dt = 50$ when $t = 0$. Tell the frequency, the period, and the amplitude of the motion represented.

4. For a straight-line motion represented by $y = 25e^{-0.035t} \sin (377t + 1)$, find the period and frequency, and show that the damping factor decreases from 1 when $t = 0$ to $\frac{1}{2}$ when t is approximately 20 units of time.

5. What must be true of k in the equation $(d^2s/dt^2) + (k\, ds/dt) + 30s = 0$ if the motion represented is oscillatory?

6. An oscillatory motion is represented by

$$\frac{d^2y}{dt^2} + \frac{1}{10}\frac{dy}{dt} + 10y = 0.$$

Find the period of oscillation of y, the damping factor, and the time required for the damping factor to decrease 50 per cent.

7. An oscillatory motion represented by an equation of the form

$$\frac{d^2x}{dt^2} + b\frac{dx}{dt} + cx = 0$$

has a frequency of oscillation $n = 60$ and a damping constant $a = \frac{1}{10}$. Find b and c.

8. Find b and c in the differential equation of exercise 7 if the period of oscillation of x is $\frac{1}{10}$ sec and the damping factor decreases 50 per cent in 30 sec.

69. Types of Damping. Resonance

Important types of motions of bodies are defined by equations having the form

$$a\frac{d^2x}{dt^2} + b\frac{dx}{dt} + cx = f(t), \tag{7}$$

where a, b, and c are constants and $a > 0$, $b > 0$, $c > 0$. Its auxiliary equation is

$$ar^2 + br + c = 0. \tag{8}$$

First, we consider three types of motion indicated by (7) with $f(t) = 0$ and: (*a*) $b^2 - 4ac > 0$; (*b*) $b^2 - 4ac = 0$; (*c*) $b^2 - 4ac < 0$.

For case (*a*), the roots α and β of (8) are real and negative, the solution of (7) has the form $x = ce^{\alpha t} + c_2 e^{\beta t}$, there is no oscillation, and the motion is said to be **overdamped.**

In case (*b*), $b^2 - 4ac = 0$, the roots α, α of (8) are equal and negative, the solution of (7) is $x = (c_1 + c_2 t)e^{\alpha t}$, the motion is nonoscillatory, and it is said to be **critically damped.**

In case (*c*), $b^2 - 4ac < 0$, the roots $-k \pm \omega i$ of (8) are imaginary, the solution has the form $x = e^{-kt}(c_1 \sin \omega t + c_2 \cos \omega t)$, and the motion indicated is said to be **damped.** In all three types of motion, x approaches zero as t becomes infinite.

When $f(t) \neq 0$, we have, in accordance with §49, $x = x_c + x_p$, where x is the solution just considered and x_p is due to $f(t)$ and may or may not be oscillatory. An interesting situation, called **resonance,** arises when, in (7), $b = 0$ and x_c and x_p have the same period. Consider, for example,

$$\frac{d^2x}{dt^2} + 4x = 8 \cos 2t.$$

The solution of this equation is

$$x = c_1 \sin 2t + c_2 \cos 2t + 2t \sin 2t. \tag{9}$$

Observe that the term $x_p = 2t \sin 2t$ oscillates and that there is no bound to its magnitude. For example, if $t = 10{,}001\pi/4$, $x_p = 10{,}001\pi/2$ units $=$ 15,721 units nearly.

EXERCISES

1. For the motion represented by

$$\frac{d^2x}{dt^2} + 4\frac{dx}{dt} + kx = 0,$$

find the numerically least integral value of k for the occurrence of: (*a*) critical damping; (*b*) overdamping; (*c*) damping. (*d*) Sketch the curve of part (*b*).

2. Name the type of damping associated with each equation:

$$(a)\ \frac{d^2x}{dt^2} + \frac{dx}{dt} + 3x = 0. \qquad (b)\ \frac{d^2x}{dt^2} + 2\frac{dx}{dt} + x = 0. \qquad (c)\ \frac{d^2x}{dt^2} + \frac{dx}{dt} + \tfrac{1}{5}x = 0.$$

3. (*a*) What is the value of ω at resonance for $d^2x/dt^2 + 64x = 64 \sin \omega t$? (*b*) Find the value of $-4t \cos 8t$ when $t = 10^6\pi$ and when $t = 10^6\pi + \frac{1}{8}\pi$.

4. Show that if α is positive the maximum value of $te^{-\alpha t}$ for t positive is e^{-1}/α. Sketch the curve $x = c_1 te^{-t/3}$ for positive values of t.

5. Show that every solution for x of (7) with $f(t) = 0$ and a, b, and c positive numbers must approach zero as t becomes infinite.

70. Forces. Accelerations. Moments

Vectors, their components along the coordinate axes, and their sum in magnitude and direction are discussed in §33. Since forces, velocities, accelerations, and other quantities defined by magnitude and direction obey the laws of vectors, the following statements relate directly to these quantities.

A vector AB (see Fig. 4) is the segment AB of a straight line containing an arrowhead pointed toward B to indicate a direction from its initial point A to its terminal point B. The length of the segment indicates the

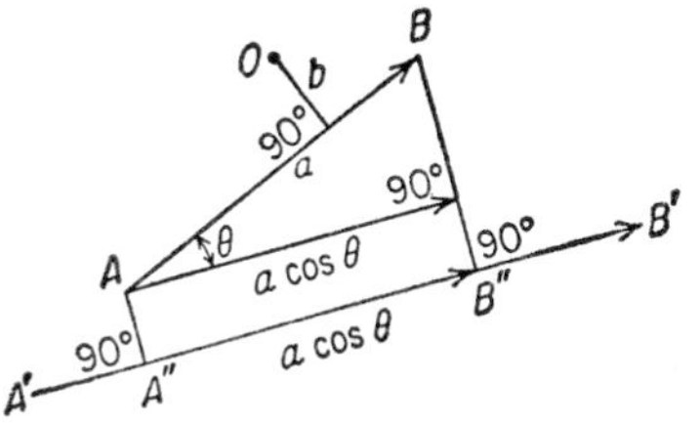

FIG. 4

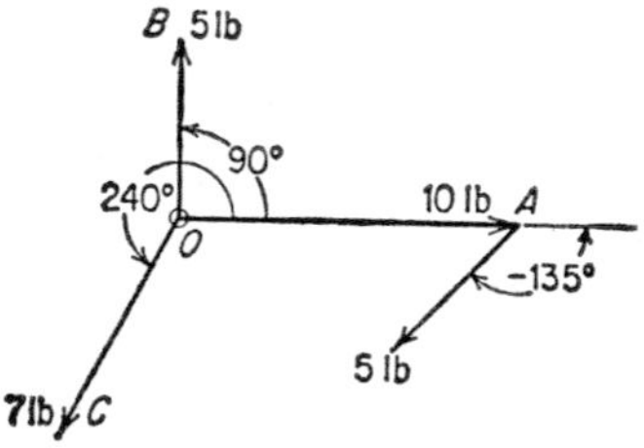

FIG. 5

magnitude of the vector, and the line with the attached arrowhead indicates direction. If, from the ends A and B of the vector, perpendiculars be dropped to the line of a vector $A'B'$ and meet it in the points A'' and B'', respectively, then the vector $A''B''$ directed from A'' to B'' is called the *component* of vector AB in the direction of $A'B'$ (see Fig. 4).

Consider a vector AB of magnitude a, making an angle θ with the positive direction of vector $A'B'$. Then, the absolute value of the quantity $a \cos \theta$ is the magnitude of the component of vector AB in the direction of $A'B'$. If $a \cos \theta$ is positive in sign, the component has the same direction as $A'B'$; if $a \cos \theta$ is negative, the component has the direction opposite to that of $A'B'$. Similarly, if a_i, θ_i $(i = 1, 2, \ldots, n)$ represent, respectively, magnitudes and angles made with vector $A'B'$ for n vectors A_iB_i, the algebraic sum $\Sigma a_i \cos \theta_i$ $(i = 1, 2, \ldots, n)$ will give in magnitude and sense along $A'B'$ the sum of the components of the n vectors in the direction of $A'B'$.

For example, the forces indicated in Fig. 5 have, as the sum of their components along OA, a vector of magnitude $10 \cos 0° + 5 \cos 90° + 7 \cos 240° + 5 \cos (-135°) = 10 - 3.50 - 3.54 = 2.96$ lb directed along OA, and as sum of components along OB a vector of $10 \cos 90° + 5 \cos 0° + 7 \cos 150° + 5 \cos 135° = 5 - (7\sqrt{3}/2) - 5/\sqrt{2} = -4.60$ lb along OB, or 4.60 lb in the direction opposite to that of OB.

Acceleration a, *like force, is a directed quantity which has components* a_x *and* a_y *in the directions of the coordinate axes*

$$a_x = \frac{d^2x}{dt^2} \qquad a_y = \frac{d^2y}{dt^2},$$

where t represents time. The statements made about forces apply generally to accelerations.

Again, consider a force represented by a vector AB lying in a fixed plane and an axis which is perpendicular to the plane and cuts it in point O (see Fig. 4). *The* **moment,** *or* **torque,** *of the force about the axis, also referred to as the* **torque about** O, *is defined to be the magnitude* a *of the force multiplied by the distance* b *from* O *to the line of action* AB *of the force.* Moment measures the tendency to cause turning. Two forces, one tending to turn a body about O in one sense and the other tending to turn it about O in the opposite sense, would have moments about O opposite in sign. For example, forces OB and OC in Fig. 5 have moments about A opposite in sign. In general, *if* θ *is the angle through which a body attached to the axis is turned from some fixed position of reference, the torque of a force is considered as positive when it tends to turn the body in the sense of increasing angle* θ *and negative when it tends to turn the body in the opposite sense.*

71. Some fundamental equations of motion

Plane motion of a rigid body is a motion such that each point in the body remains at a constant distance from a fixed plane; for example, a wheel on an automobile has plane motion when the car is moving in a straight line.

When all the particles of the body, rigid or not, have plane motion with respect to the same plane, the sum ΣF_d *of the components in any direction of all the external forces acting on it is equal to the product of the mass* m* *of the body and the component* a_d *in the same direction of the acceleration of the center of gravity of the body;* that is,

$$\Sigma F_d = ma_d. \tag{10}$$

Applying this rule for the direction of the X-axis and for the direction of the Y-axis, we obtain

$$\sum \mathbf{F}_x = \mathbf{m}\mathbf{a}_x = \mathbf{m}\frac{\mathbf{d}^2\mathbf{x}}{\mathbf{d}\mathbf{t}^2}, \qquad \sum \mathbf{F}_y = \mathbf{m}\mathbf{a}_y = \mathbf{m}\frac{\mathbf{d}^2\mathbf{y}}{\mathbf{d}\mathbf{t}^2}. \tag{11}$$

When a rigid body has plane motion, the moment, or torque T_g, *of the external forces acting on it about an axis through the center of gravity of the*

* The acceleration g of a body given it by the pull of the earth is nearly 32.2 ft/sec². For many problems in this book, the unit of mass, the **slug,** will be considered as that of a 32.2-lb body. For such problems the mass m slugs of a w-lb body will be denoted by $w/32.2$.

body and perpendicular to the plane of its motion is equal to the product of the moment of inertia I_g of the body with respect to the same axis and the angular acceleration α of the body; that is,

$$\mathbf{T}_g = \mathbf{I}_g\alpha = \mathbf{I}_g \frac{d^2\theta}{dt^2}, \tag{12}$$

where θ is the angle through which the body is turned from some fixed position of reference. When the motion is pure rotation, we may write

$$\mathbf{T} = \mathbf{I}\alpha = \mathbf{I} \frac{d^2\theta}{dt^2}, \tag{13}$$

where T is the torque of the external forces about the axis of rotation and I is the moment of inertia of the body with respect to the same axis. Note that the axis associated with (13) is not necessarily an axis through the center of gravity.

72. Oscillatory motion

Three very important types of motion are referred to as **free** motion, **damped** motion, and **forced** motion. Thus, a weight supported in a vacuum by a spring would tend to move with an oscillatory motion when displaced vertically; if air were admitted, it would tend to slow down, or *damp*, the motion; and if the supporting structure were moved up and down, a motion would be *forced* on the weight. These three types of motion or their counterparts occur in a great many physical phenomena.

Example. The force exerted by a certain spring is proportional to the amount it is stretched, and a force of 8 lb stretches it 3 in. A 16.1-lb weight hanging at rest on the spring is drawn down 6 in. and released. Describe the motion: (*a*) if there is no air resistance; (*b*) if the air resistance in pounds and one-hundredth of the speed in feet per second are equal numerically; (*c*) if, in addition to the air resistance, the supporting structure is given a motion $y = \frac{1}{2} \sin 7t$.

Solution. (*a*) Let s be the number of feet the spring is stretched (see Fig. 6*a*), and let f represent the force exerted by the spring. Then, in accordance with Hooke's law, $f = ks$. Since $f = 8$ lb when $s = \frac{1}{4}$ ft, it appears that $8 = k\frac{1}{4}$ and $k = 32$. Hence,

$$f = 32s. \tag{a}$$

From the first equation of (11), with downward considered as the positive direction, we get

$$16.1 - f = 16.1 - 32s = \frac{16.1}{32.2} \frac{d^2s}{dt^2}. \tag{b}$$

To simplify this equation, let $s = x + 16.1/32$,* so that

$$16.1 - 32s = -32x, \qquad v = \frac{ds}{dt} = \frac{dx}{dt}, \qquad a = \frac{d^2s}{dt^2} = \frac{d^2x}{dt^2}. \tag{c}$$

In accordance with (*a*), 16.1/32 is the amount the spring is stretched by its weight. Hence, the use of (*c*) amounts to specifying the position of the weight at time t by its distance from the position in which it hangs

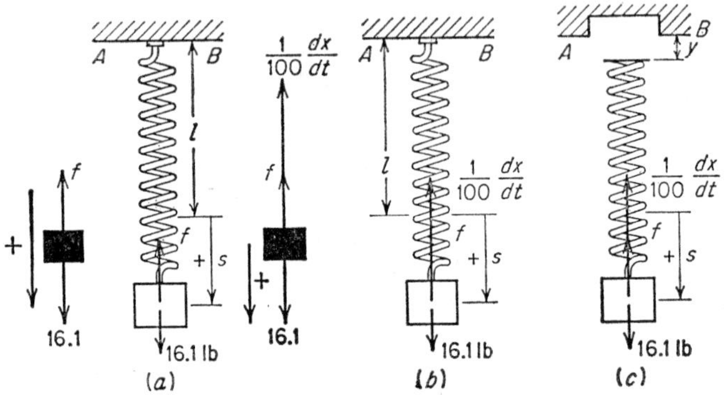

FIG. 6

in equilibrium. The use of (*c*) reduces equation (*b*) to

$$\frac{d^2x}{dt^2} + 64x = 0. \tag{d}$$

Take $t = 0$ just as the weight is released, that is, when it is at rest $\frac{1}{2}$ ft below the equilibrium position. Hence, the initial conditions are

$$x = \tfrac{1}{2}, \qquad v = 0 \qquad \textit{when } t = 0. \tag{e}$$

Applying the method of Laplace transforms, §62, to (*d*) under conditions (*e*), we get

$$p^2X - \tfrac{1}{2}p + 64X = 0,$$

$$x = T^{-1}\{X\} = T^{-1}\left\{\frac{\frac{1}{2}p}{p^2 + 64}\right\} = \tfrac{1}{2}\cos 8t. \tag{f}$$

This represents a harmonic motion with amplitude $\frac{1}{2}$ ft and period $2\pi/8 = 0.785$ sec, or frequency $8/(2\pi) = 1.27$ cycles/sec.

The solution of (*c*) subject to the initial conditions (*e*) could have been obtained by the methods of Chap. 6 instead of the method of transforms.

(*b*) The differential equation of motion in this case is obtained from (*b*) by adding $-0.01\, ds/dt$ to the force members, or by adding $0.02\, dx/dt$

* It is not necessary to introduce x to replace s as indicated; but a simpler differential equation and a simpler solution result.

to the left member of (d). This gives

$$\frac{d^2x}{dt^2} + 0.02\frac{dx}{dt} + 64x = 0. \qquad (g)$$

Solving (g) subject to initial conditions (e), we get

$$p^2X - \tfrac{1}{2}p + 0.02pX - 0.02(\tfrac{1}{2}) + 64X = 0,$$

$$x = T^{-1}\{X\} = T^{-1}\left\{\frac{\frac{1}{2}p + 0.01}{(p + 0.01)^2 + 64}\right\} \quad \text{nearly}$$

$$= e^{-0.01t}T^{-1}\left\{\frac{\frac{1}{2}(p - 0.01) + 0.01}{p^2 + 64}\right\},$$

$$\mathbf{x = e^{-0.01t}(\tfrac{1}{2}\cos 8t + 0.0006\sin 8t).} \qquad (h)$$

Here the period is the same as before, accurate to three figures. The damping factor is $e^{-0.01t}$. To get an idea of the rate of damping, notice that the damping factor is $\frac{1}{2}$ when $e^{-0.01t} = \frac{1}{2}$, or when $-0.01t = -\ln 2 = -0.693$ and $t = 69.3$ sec; that is, the magnitude of the damping factor at the end of a 69.3-sec period is one-half its magnitude at the beginning. Here again we could have used the method of Chap. 6 for solving (g) subject to conditions (e).

(c) In this case (see Fig. 6c), $s - y$ is the amount the spring is stretched, and $y = \frac{1}{2}\sin 7t$. Then,

$$f = 32(s - y) = 32(x + 16.1/32 - y) = 32x + 16.1 - 16\sin 7t. \qquad (i)$$

Substituting this value for f in (b), supplying the resisting force $-0.01\,dx/dt$, and simplifying, we get

$$\frac{d^2x}{dt^2} + 0.02\frac{dx}{dt} + 64x = 32\sin 7t. \qquad (j)$$

Solving (j) subject to the conditions (e), we get

$$p^2X - 0.5p + 0.02pX - 0.02(\tfrac{1}{2}) + 64X = \frac{224}{p^2 + 49},$$

$$X = \frac{224}{(p^2 + 49)[(p + 0.01)^2 + 64]} + \frac{0.5p + 0.01}{(p + 0.01)^2 + 64} \quad \text{nearly.} \qquad (k)$$

Using relation 19, Table 1, page 113, and others, and collecting like terms, we get

$$x = T^{-1}\{X\} = \mathbf{e^{-0.01t}(0.520\cos 8t - 1.86\sin 8t) + 2.13\sin 7t - 0.020\cos 7t,} \qquad (l)$$

approximately. Observe that the motion of the weight is composed of two motions: a damped oscillatory motion and a harmonic motion. As time increases, the damped harmonic motion dies away while the harmonic motion $2.13\sin 7t - 0.020\cos 7t$ remains. The flow of electricity in many circuits follows this same plan, being made up of two parts, a **transient part,** which quickly dies out, and a **steady-state part,** which remains indefinitely.

PROBLEMS

1. Solve parts (*a*) and (*b*) of the example by the methods of Chap. 6.

2. The force exerted by a spring is proportional to the amount that the spring is stretched and is 200 lb when the spring is stretched 1 ft. A 64-lb weight suspended by the spring as indicated in Fig. 7 is released from rest 0.4 ft below the equilibrium position. Find the equation, the amplitude, the period, and the frequency of the resulting motion. Take the mass as $\frac{64}{32} = 2$ slugs.

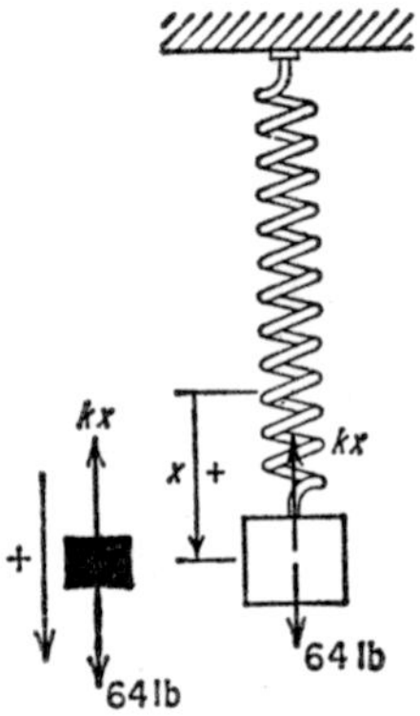

Fig. 7

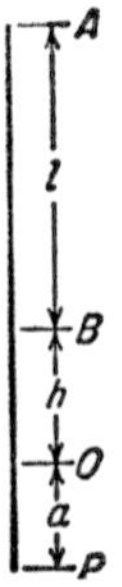

Fig. 8

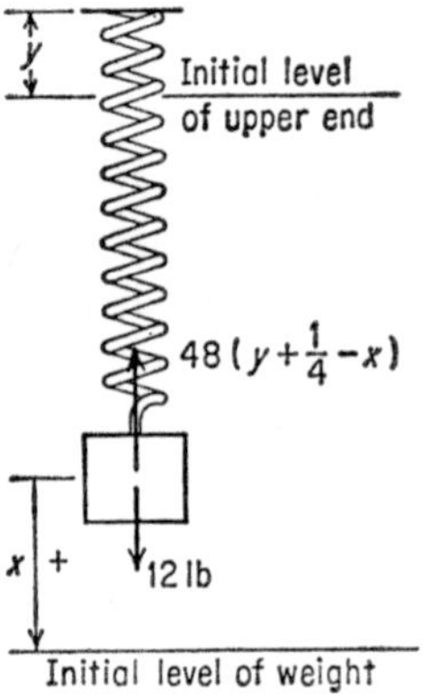

Fig. 9

3. Assume in problem 2 an additional vertical resisting force numerically equal to $0.04v$, where velocity v is in feet per second, and solve the resulting problem. Omit the part referring to amplitude. Also, find the damping factor and the time it takes it to decrease to 50 per cent of its initial value.

4. Assume the situation of problem 2, together with the additional requirement that the upper end of the spring be given the motion $y = 0.64 \sin 6t$, where y ft represents distance below the point of suspension at t sec after motion starts. Find: (*a*) the equation of the motion of the 64-lb weight; (*b*) the period of the complementary solution, that of the particular solution, and that of the motion; and (*c*) the amount the spring is stretched 1 sec after motion starts.

5. A rubber band of natural length $AB = l$ (see Fig. 8) is suspended vertically from a point A, and a weight is attached to it at B. The weight stretches the band to a length $AO = l + h$. The weight is given a displacement $OP = a$ $(a < h)$ and then released. Find the equation of the motion.

6. A spring is stretched 1 in. when a 4-lb weight is hung on it. If a 12-lb weight is hanging at rest on the spring when the upper end of the spring is given the motion $y = \sin \sqrt{3g}\, t$, find a differential equation of the motion of the weight, solve this equation, and determine all constants of integration. Find the position of the weight $50\pi/\sqrt{g}$ sec after the motion starts. *Hint:* At time t (see Fig. 9), y is the distance of the upper end above its initial position, and we let x be the distance of the weight above its initial position. Hence, at time t, the spring is stretched $y + \frac{1}{4} - x$, and the upward force on the weight is $48(y + \frac{1}{4} - x) - 12$.

7. Solve problem 6 with $y = \sin \sqrt{3g}\, t$ replaced by $y = \sin 2\sqrt{g}\, t$. Is there a theoretical upper limit to the distance of the weight from the starting point?

8. A rigid body suspended by a wire (see Fig. 10) has a motion of pure rotation about the line of the wire as an axis. If the only torque acting is a torque in the wire proportional to the angle that the body is turned from the position in which it hangs in equilibrium, find the period of the motion. *Hint:* Let θ be the angle through which the body is turned from equilibrium. Then, use (13) to obtain

$$-k^2\theta = I\frac{d^2\theta}{dt^2}.$$

9. A uniform sphere rotates about a supporting wire as an axis. If the number expressing the torque in the wire in pound-feet is equal to the number of radians

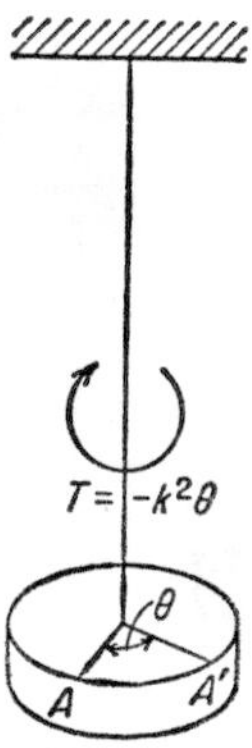

FIG. 10

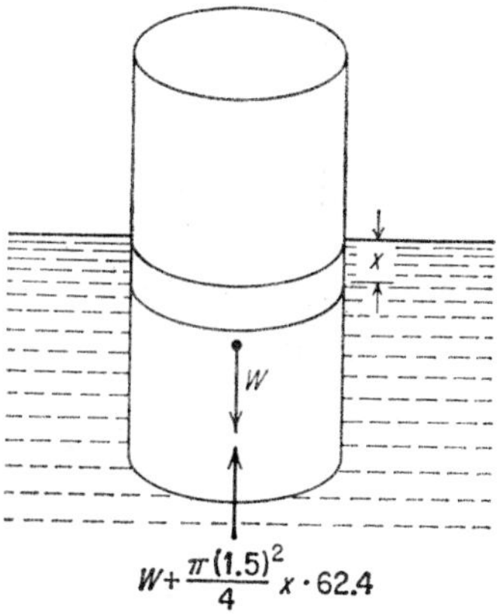

FIG. 11

through which the sphere is turned from the position in which it will hang in equilibrium, and if the sphere makes two complete oscillations per second, find the moment of inertia of the sphere with respect to the line of the wire.

10. If, for the sphere and wire of problem 9, change of motion is caused by a frictional torque proportional to the angular velocity together with the torque in the wire, and if the corresponding damping factor decreases to 25 per cent of its initial value during the first 20 sec of motion, find the equation and the period of the motion. Use the value of I found in problem 9.

11.* A cylindrical spar buoy 18 in. in diameter stands in fresh water with its axis vertical (see Fig. 11). When depressed slightly and released, its period of vibration is found to be 2.7 sec. Find the weight of the cylinder.

12. A rectangular block of wood 2 by 2 by 1 ft floats in fresh water with its 1-ft edge vertical. If the block weighs 160 lb, find the time of vibration when it is depressed slightly and released. Find also the time of vibration of the same block in a liquid of specific gravity ρ.

13. Find, approximately, the period of vibration of a simple pendulum l ft long. Assume that the angle θ between the vertical and the cord of the pendulum is always so small that $\sin\theta$ may be replaced by θ without appreciable error. *Hint:* Use Fig. 12 and apply equation (13).

★**14.*** A 10-lb weight having specific gravity 2 is immersed in water and supported

* Archimedes' principle is involved. It states that *a body in a liquid is acted upon by an upward force equal to the weight of the liquid it displaces. This force for a body floating at rest in a liquid is the weight of the body.*

by a spring which it stretches 2 in. It is drawn down 1 ft from its position of equilibrium and let go. The resistance of the liquid to the motion of the weight is proportional to its velocity. If, at the end of two complete vibrations, the value of the damping factor is 25 per cent of its initial value, find the equation of the motion and its period. Figure 13 indicates the forces acting on the body.

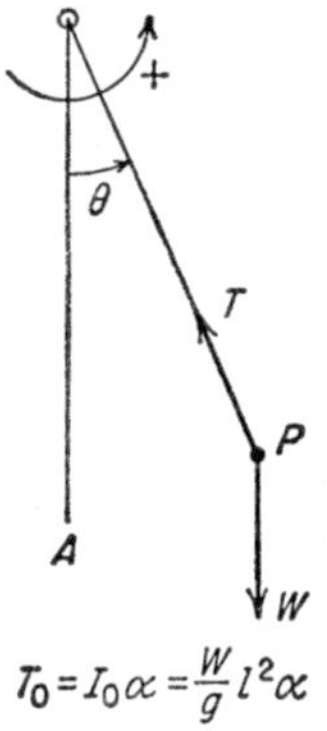

FIG. 12

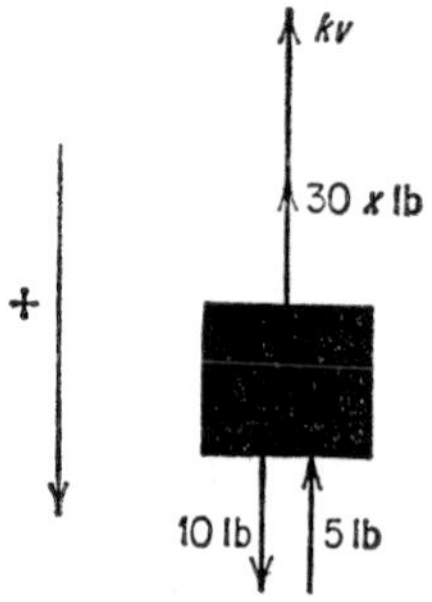

FIG. 13

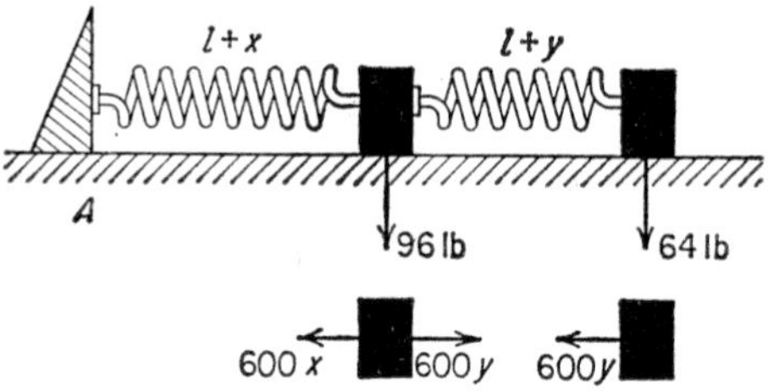

FIG. 14

15. A particle below the earth's surface is attracted toward the center of the earth with a force proportional to the distance of the particle from the center. If a particle were dropped into a smooth straight vacuum passing through the earth's center, how long would it take the particle to reach the center? Assume that the radius of the earth is 3,960 statute miles. *Hint:* $(W/32.2)a = ks$, and $a = -32.2$ ft/sec², when $s = R$.

16. If I ton-ft² is the moment of inertia of a W-ton ship about a longitudinal waterline axis, G is the center of gravity of the ship, and M a fixed point in the ship through which the buoyancy of the water acts, the differential equation

$$I\frac{d^2\theta}{dt^2} = -gW\overline{GM}\,\theta$$

applies approximately. (*a*) Find I for a 30,000-ton battleship having $\overline{GM} = 7.7$ ft and period 17 sec. (*b*) Find the period of a 1,600-ton destroyer having $\overline{GM} = 2.3$ ft and $I = 2.9 \times 10^5$ ton-ft².

17.* Figure 14 represents a 96-lb weight and a 64-lb weight moving on a smooth, straight, horizontal track subject to the action of springs, as indicated. The force exerted by each spring is $600s$, where s ft represents elongation of the spring. Assume

* Transforms should be used in solving problems 17 to 19.

that, when $t = 0$, the springs are unstretched, the 96-lb weight is moving away from A at 600 ft/sec, and the 64-lb weight is at rest. Take 3 slugs and 2 slugs as the respective masses. Find the equations of motion of the weights.

★**18.*** In Fig. 14, replace 96 lb by P lb, 64 lb by Q lb, and assume an additional force $a \sin \omega t$ acting on the P-lb block. As initial conditions, use $x = x_0$, $dx/dt = \dot{x}_0$, $y = y_0$, $dy/dt = \dot{y}_0$ when $t = 0$. Set up the differential equations for the motion, and, preferably using transforms, eliminate y from them. Then carry the solution far enough to deduce that, if $gk/Q = \omega^2$, no effect is introduced by the force $a \sin \omega t$ that could not be caused by a change of initial conditions.

★**19.** Figure 15 shows schematically a W-lb car moving rightward with velocity V ft/sec over a corduroy road such that the road imparts to the bottom of the springs the motion $y = a + b \sin \omega t$, where a, b, and ω are constants. (*a*) Assuming that x, s, l, and y have the meanings suggested by the figure and that the force of the springs is ks lb, show that

$$\frac{W}{g}\frac{d^2x}{dt^2} + k(x - l - a - b \sin \omega t) = W.$$

(*b*) In this, let $x_p = x - l - a + W/k$, $\omega_1^2 = gk/W$, solve this resulting equation, and obtain

$$x_p = c_1 \cos \omega_1 t + c_2 \cos \omega_1 t + \omega b \omega_1[\sin \omega_1 t - (\omega_1/\omega) \sin \omega t]/(\omega^2 - \omega_1^2).$$

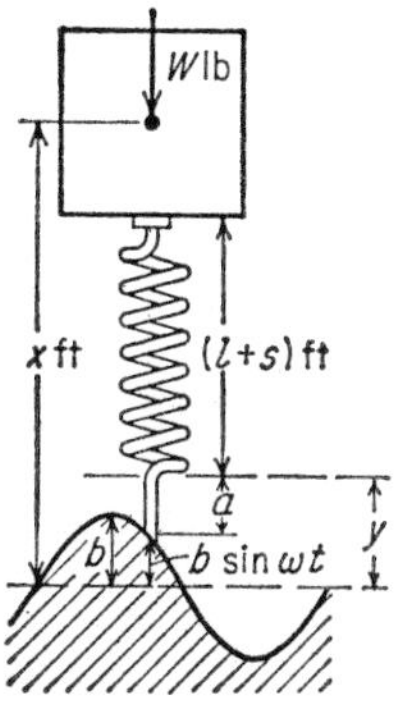

FIG. 15

The particular solution indicates the effect of the rough road. (*c*) Assume that ω/ω_1 is large, and state whether k should be large or small for slight rough-road effect. (*d*) Show that, if d is the length of road per cycle of $b \sin \omega t$, then $\omega = 2\pi V/d$. If the speed of the car is increased, will the effect of the roughness of the road be increased or decreased? (*e*) Discuss the roughness effect if ω_1 is nearly equal to ω.

73. Plane motions of bodies

In §72 motions in a straight line and simple rotary motions were considered. The equations of §71 will now be applied to the curved-line

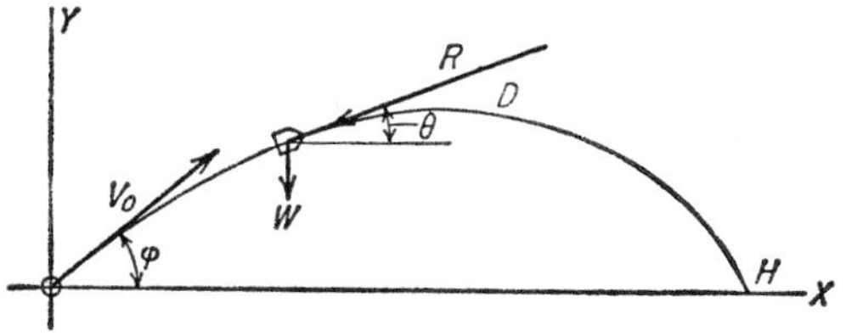

FIG. 16

motion of projectiles and of bodies rotating and translating at the same time. In Fig. 16, the curve ODH is the path, or trajectory, of a projectile fired from a gun at O, φ is the angle of departure, V_0 is the initial velocity, θ is the inclination of the tangent line to the X-axis (taken horizontal),

* This problem illustrates the use of auxiliary masses to eliminate or reduce vibratory disturbances.

OH is the range, vector W represents the force of gravity acting on the projectile, and vector R represents the force due to air resistance assumed to be acting along the tangent to the trajectory in a direction opposite to that in which the projectile is moving.

If $\dot{x} = dx/dt$ and $\dot{y} = dy/dt$, the relations between components $\dot{x}$ and $\dot{y}$ of the velocity are shown in Fig. 17. From Fig. 17, we read

$$\cos\theta = \frac{\dot{x}}{v}, \qquad \sin\theta = \frac{\dot{y}}{v}.$$

Applying equations (11) of §71 to the projectile of Fig. 16, we obtain

$$\frac{W}{g}\frac{d\dot{x}}{dt} = -R\frac{\dot{x}}{v}, \qquad \frac{W}{g}\frac{d\dot{y}}{dt} = -W - R\frac{\dot{y}}{v}, \tag{14}$$

where $\dot{x}$ and $\dot{y}$ represent, respectively, the horizontal and the vertical components of the velocity. The force R is a very complex quantity,

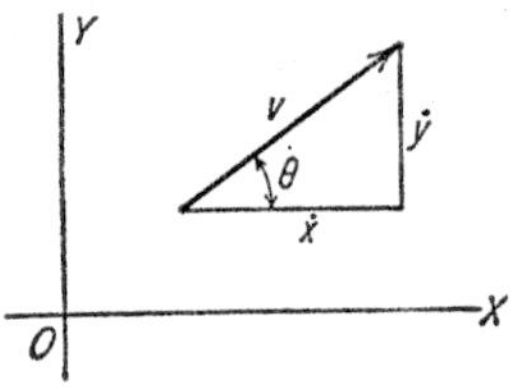

Fig. 17

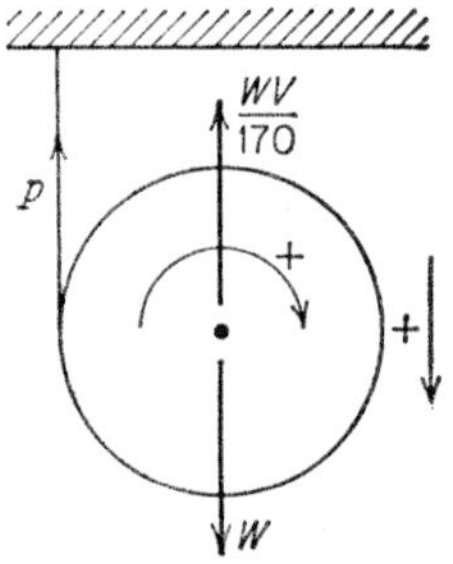

Fig. 18

so complex, in fact, that only approximations to the solutions of equations (14) can be found. Some rough approximations of special cases will appear as solutions of problems in the list of this article.

The following example will illustrate a type involving both rotation and translation.

Example. A homogeneous cylinder, having radius $= r$ ft, weight $=$ W lb, $I_g = \frac{W}{g}\frac{r^2}{2}$ (where $g = 32.2$), has a flexible cord wrapped around its central plane. One end of the cord is attached to a fixed plane as shown in Fig. 18. As the body falls, an air resistance in pounds equal numerically to $W/170$ times its velocity in feet per second retards its motion. If it starts from rest, find distance y fallen in t sec, limiting velocity, and percentage of limiting velocity acquired in 20 sec.

Solution. If y is the distance fallen from rest and θ the angle through which the body has turned, we have

$$y = r\theta, \qquad v = \frac{dy}{dt} = r\frac{d\theta}{dt}, \qquad a = \frac{d^2y}{dt^2} = r\frac{d^2\theta}{dt^2} = r\alpha. \tag{a}$$

Here, downward is considered as the positive direction and clockwise as the positive sense of rotation. Applying equations (11) and (12) to the system represented by Fig. 18, we get

$$-p - \frac{W}{170} v + W = \frac{W}{g} \frac{d^2y}{dt^2}, \tag{b}$$

$$pr = \frac{W}{g} \frac{r^2}{2} \alpha = \frac{Wr}{2g} r\alpha = \frac{Wr}{2g} \frac{d^2y}{dt^2}. \tag{c}$$

Substituting p from (c) in (b) and simplifying slightly, we obtain

$$\frac{d^2y}{dt^2} + \frac{g}{255} \frac{dy}{dt} = \frac{2g}{3}. \tag{d}$$

The initial conditions are

$$y = 0, \qquad \frac{dy}{dt} = 0 \qquad \text{when } t = 0. \tag{e}$$

Solving (d) subject to conditions (e)* by transforms, we get

$$(p^2 - 0p - 0)Y + \frac{g}{255} pY = \frac{2g}{3p},$$

$$Y = \frac{2g/3}{p^2(p + g/255)} = \frac{170}{p^2} - \frac{3(170)^2}{2gp} + \frac{3(170)^2}{2g(p + g/255)},$$

$$y = 170t + \frac{3(170)^2}{2g} (e^{-gt/255} - 1),$$

$$v = \frac{dy}{dt} = 170 - 170e^{-gt/255}. \tag{f}$$

Letting t become infinite in (f), we get

$$\lim_{t \to \infty} v = 170 \text{ ft/sec}.$$

Again, $$\frac{170(1 - e^{-20(32.2)/255})}{170} (100\%) = 92\%.$$

PROBLEMS

1. Solve equations (14) for x and y in terms of t if $R = 0$. Determine the constants of integration from the initial conditions $\dot{x} = v_0 \cos \varphi$, $\dot{y} = v_0 \sin \varphi$, $x = 0$, $y = 0$, all when $t = 0$.

2. Solve equations (14) for the special case where R is numerically equal to $0.02wv/g$ and v is the speed in feet per second. Assume that $v_0 = 3{,}000$ ft/sec, $\varphi = 30°$, and note that, when $t = 0$, $x = y = 0$, $\dot{x} = 3{,}000 \cos 30°$ ft/sec, and $\dot{y} = 3{,}000 \sin 30°$ ft/sec. Find the greatest height reached by the projectile.

3. When a projectile is fired at a small angle of elevation, the vertical component of its velocity is small and consequently the vertical component of air resistance is small. A 100-lb shell is fired with initial velocity $v_0 = 2{,}000$ ft/sec and with angle of

* Of course, the solution can be found by the methods of Chap. 6.

departure $\varphi = 5°$. Assuming in this case that air resistance is horizontal and equal numerically to $\frac{100}{25g}\frac{dx}{dt}$, derive equations similar to (14); solve these equations for dx/dt, dy/dt, x, and y, and determine the constants of integration.

4. If a projectile is fired at an angle of departure nearly equal to 90°, the horizontal component of air resistance is small. An antiaircraft gun fires a projectile of weight W with initial velocity $v_0 = 2{,}000$ ft/sec and angle of departure $\varphi = 80°$. Assume air resistance to be vertical and equal numerically to $\frac{W}{1{,}200}\frac{dy}{dt}$. Find the equations of the trajectory, the maximum height attained by the projectile, and the height of the projectile when the vertical component of its velocity is 500 ft/sec.

5. A particle of mass m slugs moves in a plane under the action of a force (see Fig. 19) always directed to a fixed point in the plane and equal in magnitude to k times the distance of the particle from the fixed point. At a certain instant, the particle is moving with velocity v_0 at right angles to a line connecting it with the fixed point and is a units from it. Find the equations of motion and tell the nature of the path. *Hint:* Apply equations (11), to obtain $m\ddot{x} = -kx$, etc.

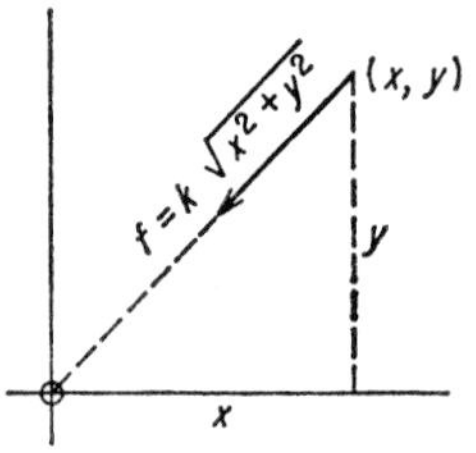

Fig. 19

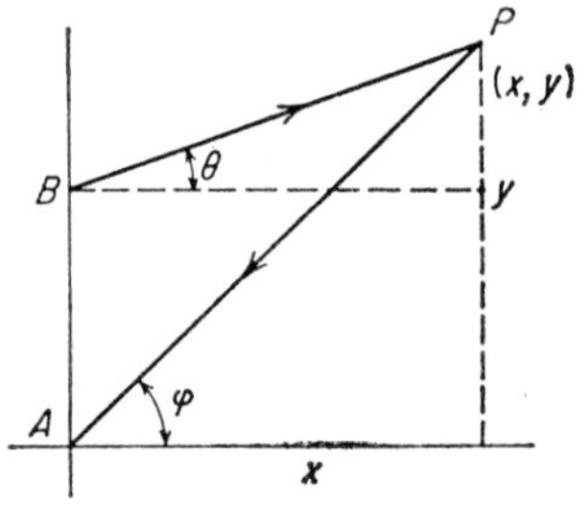

Fig. 20

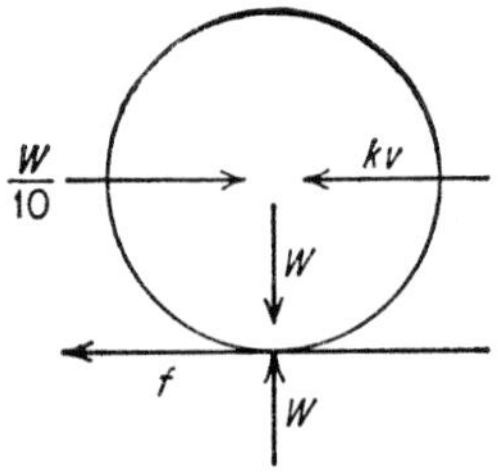

Fig. 21

6. A fixed plane contains a variable point P and two fixed points A and B. P is the position of a particle of unit mass which is acted on by two forces, one equal numerically to the magnitude of BP and exerted in the direction from B toward P, a second equal numerically to the magnitude of $2PA$ and exerted in the direction from P toward A. Find the equations of motion if $AB = 2$ ft and if the particle is initially at A moving 3 ft/sec in a direction making (*a*) an angle of 90° with AB; (*b*) an angle of 45° with AB. *Hint:* In Fig. 20, $\Sigma F_x = \overline{BP} \cos\theta - 2AP \cos\varphi = \overline{BP}(x/\overline{BP}) - 2\overline{AP}(x/\overline{AP}) = x - 2x = -x$, etc.

7. A circular cylinder having radius r, weight W, and I with respect to its axis $\frac{W}{g}\frac{r^2}{2}$ is rolling on a rough horizontal plane when two horizontal forces perpendicular to its axis are impressed on it: a constant force equal to $\frac{1}{10}W$ in the direction of motion and an oppositely directed air resistance proportional to the velocity of its axis. If no slipping occurs, if the limiting speed is 60 ft/sec, and if the initial speed is zero, describe the motion and find how far the cylinder rolls during the first minute of motion (see Fig. 21). *Hint:* Apply equations (11) and (12) of §71, eliminate f, and integrate the resulting equations.

8. The cylinder of problem 7 rolls without slipping and with axis horizontal on a rough plane inclined 30° to the horizontal. If air resistance is opposite to the direction of motion and is numerically equal to $W/600$ times the magnitude of the velocity of the axis in feet per second, find the limiting speed and the distance traversed during the first minute of motion from rest.

74. Kirchhoff's current law and electromotive-force law*

Electricity is a substance which flows through conductors such as wires. The practical unit of electricity is the **coulomb,**† and we speak of q coulombs of electricity just as we would speak of q gallons of water. A **current** of electricity is a rate of flow of this substance. A current of q coulombs of electricity per second is called q **amperes.** When a constant current of I amp flows through a wire, $q = It$ coulombs will pass any cross section of the wire in t sec.

KIRCHHOFF'S CURRENT LAW. *The excess of the current flowing into a given region at a given time over the current flowing out at the same time is the time rate of increase of quantity of electricity within the region at that time.*

If there is no accumulation of electricity within a given region, current flowing into this region equals current flowing out of it; for example, in Fig. 22,

$$i_1 = i_2 + i_3 + i_4. \qquad (15)$$

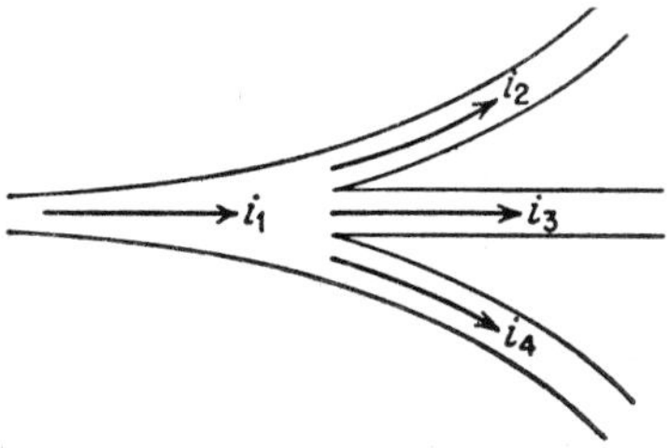

FIG. 22

If the region is the positive plate of a capacitor, electricity flows into the region but none, theoretically, flows out. Hence,

$$q = \int_c i\,dt, \tag{16}$$

where q is the charge (quantity of electricity) on the positive plate of the capacitor, i is the current, t is the time, and the subscript c on the integral sign indicates that limits are to be taken so as to obtain the total quantity of electricity on the capacitor at time t. Differentiating (16) with respect to the time, we obtain

$$\frac{dq}{dt} = i, \qquad \frac{d^2q}{dt^2} = \frac{di}{dt}. \tag{17}$$

Electromotive force (emf), also called **voltage** and **difference of potential,** causes electricity to move just as physical force causes bodies to move. The **volt** will be used as the unit.

When electricity is flowing through a coil, any change in current sets up a counter emf opposing the change in current. For this reason, an emf e_L of magnitude $e_L = L(di/dt)$ must act to cause the current to flow.

* Good reference books are G. W. Pierce, "Electric Oscillations and Waves"; F. Bedell and A. C. Crehore, "Alternating Currents"; F. W. Sears, "Principles of Physics II."

† The electron, an elemental building block of nature, carries a fixed charge of negative electricity. A coulomb consists approximately of the sum of the charges on 6.24×10^{18} electrons.

L is a constant, called **inductance.** It is analogous to the mass of a body. The practical unit of inductance is the **henry.**

Conductors offer **resistance** to the flow of electricity through them. The practical unit of resistance is the **ohm.** Resistance depends upon such things as size and kind of material. If a conductor has a resistance of R *ohms*, an emf force e_R of magnitude $e_R = Ri$ volts is required to cause a current of i amp to flow through it. Resistance is analogous to friction.

A **capacitor** consists essentially of two plates separated by a non-conducting substance, or insulator. When a current flows to one plate of a capacitor, a charge is deposited there; an equal charge opposite in sign appears at the other plate; and the current away from the capacitor is equal to the current flowing to it. The emf e_C across a capacitor having a charge of q coulombs and a capacity of C **farads** is given by

$$e_c = \frac{q}{C} = \frac{1}{C}\int_c i\,dt.$$

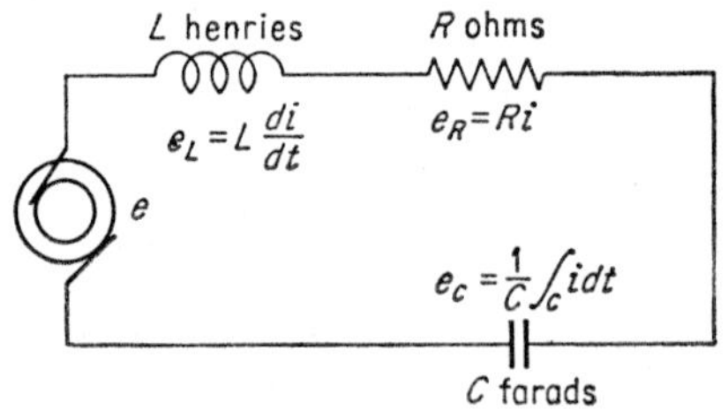

FIG. 23

Figure 23 represents the elements mentioned above, and Kirchhoff's electromotive-force law, which follows, gives an equation connecting them:

ELECTROMOTIVE-FORCE LAW. *When several elements, resistance R, inductance L, and capacitance C, all constant, are connected in series, and when an instantaneous current i is flowing in them, there is impressed in the direction of i at the terminals of this series from a source of power external to the elements a difference of potential e such that*

$$\mathbf{e} = \mathbf{L}\frac{\mathbf{di}}{\mathbf{dt}} + \mathbf{Ri} + \frac{\mathbf{1}}{\mathbf{C}}\int_c \mathbf{i\,dt}, \tag{18}$$

where $\int_c i\,dt$ *represents the total quantity of electricity on the capacitor considered.*

It is worthy of note that *Kirchhoff's laws may be applied to any part or the whole of a circuit but that, in such application, fall of potential must be considered positive in the direction of the current and negative in the opposite direction.* Also, L, R, and C do not necessarily apply to concentrated elements in a circuit but are sums of inductances, resistances, or capacitances for the part of the circuit considered.

Substitution of q for $\int_c i\,dt$, dq/dt for i, and d^2q/dt^2 for di/dt in (18) gives

$$\mathbf{L}\frac{\mathbf{d^2q}}{\mathbf{dt^2}} + \mathbf{R}\frac{\mathbf{dq}}{\mathbf{dt}} + \frac{\mathbf{q}}{\mathbf{C}} = \mathbf{e}, \tag{19}$$

and differentiation of (18) with respect to the time gives

$$\mathrm{L}\frac{d^2i}{dt^2} + \mathrm{R}\frac{di}{dt} + \frac{1}{\mathrm{C}}i = \frac{de}{dt}. \tag{20}$$

Remarks. Typical equations for electrical phenomena and mechanics of moving bodies follow:

$$LD^2q + RDq + (1/C)q = e(t), \qquad Dq = i,$$
$$mD^2s + nDs + Ks = f(t), \qquad Ds = v.$$

We see at once the following correspondence:

L	m	Conductance to mass
R	μ	Electrical resistance to a frictional resistance
$1/C$	K	Reciprocal of capacitance to spring constant or potential energy
$e(t)$	$f(t)$	Voltage to external force
q	s	Charge of electricity to distance
i	v	Current of electricity to velocity

Because of this correspondence, numerous solutions of problems of electricity involve the same mathematics as the solution of a problem in the mechanics of moving bodies. This relation is referred to as **mechanical analogue** or **electrical analogue.** It is interesting to find that one type of electronic computer solves problems of various kinds by setting up the circuit of the electric analogue and displaying the results thus obtained.

75. Simple circuits containing constant electromotive force

To illustrate the use of equations (19) and (20), consider the charging of a capacitor of capacitance C through a resistance R and an inductance L by a constant emf E. For this case, equation (19) becomes

$$LD^2q + RDq + \frac{I}{C}q = E, \tag{21}$$

where $D = d/dt$. Assume as initial conditions $q = 0$, $i = 0$ when $t = 0$. The roots of the auxiliary equation $Lm^2 + Rm + 1/C = 0$ are

$$m = \frac{-R}{2L} \pm \sqrt{\frac{R^2}{4L^2} - \frac{1}{LC}}, \quad \text{or} \quad \frac{-R}{2L} \pm \sqrt{\frac{1}{LC} - \frac{R^2}{4L^2}}\,j, \tag{22}$$

where $j^2 = -1$. First let us assume that the roots are imaginary, and let

$$a = \frac{R}{2L}, \qquad \omega_1 = \sqrt{\frac{1}{LC} - \frac{R^2}{4L^2}}. \tag{23}$$

Then we have $m = -a \pm \omega_1 j$, and the solution of (21) is

$$q = \epsilon^{-at}(c_1 \sin \omega_1 t + c_2 \cos \omega_1 t) + CE.* \tag{24}$$

* Here, ϵ (= 2.7183 approximately) is used to represent the base of natural logarithms.

Differentiating this, remembering that $i = dq/dt$, and using the initial conditions $q = 0$, $i = 0$ when $t = 0$, we obtain from (24)

$$\begin{aligned} q &= \frac{-CE}{\omega_1}\epsilon^{-at}(a \sin \omega_1 t + \omega_1 \cos \omega_1 t) + CE, \\ i &= \frac{E}{L\omega_1}\epsilon^{-at} \sin \omega_1 t. \end{aligned} \tag{25}$$

EXERCISES

1. Carry out the solution required to derive (25) by using (24), the given initial conditions, and $i = dq/dt$.

2. Taking account of (23), find the solution (25) when $R = 0$, and give the period and amplitude of both i and q.

3. If the roots of $Lm^2 + Rm + 1/C = 0$ are the real numbers α_1 and α_2, show from (20) that both are negative and that the corresponding values for q and i shrink toward zero without oscillation as t increases.

4. If $1/(LC) - R^2/(4L^2) = 0$, write the corresponding solution of (21), and show that there is no oscillation of q or i, that q approaches CE, and that i approaches 0 as t increases without bound.

5. Solve equations (19) and (17) to find i and q for a circuit in which $L = 0.1$ henry, $R = 1$ ohm, $C = 250 \times 10^{-6}$ farad, $e = E = 100$ volts if the initial conditions are $q = 0$, $i = 0$ when $t = 0$. In what time does the damping factor of the current decrease to one-tenth of its value when $t = 0$, and what is the period of the current? What are the limiting values of q and i?

6. Solve equations (17) and (19) to find i and q in terms of t for a circuit in which $L = 1$ henry, $R = 1$ ohm, $C = 4$ farads, and $e = E = 100$ volts if $q = 0$, $i = 0$ when $t = 0$. Show that the maximum value of the current is $200\epsilon^{-1}$ (where $\epsilon = 2.718$ nearly) and that the ratio of the current when $t = 10$ sec to this maximum value is $5\epsilon^{-4} < 0.1$.

7. A circuit consists of an impedance coil of inductance L and negligible resistance connected in series with a capacitor of capacitance C. Use equations (17) and (19) to find the charge q on the capacitor and current i at time t if t is the number of seconds since i was zero and q was q_0. Describe the fluctuation of i and q. *Hint:* $e = 0$.

8. Solve equations (19) and (17), with e replaced by the constant E and R by zero, for i and q in terms of t. Assume that $i = 0$, $q = 0$ when $t = 0$.

9. A circuit consists of an impedance coil having an inductance L and resistance R connected in series with a capacitor having a capacitance C. Initially the current is zero, and the charge on the capacitor is q_0. Find i and q at any time if $4L > CR^2$.

76. Simple circuits containing a sinusoidal electromotive force

The type of equation to be considered in this article has the form

$$LD^2q + RDq + \frac{1}{C}q = E \sin \omega t. \tag{26}$$

The current i is found from the equation $i = dq/dt$. The emf $e = E \sin \omega t$ is generally supplied by a dynamo.

In what follows, it will be convenient to let

$$X = L\omega - \frac{1}{C\omega}, \qquad Z = \sqrt{R^2 + X^2}. \tag{27}$$

X is called the **reactance** and Z the **impedance.**

A particular solution of (26) could be found by using any of the methods discussed in §§48 to 53. That using the symbolic operator (§52) is the shortest. From (26), by using first equation (61) of §52 and then (27) and a slight simplification, obtain

$$\begin{aligned} q_p &= \frac{E \sin \omega t}{(LD^2 + 1/C) + RD} = \frac{LD^2 + 1/C - RD}{(LD^2 + 1/C)^2 - R^2D^2} E \sin \omega t \\ &= \frac{(-L\omega^2 + 1/C)E \sin \omega t - RE\omega \cos \omega t}{(-L\omega^2 + 1/C)^2 + R^2\omega^2} \\ &= \frac{-E}{\omega Z^2} (X \sin \omega t + R \cos \omega t). \end{aligned}$$

Supplying the solution of the auxiliary equation, we obtain the general solution of (26),

$$q = q_c + q_p = \epsilon^{-at}(c_1 \sin \omega_1 t + c_2 \cos \omega_1 t) - \frac{E}{\omega Z^2} (X \sin \omega t + R \cos \omega t). \tag{28}$$

The equation of the current is obtained by differentiating (28) and replacing dq/dt by i.

The part containing the factor ϵ^{-at} generally becomes negligible in a very short time. It is called a **transient.** Transients are important in the theory of radio and of radar. The other part of the solution is permanent and is called the **steady-state solution.** Dropping the transient term from (28), we have for the steady state

$$q = \frac{-E}{\omega Z^2} (X \sin \omega t + R \cos \omega t), \tag{29}$$

and since $i = dq/dt$, for the *steady-state value* of i

$$i = \frac{dq}{dt} = \frac{E}{Z^2} (R \sin \omega t - X \cos \omega t). \tag{30}$$

77. Resonance

Equation (30) may be written in the form

$$i = \frac{E}{Z} \sin\left(\omega t - \tan^{-1} \frac{X}{R}\right), \tag{31}$$

where the quadrant of $\tan^{-1} (X/R)$ is that of point (X,R) when plotted in rectangular coordinates. Observe that the amplitude of i,

$$\frac{E}{Z} = \frac{E}{\sqrt{R^2 + X^2}} = \frac{E}{\sqrt{R^2 + [L\omega - 1/(C\omega)]^2}}, \tag{32}$$

will be a maximum for given values of L, R, E, and ω when C is chosen so that $X = 0$, that is, so that

$$L\omega - \frac{1}{C\omega} = 0, \qquad \text{or} \qquad \omega = \frac{1}{\sqrt{LC}}. \tag{33}$$

With this condition is associated the name *current resonance*. A person tuning a radio in to a station takes advantage of current resonance.

EXERCISES

1. Reproduce the solution of (26) to obtain (28) without using the text.

2. Obtain the steady-state equation for i by differentiating (29).

3. A sinusoidal emf of frequency $200/\pi$ cycles/sec and maximum value 110 volts is connected in series in a circuit with an inductance of 0.1 henry, a resistance of 10 ohms, and a capacitor of capacity 250×10^{-6} farad. Find the steady-state solution of i and q in terms of t and the maximum values of the steady-state charge on the capacitor and the current.

4. If $e = E \sin \omega t$ in the circuit of Fig. 23, derive the steady-state solution for i and q: (*a*) when $R = 0$ and there is no capacitor; (*b*) when $L = 0$ and there is no capacitor; (*c*) when $L = 0$ and $R = 0$; (*d*) when $L = 0$; (*e*) when there is no capacitor; (*f*) when $R = 0$.

5. Find the expression of i in terms of t for the circuit of Fig. 23 provided that $e = 20 \sin 500t$, $R = 2$ ohms, $L = 0.2$ henry, $C = 20 \times 10^{-6}$ farad and if i and q are zero when $t = 0$. Find the value of the damping factor of the transient at time $t = 1$ sec.

6. Use (33) to find C at current resonance when the frequency is 10^5 cycles/sec and $L = 6 \times 10^{-6}$ henry. If $R = 100$ ohms, find the ratio of the maximum current E/Z from (31) at current resonance to the current in the same circuit with no capacitor.

78. Applications of Kirchhoff's laws to networks

The emf law and the current law stated in §74 may be applied when elements involving inductance, resistance, and capacitance are connected in a more or less complicated network. Equations can be obtained by applying the emf law to complete circuits or the current law at points where two or more conductors meet.

For example, in Fig. 24, apply the current law at A and at B to obtain

$$i = i_1 + i_2, \qquad i_2 = i_3 + i_4.$$

Apply the emf law to circuit $LAGF$ to obtain

$$R_1 i_1 + \frac{q_1}{C_1} = E, \qquad i_1 = \frac{dq_1}{dt}.$$

Also, apply the emf law to the circuits $LABHDF$ and $BKDH$ to obtain

$$R_2 i_2 + L_3 \frac{di_3}{dt} = E, \qquad R_4 i_4 + \frac{q_4}{C_4} - L_3 \frac{di_3}{dt} = 0, \qquad i_4 = \frac{dq_4}{dt}.$$

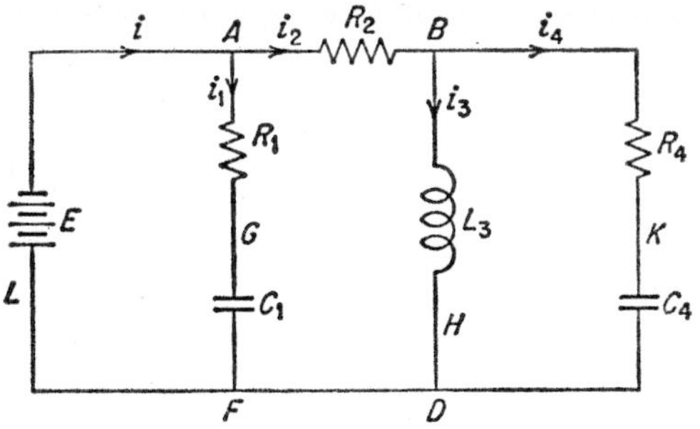

FIG. 24

Observe in this last circuit that there was no externally applied emf and that a negative sign was given to $L_3(di_3/dt)$ because, in following the circuit in the direction B to K to D to H, the element of inductance L_3 was traversed opposite to the direction of the assumed current i_3. Solving the equations just derived, we could find the current in each branch of the network and the charge of electricity on each capacitor at time t.

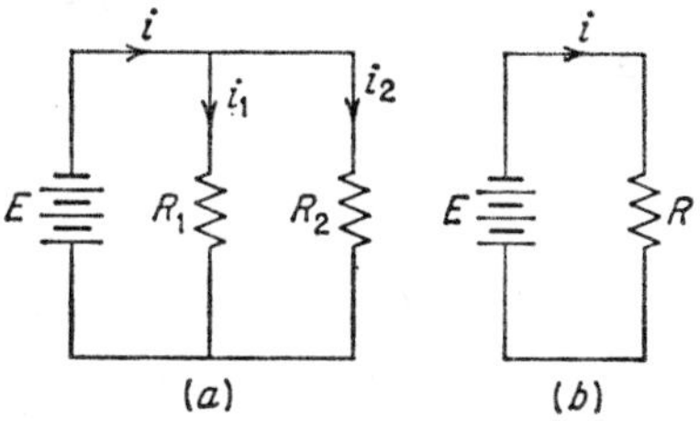

FIG. 25

As another application, apply Kirchhoff's laws to the circuits of Fig. 25*a*. We have

$$R_1 i_1 = E, \qquad R_2 i_2 = E, \qquad i = i_1 + i_2. \tag{34}$$

Substituting i_1 and i_2 from the first two equations of (34) in the third and transforming slightly, we have

$$i = E\left(\frac{1}{R_1} + \frac{1}{R_2}\right), \qquad \text{or} \qquad \frac{i}{1/R_1 + 1/R_2} = E. \tag{35}$$

Comparing this last equation with $Ri = E$ from Fig. 25*b*, it appears that two resistances R_1 and R_2 in parallel are together equivalent to a resistance $R = 1/(1/R_1 + 1/R_2)$.

In general, to find the currents in the branches of a network and the charges on the capacitors, proceed as follows: (1) *Draw a figure representing the elements involved, indicating inductance by* , *resistance by* , *and a capacitor by* ; (2) *draw arrowheads to indicate the assumed directions of currents through the various branches;* (3) *apply the current law at points where conductors intersect and the emf law to complete circuits to find as many independent equations as are necessary to determine the unknown quantities involved;* (4) *solve these equations for the unknowns.* The following example will illustrate the procedure:

Example. An impedance coil which has a resistance of 14 ohms and an inductance of 0.05 henry and a branch having a noninductive resistance of 15 ohms and a capacitor of capacity 10^{-4} farad in series are connected in parallel across the terminals of a 220-volt source of emf. Find expressions in terms of the time for the charge on the capacitor, the current in the impedance coil, the current in the noninductive resistance, and the total current.

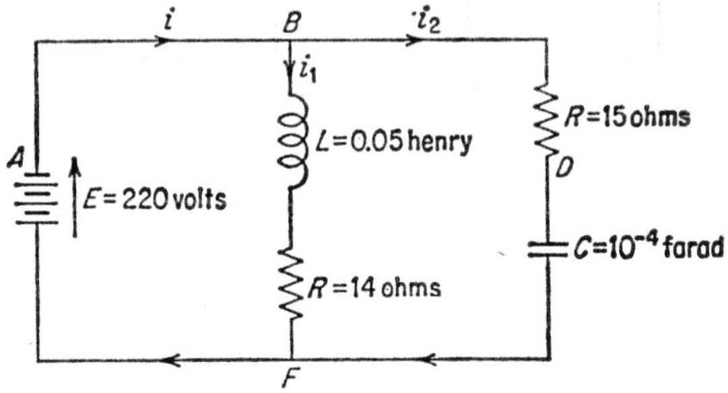

FIG. 26

Solution. Figure 26 represents the circuit with indicated elements and currents. The current law applied at point B gives

$$i = i_1 + i_2. \tag{a}$$

The emf law applied to circuit $ABFA$ gives

$$0.05\,\frac{di_1}{dt} + 14i_1 = 220, \tag{b}$$

and, applied to circuit $ABDFA$, it gives

$$15i_2 + 10^4\textstyle\int_c i_2\,dt = 220. \tag{c}$$

Finally, we have from equation (16) of §74

$$q = \int_c i_2\,dt, \qquad i_2 = \frac{dq}{dt}. \tag{d}$$

Elimination of i_2 from (c) by using (d) gives

$$15\,\frac{dq}{dt} + 10^4 q = 220. \tag{e}$$

The solution of equation (e), subject to the condition $q = 0$ when $t = 0$, is

$$\mathbf{q = 0.022(1 - \epsilon^{-2,000t/3}).}$$

Therefore,
$$\mathbf{i_2 = \frac{dq}{dt} = \frac{44}{3}\,\epsilon^{-2,000t/3}.}$$

The solution of (*b*), subject to the condition $i_1 = 0$ when $t = 0$, is

$$\mathbf{i}_1 = \mathbf{15.71(1} - \epsilon^{-280t}).$$

Finally, $$\mathbf{i} = \mathbf{i}_1 + \mathbf{i}_2 = \mathbf{15.71(1} - \epsilon^{-280t}) + \frac{\mathbf{44}}{\mathbf{3}} \epsilon^{-2,000t/3}.$$

As the values of ϵ^{-280t} and $\epsilon^{-2,000t/3}$ are practically zero after a fraction of a second, it appears that the capacitor very soon is practically charged and that the inductance in *BF* opposes the current for only a small fraction of a second. Hence, we have practically $q = 0.022$ coulomb and $i = 15.71$ amp in a very short time.

PROBLEMS

1. For the system represented in Fig. 27, obtain by the current law at point *A* $i = i_1 + i_2$ and from the emf law applied to circuits *AFHG* and *ABHG*

$$L\frac{di_1}{dt} = E \sin \omega t, \qquad Ri_2 = E \sin \omega t.$$

Solve these equations for i_1, i_2, and i in terms of t, and determine a constant of integration by using the condition $i = 0$ when $t = 0$.

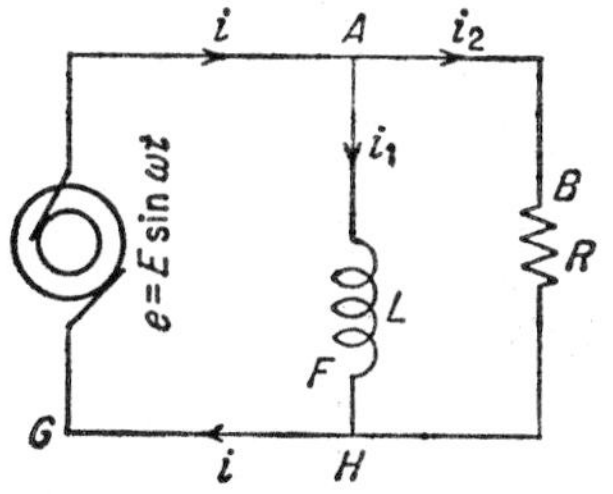

FIG. 27

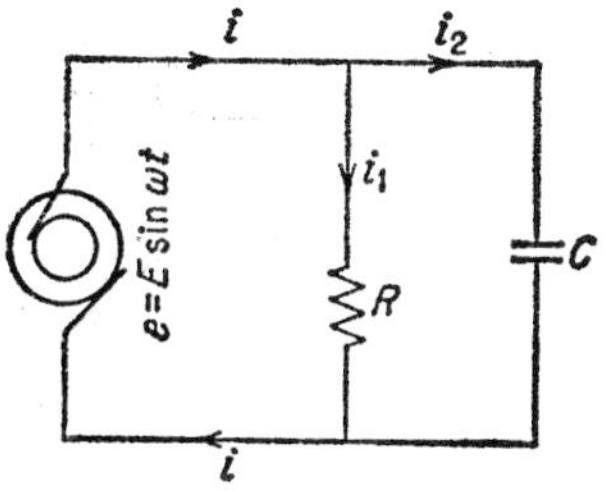

FIG. 28

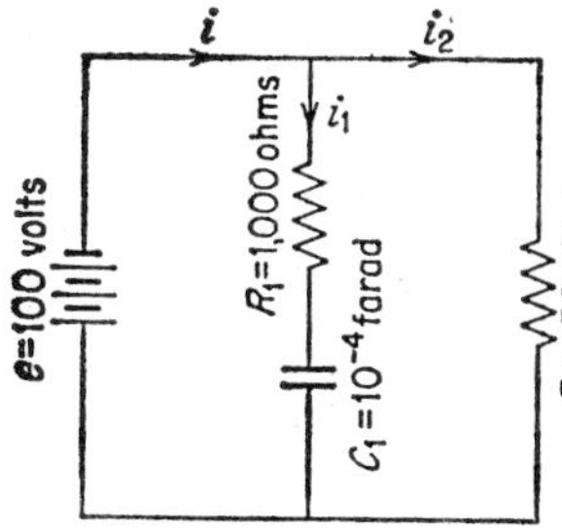

FIG. 29

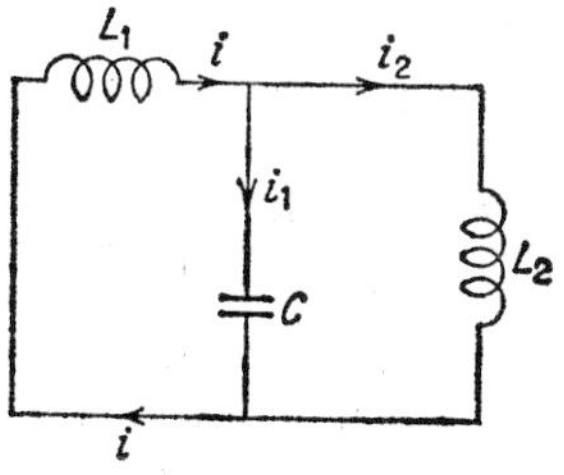

FIG. 30

2. From Fig. 28, derive by Kirchhoff's laws

$$i = i_1 + i_2, \qquad Ri_1 = E \sin \omega t, \qquad \frac{1}{C}\int_c i_2\, dt = \frac{q}{C} = E \sin \omega t.$$

Find q, i_1, i_2, and i in terms of t.

3. For the system indicated in Fig. 29, derive three equations by applying Kirchhoff's laws. Assume that the charge on the capacitor is zero when $t = 0$, and deduce that $i_2 = 2$ amp always and that $i_1 = \frac{1}{10}\epsilon^{-10t}$ and therefore rapidly approaches zero.

4. Replace the 100-volt emf in Fig. 29 by a sinusoidal emf represented by 100 sin 400t, and then find q, i_1, and i_2 at time t. Assume that the charge on the capacitor is zero when $t = 0$.

5. If initially the charge on the capacitor of Fig. 30 is q_0 and $i_1 = 0$, show that $q = q_0 \cos \sqrt{(L_1 + L_2)/(CL_1L_2)}\, t$. *Hint:* $e = 0$.

6. Find i in terms of the time t in the system represented by Fig. 31 if all initial currents and the initial charge on the capacitor are zero.

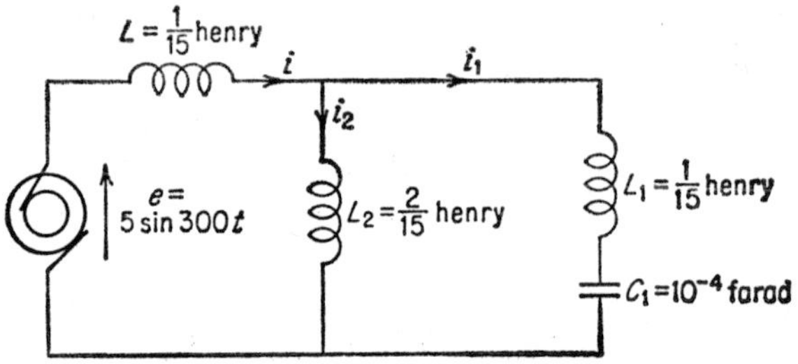

FIG. 31

7. Find i in terms of the time t in the system represented in Fig. 32 if the initial currents and the initial charges on the capacitors are zero and $\omega \neq 1/\sqrt{L(C_1 + C_2)}$.

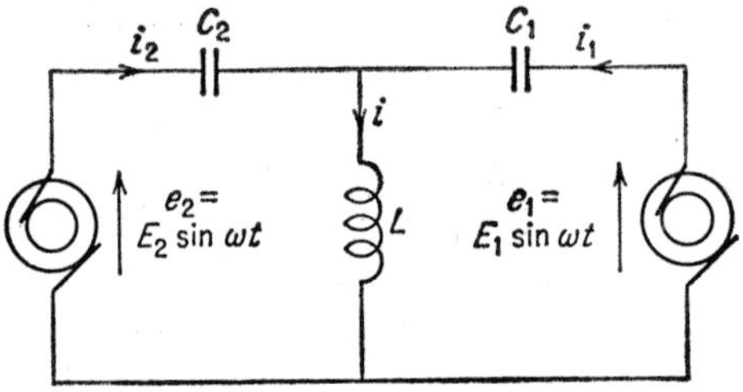

FIG. 32

8. Show that the current i indicated in Fig. 33 is the same as it would be if the three inductances were replaced by a single inductance of magnitude $1/(1/L_1 + 1/L_2 + 1/L_3)$ in series with the emf. Also, show that, in the same sense, the three capacitors in parallel in Fig. 34 are equivalent to a single one of capacity $C_1 + C_2 + C_3$.

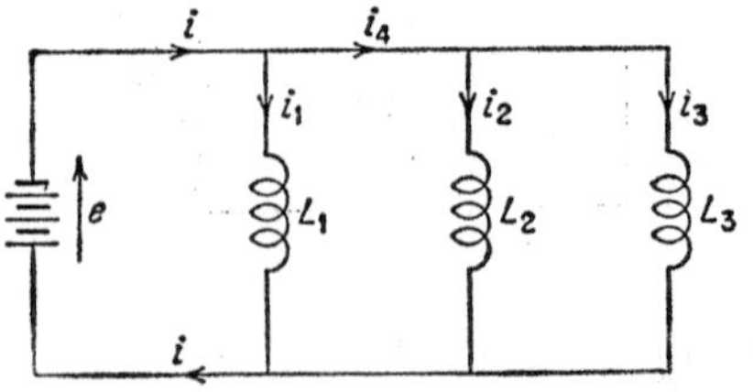

FIG. 33

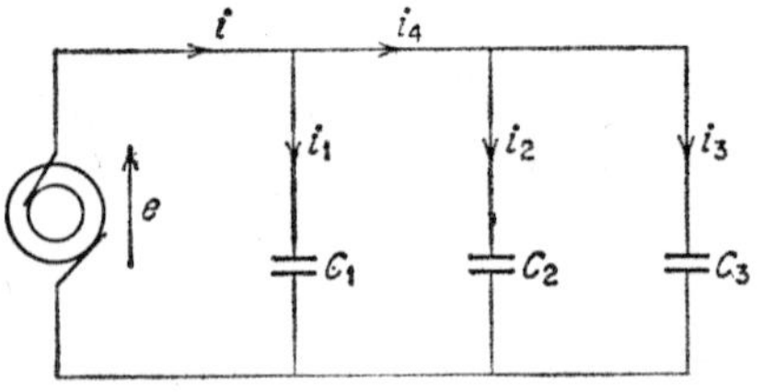

FIG. 34

★9. A hot-wire galvanometer having a resistance of 5 ohms is shunted with a capacitor of capacitance $C = 5 \times 10^{-8}$ farad, as indicated in Fig. 35. If effective current is $1/\sqrt{2}$ times maximum current, find the ratio of the effective current i_1 through the galvanometer to the total effective current i when: (a) $\omega = 2 \times 10^4$; (b) $\omega = 2 \times 10^5$; (c) $\omega = 2 \times 10^6$; (d) $\omega = 2 \times 10^7$.

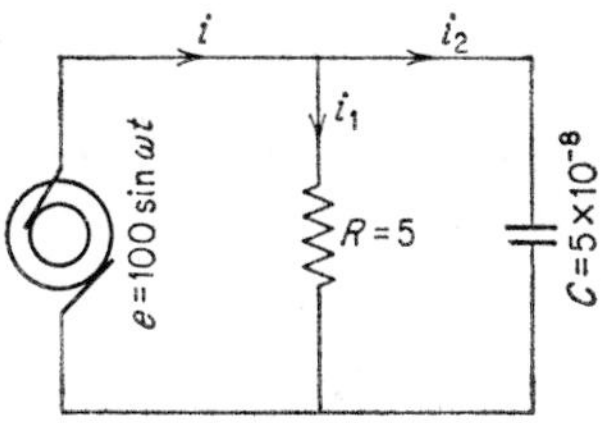

FIG. 35

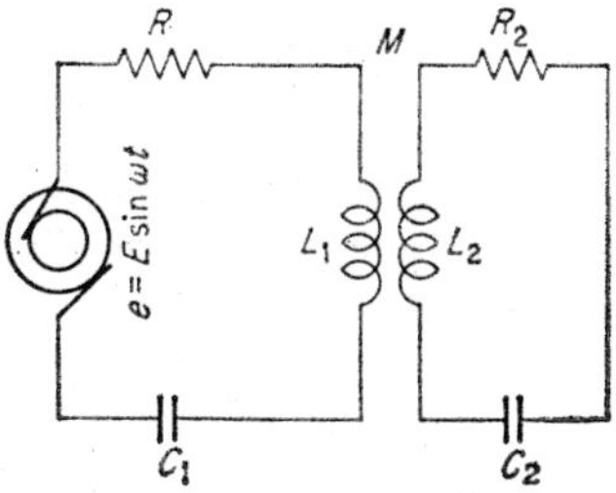

FIG. 36

★**10.** The equations for the coupled circuits represented in Fig. 36 are

$$(L_1D + R_1)i_1 + MDi_2 + (1/C_1)q_1 = E \sin \omega t, \qquad Dq_1 = i_1,$$
$$MDi_1 + (L_2D + R_2)i_2 + (1/C_2)q_2 = 0, \qquad Dq_2 = i_2.$$

Solve these equations for q_1 and i_2, assuming that $R_1 = R_2 = 0$, $C_2 = \infty$, $L_1L_2 > M^2$, and $q_1 = i_1 = i_2 = 0$ when $t = 0$. Let $L_2/[C_1(L_1L_2 - M^2)] = \omega_1^2$ and $L_2E/(L_1L_2 - M^2) = a$.

79. Review problems

In the following problems D represents d/dt.

PROBLEMS

1. The equation $D^2y + y = 0$ represents a simple harmonic motion. Finds its period, frequency, and amplitude if $y = 5$, $Dy = 0$ when $t = 0$.

2. Solve the differential equation

$$D^2x + Dx + \tfrac{37}{4}x = 0,$$

and determine the constants of integration by using the conditions $x = 0$, $dx/dt = 6$ when $t = 0$. Find x in terms of the time, the period of oscillation of x, and the magnitude of the damping factor after 3 sec.

3. Solve the differential equation

$$9D^2x + 3aDx + 82x = 0,$$

and determine a and the constants of integration if $dx/dt = 6$, $x = 0$ when $t = 0$ and if the damping factor decreases 50 per cent in 2.08 units of time. Also, find the period.

4. Find b and c in $(D^2 + bD + c)x = 0$ if the corresponding period is $\frac{1}{60}$ sec and the damping factor decreases 50 per cent in 0.1 sec.

5. In the equation $(D^2 + 0.01D + c)x = 0$, find c if the corresponding damping is critical.

6. Find the relation satisfied by a, b, and c for a motion defined by $(aD^2 + bD + c)x = 0$ if the motion is: (a) overdamped; (b) critically damped; (c) damped oscillatory; (d) undamped.

7. A particle of mass 1 slug moves toward a fixed center of force which repels it with a magnitude in pounds equal to k times the distance of the particle from the center. Initially, the particle is distant a from the center and is moving toward it with a velocity equal in magnitude to $\sqrt{ka^2}$. Prove that the particle will continually approach but never reach the center.

8. A body falling from rest in a heavy fluid acquires a velocity which approaches 10 ft/sec as a limit. Assuming the resistance of the medium to be proportional to the velocity and the buoyancy of the fluid to be one-half the weight of the body, find the factor of proportionality and the distance traversed during the first 10 sec.

9. A body of weight w lb moves vertically under the force of gravity and under the action of a force opposite to the direction of motion and equal numerically to $0.4wv/32.2$, where v is the speed in feet per second. Taking y as the distance above the ground, study the motion under the conditions $y = 0$, $v = 100$ when $t = 0$.

10. A sphere of uniform density and diameter 5 ft sinks 1 ft in salt water weighing 64 lb/ft³. It is depressed slightly and released. Find the period of the resulting motion. By Archimedes' principle, the weight of the sphere is $\frac{13}{6}\pi 64$ lb.

11. Solve (21), §75, and $Dq = i$ if $R = 0$, $E = 0$, and, initially, $t = 0$, $q = q_0$, $i = 0$.

12. For a simple circuit, $L = 0.1$ henry, $R = 1$ ohm, $c = 250 \times 10^{-6}$ farad, and $e = 0$. If initially $t = 0$, $q = 0.05$ coulomb, and $i = -0.25$ amp, find i and q in terms of t, the period of the current, and the limiting values of i and q.

13. Find the charge on the capacitor of Fig. 37 at time t if initially there is no charge on the capacitor and no current through the inductance.

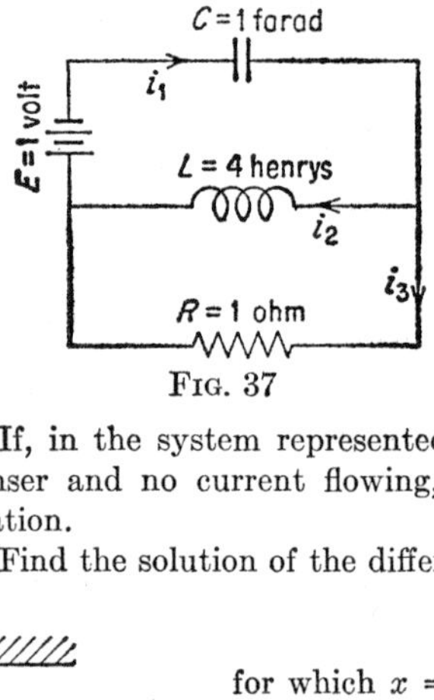

FIG. 37

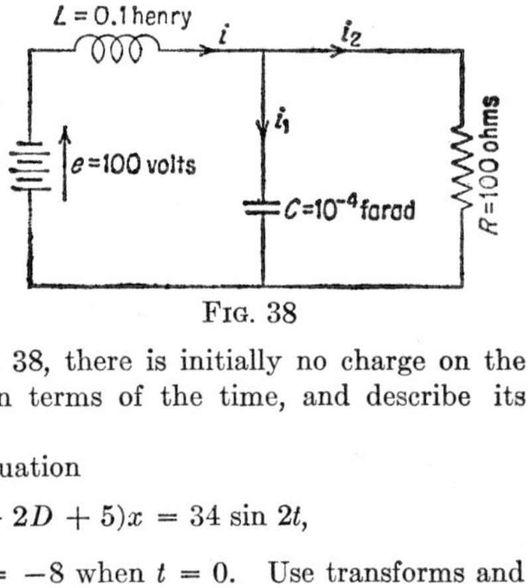

FIG. 38

14. If, in the system represented by Fig. 38, there is initially no charge on the condenser and no current flowing, find i in terms of the time, and describe its fluctuation.

15. Find the solution of the differential equation

$$(D^2 + 2D + 5)x = 34 \sin 2t,$$

for which $x = 0$, $Dx = -8$ when $t = 0$. Use transforms and relation 19 of Table 1, page 113. Give the amplitude and period of the permanent part of the solution, and show that the part having the factor e^{-t} is less than 0.005 when t is 9 sec or more.

16. If the capacitors of problem, 10, §78, are omitted, the corresponding equations are

$$(L_1D + R_1)i_1 + MDi_2 = E \sin \omega t,$$
$$MDi_1 + (L_2D + R_2)i_2 = 0.$$

Find i_1 and i_2 for these, assuming that $R_1 = 0$, $L_1L_2 = M^2$ and that $i_1 = i_2 = 0$ when $t = 0$.

★17. Figure 39 represents a 64.4-lb weight and a 32.2-lb weight hung from a ceiling and connected by springs having the indicated spring constants. When $t = 0$, the weights are at rest and the springs have natural unstretched lengths. Find the amounts x ft and y ft the springs are stretched at time t.

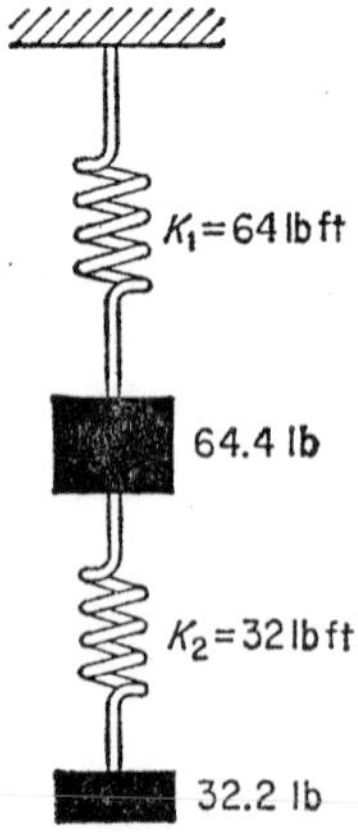

FIG. 39

CHAPTER 9

MISCELLANEOUS DIFFERENTIAL EQUATIONS OF ORDER HIGHER THAN THE FIRST

80. Reduction of order by substitution

In Chap. 6, we found general methods for solving linear equations with constant coefficients. This was unusual, for we cannot solve most equations of order higher than the first in finite form. Certain types, however, are readily solvable. One method of attack is to *make such a substitution as to reduce the order and then try to solve the result.* For example, consider the equation

$$\frac{d^ny}{dx^n} = f(x). \tag{1}$$

To solve this, substitute p for $d^{n-1}y/dx^{n-1}$, and obtain

$$\frac{d^ny}{dx^n} = \frac{d}{dx}\left(\frac{d^{n-1}y}{dx^{n-1}}\right) = \frac{dp}{dx} = f(x). \tag{2}$$

Therefore,

$$p = \int f(x)\,dx + c_1, \qquad \text{or} \qquad \frac{d^{n-1}y}{dx^{n-1}} = \int f(x)\,dx + c_1. \tag{3}$$

Clearly, we can treat equation (3) in a similar manner and obtain

$$\frac{d^{n-2}y}{dx^{n-2}} = \int \left[\int f(x)\,dx\right] dx + c_1x + c_2, \tag{4}$$

and it appears that we may continue this process until we find y in terms of x by n successive integrations.

Various types of differential equations with appropriate substitutions will be considered in the following sections.

81. Dependent variable absent

If an equation contains derivatives of the dependent variable y but does not contain y directly, then the substitution

$$p = \frac{dy}{dx}, \qquad \frac{dp}{dx} = \frac{d^2y}{dx^2}, \qquad \ldots, \qquad \frac{d^{n-1}p}{dx^{n-1}} = \frac{d^ny}{dx^n} \tag{5}$$

will reduce the order of the equation by unity; if the result can be solved for p in terms of x,

$$p = \frac{dy}{dx} = f(x), \tag{6}$$

a single integration will give y in terms of x. In fact, if d^ky/dx^k is the derivative of lowest order in an equation which does not contain y directly, then the substitution

$$p = \frac{d^ky}{dx^k}, \quad \frac{dp}{dx} = \frac{d^{k+1}y}{dx^{k+1}}, \quad \dots, \quad \frac{d^{n-k}p}{dx^{n-k}} = \frac{d^ny}{dx^n} \tag{7}$$

will reduce the order by k; if the result can be solved for p in terms of x,

$$p = \frac{d^ky}{dx^k} = f_1(x), \tag{8}$$

y may be found in terms of x by k successive integrations, as indicated in §80.

Example. Solve

$$(1 + x^2)\frac{d^2y}{dx^2} + x\frac{dy}{dx} + ax = 0. \tag{a}$$

Solution. In equation (a), substitute

$$p = \frac{dy}{dx}, \quad \frac{dp}{dx} = \frac{d^2y}{dx^2} \tag{b}$$

and obtain

$$(1 + x^2)\frac{dp}{dx} + px + ax = 0. \tag{c}$$

Separating the variables in equation (c) and integrating, we have

$$p + a = c_1(1 + x^2)^{-\frac{1}{2}}.$$

Replacing p by dy/dx and integrating, we obtain

$$\mathbf{y = -ax + c_1 \sinh^{-1} x + c_2.}$$

EXERCISES

Solve the following differential equations, and determine the constants of integration where sufficient conditions are given:

1. $\dfrac{d^2y}{dx^2} = 12x.$

2. $x^3\dfrac{d^3y}{dx^3} = 12.$

3. $x\dfrac{d^2y}{dx^2} + \dfrac{dy}{dx} = 0.$

4. $x^2\dfrac{d^2y}{dx^2} + \left(\dfrac{dy}{dx}\right)^2 = 0.$

5. $\dfrac{d^2y}{dx^2} + 24x = 0;\ y = -28,\ \dfrac{dy}{dx} = -10$ when $x = 1.$

6. $x\dfrac{d^3y}{dx^3} - 2\dfrac{d^2y}{dx^2} = 12x^3$; $y = 0$, $\dfrac{dy}{dx} = 1$, $\dfrac{d^2y}{dx^2} = 0$ when $x = 1$.

7. $a\dfrac{d^3y}{dx^3} = \sqrt{a^2 + \left(\dfrac{d^2y}{dx^2}\right)^2}$; $y = 0$, $\dfrac{dy}{dx} = -a^2$, $\dfrac{d^2y}{dx^2} = 0$ when $x = 0$, $a > 0$.

82. Independent variable absent

If p is substituted for dy/dx, we have

$$\frac{dy}{dx} = p, \qquad \frac{d^2y}{dx^2} = \frac{dp}{dy}\frac{dy}{dx} = \frac{p\,dp}{dy},$$
$$\frac{d^3y}{dx^3} = \frac{d}{dy}\left(p\frac{dp}{dy}\right)\frac{dy}{dx} = p^2\frac{d^2p}{dy^2} + p\left(\frac{dp}{dy}\right)^2, \qquad \text{etc.} \tag{9}$$

Therefore, if a differential equation does not contain x directly, the substitution (9) will give a new differential equation in p and y of order one less than that of the original equation. If this new equation can be solved for p in terms of y to get

$$p = \frac{dy}{dx} = f(y), \tag{10}$$

then x may be found in terms of y from

$$x = \int \frac{dy}{f(y)} + c. \tag{11}$$

Example. Solve

$$y\frac{d^2y}{dx^2} + \left(\frac{dy}{dx}\right)^2 = \frac{dy}{dx}. \tag{a}$$

Solution. Substitution of

$$p = \frac{dy}{dx}, \qquad \frac{p\,dp}{dy} = \frac{d^2y}{dx^2} \tag{b}$$

in (a) gives

$$yp\frac{dp}{dy} + p^2 = p, \qquad \text{or} \qquad p\left(y\frac{dp}{dy} + p - 1\right) = 0. \tag{c}$$

From (c),

$$y\frac{dp}{dy} + p - 1 = 0, \qquad p = 0. \tag{d}$$

Hence,

$$\frac{dp}{p-1} + \frac{dy}{y} = 0. \tag{e}$$

The solution of (e) is

$$p = 1 + \frac{c_1}{y}. \tag{f}$$

Replacing p by dy/dx and separating the variables, we obtain

$$\frac{y\,dy}{y + c_1} = dx. \tag{g}$$

The solution of (g) is

$$\mathbf{x} = \mathbf{y} - \mathbf{c}_1 \ln (\mathbf{y} + \mathbf{c}_1) + \mathbf{c}_2.$$

From the second equation of (d) or by inspection, it appears that $y = c$ satisfies equation (a).

EXERCISES

Solve the following differential equations, and determine constants of integration when initial conditions are given:

1. $y \dfrac{d^2y}{dx^2} + \left(\dfrac{dy}{dx}\right)^2 = 0.$

2. $y^2 \dfrac{d^2y}{dx^2} + \left(\dfrac{dy}{dx}\right)^3 = 0.$

3. $y \dfrac{d^2y}{dx^2} + 2\left(\dfrac{dy}{dx}\right)^2 = 0.$

4. $y \dfrac{d^2y}{dx^2} + (1 + y)\left(\dfrac{dy}{dx}\right)^2 = 0.$

5. $\dfrac{d^2s}{dt^2} = \dfrac{1}{s^3}.$

6. $\dfrac{d^2s}{dt^2} = 64 - \left(\dfrac{ds}{dt}\right)^2.$

7. $y \dfrac{d^2y}{dx^2} + 4y^2 - \dfrac{1}{2}\left(\dfrac{dy}{dx}\right)^2 = 0;\ y = 1,\ \dfrac{dy}{dx} = \sqrt{8}$ when $x = 0.$

★8. $\dfrac{d^2s}{dt^2} = 100 - \left(\dfrac{ds}{dt}\right)^2;\ s = 0,\ \dfrac{ds}{dt} = 26$ when $t = 0.$

★9. $2 \dfrac{d^2y}{dx^2} = e^y;\ y = 0,\ \dfrac{dy}{dx} = 0$ when $x = 0.$

10. A ring slides from a point A to a lower point B under the influence of gravity. The ring is smooth, and the time required is minimum.* By higher mathematics, it is proved that the path followed satisfies the equation $1 + (dy/dx)^2 + 2y\, d^2y/dx^2 = 0$. First prove that $(dy/dx)^2 = c_1/y - 1$. Let $y = 2c_1 \sin^2 \frac{1}{2}\theta$, and show that $x = c_1(\theta - \sin \theta) + c_2$.

11. A certain curve connecting two points A and B passes through (0,1) with slope zero. When revolved about the X-axis, it generates a surface of minimum area (see Fig. 1). This will be true provided that the equation of the curve satisfies $1 + (dy/dx)^2 = y\, d^2y/dx^2$. Find the equation of the curve.†

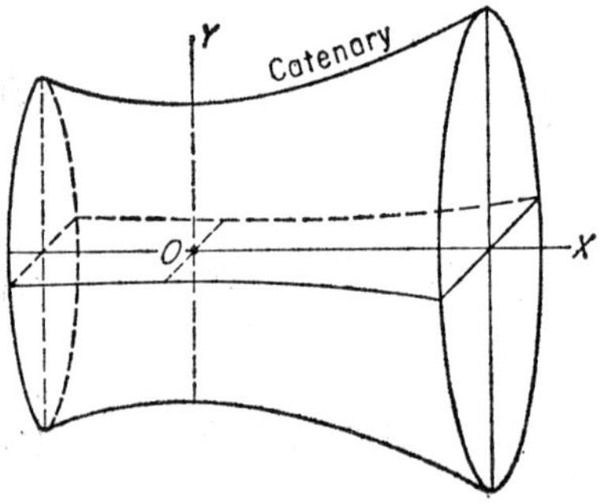

FIG. 1

83. Method based on factorization of the operator

Operators in the form of polynomials in D with variable coefficients are defined by relations (1), (2), (3), and (4), §42. If P, Q, R, S, and u are functions of x, we get from (3) and (4), §42,

$$(PD + Q)(RD + S)y = (PD + Q)u, \qquad \text{where } u = (RD + S)y.$$

* The curve, called the **brachistochrone,** has the shape of a cycloid.

† The curve is that of a uniform, perfectly flexible string hanging under its own weight. It is called a **catenary.**

Also, the student may verify that $(PD + Q)(RD + S)u$ is equal to

$$P\frac{dR}{dx}\frac{du}{dx} + PR\frac{d^2u}{dx^2} + P\left(S\frac{du}{dx} + u\frac{dS}{dx}\right) + QR\frac{du}{dx} + QSu.$$

Note that, if O_1 and O_2 are operators, O_1O_2y may not equal O_2O_1y. Note, for example, that

$$(D - x)(D - x^2)y = D^2y - x^2Dy - 2xy - xDy + x^3y,$$
$$(D - x^2)(D - x)y = D^2y - xDy - y - x^2Dy + x^3y.$$

To solve a differential equation having the form

$$(PD + Q)(RD + S)y = f(x),$$

set $(RD + S)y = u$, solve the result to find $u = \varphi(x)$, and then solve $(RD + S)y = \varphi(x)$. The difficulty comes in transforming an operator to the factored form. The following examples illustrate methods of solution using operators:

Example 1. Solve

$$x^2D^2y + (5x - x^2)Dy + (3 - 2x)y = 4e^x. \qquad (a)$$

Solution. Assume the left member to be

$$(xD + M)(xD + N)y,$$

or

$$x^2D^2y + x(M + N + 1)Dy + (MN + xN')y, \qquad (b)$$

where M and N are functions of x. If expression (b) equals the left side of (a), we must have

$$x(M + N + 1) = x(5 - x), \qquad MN + xN' = 3 - 2x. \qquad (c)$$

Substituting $M = 4 - x - N$ from the first of (c) in the second, we get

$$(4 - x)N - N^2 + xN' = 3 - 2x. \qquad (d)$$

We attempt to find a solution of (d) by letting

$$N = ax + b \qquad (e)$$

in (d), equating coefficients of like powers of x, and determining a and b. This gives

$$(4 - x)(ax + b) - (a^2x^2 + 2axb + b^2) + xa = 3 - 2x;$$
$$-a - a^2 = 0, \qquad 5a - b - 2ab = -2, \qquad 4b - b^2 = 3.$$

These are satisfied by $a = -1$, $b = 3$. Therefore,

$$N = -x + 3, \qquad M = 4 - x + x - 3 = 1, \qquad (f)$$

and the given equation may be written

$$(xD + 1)(xD + 3 - x)y = 4e^x. \qquad (g)$$

Now, let $z = (xD + 3 - x)y$ in (g), and solve the resulting linear equation by the method of §25 to get

$$(xD + 1)z = 4e^x,$$
$$xz = 4e^x + c. \qquad (h)$$

Now, replacing z in (h) by its equal $(xD + 3 - x)y$ and solving the resulting linear equation for y, we get

$$x(xD + 3 - x)y = 4e^x + c,$$
$$\mathbf{x^3y = c_1(x + 1) + (c_2 + 2x^2)e^x.}$$

Example 2.* (a) Show that, if M and N are functions of x, and c a constant, then

$$[MD^2 + (Mc + N)D + cN]y = (MD + N)(D + c)y.$$

(b) Solve $[x^3D^2 + (x^3 - x^2)D - x^2]y = 2x^4$.

Solution. (a) This part is left as an exercise.

(b) Taking $M = x^3$, $N = -x^2$, $c = 1$ in part (a) of this example, we get

$$[x^3D^2 + (x^3 - x^2)D - x^2]y = (x^3D - x^2)(D + 1)y.$$

Therefore, the given equation may be written

$$(x^3D - x^2)(D + 1)y = 2x^4.$$

In this, let $(D + 1)y = z$, and solve for z to get

$$z = 2x^2 + cx.$$

In this, replace z by its equal $(D + 1)y$, solve the resulting equation, and obtain

$$\mathbf{y = c_2e^{-x} + cx - c + 2x^2 - 4x + 4.}$$

EXERCISES

1. Show that $(xD - 1)(D - x^2)y = [xD^2 - (x^3 + 1)D - x^2]y$.

2. Show that $(D + x^2)(xD - 4)y - (xD - 4)(D + x^2)y = (D - 2x^2)y$.

3. Solve $(xD - 2)(xD + x + 1)y = 0$.

4. Factor the operator: $D^2 + D - 1 - x - x^2$.

5. Factor the operator: $x^2D^2 + x^2D - 2 - x$.

Solve the following differential equations:

6. $(xD^2 - D)y = 12$.

7. $(x^2D^2 - xD + 1)y = 12x^2$.

8. $[xD^2 + (2 - x)D - 1]y = e^x$.

9. $[xD^2 + (3 - 2x^2)D - 4x]y = 4xe^{x^2}$.

Exercises 10, 11, and 12 are of the type of example 2. Solve them:

10. $[xD^2 + (2x - 1)D - 2]y = 4x^2$.

11. $[x^2D^2 + (2x^2 - x)D - 2x]y = 0$.

* Numerous simple special cases of solutions by operators can be devised. Example 2 furnishes a case for which factorization of the operator by algebraic processes applies.

12. $[x^3D^2 + (5x^3 - x^2)D + 2(3x^3 - x^2)]y = 0.$

★**13.** Factor $xD^2 + (1 + x^2)D + 2x$. It may be necessary to try $(xD + M)(D + N)$ and $(D + M)(xD + N)$ to obtain a solution.

14. Solve $[D^2 + (1 + \cot x)D + \cot x - \csc^2 x]y = 2e^x$.

84. Euler's linear equation

The equation

$$x^n \frac{d^ny}{dx^n} + A_1x^{n-1}\frac{d^{n-1}y}{dx^{n-1}} + \cdots + A_{n-1}x\frac{dy}{dx} + A_ny = X, \qquad (12)$$

where the A's are constant and X represents a function of x, is often referred to as **Euler's differential equation.** The substitution

$$z = \ln x, \qquad dz/dx = 1/x = e^{-z} \qquad (13)$$

reduces this to the linear equation with constant coefficients. Using the notation

$$\frac{d^ky}{dz^k} = D^ky, \qquad (14)$$

we have

$$\begin{aligned}
\frac{dy}{dx} &= \frac{dy}{dz}\frac{dz}{dx} = \frac{1}{x}\frac{dy}{dz} = \frac{1}{x}Dy,\\
\frac{d^2y}{dx^2} &= \frac{d(dy/dx)}{dz}\frac{dz}{dx} = \frac{1}{x^2}\frac{d^2y}{dz^2} - \frac{1}{x^2}\frac{dy}{dz} = \frac{1}{x^2}D(D-1)y,\\
\frac{d^3y}{dx^3} &= \frac{1}{x^3}D^2(D-1)y - \frac{2}{x^3}D(D-1)y = \frac{1}{x^3}D(D-1)(D-2)y, \qquad (15)\\
&\cdots\cdots\cdots\cdots\cdots\cdots\cdots\cdots\cdots\cdots,\\
\frac{d^ny}{dx^n} &= \frac{1}{x^n}D(D-1)\cdots(D-n+1)y.
\end{aligned}$$

Substitution of the values of d^ky/dx^k from (15) in (12) evidently gives a linear equation with constant coefficients. Solving this equation by the methods of Chap. 6, and replacing z by $\ln x$ in the result, obtain the solution of (12).

Example. Solve

$$x^3\frac{d^3y}{dx^3} + 6x^2\frac{d^2y}{dx^2} + 8x\frac{dy}{dx} - 8y = x^2. \qquad (a)$$

Solution. Using (13) to (15), we have

$$\frac{x^3}{x^3}D(D-1)(D-2)y + 6\frac{x^2}{x^2}D(D-1)y + 8\frac{x}{x}Dy - 8y = e^{2z}, \qquad (b)$$

$$(D^3 + 3D^2 + 4D - 8)y = e^{2z}. \qquad (c)$$

The solution of equation (c) is

$$y = c_1e^z + e^{-2z}(c_2 \sin 2z + c_3 \cos 2z) + \tfrac{1}{20}e^{2z}. \qquad (d)$$

Replacing z in (d) by $\ln x$ from (13), we have

$$\mathbf{y = c_1x + \frac{1}{x^2}[c_2 \sin (2 \ln x) + c_3 \cos (2 \ln x)] + \tfrac{1}{20}x^2.}$$

EXERCISES

1. $x^3 \dfrac{d^3y}{dx^3} + 3x^2 \dfrac{d^2y}{dx^2} - 6x \dfrac{dy}{dx} - 6y = 0.$

2. $x^2 \dfrac{d^2y}{dx^2} + x \dfrac{dy}{dx} - 9y = x^n \ (n \neq \pm 3).$

3. $(x - 1)^3 \dfrac{d^3y}{dx^3} + 2(x - 1)^2 \dfrac{d^2y}{dx^2} - 4(x - 1) \dfrac{dy}{dx} + 4y = 4 \ln (x - 1)$; let $z = \ln (x - 1)$.

4. $x \dfrac{d^3y}{dx^3} + 2 \dfrac{d^2y}{dx^2} = 0.$

85. Second-order linear equation

The general linear equation of the second order has the form

$$\frac{d^2y}{dx^2} + f_1(x) \frac{dy}{dx} + f_2(x)y = f_3(x). \tag{16}$$

To get an idea of how this may be solved, let us try the substitution

$$y = v(x) \cdot \varphi(x). \tag{17}$$

Substituting y from (17) in (16) and rearranging the terms, we find

$$\varphi \frac{d^2v}{dx^2} + \left(2 \frac{d\varphi}{dx} + f_1\varphi\right) \frac{dv}{dx} + \left(\frac{d^2\varphi}{dx^2} + f_1 \frac{d\varphi}{dx} + f_2\varphi\right) v = f_3. \tag{18}$$

If now $\varphi(x)$ is chosen so that the coefficient of v in (18) is zero, that is, if

$$\frac{d^2\varphi}{dx^2} + f_1 \frac{d\varphi}{dx} + f_2\varphi = 0, \tag{19}$$

equation (18) does not contain v. Hence, the method of §81 may be applied to solve it. In other words, if $y = \varphi(x)$ *is any particular solution of the equation obtained by setting the left-hand member of* (16) *equal to zero, then the substitution* (17) *applied to* (16) *reduces it to an equation that can be solved by methods already considered.*

Example. Solve

$$(1 + x) \frac{d^2y}{dx^2} + (4x + 5) \frac{dy}{dx} + (4x + 6)y = e^{-2x}. \tag{a}$$

Solution. First we try to find a particular solution of

$$(1 + x) \frac{d^2y}{dx^2} + (4x + 5) \frac{dy}{dx} + (4x + 6)y = 0. \tag{b}$$

Often, particular solutions are obtained by trial. The usual plan is to substitute simple expressions, such as $y = e^{ax}$, $y = x^a$, $y = x + a$, y = polynomial in x, in the equation to be solved, and then try to determine the arbitrary constants so that the equation will be satisfied. Substituting $y = e^{ax}$ in (*b*), we find, after slight simplification,

$$[(a^2 + 5a + 6) + x(a^2 + 4a + 4)]e^{ax} = 0. \tag{c}$$

This will be true, if

$$a^2 + 5a + 6 = 0 \quad \text{and} \quad a^2 + 4a + 4 = 0.$$

Both of these equations have a root -2. Hence, $y = e^{-2x}$ is a particular solution. Therefore, in accordance with (17), we substitute

$$y = ve^{-2x} \tag{d}$$

in (*a*) to obtain, after considerable simplification,

$$(1 + x)\frac{d^2v}{dx^2} + \frac{dv}{dx} = 1. \tag{e}$$

The solution of this equation, found by the method of §81, is

$$v = x + c_1 \ln (x + 1) + c_2. \tag{f}$$

Substitution of this value of v in (*d*) gives the required solution of (*a*):

$$\mathbf{y = e^{-2x}[x + c_1 \ln (x + 1) + c_2].}$$

EXERCISES

1. $(x^2 - 1)\dfrac{d^2y}{dx^2} + x\dfrac{dy}{dx} - y = 0$; let $y = vx$.

2. $x^2\dfrac{d^2y}{dx^2} + x^2\dfrac{dy}{dx} + (x - 2)y = 0$. *Hint:* Try $y = x^n$.

3. $(x^2 + 1)\dfrac{d^2y}{dx^2} - 2x\dfrac{dy}{dx} + 2y = 6(1 + x^2)^2$; let $y = vx$.

4. $x\dfrac{d^2y}{dx^2} - (x + 3)\dfrac{dy}{dx} + 3y = 4x^4e^x$.

5. $\sin^2 x\dfrac{d^2y}{dx^2} - \sin x \cos x\dfrac{dy}{dx} + y + \sin^3 x = 0$.

86. Review exercises.

In the following exercises D means d/dx.

EXERCISES

Solve the following differential equations, and determine the constants when initial conditions are given:

1. $xD^2y + Dy = 16x^3$.

2. $(x + 1)D^2y - (x + 2)Dy = 0$.

3. $D^2y + \cos x(Dy)^2 = 0$; $y = 0$, $Dy = \frac{5}{8}$ when $x = \frac{1}{2}\pi$.

4. $D^2y = -100 - (Dy)^2$; $y = 0$, $Dy = 24$ when $x = 0$.

5. $D^2y + yDy + (Dy)^2 = 0$; $y = 0$, $Dy = 1$ when $x = 0$.

★**6.** $aD^3y = \sqrt{1 + (D^2y)^2}$; $y = 0$, $Dy = -a$, $D^2y = 0$ when $x = 0$.

7. $(xD - 2)(D + 2x - 1/x)y = 4x^4e^{-x^2}$.

8. $(D^2 - 4xD - 2 + 4x^2)y = 2e^{x^2}$.

9. $[D^2 + (1 - 2x)D - 1 - x + x^2]y = e^{x^2/2}$.

10. $[x^2D^2 + x^2D - (x + 2)]y = 0$.

11. $(2x^2D^2 + xD - 3)y = 12 \ln x$.

★**12.** $(x^3D^3 + 3x^2D^2 + 4xD)y = \sin(\sqrt{3} \ln x)$.

13. $[(2x^2 + x)D^2 - D - 4]y = 0$. *Hint:* Try $y = x^m$.

14. $xD^2 + (x - 1)D + (3 - 12x)y = 0$.

15. At any point a distance r from the common center of two concentric spheres, the differential equation for the potential v due to an electric charge on the inner sphere is

$$\frac{d^2v}{dr^2} + \frac{2}{r}\frac{dv}{dr} = 0.$$

Solve for v in terms of r, given $v = v_1$, when $r = r_1$, and $v = v_0$, when $r = r_0$.

16. Apply (49), §51, repeatedly to $dy/dx = e^{-z}D(y)$ to derive from (13) and (14), §84, the last line of formula (15), §84. Note that

$$d^2y/dx^2 = (dz/dx)D[e^{-z}D(y)] = e^{-2z}(D - 1)Dy.$$

CHAPTER 10

APPLICATIONS

87. Radius of curvature

Some problems relating to the radius of curvature are rather interesting. As an illustration, consider the following:

Example. Find the equation of the curve whose radius of curvature is double the normal and oppositely directed.

Solution. Equating the expression for the radius of curvature and twice the expression for the normal (see Fig. 1), obtain

$$\left[1+\left(\frac{dy}{dx}\right)^2\right]^{\frac{3}{2}} \div \frac{d^2y}{dx^2} = \pm 2y\sqrt{1+\left(\frac{dy}{dx}\right)^2}. \qquad (a)$$

Assuming that the radius of curvature R is positive and is directed from the curve toward the center of curvature, and that the normal N is directed from the curve toward the X-axis, we see that y and d^2y/dx^2 will have the same sign when R and N are directed oppositely. Hence, the plus sign in (a) must be used. Substitution of p for dy/dx and $p\,dp/dy$ for d^2y/dx^2 in (a) gives

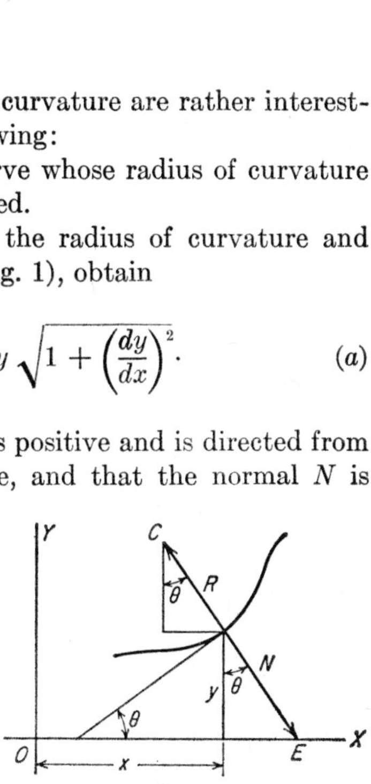

FIG. 1

$$\frac{(1+p^2)^{\frac{3}{2}}}{p\,dp/dy} = 2y(1+p^2)^{\frac{1}{2}}. \qquad (b)$$

Separating the variables and integrating (b), we obtain

$$\ln(1+p^2) = \ln\frac{y}{c}, \qquad \text{or} \qquad \frac{dy}{dx} = \pm\sqrt{\frac{y}{c}-1}. \qquad (c)$$

Integrating (c) and simplifying, we obtain

$$(x - c_1)^2 = 4cy - 4c^2. \qquad (d)$$

This represents a system of parabolas with their axes parallel to the Y-axis.

PROBLEMS

Determine the curves for which the radius of curvature:

1. Is equal to the normal and in the same direction.
2. Is equal to the normal and in the opposite direction.
3. Varies as the cube of the normal.
4. Projected on the X-axis equals the abscissa.
5. Projected on the X-axis is the negative of the abscissa.
6. Projected on the X-axis is twice the abscissa.

7. Find the equation of all plane curves which have a constant radius of curvature.

8. Integrate completely the differential equation of the curve in which the projection of the radius of curvature upon the X-axis is constant.

88. Cables. The catenary

Figure 2 represents a loaded cable. Let us assume that it is perfectly flexible, inextensible, homogeneous, and hanging from two points under the action of gravity on a load distributed along it in a continuous way. Let H be the tension in the cable at its lowest point A, T the tension at any point B of the cable, and L the resultant force of gravity exerted between A and B. Since the forces T, H, and L are in equilibrium,

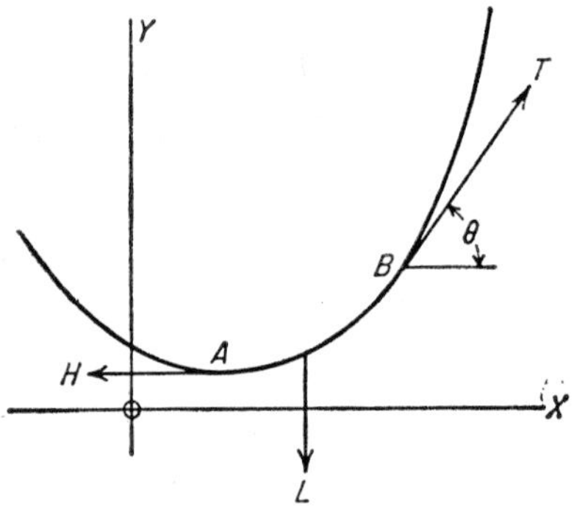

FIG. 2

$$T \cos \theta = H, \tag{1}$$
$$T \sin \theta = L, \tag{2}$$

where θ is the angle between the direction of force T and the horizontal. Evidently, the tension H at A is horizontal, and the tension T at B is directed along the tangent to the curve of the cable; hence, if we take the X-axis horizontal and the Y-axis vertical, we have $\tan \theta = dy/dx$. Then division of (2) by (1), member by member, gives

$$\tan \theta = \frac{dy}{dx} = \frac{L}{H}. \tag{3}$$

Differentiating both sides, we obtain

$$\frac{d^2y}{dx^2} = \frac{1}{H}\frac{dL}{dx} \tag{4}$$

as the differential equation of the curve of the cable.

The curve in which a uniform chain hangs under its own weight is called the **catenary**. In this case, we have

$$L = ws, \tag{5}$$

where s represents the arc length AB in Fig. 2 and w represents weight per unit length of the chain. Substitution of L from (5) in (4) gives

$$\frac{d^2y}{dx^2} = \frac{w}{H}\frac{ds}{dx} = \frac{w}{H}\sqrt{1 + \left(\frac{dy}{dx}\right)^2}. \tag{6}$$

Substituting in (6) p for dy/dx and dp/dx for d^2y/dx^2, we obtain

$$\frac{dp}{dx} = \frac{w}{H}\sqrt{1 + p^2}. \tag{7}$$

Integrating (7), we obtain

$$\sinh^{-1} p = \frac{w}{H}x + c_1, \qquad \text{or} \qquad p = \sinh\left(\frac{w}{H}x + c_1\right). \tag{8}$$

Replacing p by dy/dx in (8) and integrating, we find

$$y = \frac{H}{w}\cosh\left(\frac{w}{H}x + c_1\right) + c_2. \tag{9}$$

Taking the origin H/w units below the lowest point on the curve, we have $y = H/w$, $dy/dx = 0$ when $x = 0$. Using these values in (8) and (9) and remembering that $\cosh^2\theta - \sinh^2\theta = 1$, we get

$$\mathbf{y = \frac{H}{w}\cosh\frac{w}{H}x.} \tag{10}$$

PROBLEMS

1. Find the curve in which the cable of a suspension bridge hangs, if it carries a uniform horizontal load of w lb/ft run; neglect the weight of the cable. *Hint:* In equation (3), $L = wx$.

2. Set up the differential equation for the cable of problem 1 if its weight per running foot is assumed constant and taken into account.

3. Slender uniform rods all of the same diameter are suspended from a string to which each is knotted; two consecutive rods just touch, and they hang so that their ends are in a straight horizontal line. Neglecting the diameter of the rods, find the equation of the curve of the string. *Hint:* dL in equation (4) $= ky\,dx$ (see Fig. 3).

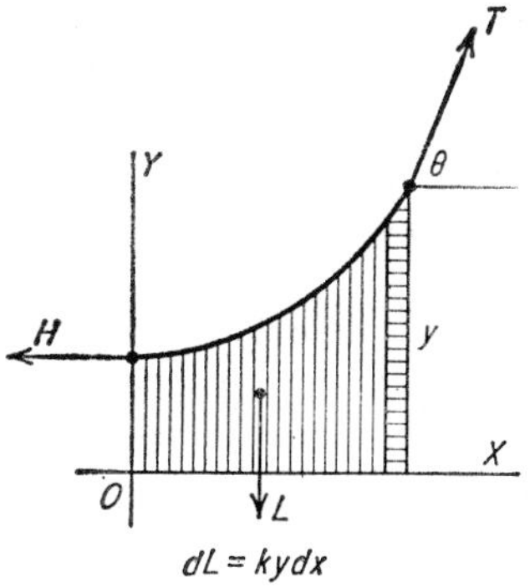

FIG. 3

4. What would be the equation of the curve of the string in problem 3 if all the rods were of the same length instead of having their ends in a straight line?

5. Set up the differential equation for the string of problem 3 if its weight per running foot is assumed constant and taken into account.

6. Find the shape of the arch of a stone-arch bridge if the resultant stress at any point of the arch due to the weight of the masonry above is directed along the tangent to the arch at the point. Assume that the masonry is uniform in density and that the surface of the road is horizontal (see Fig. 4).

7. If an arch carries, in addition to the load of problem 6, a layer of material spread uniformly over the horizontal road surface, the density of the layer being k times that of the masonry, what would be the shape of the arch?

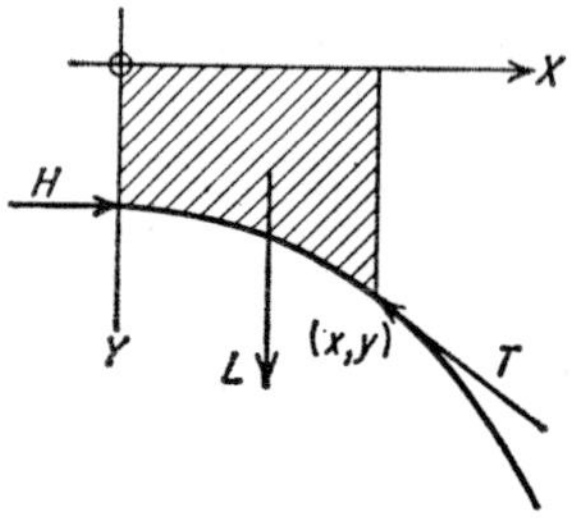

FIG. 4

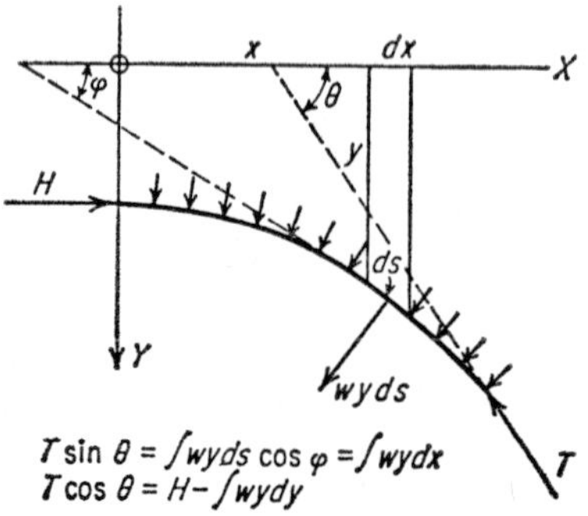

FIG. 5

★8. An arch is the bottom of a canal carrying a water load. Find the equation of its curve, assuming that the stress at each point due to the weight of the water is directed along the tangent. Neglect the weight of the arch, and note that the water pressure at each point is directed along the normal to the arch through the point (see Fig. 5).

★9. Solve problem 8 if the water is covered with a uniform layer of fluid having specific gravity k.

★10. A uniform cable $2l$ units long has its ends attached at two points, A and B, and hangs under its own weight. A horizontal line through B meets a vertical line through A at point C. If $AC = 2b$ units and $BC = 2c$ units, find the coordinates of the mid-point of line AB referred to a set of rectangular axes with origin at the lowest point of the cable and X-axis horizontal.

89. Equation of elastic curve. Beams

Consider a horizontal beam acted upon by vertical loads, and assume that the forces due to these loads lie in a vertical plane containing the

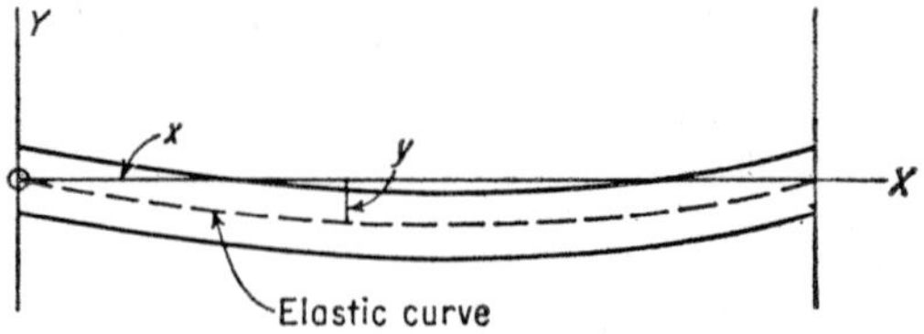

FIG. 6

centroidal axis (central longitudinal axis) of the beam and that they are such that no part of the beam is stressed beyond its elastic limit. These stresses cause the beam to bend, as indicated in Fig. 6, and the curve of its centroidal axis is called the **elastic curve** of the stressed beam. An important problem in the consideration of strength of materials is to find the equation of this elastic curve. If a beam is loaded as just indicated, is made of uniform material satisfying Hooke's law, and fulfills certain other conditions relating to shape and to properties of materials, it can be shown that its elastic curve satisfies approximately the differential equation

$$\mathbf{EI}\frac{\mathbf{d^2y}}{\mathbf{dx^2}} = \mathbf{M}, \tag{11}$$

where the X-axis is horizontal along the beam, the Y-axis is vertical, E is the modulus of elasticity of the material of the beam, I is the moment of inertia of the cross section of the beam perpendicular to its axis with respect to a horizontal line in the cross section passing through its centroid, and M is the **bending moment** at the cross section. Since the

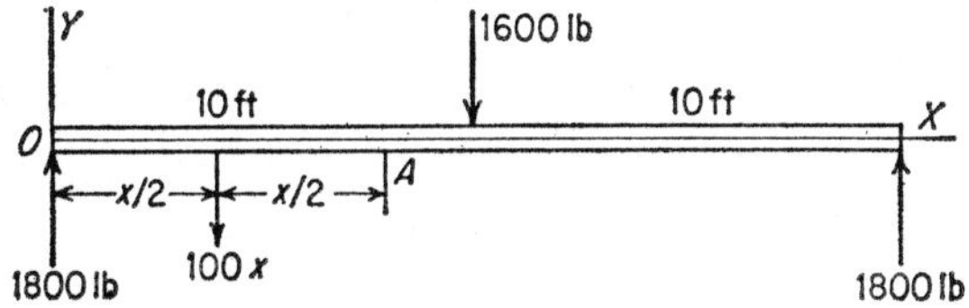

FIG. 7

material of the beam is uniform, E *is constant*, and if the beam has a uniform cross section, I *is constant*.

The bending moment M at any cross section may be found by taking the algebraic sum of the moments of the external forces on the part of the beam on one side of the cross section about a horizontal line in this cross section. In finding the bending moment, *consider upward forces as giving positive moments and downward forces negative moments* about the horizontal line in the cross section. Consider, for example, the beam of Fig. 7 loaded as indicated in addition to a uniform running load of 100 lb/ft. To find the bending moment at point A, consider the forces to the left of A: 1,800 lb at O with arm x ft, and $100x$ lb of running load downward and thought of as concentrated at the center of OA. Taking moments about A, we have

$$M = 1{,}800x - 100x\frac{x}{2} = 1{,}800x - 50x^2.$$

Example. A uniform beam (see Fig. 8) l ft long is fixed at both ends and carries a uniformly distributed load of w lb/ft length. Find the equation of its elastic curve and its maximum deflection.

Solution. Since the beam is fixed at the ends, the elastic curve is horizontal at both ends. Hence, taking the origin at the left end, we have

$$y = 0, \quad \frac{dy}{dx} = 0 \quad \text{when } x = 0,$$
$$y = 0, \quad \frac{dy}{dx} = 0 \quad \text{when } x = l. \tag{a}$$

The forces acting on the beam to the left of the cross section x ft from the left end are (1) wx lb due to the running load, (2) a supporting force at the left end, (3) a couple exerted by the masonry. Writing f for the supporting force and A for the moment of the couple, we have for the

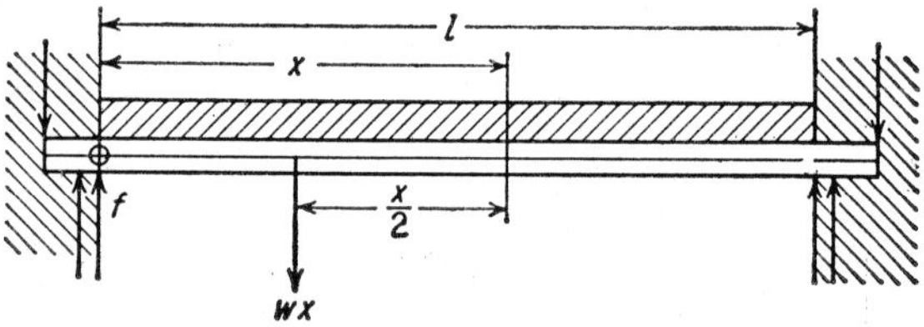

FIG. 8

bending moment x ft from the left end (see Fig. 8)

$$M = A + fx - wx\frac{x}{2}. \tag{b}$$

Substitution of M from (b) in (11) gives

$$EI\frac{d^2y}{dx^2} = A + fx - w\frac{x^2}{2}. \tag{c}$$

Integrating (c), we obtain

$$EI\frac{dy}{dx} = Ax + f\frac{x^2}{2} - \frac{wx^3}{6} + c_1, \tag{d}$$

$$EIy = \frac{Ax^2}{2} + f\frac{x^3}{6} - w\frac{x^4}{24} + c_1x + c_2. \tag{e}$$

Substituting the conditions (a) in (d) and (e), we get

$$c_1 = 0, \quad c_2 = 0, \quad Al + f\frac{l^2}{2} - w\frac{l^3}{6} = 0, \quad \frac{Al^2}{2} + \frac{fl^3}{6} - \frac{wl^4}{24} = 0,$$

or

$$c_1 = 0, \quad c_2 = 0, \quad f = \frac{wl}{2}, \quad A = \frac{-wl^2}{12}. \tag{f}$$

Substituting in (e) the values of c_1, c_2, f, and A from (f) and simplifying, we have the equation of the elastic curve,

$$\mathbf{y} = \frac{-\mathbf{w}}{\mathbf{24EI}}(\mathbf{x^2l^2} - \mathbf{2x^3l} + \mathbf{x^4}). \tag{g}$$

Here, $-y$ represents the deflection of the beam x ft from the left end, and since the maximum deflection (d_{max}) will evidently be at the center of the beam where $x = l/2$, we have, from (g),

$$d_{max} = (-y)_{x=l/2} = \frac{w}{24EI}\left(\frac{l^4}{4} - 2\frac{l^4}{8} + \frac{l^4}{16}\right) = \frac{\mathbf{wl^4}}{\mathbf{384EI}}.$$

PROBLEMS

1. A beam (see Fig. 9) l ft long is simply supported at its ends and carries a uniform load of w lb/ft run. Show that the bending moment at a point x ft from the left end is $\frac{1}{2}wlx - \frac{1}{2}wx^2$, and use this in equation (11) to find the deflection y at this point. Also, find the maximum deflection.

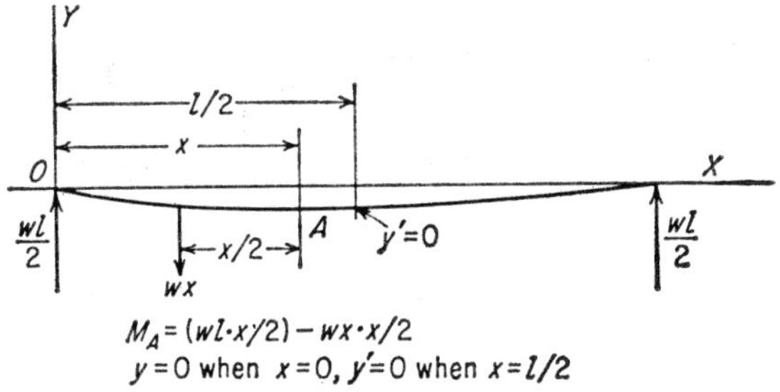

FIG. 9

2. A beam l ft long and simply supported carries a load of P lb at its center. Find its deflection x ft from the left end and its maximum deflection. *Hint:* Draw a figure of the beam like Fig. 9, and observe that $M = \frac{1}{2}Px$ if $x < \frac{1}{2}l$.

3. Using the answers to problems 1 and 2, write a formula for the maximum deflection of a beam simply supported at its ends and carrying a uniformly distributed load of w lb/ft and P lb, at its center.

4. Using the formulas from problems 1 to 3, find the maximum deflection of a simply supported steel beam 20 ft long, having $E = 30 \times 10^6$ lb/in.^{2}, $I = 54$ in.^{4}, if the loading is: (a) 5,000 lb at center; (b) 40 lb/in. uniformly distributed; (c) the combined loading just mentioned.

5. A beam fixed at one end and unsupported at the other (see Fig. 10) is called a **cantilever beam.** Find the deflection x ft from the fixed end of a cantilever beam

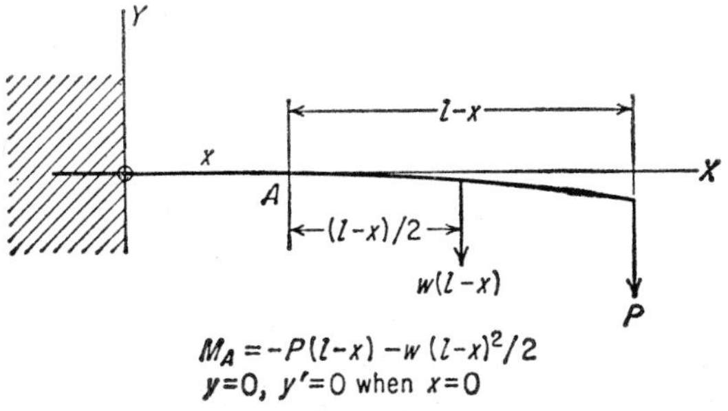

FIG. 10

l ft long if it carries a load of: (*a*) P lb at the fixed end ($w = 0$ in Fig. 10); (*b*) w lb/ft run ($P = 0$ in Fig. 10); (*c*) w lb/ft run and P lb at its fixed end.

★**6.** Figure 11 represents a cantilever beam carrying a uniformly distributed load of w lb/ft, fixed at one end and simply supported at the other so that the right end is on a level with the left end. Since force R is unknown, it must be determined like a constant of integration by using an initial condition. Find the equation of the elastic curve of the beam. Also, find the value of x/l at the point where the deflection is maximum.

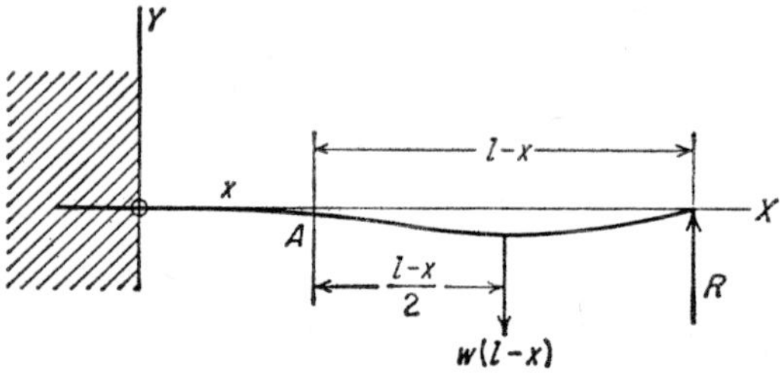

FIG. 11

7. Find the equation of the elastic curve of a uniform beam fixed at both ends and carrying a load P at its center.

★**8.** Figure 12 represents a uniform beam AB with a concentrated load P at C twice as far from A as from B. The supporting forces $\frac{1}{3}P$ and $\frac{2}{3}P$ are indicated. If y_1 is the deflection for part AC and y_2 for part CB, we have

$$EI\frac{d^2y_1}{dx^2} = \frac{1}{3}Px, \qquad EI\frac{d^2y_2}{dx^2} = \frac{1}{3}Px - P(x - 2a),$$

with the initial conditions $y_1 = 0$ when $x = 0$, $y_2 = 0$ when $x = 3a$, $y_1 = y_2$ and $dy_1/dx = dy_2/dx$ when $x = 2a$. Integrate the two equations, using the initial conditions to determine constants, and thus find the equations of the elastic curves of the parts of the beam. Also, find the maximum deflection.

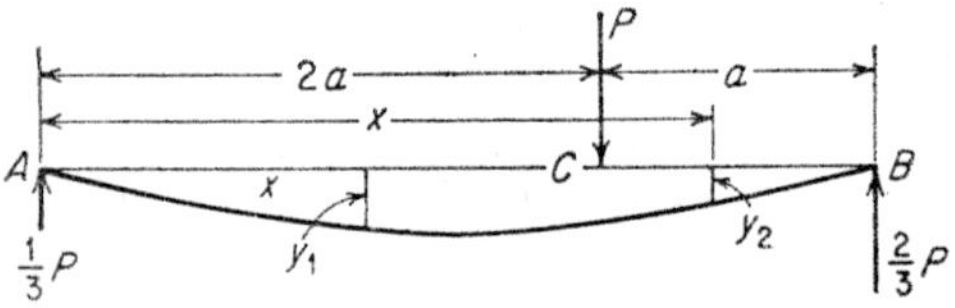

FIG. 12

★**9.** Solve problem 8, and then find the maximum deflection of the beam of Fig. 12 with the same loading, assuming that it is fixed at both ends. Observe in this case that the supporting force and the couple at A must be found by using initial conditions.

★**10.** A cantilever beam l ft long carries a load of material whose width and density are uniform and whose depth is directly proportional to its distance from the free end. Find the maximum deflection of the beam.

★**11.** Find the equation of the elastic curve of a beam fixed at both ends and carrying a concentrated load P, distant a ft from the left end and b ft from the right end.

90. Columns

Beams placed vertically to support vertical loads are often called **columns.** This section will deal mainly with the four types represented in Figs. 13 to 16. The plane of the elastic curve of a column contains

Both ends free to turn

FIG. 13

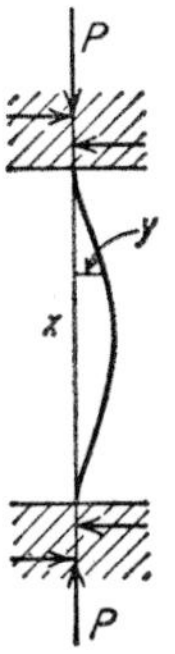

Both ends fixed

FIG. 14

Base fixed, top free

FIG. 15

Base fixed, top in vertical line through base

FIG. 16

the axis of each cross section about which the moment of inertia is greatest. If now we think of the column as placed horizontally without relative change of forces acting on it, and with the plane of the elastic curve vertical (see Fig. 17), we may apply formula (11) of §89 to obtain an approximation to the equation of the elastic curve of the column.

Example. Approximate the equation of the elastic curve of a column (Fig. 17) with both ends free to turn, and find the buckling stress.

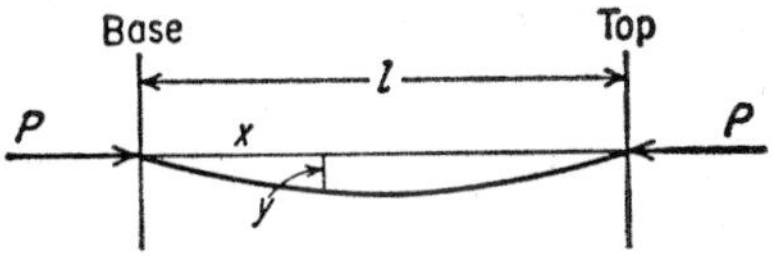

FIG. 17

Solution. Neglecting the weight of the beam, and applying (11) of §89, obtain (see Fig. 17)

$$EI\frac{d^2y}{dx^2} = -Py.$$

The general solution of this equation is

$$y = c_1 \sin \omega x + c_2 \cos \omega x, \qquad \omega = \sqrt{\frac{P}{EI}}. \tag{a}$$

As initial conditions, we have

$$y = 0 \qquad \text{when } x = 0 \text{ and when } x = l. \tag{b}$$

Since $y = 0$ when $x = 0$, we have from (a) $c_2 = 0$, and

$$y = c_1 \sin \omega x. \tag{c}$$

The second condition of (*b*), $y = 0$ when $x = l$, will be satisfied if $c_1 = 0$. In this case, $y = 0$ for all values of x, and the beam is straight. Also, $y_l = c_1 \sin \omega l = 0$ if $\omega l = \pi$; or since $\omega = \sqrt{P/(EI)}$, $P = \pi^2 EI/l^2$. Hence, if A is the area of the horizontal cross section of a column, the stress p, or force per square unit for buckling, is

$$p = \frac{P}{A} = \frac{\pi^2 EI}{Al^2}. \tag{d}$$

Since we cannot have much deflection without disagreement with the conditions of §89, a column should not be loaded so that buckling impends.* Also, note that, if l is very small, p from (*d*) is very large and has no design value. Actually, formula (*d*) is useful only for a limited range of $I/(Al^2)$. The student may consult a book on the *strength of materials* for a detailed treatment of columns.

PROBLEMS

1. Show for the column represented by Fig. 14 that $EI\, d^2y/dx^2 = -Py + G$, where G is a constant. Check that the initial conditions are $x = 0$, $y = 0$, $dy/dx = 0$, both when $x = 0$ and when $x = l$. Show that $y = (G/P)(1 - \cos \omega x)$, where $\omega = \sqrt{P/EI}$, and that for buckling $P = 4\pi^2 EI/l^2$.

2. In the solution of problem 1, you took $\omega l = 2\pi$ to provide that $1 - \cos \omega l = 0$. Show that, if you had used $\omega l = 4\pi$, the corresponding P would have been four times as large. Sketch the corresponding elastic curve of the beam, and thus show that it consists essentially of two beams each having one-half the length of the original one.

3. Figure 15 represents a column with fixed base and top free to move. Show that for buckling $P = \frac{1}{4}\pi^2 EI/l^2$.

4. For problem 3, discuss the elastic curve and the strength of the beam corresponding to a value of $3\pi/2$ instead of $\pi/2$ for ωl to provide that $\cos \omega l = 0$.

★5. Figure 16 represents a column with base fixed and top free to turn but held on a vertical line through the base. Prove that for buckling $\tan \omega l = \omega l$, where $\omega = \sqrt{P/(EI)}$. Then show that, if A is the cross-sectional area of the column, assumed uniform, stress $p = P/A = (4.4934)^2 EI/(Al^2)$, approximately.

6. For a round steel column supported as indicated in Fig. 16 and having $E = 30 \times 10^6$ lb/in.² and radius 2 in., show that $p = 6.057 \times 10^8/l^2$ lb/in.², where l is length in inches. Show that this is greater than 30,000 lb/in.² (the elastic limit of steel) when $l < 142.1$ in.

91. Motion of a particle in a plane

Polar coordinates lend themselves to the solution of certain problems more readily than rectangular coordinates. Accordingly, we shall find an expression for the component a_ρ of the acceleration in the direction of the radius vector and an expression for the component a_θ at right

* Since amplitude c_1 in (*c*) is independent of p, it is not determined and the maximum deflection of a buckling column seems to be arbitrary. However, Prof. R. P. Bailey, using a more accurate formula than (11), §89, has shown that amplitude of deflection depends on stress p.

angles to the radius vector for the motion of a particle in a plane. The component a_ρ is the projection of the acceleration vector a on the radius vector, or, what amounts to the same thing, the sum of the projections of the components of a on the radius vector. Hence, denoting derivatives with respect to t by dots thus,

$$\frac{dx}{dt} = \dot{x}, \qquad \frac{d^2x}{dt^2} = \ddot{x}, \qquad \frac{d\rho}{dt} = \dot{\rho}, \qquad \frac{d\theta}{dt} = \dot{\theta}, \qquad \text{etc.,} \tag{12}$$

we see from Fig. 18 that

$$a_\rho = \ddot{x} \cos \theta + \ddot{y} \sin \theta \tag{13}$$

and

$$a_\theta = -\ddot{x} \sin \theta + \ddot{y} \cos \theta. \tag{14}$$

Repeated differentiation of each of the equations

$$x = \rho \cos \theta, \qquad y = \rho \sin \theta \tag{15}$$

with respect to the time gives

$$\dot{x} = \dot{\rho} \cos \theta - \rho\dot{\theta} \sin \theta, \qquad \dot{y} = \dot{\rho} \sin \theta + \rho\dot{\theta} \cos \theta, \tag{16}$$

$$\ddot{x} = \ddot{\rho} \cos \theta - 2\dot{\rho}\dot{\theta} \sin \theta - \rho\dot{\theta}^2 \cos \theta - \rho\ddot{\theta} \sin \theta, \tag{17}$$

$$\ddot{y} = \ddot{\rho} \sin \theta + 2\dot{\rho}\dot{\theta} \cos \theta - \rho\dot{\theta}^2 \sin \theta + \rho\ddot{\theta} \cos \theta. \tag{18}$$

Substituting the values of $\ddot{x}$ and $\ddot{y}$ from (17) and (18) in (13) and (14) and simplifying, we have

$$a_\rho = \ddot{\rho} - \rho\dot{\theta}^2, \tag{19}$$

$$a_\theta = \rho\ddot{\theta} + 2\dot{\rho}\dot{\theta} = \frac{1}{\rho}\frac{d}{dt}(\rho^2\dot{\theta}). \tag{20}$$

Similarly, it is easy to show that the component v_ρ of the velocity along the radius vector and the component v_θ at right angles to it are

$$v_\rho = \dot{\rho}, \qquad v_\theta = \rho\dot{\theta}. \tag{21}$$

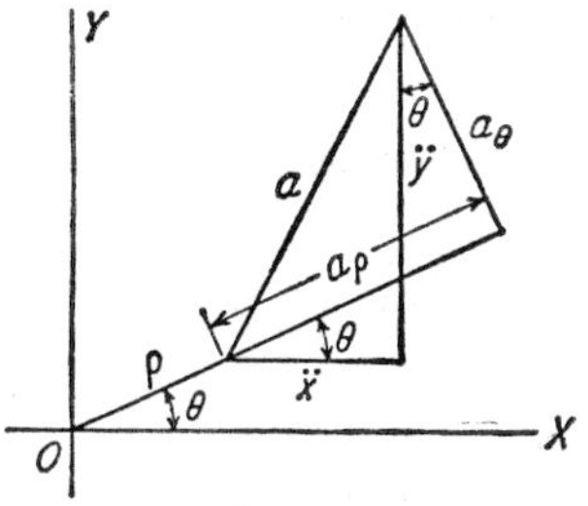

FIG. 18

The following example illustrates substantially the method of deducing mathematically the equation of the path of a planet moving about a sun. The basic assumption, conceived by Isaac Newton, is that *two particles attract each other with a force directly proportional to their masses and inversely proportional to the square of the distance between them and directed along a straight line connecting them.* Hence, assuming that bodies act as particles, that one, a sun, is so large relative to the other, a planet, that we may think of the sun as fixed at the pole of a system of polar coordinates (see Fig. 19), and using (10), §71, with (19) and (20), we get for the planet

$$m(\ddot{\rho} - \rho\dot{\theta}^2) = -\frac{mk}{\rho^2}, \qquad \frac{1}{\rho}\frac{d}{dt}(\rho^2\dot{\theta}) = 0. \tag{22}$$

To avoid unwieldy constants, a special case is considered.

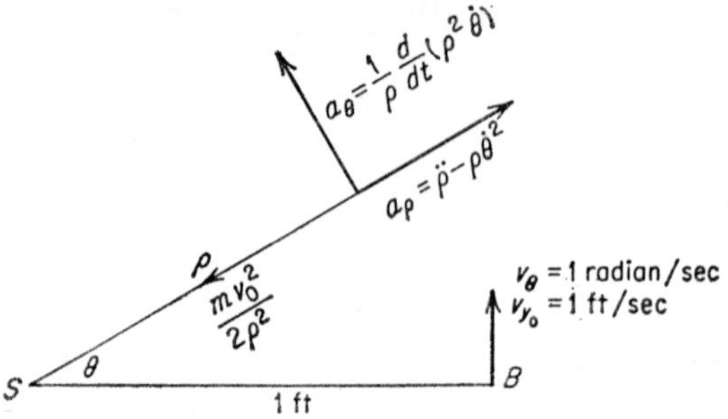

FIG. 19

Example. A particle P of mass 1 slug and coordinates (ρ ft, θ radians) moves about the fixed pole S under the action of an attractive force of magnitude $5/(9\rho^2)$ lb always directed toward the pole. Find the equation of the path of the particle if

$$\rho = 1 \text{ ft}, \qquad \dot\rho = 0, \qquad \dot\theta = 1 \text{ radian/sec} \qquad \text{when } \theta = 0. \tag{a}$$

Solution. Equations (22) for the motion considered are

$$1 \cdot a_\rho = \ddot\rho - \rho\dot\theta^2 = -\tfrac{5}{9}(1/\rho^2), \tag{b}$$
$$1 \cdot a_\theta = (1/\rho)\, d(\rho^2\dot\theta)/dt = 0. \tag{c}$$

From (c) and the conditions $\rho = 1$, $\dot\theta = 1$, $\theta = 0$ from (a),

$$\rho^2\dot\theta = 1^2 \cdot 1 = 1. \tag{d}$$

Replacing, in (b), $\ddot\rho$ by $\dot\rho\, d\dot\rho/d\rho$, $\dot\theta$ by $1/\rho^2$, solving the resulting equation, using conditions (a) to determine the constants of integration, and simplifying, we get

$$\dot\rho = \sqrt{-\frac{1}{\rho^2} + \frac{10}{9\rho} - \frac{1}{9}}. \tag{e}$$

In (e), replace dt by $\rho^2\, d\theta$ from (d), in the result replace ρ by $1/u$, $d\rho$ by $-(1/u^2)\, du$, simplify, separate the variables, and perform integrations to obtain

$$\frac{du}{\sqrt{-u^2 + \frac{10}{9}u - \frac{1}{9}}} = -d\theta,$$
$$\sin^{-1}\frac{2u - \frac{10}{9}}{\frac{8}{9}} = -\theta + c. \tag{f}$$

In (f), replace u by $1/\rho$, use conditions (a) to show that $c = \frac{1}{2}\pi$, solve the result for ρ, and obtain

$$\rho = \frac{\frac{9}{5}}{1 + (\frac{4}{5})\cos\theta}. \tag{g}$$

By means of analytic geometry, we deduce from (g) that the path is an ellipse having eccentricity $e = \frac{4}{5}$, semiaxes 3 ft and 5 ft, and area $A = \pi ab = 15\pi$ ft^2. From (d) we see that the rate of change of area, $\frac{1}{2}\rho^2\dot\theta = \frac{1}{2}$, is constant and therefore that area A (of ellipse) $= \pi ab = 15$ ft^2 divided by the rate $\frac{1}{2}$ ft²/sec gives the period P. In symbols,

$$P = \frac{A}{\frac{1}{2}} = (15\pi)2 = 94.2 \text{ sec}$$

PROBLEMS

1. A particle of weight w lb moves in a straight line from a distance a toward a charged point which attracts with a force whose magnitude in pounds is equal numerically to $w/(2gr^2)$, r denoting the distance of the particle from the point. If the particle had an initial velocity toward the point of $1/\sqrt{a}$, how long will it take to traverse half the distance to the point? Use (10) of §71.

2. A particle moves in a straight line from rest at a distance a toward a center of attraction, the attraction varying inversely as the cube of the distance. How long will it take the particle to reach the center? Use (10) of §71.

3. The areal velocity of a moving particle P with reference to a fixed point A is the rate at which the line AP generates area. Prove that a particle moving in a plane through a point A under the action of a force always directed toward point A has a constant areal velocity with respect to A. *Hint:* First show that a_θ in equation (20) of this section is zero.

4. A particle moves so that its radial acceleration is always 1 ft/sec² and the angular velocity of its radius is always 2 radians/sec. If $\rho = \frac{3}{4}$, $\theta = 0$, and $\dot{\rho} = 6$ when $t = 0$, find ρ and θ in terms of t. Also, find a_θ in terms of t.

5. A particle moves so that its radial velocity $\dot{\rho}$ is always 1 ft/sec, and the force on the particle is directed along the radius vector. If initially $\rho = 1$, $\theta = 0$, $\dot{\theta} = 2$ when $t = 0$, find ρ, θ, and the magnitude of the force in terms of t.

6. Prove that a particle moving with constant speed under the action of a force always directed toward a fixed point A in its plane of motion must move in a circle with A as center or move in a straight line.

7. Take $k = \frac{1}{2}$ in (22), and solve the equations subject to initial conditions $\rho = 1$, $\dot{\rho} = 0$, $\dot{\theta} = 1$ radian/sec, $\theta = 0$.

8. Solve equation (22) with k replaced by n subject to the initial conditions $\rho = 1$ ft, $\dot{\rho} = 0$, $\theta = 1$ radian/sec, when $\theta = 0$. Recalling that $\rho = a/(1 \pm e \cos \theta)$ is an ellipse, parabola, or hyperbola according as $e < 1$, $e = 1$, $e > 1$, discuss the solution when: (*a*) $n > 1$; (*b*) $n = \frac{1}{2}$; (*c*) $n < 0$; (*d*) $n = 0$; (*e*) $n = 1$; (*f*) $0 < n < \frac{1}{2}$; (*g*) $\frac{1}{2} < n < 1$.

9. A particle of mass m at point P situated b units from a fixed point A is moving at right angle to AP with velocity v_0. Taking AP as initial line and A as pole, find the equation of the path of the particle if it is acted on by a force always directed toward point A and equal in magnitude to $\frac{1}{2}nmbv_0^2/\rho^2$, where n is real and positive. Discuss the curve: (*a*) when $n = 1$; (*b*) when $n = 2$.

10. An airplane flying 105 miles/hr at a height of 2,000 ft lets fall a dummy weighing 180 lb. If v_x and v_y are, respectively, the horizontal component and the vertical component of the velocity, in feet per second, and if air resistance in pounds has a vertical component equal numerically to $0.006\ v_y^2$ and a horizontal component of $0.006v_x^2$, find: (*a*) the equation of the path; (*b*) the time of descent; (*c*) the horizontal distance traveled while coming down.

92. Review problems

In the following problems r and θ are used for polar coordinates, and dots denote derivatives with respect to time.

PROBLEMS

1. Using polar coordinates r and θ, find the equation of the curve for which the curvature equals $d\theta/ds$, where s denotes arc length. Use the formula for curvature $K = (r^2 + 2r'^2 - r'')/(r^2 + r'^2)^{\frac{3}{2}}$.

★2. A particle moves at 10 ft/sec along a curve having a curvature equal to the reciprocal of the x-component of velocity. Find the equation of the curve if at time $t = 0$ it passes through (0,0) tangent to the X-axis with $\dot{x}$ positive. Use the formula for curvature $K = (\dot{x}\ddot{y} - \dot{y}\ddot{x})/(\dot{x}^2 + \dot{y}^2)^{\frac{3}{2}}$.

3. Find a formula for the equation of the elastic curve of a beam l ft long, simply supported at the ends, and carrying a load proportional to distance from the left end (see Fig. 20). Note that at x ft from the left $M = \frac{1}{6}wl^2x - \int_0^x (wy\,dy)(x - y)$.

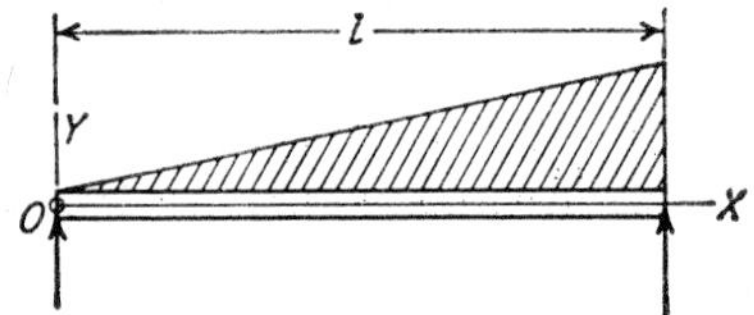

FIG. 20

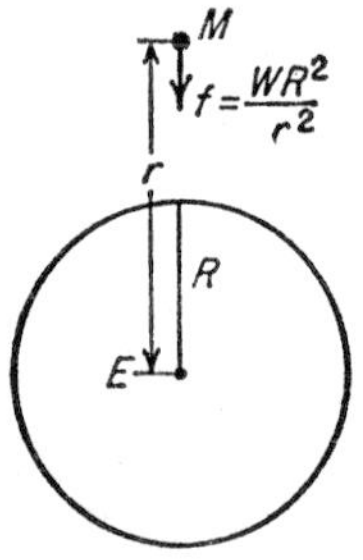

FIG. 21

4. Solve problem 3 modified by the specification that the beam be fixed horizontally in a wall at: (*a*) the left end; (*b*) both ends.

5. Figure 21 represents the earth without air, with center E and radius R ft, and a w-lb mass M distant r ft from E and moving in a vertical straight line relative to E. The force exerted on M is $-w$ lb when $r = R$ and $-wR^2/r^2$ when $r > R$. Take as initial conditions

$$t = 0, \qquad r = R, \qquad v_0 \text{ (of } M) = \dot{r}_0 = v_0.$$

Neglecting all motions of the earth E and M except relative motions show that: (*a*) if $v_0^2 = 2gR$,* r will always be positive and therefore M will not return to the earth; also show that $\dot{r} \to 0$ as $r \to \infty$; (*b*) if $v_0^2 < 2gR$, the body will return to the earth; also explain the significance of the signs $\pm$ for $\dot{r}$; (*c*) if $v_0^2 > 2gR$, then as $r \to \infty$, $\dot{r}$ does not approach zero; (*d*) if $2gR > v_0^2$, the maximum value of r is $2gR^2/(2gR - v_0^2)$.

6. For the body M of problem 5 with $v_0^2 < 2gR$, and $\dot{r} > 0$, find t in terms of r and the value of t when r is maximum.

7. A particle moves in a plane under the action of a force always directed toward a fixed point A in its plane; the velocity of the particle is $k\rho^n$, where ρ is its distance from A and the values of k† and n are constant. Find the equation of its path. Tell the nature of its path when: (*a*) $n = 0$; (*b*) $n = -2$; (*c*) $n = 1$; (*d*) $n = -3$.

8. Prove that the force in problem 7 is $k^2nm\rho^{2n-1}$, where m is the mass of the particle.

* The velocity $\sqrt{2gR}$ for v_0 is called the **escape velocity.** It is approximately 7 miles/sec.

† The dimensions of k are $L^{1-n}T^{-1}$.

CHAPTER 11

EXISTENCE THEOREMS AND APPLICATIONS

93. Foreword

Most of the theory used in the preceding chapters relates to the solutions of special types of differential equations in two unknowns. This chapter will provide a broad view of the field of differential equations by means of general existence theorems. It will indicate new points of view and methods. Also, it will give deeper insight into the general methods of the following chapters.

94. Replacement of differential equations by a system of the first order and the first degree

The solution of each set of equations already treated consisted of as many nondifferential relations as there were differential equations in the set. Also, the number of constants of integration was the same as the number of given equations. In general, it can be proved that *the general solution of a set of n first-order and first-degree differential equations in $n + 1$ variables consists of n nondifferential relations among these variables and n constants of integration.*

In this section, we shall indicate how the problem of finding the solution of n differential equations in $n + 1$ unknowns can be reduced to that of solving a set of differential equations of the first order and the first degree.

To get an idea of the method of procedure, consider the special system

$$\frac{d^3y}{dx^3} = x + \frac{d^2y}{dx^2}\frac{dz}{dx}, \qquad \frac{d^2z}{dx^2} = zy + \frac{dy}{dx}\frac{dz}{dx}. \tag{1}$$

Making the substitutions $dy/dx = y_1$, $dz/dx = z_1$, $dy_1/dx = y_2$ in (1), we obtain the equivalent system of the first order and the first degree:

$$\begin{aligned} &\frac{dy}{dx} = y_1, \qquad \frac{dz}{dx} = z_1, \qquad \frac{dy_1}{dx} = y_2, \\ &\frac{dy_2}{dx} = x + y_2z_1, \qquad \frac{dz_1}{dx} = zy + y_1z_1. \end{aligned} \tag{2}$$

Solving equations (2) and eliminating y_1, z_1, and y_2 from the resulting five equations, we obtain two equations in x, y, z, and the five constants of integration. These two equations constitute the general solution of equations (1).

Now, consider a set of n independent differential equations in n dependent variables and an independent variable. Substitute a new variable for each derivative of a dependent variable, up to the next to the highest-ordered one, and solve the resulting system of the first order for the derivatives contained in it. This set of equations, together with the substitution set, constitutes a system of differential equations of the first order and first degree which is equivalent to the original system.

EXERCISES

1. Replace, in accordance with the principle stated above, each of the following sets of differential equations by an equivalent set of the first order and the first degree:

(a) $\dfrac{d^2y}{dx^2} + x^2\dfrac{dy}{dx} + x^3y = 0.$ (b) $\dfrac{d^2y}{dx^2} + P(x)\dfrac{dy}{dx} + Q(x)y = 0.$

(c) $\dfrac{d^3y}{dt^3} = 3y + \dfrac{d^2y}{dt^2} + \dfrac{d^2x}{dt^2}, \dfrac{d^3y}{dt^3} = 3x - \dfrac{d^2y}{dt^2}.$

2. To solve $d^2y/dx^2 + y = 0$, derive, from the equivalent system $dy/dx = z$, $dz/dx = -y$, first $y^2 + z^2 = c_1^2$ and then, from $dy = \pm\sqrt{c_1^2 - y^2}\,dx$, get $y = c_1 \sin(x + c_2)$.

For each equation, write an equivalent system of the first order, and, using the method suggested in exercise 2, find the solution of the given equation:

3. $x^2\dfrac{d^2y}{dx^2} - x\dfrac{dy}{dx} - x^2 - 2 = 0.$ **4.** $\dfrac{d^2y}{dx^2} + x\dfrac{dy}{dx} + x = 0.$

5. Write a system of equations of the first order and first degree, equivalent to a linear nth-order differential equation in two variables. How many constants of integration would appear in the solution of this system?

95. Existence theorems

Theorem I, stated below but not proved, includes as special cases the theorems of §5 and other theorems of this section; it gives sufficient but not necessary conditions for the existence of solutions of systems of differential equations, and it also indicates the nature of those solutions.

THEOREM I. *For a system of differential equations*

$$\frac{dy_i}{dx} = f_i(x, y_1, y_2, \ldots, y_n), \qquad i = 1, 2, \ldots, n, \tag{3}$$

there exists a unique set of continuous solutions $y_1(x), y_2(x), \ldots, y_n(x)$ *of the given equations which take on the values* $y_1^0, y_2^0, \ldots, y_n^0$ *when* $x = x_0$, *provided that the functions*

$$f_1, f_2, \ldots, f_n, \qquad \frac{\partial f_i}{\partial y_1}, \ldots, \frac{\partial f_i}{\partial y_n}, \qquad i = 1, 2, \ldots, n, \tag{4}$$

are continuous and single-valued in the regions defined by

$$|\mathbf{x} - \mathbf{x}_0| \leqq \mathbf{a}, \qquad |\mathbf{y}_1 - \mathbf{y}_1^0| \leqq \mathbf{b}_1, \quad \ldots, \quad |\mathbf{y}_n - \mathbf{y}_n^0| \leqq \mathbf{b}_n, \tag{5}$$

where the values of a and the b's are all greater than zero.

In accordance with §94, the equation

$$\frac{d^n y_1}{dx^n} = f\left(x, y_1, \frac{dy_1}{dx}, \frac{d^2 y_1}{dx^2}, \ldots, \frac{d^{n-1} y_1}{dx^{n-1}}\right), \tag{6}$$

is equivalent to the system

$$\frac{dy_1}{dx} = y_2, \qquad \frac{dy_2}{dx} = y_3, \qquad \ldots, \qquad \frac{dy_{n-1}}{dx} = y_n,$$
$$\frac{dy_n}{dx} = f(x, y_1, y_2, \ldots, y_{n-1}). \tag{7}$$

For the system (7), the expressions of line (4) are

$$y_2, y_3, \ldots, y_{n-1}, \qquad \frac{\partial f}{\partial y_i}, \qquad i = 1, 2, \ldots, n-1. \tag{8}$$

Hence, we have the following theorem:

THEOREM II. *For a differential equation*

$$\frac{d^n \mathbf{y}}{d\mathbf{x}^n} = \mathbf{f}\left(\mathbf{x}, \mathbf{y}, \frac{d\mathbf{y}}{d\mathbf{x}}, \frac{d^2\mathbf{y}}{d\mathbf{x}^2}, \ldots, \frac{d^{n-1}\mathbf{y}}{d\mathbf{x}^{n-1}}\right), \tag{9}$$

there exists a unique continuous solution $y(x)$ having continuous derivatives $d^k y/dx^k$, $k = 1, 2, \ldots, n-1$, such that

$$\mathbf{y} = \mathbf{a}_0, \qquad \frac{d\mathbf{y}}{d\mathbf{x}} = \mathbf{a}_1, \qquad \frac{d^2\mathbf{y}}{d\mathbf{x}^2} = \mathbf{a}_2, \qquad \ldots, \qquad \frac{d^{n-1}\mathbf{y}}{d\mathbf{x}^{n-1}} = \mathbf{a}_{n-1} \tag{10}$$

when $x = x_0$, provided that the functions

$$\mathbf{f}, \qquad \frac{\partial \mathbf{f}}{\partial \mathbf{y}}, \qquad \frac{\partial \mathbf{f}}{\partial (d^k\mathbf{y}/d\mathbf{x}^k)}, \qquad \mathbf{k} = 1, 2, \ldots, \mathbf{n} - 1 \tag{11}$$

are continuous and single-valued in the regions defined by

$$|\mathbf{x} - \mathbf{x}_0| \leqq \mathbf{b}, \qquad |\mathbf{y} - \mathbf{a}_0| \leqq \mathbf{b}_0, \qquad \left|\frac{d\mathbf{y}}{d\mathbf{x}} - \mathbf{a}_1\right| \leqq \mathbf{b}_1, \qquad \ldots,$$
$$\left|\frac{d^{n-1}\mathbf{y}}{d\mathbf{x}^{n-1}} - \mathbf{a}_{n-1}\right| \leqq \mathbf{b}_{n-1}, \tag{12}$$

where the values b, b_i, $i = 0, 1, \ldots, n-1$, are all greater than zero.

Consider, for example, $x(x-4)\,dy/dx = 4$. Here there is only the one equation $dy/dx = 1/[x(x-4)]$. The functions (11) are $1/[x(x-4)]$, 0. These are continuous in every region not containing points for which $x = 1$ or $x = 4$; therefore, in every such region there is a unique solution through every point in it. Thus, a solution passes through every point in $|x - 5| < 1$, $|y - 11| < m$, m arbitrary. Nothing is said regarding a region such as $|x - 5| < 6$, $|y - 11| < 24$ by Theorem II. However, the solution of $x(x - 4)\, dy/dx = 4$ is $y = \ln |(x - 4)/x| + c$, and y does not exist for points having abscissas 0 or 4.

Let f_1, f_2, and f_3 represent functions of x, and consider

$$\frac{d^2y}{dx^2} + f_1\frac{dy}{dx} + f_2y = f_3. \tag{13}$$

A system equivalent to (13) is

$$\frac{dy}{dx} = y_1, \qquad \frac{dy_1}{dx} = -f_1y_1 - f_2y + f_3, \tag{14}$$

and the expressions corresponding to (11) are

$$-f_1y_1 - f_2y + f_3,\ y_1,\ 1,\ -f_1,\ -f_2. \tag{15}$$

If the functions x, f_1, f_2, and f_3 are polynomials, functions (15) are single-valued and continuous everywhere and there is a solution of (14), and therefore of (13), for every choice of a point in the plane and a direction associated with it.

If the functions $f_1(x)$, $f_2(x)$, $f_3(x)$ are single-valued and continuous in a region $|x - a| \leqq b$, the functions in (15) are single-valued and continuous in x, y, and y_1, and a unique solution $y(x)$ of (13) exists such that $y_1(x) = y'(x)$, $y = \beta$, $y_1 = \gamma$ when $x = \alpha$ provided that $|\alpha - a| < b$, $|\beta| < m$, $|y_1| < n$, where m and n are any positive numbers.

Theorems I and II may not indicate solutions which exist. Thus $x\, dy/dx - y = 0$ has the solution $y = cx$ through (0,0) although the conditions of Theorem II that $\partial(dy/dx)/\partial y$ be continuous at $x = 0$ are not satisfied. Note, however, that $y = cx$ is not unique since c is arbitrary. Also, note that there is no solution through $(0,a)$, $a \neq 0$. Of course, there is a unique solution through every point (a,b), $a \neq 0$.

In dealing with a system of m consistent and independent equations in $n + 1$ variables, it is possible to replace $n - m$ variables by arbitrary functions of the remaining $m + 1$ unknowns and then apply Theorem II to the result. A single total differential equation in three variables is a case in point. As in the case of total differential equations, a number of equations connecting the variables may often be found by solving exact equations or integrable equations derived from the given set.

EXERCISES

1. State Theorem II for $n = 1$, and observe that the result is Theorem I of §5.

2. Is a unique solution of $x\, d^2y/dx^2 - y = 0$, satisfying the condition $y = 2$ when $x = 0$, to be expected? Why?

3. For $dy/dx = y^{\frac{1}{3}}$, the conditions of Theorem II with $n = 1$ are satisfied in the whole XY-plane. What solution passes through (0,0)?

4. What condition of Theorem II with $n = 1$ is not satisfied by $dy/dx = 3y/x$ at (0,0)? $y = y_0(x/x_0)^3$ satisfies $dy/dx = 3y/x$ if $x_0 \neq 0$. Does $y = cx^3$ have at (0,0) the slope given by $dy/dx = 3y/x$?

5. Does Theorem II show that the graph of the solution of

$$\frac{dy}{dx} = 2, \qquad \frac{dz}{dx} = x + y + z$$

consists of a unique curve through every point of space? Solve the equations, and find the solution for which $y = 5$, $z = -10$ when $x = 0$.

6. Show that the solution of

$$x^2\frac{d^2y}{dx^2} - 2x\frac{dy}{dx} + 2y = 2x^3$$

could be obtained from the solution of

$$\frac{dy}{dx} = z, \qquad \frac{dz}{dx} = \frac{2xz - 2y}{x^2} + 2x.$$

In accordance with Theorem II, would you expect a unique solution of the pair of equations for which $y = 0$, $z = 1$ when $x = 0$?

Show that the general solution of the pair of equations is $y = c_1x^2 + c_2x + x^3$, $z = 2c_1x + c_2 + 3x^2$ and that an infinite number of solutions $y = c_1x^2 + x + x^3$, $z = 2c_1x + 1 + 3x^2$ satisfy the conditions $y = 0$, $z = 1$ when $x = 0$.

7 Discuss the existence of solutions of

$$P(x)\frac{d^2y}{dx^2} + Q(x)\frac{dy}{dx} + R(x)y = 0$$

by using Theorem II.

8. For $d^3y/dx^3 = 1/(d^2y/dx^2)$, write the corresponding expressions (11), and observe that $\partial[1/(d^2y/dx^2)]/\partial(d^2y/dx^2)$ is not continuous at points where $d^2y/dx^2 = 0$. What feature of the solution $y = \frac{1}{15}(2x + c_1)^{\frac{5}{2}} + c_2x + c_3$ of $d^3y/dx^3 = 1/(d^2y/dx^2)$ corresponds to this discontinuity?

9. Use Theorem II to find the values of a at which irregularities are to be expected in the solution of

$$x(x - 1)\frac{d^2y}{dx^2} + (4x - 2)\frac{dy}{dx} + 2y = 0$$

subject to the condition $y = 0$, $dy/dx = 1$ when $x = a$. Does the general solution $y = (c_1/x) + c_2/(x - 1)$ bear out your answer?

96. Differential equations of the first order and first degree in the unknowns

By using §94, we are enabled to write a set of equations of form (3), §95, equivalent to a very general set of equations. For this reason and for future reference, we are considering equations of type (3), §95, not readily solvable by methods used earlier.

Consider the equations

$$\begin{aligned} P_1\,dx + Q_1\,dy + R_1\,dz &= 0,\\ P_2\,dx + Q_2\,dy + R_2\,dz &= 0, \end{aligned} \tag{16}$$

in which the P's, Q's, and R's represent functions of x, y, and z. A solution consists of two nondifferential equations in x, y, and z which satisfy both equations. *The main method of solution consists in* (1) *combining the given equations and others derived from them so as to obtain an equation in two unknowns, or an equation which is the result of equating to zero the total derivative of some expression involving the variables;* (2) *integrating the equations thus obtained and combining the results with the given differential equations to obtain other relations among the variables.*

Dividing equations (1) by dz and solving the results for dx/dz and dy/dz, we obtain

$$\frac{dx}{dz} = \frac{P}{R}, \quad \frac{dy}{dz} = \frac{Q}{R}, \quad \text{or} \quad \frac{dx}{P} = \frac{dy}{Q} = \frac{dz}{R}, \tag{17}$$

where

$$P:Q:R = \begin{vmatrix} Q_1 & R_1 \\ Q_2 & R_2 \end{vmatrix} : \begin{vmatrix} R_1 & P_1 \\ R_2 & P_2 \end{vmatrix} : \begin{vmatrix} P_1 & Q_1 \\ P_2 & Q_2 \end{vmatrix}. \tag{18}$$

From (17), we may write

$$\frac{l\,dx}{lP} = \frac{m\,dy}{mQ} = \frac{n\,dz}{nR}, \tag{19}$$

and then apply the theorem that in a continued proportion the sum of the antecedents is to the sum of the consequents as any antecedent is to its consequent, to obtain

$$\frac{dx}{P} = \frac{dy}{Q} = \frac{dz}{R} = \frac{l\,dx + m\,dy + n\,dz}{lP + mQ + nR}, \tag{20}$$

where l, m, and n are functions of x, y, and z at our disposal. (1) *It may happen that, by suitably choosing l, m, and n, we can find an equation in only two variables or an equation readily integrable.* In either case, an integration gives us a required relation. (2) *Again we may be able to choose l, m, and n so that $lP + mQ + nR = 0$ and so that $l\,dx + m\,dy + n\,dz = du$, where u is some function of x, y, and z.* In this case, since $lP + mQ + nR = 0$ and since the last fraction in (20) is finite, it follows that $l\,dx + m\,dy + n\,dz = 0$; that is, $du = 0$, and *$u = c$ (constant) is a required relation.* The examples will illustrate these methods of procedure and also an elimination method.

Example 1. Solve

$$\frac{dx}{xz} = \frac{dy}{yz} = \frac{2\,dz}{x + y}. \tag{a}$$

Solution. Integration of the equation of the first two ratios gives

$$y = c_1x. \tag{b}$$

Writing equations (20) for (a) with $l = 1$, $m = 1$, $n = 0$, we obtain

$$\frac{2\,dz}{x + y} = \frac{dx + dy}{z(x + y)}. \tag{c}$$

Multiplying through by $z(x + y)$ and integrating, we have

$$\mathbf{x + y = z^2 + c_2}. \tag{d}$$

Equations (b) and (d) constitute the solution.

It is instructive to note that, after finding equation (b), we could have substituted c_1x from (b) for y in $dx/xz = 2\,dz/(x + y)$ and integrated the resulting equation in x and z to obtain

$$x + c_1x = z^2 + c, \qquad \text{or} \qquad x + y = z^2 + c.$$

Also, we could have noticed that

$$P + Q - 2zR = xz + yz - xz - yz = 0$$

and therefore that

$$l\,dx + m\,dy + n\,dz = dx + dy - 2z\,dz = 0.$$

Hence,

$$x + y - z^2 = c.$$

Example 2. Solve

$$dx = \frac{dy}{-5x + 12y - 5z} = \frac{dz}{x + 2y + z}. \tag{a}$$

Solution. Write

$$\frac{dy}{dx} = -5x + 12y - 5z, \qquad \frac{dz}{dx} = x + 2y + z. \tag{b}$$

Differentiate the first of (b) to obtain

$$\frac{d^2y}{dx^2} = -5 + 12\frac{dy}{dx} - 5\frac{dz}{dx}, \tag{c}$$

in (c) replace dz/dx by its value from the second equation of (b), in the result replace z by its value from the first of (b), and simplify to obtain

$$\frac{d^2y}{dx^2} - 13\frac{dy}{dx} + 22y = -5. \tag{d}$$

Solve (d) for y, and substitute the result in the first of (b) to obtain, after slight simplification,

$$\begin{aligned} y &= c_1e^{2x} + c_2e^{11x} - \tfrac{5}{22}, \\ 5z &= 10c_1e^{2x} + c_2e^{11x} - 5x - \tfrac{30}{11}. \end{aligned} \tag{e}$$

Equations (e) constitute the solution of (a).

EXERCISES

1. $\dfrac{dx}{y} = \dfrac{dy}{x} = \dfrac{dz}{z}$.

2. $\dfrac{dx}{ayz} = \dfrac{dy}{bzx} = \dfrac{dz}{cxy}$.

3. $y\,dx + (y - 2x)\,dy + yz\,dz = 0,\ (x - y)\,dy - yz\,dz = 0.$

4. $z\,dx + (y - x)\,dy + z\,dz = 0,\ 2z\,dx - (2x + y)\,dy - z\,dz = 0.$

5. $(x + z)\,dx + (x - z)\,dy - (x + z)\,dz = 0,\ x(x + z)\,dx + y(z - x)\,dy - z(x + z)\,dz = 0.$

6. $\dfrac{dx}{y} = \dfrac{dy}{x} = \dfrac{2\,dz}{1 - z^2}.$ **7.** $\dfrac{dx}{x^2 - y^2 - z^2} = \dfrac{dy}{2xy} = \dfrac{dz}{2xz}.$

8. $\dfrac{dx}{x(y - z)} = \dfrac{dy}{y(z - x)} = \dfrac{dz}{z(x - y)}.$ **9.** $\dfrac{dx}{y - xz} = \dfrac{dy}{x + yz} = \dfrac{dz}{x^2 + y^2}.$

10. $\dfrac{dx}{x^2 - y^2 - yz} = \dfrac{dy}{x^2 - y^2 - xz} = \dfrac{dz}{z(x - y)}.$

11. $\dfrac{dx}{ny - mz} = \dfrac{dy}{lz - nx} = \dfrac{dz}{mx - ly}.$

12. $\dfrac{dx}{-1 - xz^2} = \dfrac{dy}{1 + yz^2} = \dfrac{dz}{z^2(y - x)}.$

13. $\dfrac{dx}{y} = \dfrac{dy}{x} = \dfrac{dz}{w} = \dfrac{dw}{z}.$

14. $\dfrac{dx}{w - z} = \dfrac{dy}{w - z} = \dfrac{dz}{x + y - 2w} = \dfrac{dw}{2z - x - y}.$

Using the method of example 2, solve the following systems of equations:

15. $dx = \dfrac{dy}{10x - y + 5z} = \dfrac{dz}{2x - y + z}.$

16. $dx = \dfrac{dy}{2e^x + y + z} = \dfrac{dz}{4e^x + y + z}.$ **17.** $dx = \dfrac{dy}{6x^2 - y + 3z} = \dfrac{dz}{2x^2 + y + z}.$

18. $dx = \dfrac{dy}{a \sin 2x + y + 2z} = \dfrac{dz}{-a \cos 2x - y - z}.$

19. State sufficient conditions that equations (16) have a solution.

97. Total differential equations

The number of variables in a system of differential equations may exceed the number of equations by more than one. We shall consider here only the special case of one first-order first-degree differential equation in three variables. Under certain conditions, such an equation is integrable; for example, the solution of

$$2x\,dx + 2y\,dy + 2z\,dz = 0 \tag{21}$$

evidently is

$$x^2 + y^2 + z^2 = c, \tag{22}$$

and, in general, the solution of

$$\frac{\partial f(x,y,z)}{\partial x}\,dx + \frac{\partial f(x,y,z)}{\partial y}\,dy + \frac{\partial f(x,y,z)}{\partial z}\,dz = 0 \tag{23}$$

is

$$f(x,y,z) = c. \tag{24}$$

The object of this section is to arrive at the condition of integrability of an equation

$$P\,dx + Q\,dy + R\,dz = 0, \tag{25}$$

where P, Q, and R are continuous functions of x, y, and z, possessing continuous first partial derivatives with respect to x, y, and z.

If (25) is integrable, there exists a function $\mu(x,y,z)$ such that the expression

$$\mu P\,dx + \mu Q\,dy + \mu R\,dz \tag{26}$$

is exactly the derivative of some function, say $f(x,y,z)$. Hence, comparing the left-hand member of (23) with (26) and using subscripts to indicate partial differentiation, we get

$$f_x = \mu P, \qquad f_y = \mu Q, \qquad f_z = \mu R. \tag{27}$$

Since $f_{xy} = f_{yx}$, we have, from (27),

$$\mu P_y + P\mu_y = \mu Q_x + Q\mu_x. \tag{28}$$

Similarly,

$$\mu Q_z + Q\mu_z = \mu R_y + R\mu_y, \tag{29}$$

$$\mu R_x + R\mu_x = \mu P_z + P\mu_z. \tag{30}$$

Multiplying equation (28) by R, (29) by P, and (30) by Q, adding the results, and rearranging, we have

$$\mathbf{P(Q_z - R_y) + Q(R_x - P_z) + R(P_y - Q_x) = 0.} \tag{31}$$

This equation states a necessary condition that (25) be integrable; we shall prove that it is also a sufficient one.

Since the equation $P\,dx + Q\,dy = 0$ is always integrable if z is considered constant, there will be no loss in generality in assuming that $P\,dx + Q\,dy$ is an exact equation with respect to x and y. The solution of

$$P\,dx + Q\,dy = 0, \tag{32}$$

considering z as constant, may now be written in the form

$$f(x,y,z) + \varphi(z) = 0, \tag{33}$$

where φ represents an arbitrary function of z. Since $P\,dx + Q\,dy$ has been assumed to be an exact differential, we may write

$$P_y = Q_x, \qquad P = f_x, \qquad Q = f_y. \tag{34}$$

Taking account of (34), we may write $P\,dx + Q\,dy + R\,dz = 0$ in the form

$$f_x\,dx + f_y\,dy + f_z\,dz + (R - f_z)\,dz = 0, \tag{35}$$

or

$$df + (R - f_z)\,dz = 0. \tag{36}$$

Equation (36) can be integrated if there exists a relation independent of x and y between $R - f_z$ and f; that is, $R - f_z$ is a function of f and z, say $\psi(f,z)$. In this case,

$$(R - f_z)_x = \psi_f f_x, \qquad (R - f_z)_y = \psi_f f_y. \tag{37}$$

Eliminating ψ_f from (37) and performing indicated partial differentiations on $R - f_z$, we get the following necessary and sufficient condition that $\psi(f,z)$ exist:

$$f_x(R_y - f_{zy}) - f_y(R_x - f_{zx}) = 0. \tag{38}$$

From (34),

$$f_x = P, \qquad f_y = Q, \qquad f_{zy} = (f_y)_z = Q_z, \qquad f_{zx} = (f_x)_z = P_z.$$

Substituting these results in (38), we get

$$P(R_y - Q_z) - Q(R_x - P_z) = 0. \tag{39}$$

Since, from (34), $P_y - Q_x = 0$, it appears that (39) is the same as (31) with the signs changed. Hence, if (31) holds, (36) can be expressed in terms of two variables f and z and solved. Since (36) and (35) are the same equation, this solution with f replaced by its value in terms of x, y, and z will be the integral of (25).

The proof just given suggests the following rule:

RULE. *To integrate a total differential equation*

$$\mathbf{P\,dx + Q\,dy + R\,dz = 0} \tag{40}$$

which satisfies the condition (31), *first integrate the equation*

$$\mathbf{P\,dx + Q\,dy = 0},$$

treating z as constant, to obtain

$$f(x,y,z) = C. \tag{41}$$

Find df, and change the given equation (40) *to the form* (36) *with R and f expressed in terms of f and z, solve this equation, and in the result replace f by its equal in terms of x, y, and z.*

If (40) is not integrable, we may assume any second relation

$$\varphi(x,y,z) = 0 \tag{42}$$

and solve it simultaneously with (40) to get a particular solution.

Example 1. Solve

$$yz^2\,dx - xz^2\,dy - (2xyz + x^2)\,dz = 0. \tag{a}$$

Solution. Substitution from (a) in (31) shows that (a) is integrable. A solution of

$$yz^2\,dx - xz^2\,dy = 0, \tag{b}$$

got by considering z as constant, is $f(x,y,z) = y/x = c$. Hence, we write

$$f = y/x, \qquad x^2\,df = x\,dy - y\,dx. \tag{c}$$

Substituting, from (c), $x^2\,df$ for $x\,dy - y\,dx$ and xf for y in (a), we get

$$z^2x^2\,df + (2x^2fz + x^2)\,dz = 0. \tag{d}$$

Dividing (d) through by x^2 and solving the resulting linear equation by a method of §25, we get

$$fz^2 = c - z. \tag{e}$$

In this, replace f by y/x from (c), change slightly, and obtain

$$\mathbf{yz^2 = x(c - z).}$$

Example 2. Prove that

$$dx + dy + y\,dz = 0 \tag{a}$$

is not integrable, and then solve it simultaneously with

$$x - y + z = d. \tag{b}$$

Solution. The equation (31), §97, is not satisfied by (a). The derivative of (b) is

$$dx - dy + dz = 0. \tag{c}$$

Solving (a) and (c) simultaneously for dx/dz and dy/dz, we find

$$\frac{dx}{y+1} = \frac{dy}{y-1} = \frac{dz}{-2}. \tag{d}$$

The solution of (d) is

$$x = y + 2\ln(y - 1) + c_1, \qquad \mathbf{y = 1 + ce^{-z/2}}. \tag{e}$$

Equation (b) and either of the equations (e), considered simultaneously, constitute a solution.

EXERCISES

Apply the condition (31), §97, of integrability, and find the solutions of the differential equations numbered 1 to 11:

1. $x\,dy - y\,dx - 2x^2z\,dz = 0.$ **2.** $(2y - z)\,dx + 4\,dy - 2\,dz = 0.$

3. $x\,dy + y\,dx + (2xy - z)\,dz = 0.$
4. $z(y\,dx - x\,dy) - (2xy + 3x^2z^3)\,dz = 0.$
5. $2x\,dx + 2y\,dy + (x^2 + y^2 + e^{-z})\,dz = 0.$
6. $2xy^2z\,dx + (1 + 2x^2yz)\,dy + x^2y^2\,dz = 0.$
7. $(2x - yz)\,dx - xz\,dy + (x^2 - xyz - xy)\,dz = 0.$
8. $z\,dx + z\,dy + [2(x + y) + \sin z]\,dz = 0.$
9. $(1 + z)(x\,dy + y\,dx) + (2xy - 4z)\,dz = 0.$
10. $\sin z\,dx + \cos z\,dy + [(x + y)\cos z + (x - y)\sin z - e^{-z}\tan z]\,dz = 0.$
11. $yz\,dx - (xz + x^2)\,dy - (xy + x^2)\,dz = 0.$

12. Find the condition that $dz = M\,dx + N\,dy$ be integrable: (a) if M and N represent functions of x, y, and z; (b) if M and N are functions of x and y only.

13. Solve simultaneously

$$z\,dx + x\,dy + y\,dz = 0,$$
$$ax + 2by - (a + 2b)z = c.$$

98. Geometrical interpretation

It is proved in calculus that the normal to a surface $f(x,y,z) = 0$ at a point (x,y,z) on the surface has as direction numbers $\partial f/\partial x$, $\partial f/\partial y$, $\partial f/\partial z$ evaluated at (x,y,z). Hence, if $f(x,y,z) = 0$ is a solution of equation (40) of §97, equations (27) show that a line through (x,y,z) having direction numbers P, Q, R meets $f(x,y,z) = 0$ in (x,y,z) at right angles. Now, the curves having tangents with direction numbers P, Q, R are defined by

$$\frac{dx}{P} = \frac{dy}{Q} = \frac{dz}{R}. \tag{43}$$

Hence *the curves defined by* (43) *meet at right angles the surfaces defined by the solution of an integrable equation* (40), §97. Figure 1 indicates the relation.

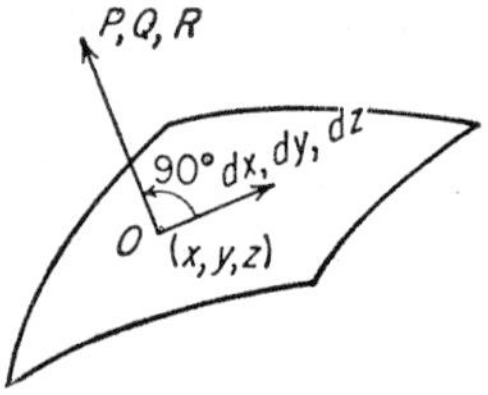

FIG. 1

Example. Find the equation of the surfaces cutting at right angles the curves defined at points (x,y,z) by

$$dx/(2x) = dy/(2y) = dz/z. \qquad (a)$$

Also, find the equations of the curves.

Solution. The equation of the required system of surfaces is

$$2x\,dx + 2y\,dy + z\,dz = 0, \qquad (b)$$

and, by inspection, we see that its solution is

$$2x^2 + 2y^2 + z^2 = c. \qquad (c)$$

This represents a family of ellipsoids. The following solution of equations (a) is easily found:

$$x = c_1y, \qquad x = c_2z^2. \qquad (d)$$

99. Fields of force in space

Integrable differential equations in three unknowns have important applications to fields of force in space. A force having magnitude r and direction making angles α, β, and γ with the X-, Y-, and Z-axes, respectively, is denoted by the symbol $[X,Y,Z]$, where

$$X = r\cos\alpha, \qquad Y = r\cos\beta, \qquad Z = r\cos\gamma. \tag{44}$$

The sum of two forces $[X_1,Y_1,Z_1]$ and $[X_2,Y_2,Z_2]$ is defined by

$$[X_1,Y_1,Z_1] + [X_2,Y_2,Z_2] = [X_1 + X_2,\ Y_1 + Y_2,\ Z_1 + Z_2]. \tag{45}$$

Just as in §33, a field of force is defined by

$$[P(x,y,z),Q(x,y,z),R(x,y,z)],$$

its **equipotential surfaces** are represented by

$$\mathbf{P\,dx + Q\,dy + R\,dz = 0} \tag{46}$$

provided that this equation is integrable, and the **lines of force** of the field are given by

$$\frac{\mathbf{dx}}{\mathbf{P}} = \frac{\mathbf{dy}}{\mathbf{Q}} = \frac{\mathbf{dz}}{\mathbf{R}}. \tag{47}$$

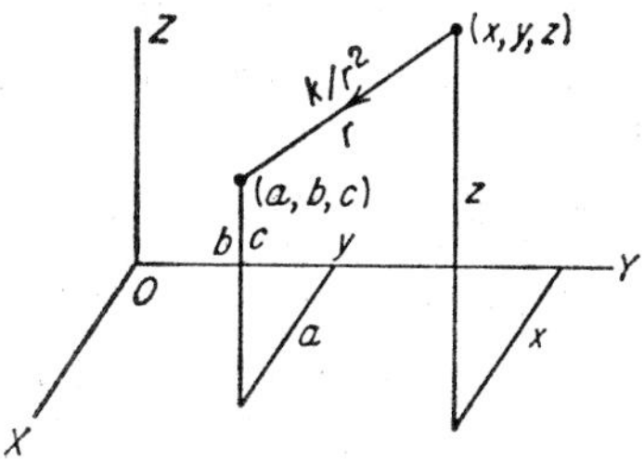

FIG. 2

Example. Find the equations of the lines of force and of the equipotential surfaces of a field of force in space due to a negative charge of electricity fixed at the point (a,b,c).

Solution. Figure 2 represents a negative charge of electricity fixed at point (a,b,c), point (x,y,z) distant r from (a,b,c), and the force at (x,y,z), due to the charge, of magnitude* k/r^2 and directed from (x,y,z) toward (a,b,c). From Fig. 2, we get

$$r = \sqrt{(x-a)^2 + (y-b)^2 + (z-c)^2},$$
$$\cos\alpha = \frac{x-a}{r}, \qquad \cos\beta = \frac{y-b}{r}, \qquad \cos\gamma = \frac{z-c}{r}. \tag{a}$$

The field of force $[P,Q,R]$ is given by

$$[P,Q,R] = \left[\frac{k(x-a)}{r^3}, \frac{k(y-b)}{r^3}, \frac{k(z-c)}{r^3}\right]. \tag{b}$$

From (47) and (b), we get, after slight simplification, for the lines of force

$$\frac{dx}{x-a} = \frac{dy}{y-b} = \frac{dz}{z-c}. \tag{c}$$

A general solution of (c) is

$$x - a = c_1(y-b), \qquad x - a = c_2(z-c). \tag{d}$$

From (46) and (b), we get, after slight simplification, for the equipotential surfaces

$$(x-a)\,dx + (y-b)\,dy + (z-c)\,dz = 0. \tag{e}$$

A general solution of (e) is

$$(x-a)^2 + (y-b)^2 + (z-c)^2 = c_1^2. \tag{f}$$

This represents all spheres having (a,b,c) as center.

* See the example of §33.

EXERCISES

Find the equations of the set of curves cutting at right angles the family of surfaces:

1. $x^2 + y^2 + z^2 = c^2$.
2. $x^2 + 3y^2 - z^2 = c^2$.
3. $2x^2 - 3y^2 - 4z^2 = c$.
4. $xyz = c$.

Find the equation of the family of surfaces orthogonal to the family of curves defined by:

5. $\dfrac{dx}{2x + y} = \dfrac{dy}{x + z} = \dfrac{dz}{y}$.
6. $\dfrac{dx}{y} = \dfrac{dy}{-x} = \dfrac{dz}{2x^2z}$.
7. $x\,dx = (3 - z)\,dz = y\,dy$.
8. $x^2 + 2y^2 + 3z^2 = a^2$, $z = b$.
9. $z\,dx + x\,dz = 0$, $yz\,dx + z^2\,dy + y(x + z)\,dz = 0$.

Find the equation of the lines of force and of the equipotential surfaces for the fields of force defined as follows:

10. $[3x,2y,-z]$.
11. $[a/x,b/y,c/z]$.
12. $[x, y, 2x^2 + 2y^2 + 3z]$.
13. $[ayz,bzx,cxy]$.

★**14.** Find the equation of the equipotential surfaces for a field of force due to a charge q_1 of electricity at $(-a,0,0)$ and a charge q_2 at $(a,0,0)$ if: (*a*) $q_1 = q_2$; (*b*) $q_1 = -q_2$.

★**15.** Find the equation of the streamlines for the field of force considered in problem 14. *Hint:* To perform the integration involved, note first that $y = c_1z$. Pattern your solution after that of the example of §33.

100. Review exercises

The material of this chapter consists essentially of existence theorems, §95, and total differential equations, §97.

EXERCISES

1. Use §94 to write a system of differential equations of the first order equivalent to

$$(x - 2)xD^3y - xD^2z + y + 2z = 0, \qquad (x - 3)D^2y + (x - 4)D^2z = 0.$$

If (a,b,c) represents a point through which a solution curve of this system is to pass, for what values of a does Theorem I, §95, fail to guarantee a solution?

2. For the system

$$(x - 2)(y + 2)\frac{dy}{dx} = (3x - 2z)y, \qquad (z^2 + 2x^2)\frac{dz}{dx} = y^{\frac{1}{3}} + z^{\frac{1}{3}},$$

state, for each of the following regions, whether Theorem I, §95, guarantees a solution curve through each of its interior points: (*a*) $|x - 4| \leqq 1$, $|y - 6| \leqq 1$, $|z| > 0.1$; (*b*) $|x| \leqq 1$, $|y + 2| \leqq 1$, $|z| > 0$; (*c*) $|x| \leqq 1$, $|y + 4| \leqq 1$, $|z| \leqq 1$; (*d*) $|x - 2{,}003| \leqq 2{,}000$, $|y - 2{,}003| \leqq 2{,}000$, $|z| \geqq 0.01$.

3. For which of the following equations does an integrating factor exist?

(*a*) $(0.4x - 0.2y)\,dx + (0.1y + z)\,dy + (10z + 2x)\,dz = 0$.
(*b*) $(2x - 2y)\,dx + (2y - 2x)\,dy + (3x^2 - 6xy + 3y^2 - 10\cos z)\,dz = 0$.
(*c*) $(3y + z^3)\,dx + xz\,dy + (xz^3 - 2xy)\,dz = 0$.
(*d*) $2zy\,dx + 3xz\,dy - xy\,dz = 0$.

4. Solve equations (*b*) and (*d*) of exercise 3.
5. Solve $(zy + z^4)\,dx + xz\,dy + (xz^3 - 2xy)\,dz = 0$.
6. Solve $dx/(y - z) = dy/(z - x) = dz/(x - y)$.

Use the method of example 2, §96, to solve:

7. $dy/dx = x + z,\ dz/dx = x + y$.
8. $dy/dx = 2x + y + z,\ dz/dx = 4x - y + z$.

Find the equations of the lines of force and of the equipotential surfaces for the fields of force defined by:

9. $[x + y,\ x - y,\ z]$.

10. $[3zx,\ zy,\ 3x^2 + 2y^2 - z^2]$.

★11. $\left[\dfrac{k(x + a)}{r_1^2} + \dfrac{k(x - a)}{r_2^2}, \dfrac{ky}{r_1^2} + \dfrac{ky}{r_2^2}, \dfrac{kz}{r_1^2} + \dfrac{kz}{r_2^2}\right]$, where r_1 and r_2 are the respective distances from $(-a,0,0)$ and $(a,0,0)$ to (x,y,z).

★12. $\left[\dfrac{k(x + a)}{r_1^5} + \dfrac{k(x - a)}{r_2^5}, \dfrac{ky}{r_1^5} + \dfrac{ky}{r_2^5}, \dfrac{kz}{r_1^5} + \dfrac{kz}{r_2^5}\right]$.

CHAPTER 12

SOLUTION BY SERIES

101. Introduction

The preceding chapters have been concerned mainly with solving special types of differential equations. This chapter is concerned with a general method called **integration in series.** This method may be applied to solve a large variety of differential equations, and it generally gives the complete solution.

It will be convenient to use the summation notation, which is expressed by

$$\sum_{n=p}^{q} a_n x^n = a_p x^p + a_{p+1}x^{p+1} + \cdots + a_q x^q, \qquad p \leqq q, \tag{1}$$

and this will be endless if q is infinite. Observe that

$$\sum_{n=p}^{\infty} \mathbf{a}_n \mathbf{x}^n = \sum_{n=0}^{\infty} \mathbf{a}_{n+p}\mathbf{x}^{n+p}. \tag{2}$$

As an example of the use of (1) and (2), note that

$$\sum_{n=0}^{\infty} a_n x^n = \sum_{n=0}^{5} a_n x^n + \sum_{n=6}^{\infty} a_n x^n = \sum_{n=0}^{5} a_n x^n + \sum_{n=0}^{\infty} a_{n+6} x^{n+6}. \tag{3}$$

The following facts concerning infinite series are involved in this chapter: If two infinite power series,

$$\begin{aligned} \sum_{n=0}^{\infty} a_n(x-a)^n &= a_0 + a_1(x-a) + a_2(x-a)^2 + \cdots, \\ \sum_{n=0}^{\infty} b_n(x-a)^n &= b_0 + b_1(x-a) + b_2(x-a)^2 + \cdots, \end{aligned} \tag{4}$$

are absolutely convergent in an interval $a - r < x < a + r$, then, within this same interval of convergence, they represent continuous functions of x, say $\varphi(x-a)$ and $\psi(x-a)$, and

$$\varphi(x-a) + \psi(x-a) = a_0 + b_0 + (a_1 + b_1)(x-a) + \cdots + (a_n + b_n)(x-a)^n + \cdots, \tag{5}$$

$$\frac{d^k[\varphi(x-a)]}{dx^k} = \sum_{n=0}^{\infty} \frac{d^k}{dx^k} a_n (x-a)^n, \qquad \frac{d^k[\psi(x-a)]}{dx^k} = \sum_{n=0}^{\infty} b_n \frac{d^k}{dx^k} (x-a)^n. \quad (6)$$

A similar statement applies to any finite number of infinite series.*

If for all values of x in a finite interval

$$\sum_{n=0}^{\infty} a_n x^n = \sum_{n=0}^{\infty} b_n x^n, \qquad \textit{then} \qquad a_n = b_n, \qquad n = 0, 1, \ldots, \infty. \quad (7)$$

Cauchy's **ratio test** *states that a series of positive constants* $\sum_{n=0}^{\infty} A_n$ *is absolutely convergent if*

$$\lim_{n\to\infty} |A_n/A_{n+1}| > 1. \quad (8)$$

Thus, for x a fixed number, the series $\sum_{n=0}^{\infty} 8^{-n}(x-5)^{3n}$ converges absolutely if

$$\lim_{n\to\infty} |8^{-n}(x-5)^{3n}/[8^{-(n+1)}(x-5)^{3(n+1)}]| > 1, \quad \text{or} \quad \lim_{n\to\infty} |8/(x-5)^3| > 1.$$

Evidently, this will hold if $|x-5| < 2$, or $5 - 2 < x < 5 + 2$.

EXERCISES

1. If, for every value of x, $\sum_{n=5}^{\infty} \frac{5x^n}{n!} = \sum_{m=0}^{\infty} a_m x^m$, find the values of the constants a_m.

2. Show that† $\sum_{n=0}^{\infty} \frac{x^n 2^n}{n!} = 1 + 2x + 2x^2 + \sum_{n=0}^{\infty} \frac{x^{n+3}2^{n+3}}{(n+3)!}$.

3. Using (2), show that $\sum_{r=0}^{\infty} \frac{rx^r}{r!} = \sum_{r=1}^{\infty} \frac{x^r}{(r-1)!} = \sum_{s=0}^{\infty} \frac{x^{s+1}}{s!}$.

4. Using (2), show that $\sum_{r=6}^{\infty} \frac{(x+3)x^r}{r!} = \sum_{s=0}^{\infty} \frac{x^{s+7} + 3x^{s+6}}{(s+6)!}$.

5. Show that

$$\sum_{n=0}^{\infty} [n(n-1)a_n x^{n-2} - a_n x^{n+1}] = \sum_{n=-3}^{\infty} (n+3)(n+2)a_{n+3}x^{n+1} - \sum_{n=0}^{\infty} a_n x^{n+1}.$$

* See R. Courant, "Differential and Integral Calculus," vol. I, pp. 401–404, Interscience Publishers, Inc., New York.

† Assume that $0! = 1$ and $1! = 1$, $n! = 1 \cdot 2 \cdot 3 \cdots n$.

6. Use (8) in determining the interval of absolute convergence of each series:

(a) $\sum_{n=0}^{\infty} 9^{-n}x^{2n}$. (b) $\sum_{n=0}^{\infty} \frac{4^{-n}(x-3)^{2n}}{n+1}$. (c) $\sum_{n=1}^{\infty} \frac{(-1)^{n+1}x^{2n-1}}{(2n-1)!}$.

102. Integration in series

When an equation cannot be solved by any of the methods already discussed, we may try to find a convergent series which will express the value of the dependent variable in terms of the independent variable to any required degree of accuracy. We shall solve a problem to illustrate a method of finding such a series.

Example 1. Solve the following differential equation for y as a power series in x:

$$\frac{d^2y}{dx^2} - xy = 0. \tag{a}$$

Solution. Assume that there exists a solution having the form

$$y = c_0 + c_1x + c_2x^2 + \cdots + c_nx^n + \cdots, \tag{b}$$

or, using the summation notation,

$$y = \sum_{n=0}^{\infty} c_nx^n, \tag{c}$$

where the c's are constants to be determined. Substitute y from (b) in (a) to obtain

$$\begin{aligned}2c_2 + 2\cdot 3c_3x + 3\cdot 4c_4x^2 + \cdots + n(n-1)c_nx^{n-2} + \cdots \\ - c_0x - c_1x^2 - \cdots - c_{n-3}x^{n-2} - \cdots = 0.\end{aligned} \tag{d}$$

Since (b) is a solution of (a), equation (d) is an identity. Hence, equating the coefficients of x to zero, obtain

$$\begin{gathered}2c_2 = 0, \quad 3\cdot 2c_3 - c_0 = 0, \quad 4\cdot 3c_4 - c_1 = 0, \quad \ldots, \\ n(n-1)c_n - c_{n-3} = 0.\end{gathered} \tag{e}$$

Solving equations (e) for $c_2, c_3, \ldots$ in terms of c_0 and c_1, we find

$$\begin{gathered}c_2 = 0, \quad c_3 = \frac{c_0}{2\cdot 3}, \quad c_4 = \frac{c_1}{3\cdot 4}, \quad c_5 = 0, \\ c_6 = \frac{c_3}{5\cdot 6} = \frac{c_0}{2\cdot 3\cdot 5\cdot 6}, \quad c_7 = \frac{c_4}{6\cdot 7} = \frac{c_1}{3\cdot 4\cdot 6\cdot 7}, \\ \ldots, \quad c_n = \frac{c_{n-3}}{n(n-1)}.\end{gathered} \tag{f}$$

We may write the first six terms of the solution by substituting the values from (f) in (b) to obtain

$$y = c_0 + c_1x + \frac{c_0}{2 \cdot 3} x^3 + \frac{c_1}{3 \cdot 4} x^4 + \frac{c_0}{2 \cdot 3 \cdot 5 \cdot 6} x^6 + \frac{c_1}{3 \cdot 4 \cdot 6 \cdot 7} x^7 + \cdots . \quad (g)$$

This is the important part of the solution for values of x near zero.

However, a law for writing any number of terms is desired. By rearranging the values for the c's found in (f) and by using the last equation of (f) successively for different values of n, we find

$$c_0 = c_0, \quad c_1 = c_1, \quad c_2 = 0, \quad c_3 = \frac{c_0}{2 \cdot 3}, \quad c_4 = \frac{c_1}{3 \cdot 4},$$
$$c_5 = 0, \quad c_6 = \frac{1 \cdot 4c_0}{6!}, \quad c_7 = \frac{2 \cdot 5c_1}{7!}, \quad c_8 = 0, \quad (h)$$
$$c_{3n} = \frac{1 \cdot 4 \cdot 7 \cdots (3n - 2)c_0}{(3n)!}, \quad c_{3n+1} = \frac{2 \cdot 5 \cdot 8 \cdots (3n - 1)c_1}{(3n + 1)!},$$
$$c_{3n+2} = 0.$$

Substituting the values of the c's from (h) in (b), we obtain

$$y = c_0\left[1 + \frac{x^3}{3!} + \cdots + \frac{1 \cdot 4 \cdot 7 \cdots (3n - 2)}{(3n)!} x^{3n} + \cdots\right] + c_1\left[x + \frac{2x^4}{4!} + \cdots + \frac{2 \cdot 5 \cdot 8 \cdots (3n - 1)x^{3n+1}}{(3n + 1)!} + \cdots\right], \quad (i)$$

or, using the summation notation,

$$\mathbf{y} = \mathbf{c}_0 + \mathbf{c}_1\mathbf{x} + \mathbf{c}_0 \sum_{n=1}^{\infty} \frac{\mathbf{1 \cdot 4 \cdot 7 \cdots (3n - 2)}}{\mathbf{(3n)!}} \mathbf{x}^{3n} + \mathbf{c}_1 \sum_{n=1}^{\infty} \frac{\mathbf{2 \cdot 5 \cdot 8 \cdots (3n - 1)x}^{3n+1}}{\mathbf{(3n + 1)!}}. \quad (j)$$

By applying Cauchy's ratio test we find that the two series of (i) are absolutely convergent for all values of x. Hence, in accordance with §101, each series represents, for all values of x, a function of x, their sum represents a function of x, and their derivatives may be found by using term-by-term differentiation. We can see by the method of derivation of (i), or by direct trial, that (i) satisfies (a). Also, we know by Theorem II, §95, that there is a unique solution of (a) satisfying the condition $y = c_0$, $dy/dx = c_1$ when $x = 0$, and since (i) satisfies these conditions, it is that unique solution. Like arguments could be used to validate all the other solutions of this chapter.

Alternate solution. A shorter solution results from using the summation notation. Substituting $y = \sum_{n=0}^{\infty} c_n x^n$ in (a), we get directly

$$\frac{d^2y}{dx^2} - xy = \sum_{n=0}^{\infty} \left[n(n-1)c_n x^{n-2} - c_n x^{n+1} \right]$$
$$= \sum_{n=-3}^{\infty} (n+3)(n+2)c_{n+3}x^{n+1} - \sum_{n=0}^{\infty} c_n x^{n+1} = 0. \qquad (k)$$

If we take $c_2 = 0$, we see that the three terms of the first sum in line (k) are zero, when $n = -3, -2$, and -1; hence, all terms in line (k) will vanish if $(n+2)(n+3)c_{n+3} = c_n$. In other words, $y = \sum_{n=0}^{\infty} c_n x^n$ satisfies $d^2y/dx^2 - xy = 0$, if

$$c_0 = c_0, \qquad c_1 = c_1, \qquad c_2 = 0, \qquad c_{n+3} = c_n/[(n+2)(n+3)], \qquad (l)$$

where $n = 1, 2, \ldots$. Using $n = 0, 1, 2, 3, \ldots$ in line (l), we obtain

$$c_3 = c_0/(2 \cdot 3), \qquad c_4 = c_1/(3 \cdot 4), \qquad c_5 = c_2/(4 \cdot 5),$$
$$c_6 = c_3/(5 \cdot 6) = c_0/(2 \cdot 3 \cdot 5 \cdot 6) = 4c_0/6!,$$
$$c_7 = c_4/(6 \cdot 7) = 2 \cdot 5c_1/7!,$$

and so on, until we get equations (h). We then write the answer (i) or (j).

Example 2. Find, by using a Maclaurin series, the solution of

$$\frac{d^2y}{dx^2} - x\frac{dy}{dx} - 2y = 0, \qquad (a)$$

for which $y' = 0$, $y = 1$ when $x = 0$.

Solution. Using the notation $y^{(k)} = (d^ky)/dx^k$, we obtain from (a)

$$\begin{aligned} y^{(2)} &= xy^{(1)} + 2y, \\ y^{(3)} &= xy^{(2)} + 3y^{(1)}, \\ y^{(4)} &= xy^{(3)} + 4y^{(2)}, \\ &\cdots\cdots\cdots\cdots \\ y^{(n)} &= xy^{(n-1)} + ny^{(n-2)}. \end{aligned} \qquad (b)$$

In (b), substitute 0 for x, 1 for y, 0 for $y^{(1)}$, and solve the resulting equations for $y_0^{(2)}, y_0^{(3)}, \ldots, y_0^{(2n-1)}, y_0^{(2n)}$, to get

$$y_0^{(2)} = 2, \qquad y_0^{(3)} = 0, \qquad y_0^{(4)} = 2 \cdot 4, \qquad \ldots, \qquad y_0^{(2n-1)} = 0,$$
$$y_0^{(2n)} = 2 \cdot 4 \cdots 2n. \qquad (c)$$

Observing that $2 \cdot 4 \cdot 6 \cdots 2n = 2^n n!$, and substituting the values (*c*) in Maclaurin's series,

$$y = y_0 + y_0^{(1)}x + (1/2!)y_0^{(2)}x^2 + (1/3!)y_0^{(3)}x^3 + \cdots + [1/(n)!]y_0^{(n)}x^n + \cdots, \qquad (d)$$

we get after slight simplification

$$\mathbf{y} = \mathbf{1} + \frac{\mathbf{x}^2}{\mathbf{1}} + \frac{\mathbf{x}^4}{\mathbf{1 \cdot 3}} + \frac{\mathbf{x}^6}{\mathbf{1 \cdot 3 \cdot 5}} + \cdots + \frac{\mathbf{x}^{2n}}{\mathbf{1 \cdot 3 \cdot 5} \cdots \mathbf{(2n-1)}} + \cdots. \qquad (e)$$

Remark. Most of the problems in the following exercises can be solved by using Maclaurin's series or Taylor's series.

EXERCISES

Solve differential equations 1 to 6 by using infinite series of form (*b*) of example 1. *D* means d/dx.

1. $Dy - y = 0$.

2. $Dy - 2xy = 0$.

3. $D^2y - x^2y = 0$.

4. $(x^2 + 1)D^2y + 6xDy + 6y = 0$.

5. $(x^2 - 1)D^2y - 6y = 0$.

6. $x^2D^2y - 4xDy + 6y = 0$.

7. Find a solution of $(x^2 - 2x)D^2y + 6(x - 1)Dy + 6y = 0$ in series having the form

$$y = \sum_{n=0}^{\infty} c_n(x - 1)^n.$$

8. Find a solution of $(x^2 + 2x)D^2y + 8(x + 1)Dy + 12y = 0$ in a series having the form

$$y = \sum_{n=0}^{\infty} c_n(x + 1)^n.$$

Use series proceeding in powers of x to find the first five terms in the solutions of equations 9 and 10. Avoid the method using summation symbols.

9. $(x - 1)D^2y + y = 0$.

10. $(x^2 + 1)D^2y + xDy + xy = 0$.

11. Find a particular solution of $x^2(dy/dx) - y = 5x^{-3} + 3x^{-2}$ by series. If $y = c_3x^{-3} + c_4x^{-4} + \cdots + c_nx^{-n} + \cdots$, show that $c_3 = -1$, that $c_4 = -1$, $c_5 = \frac{1}{5}$, etc.

★12. The theory of the oscillator in quantum mechanics uses those solutions of the equation

$$-\frac{d^2u}{dx^2} + x^2u = (2n + 1)u, \qquad n \text{ constant}, \qquad (a)$$

that remain finite as x increases without limit. Find these solutions.

First show that $u = e^{-\frac{1}{2}x^2}$ satisfies (*a*) when $n = 0$. Then let

$$u = ve^{-\frac{1}{2}x^2}$$

in (*a*), and deduce the equation

$$\frac{d^2v}{dx^2} - 2x\frac{dv}{dx} + 2nv = 0. \qquad (b)$$

Next solve (*b*) to obtain the solutions v_1 and v_2 as infinite series. Now show that the solutions of (*a*)

$$u = v_1e^{-\frac{1}{2}x^2}, \qquad u = v_2e^{-\frac{1}{2}x^2} \qquad (c)$$

satisfy the required condition when and only when n is zero or a positive integer. Write the solutions (*c*) when $n = 0$, $n = 2$, and $n = 3$.

★**13.** Find the general solution of $D^2y + xDy + 2y = x$.

103. Solution involving a more general type of series

A function $f(x)$ is analytic at a value a of x if it can be expanded in an infinite series having the form

$$f(x) = a_0 + a_1(x - a) + a_2(x - a)^2 + \cdots + a_n(x - a)^n + \cdots, \qquad (9)$$

which converges absolutely in an interval $a - r < x < a + s$, where $r > 0$ and $s > 0$.

Series solutions in powers of $x - a$ of a differential equation

$$D^2y + p(x)Dy + q(x)y = 0 \qquad (10)$$

exist if D means d/dx and $p(x)$ and $q(x)$ are analytic at $x = a$. They can be found by the method used in §102.

This section and the next will deal mainly with differential equations having the form

$$D^2y + \frac{p(x)}{x}Dy + \frac{q(x)}{x^2}y = 0, \qquad (11)$$

where at least one of the functions $p(x)/x$, $q(x)/x^2$ is not analytic at $x = 0$. In this section, we shall derive solutions of equations of type (11) by using series having the form

$$y = x^m(c_0 + c_1x + c_2x^2 + \cdots + c_nx^n + \cdots), \qquad (12)$$

where m is a real number. The next section will deal with special cases of (11) in which series of form (12) play a prominent role.

If y in (11), *cleared of fractions, is replaced by x^m, the equation obtained by equating to zero the coefficient of the lowest* (*or highest, in case a series of descending powers is used*) *power of x in the result is called the* **indicial equation.**

Example. Solve $2x^2D^2y + 3xDy - (x^2 + 1)y = 0$.

Solution. Substituting y from (12) in the given equation, obtain after some simplification

$$c_0[2m(m-1)+3m-1]+c_1[2(m+1)m+3(m+1)-1]x$$
$$+\sum_{n=2}^{\infty}\{[2(n+m)(n+m-1)+3(n+m)-1]c_n-c_{n-2}\}x^n=0. \quad (a)$$

The number m being at our disposal is chosen so as to make the first term of (a) vanish. Therefore, let

$$(m+1)(2m-1)=0, \qquad m=-1, \qquad m=\tfrac{1}{2}. \quad (b)$$

To dispose of the second term of (a), take $c_1 = 0$. From the third part of (a), obtain

$$c_n=\frac{c_{n-2}}{(n+m+1)[2(n+m)-1]}. \quad (c)$$

Substituting -1 from (b) for m in (c), obtain

$$c_n=\frac{c_{n-2}}{n(2n-3)}. \quad (d)$$

Now using $m = -1$, $c_0 = c_0$, $c_1 = 0$, and (d) with $n = 2, 4, 6, \ldots$ in (12) we obtain

$$\mathbf{y}_1=\mathbf{c}_0\mathbf{x}^{-1}\left(1+\frac{\mathbf{x}^2}{2\cdot 1}+\frac{\mathbf{x}^4}{2\cdot 4\cdot 1\cdot 5}+\frac{\mathbf{x}^6}{2\cdot 4\cdot 6\cdot 1\cdot 5\cdot 9}+\cdots\right). \quad (e)$$

Similarly, substituting $\frac{1}{2}$ from (b) for m in (c), obtain

$$c_n=\frac{c_{n-2}}{(2n+3)n}. \quad (f)$$

Then, using in (12) $m = \frac{1}{2}$, $c_0 = b$, $c_1 = 0$, and (f) with $n = 2, 4, 6, \ldots,$ we get

$$\mathbf{y}_2=\mathbf{b}\mathbf{x}^{\frac{1}{2}}\left(1+\frac{\mathbf{x}^2}{2\cdot 7}+\frac{\mathbf{x}^4}{2\cdot 4\cdot 7\cdot 11}+\frac{\mathbf{x}^6}{2\cdot 4\cdot 6\cdot 7\cdot 11\cdot 15}+\cdots\right). \quad (g)$$

The general solution is

$$\mathbf{y}=\mathbf{y}_1+\mathbf{y}_2. \quad (h)$$

When the degree in m of the indicial equation is less than the order of the equation to be solved, a solution may be found by using a series of descending powers of x, having the form

$$y=x^m(c_0+c_1x^{-1}+c_2x^{-2}+\cdots).$$

The procedure in this case is the same as when equation (1) is used. Exercises 9 to 11 below involve this type of expansion.

EXERCISES

Solve the following differential equations:

1. $2xD^2y+Dy-2y=0.$

2. $(x^3-x)D^2y+(8x^2-2)Dy+12xy=0.$

3. $xD^2y + 3Dy - x^2y = 0.$ **4.** $x^2D^2y + (x + 2x^2)Dy - 4y = 0.$

5. Show that the regular procedure gives as the solution of $x^2D^2y - x^2Dy + (x - 2)y = 0$

$$y = c_0x^2\left(1 + \frac{1}{4}x + \frac{1}{4\cdot 5}x^2 + \cdots\right) + c_1x^{-1}\left(1 + x + \frac{1}{2!}x^2 + \frac{1}{3!}x^3 + \cdots\right).$$

Then show that this can be written

$$y = c_1\left(x^{-1} + 1 + \frac{1}{2}x\right) + cx^2\left(1 + \frac{1}{4}x + \frac{1}{4\cdot 5}x^2 + \cdots\right),$$

where $c = c_0 + \frac{1}{6}c_1$.

6. $(x^3 - x)D^2y + (4x^2 - 2)Dy + 2xy = 0.$

7. $(x - x^2)D^2y - (x + 1)Dy + y = 0.$

8. $x^4D^2y + xDy + y = 0.$ *Hint:* Let $y = x^m(c_0 + c_1x^{-1} + c_2x^{-2} + \cdots).$

9. Show that the solution of $(x^4 - x^2)D^2y + 2xDy - (2 + 2x^2)y = 0$ is

$$y = Ax^2 + Bx(1 - x^2 - \tfrac{1}{3}x^4 - \tfrac{1}{5}x^6 - \tfrac{1}{7}x^8 - \cdots).$$

Show that

$$y = cx^{-1}(1 + \tfrac{3}{5}x^{-2} + \tfrac{3}{7}x^{-4} + \tfrac{3}{9}x^{-6} + \cdots)$$

is also a solution which converges when $|x| > 1$. Note that the series in the first solution converges when $|x| < 1$ and that y does not exist for either solution when $x = 1$. It is interesting to observe that the conditions of Theorem II in §95 for the given differential equation are not satisfied for a region in which x may be zero, 1, or -1.

10. To solve $x^4D^2y + xDy - 2y = 0$, let $y = x^m(c_0 + c_1x + c_2x^2 + \cdots)$ to obtain the solution $y = cx^2(1 - x^2 + 3x^4 - 3\cdot 5x^6 + \cdots)$, and show that this series diverges for all values of x except zero. Solve the differential equation by using $y = x^m(c_0 + c_1x^{-1} + c_2x^{-2} + \cdots)$, and show that the series thus obtained converges for all values of x except zero.

11. Show that a solution of

$$(x^4 - x^2)D^2y - (2x^3 - 3x)Dy + (2x^2 - 3)y = 0$$

is

$$y = c_0x + c_1x^3\left(1 + \frac{1}{4}x^2 + \frac{1\,3}{4\,6}x^4 + \frac{1\cdot 3\cdot 5}{4\cdot 6\cdot 8}x^6 + \cdots\right).$$

Also, derive the solution

$$y = cx^2\left[1 + \frac{(-1)}{2}x^{-2} + \frac{(-1)(1)}{2\cdot 4}x^{-4} + \frac{(-1)(1)(3)}{2\cdot 4\cdot 6}x^{-6} + \cdots\right].$$

★**12.** $x^3D^3y + 6x^2D^2y + 6xDy + a^3x^3y = 0.$

★**13.** Find a particular solution of $x^2D^2y + xDy - (1 + x^2)y = x^{\frac{3}{2}}$.

104. Indicial equation has roots differing by an integer

While the statements made below refer to second-order equations at $x = 0$, they may easily be extended to apply for linear equations of any order at $x = a$. When two roots of the indicial equation for an equation of type (11) of §103 are equal, the process of §103 fails to give the general solution at $x = 0$ and the same thing may be true when two roots differ by an integer. The following example will illustrate the procedure to be used in solving such equations:

Example. Solve

$$x^2D^2y + 2xDy - xy = 0. \tag{a}$$

Solution. In the given equation substitute

$$y = x^m(c_0 + c_1x + c_2x^2 + \cdots + c_nx^n + \cdots). \tag{b}$$

Collect the coefficients of like terms, and simplify to obtain

$$c_0(m^2 + m) + \sum_{n=1}^{\infty} [c_n(n + m)(n + m + 1) - c_{n-1}]x^n = 0. \tag{c}$$

Solving the indicial equation for m, we get

$$c_0(m^2 + m) = 0, \qquad m = 0, -1. \tag{d}$$

Equating the coefficient of x^n to 0 in (c) and solving for c_n, we obtain

$$c_n = \frac{c_{n-1}}{(m + n)(m + n + 1)}. \tag{e}$$

Solve (e) for the c's in terms of c_0, and substitute the results in (b) to obtain

$$\begin{aligned} Y &= c_0x^m\left[m+1+\frac{x\cancel{(m+1)}}{\cancel{(m+1)}(m+2)}+\frac{x^2}{(m+2)^2(m+3)}+\cdots\right] \\ &= c_0x^m\left[m+1+\sum_{n=1}^{\infty}\frac{x^n}{(m+2)^2(m+3)^2\cdots(m+n)^2(m+n+1)}\right], \end{aligned} \tag{f}$$

where we have replaced c_0 by $c_0(m + 1)$ to avoid a zero in denominators when $m = -1$ from (d). Substituting $m = 0$ from (d) in (f), we obtain one solution of (a):

$$\begin{aligned} y_1 &= c_0\left(1 + \frac{x}{1 \cdot 2} + \frac{x^2}{2^2 \cdot 3} + \frac{x^3}{2^2 \cdot 3^2 \cdot 4} + \cdots\right) \\ &= c_0 \sum_{n=0}^{\infty} \frac{x^n}{n!(n + 1)!}. \end{aligned} \tag{g}$$

If we replace m in (f) by -1, we duplicate (g) and must seek further. Replacing y in the left-hand member of (a) by Y from (f), obtain

$$x^2D^2Y + 2xDY - xY = c_0(m + 1)(m + 1)mx^m \tag{h}$$

no matter what value m may have. Now, taking the derivative of (h) partially with respect to m and noting that $\partial(D^kY)/\partial m = D^k(\partial Y/\partial m)$, obtain

$$x^2D^2\left(\frac{\partial Y}{\partial m}\right) + 2xD\left(\frac{\partial Y}{\partial m}\right) - x\frac{\partial Y}{\partial m} = c_0(m+1)(3m+1)x^m + c_0m(m+1)^2x^m \ln x. \quad (i)$$

Since, when $m = -1$, the right-hand member of (i) is zero, we see that

$$\mathbf{y}_2 = \left(\frac{\partial \mathbf{Y}}{\partial \mathbf{m}}\right)_{m=-1} \quad (j)$$

is a solution of (a). The general solution of (a) then is

$$\mathbf{y} = \mathbf{A}\mathbf{y}_1 + \mathbf{B}(\partial \mathbf{Y}/\partial \mathbf{m})_{m=-1}. \quad (k)$$

In finding $\partial Y/\partial m$, formula (14) below, got by logarithmic differentiation, is useful. If

$$f(m) = \frac{(m-a_1)(m-a_2)\cdots(m-a_n)}{(m-b_1)(m-b_2)\cdots(m-b_t)}, \quad (13)$$

then

$$\frac{\partial f(m)}{\partial m} = f(m)\left(\sum_{k=1}^{n}\frac{1}{m-a_k} - \sum_{k=1}^{t}\frac{1}{m-b_k}\right). \quad (14)$$

From (f) we get

$$\frac{\partial Y}{\partial m} = Y\ln x + c_0x^m\left[1 - \frac{x}{(m+2)^2} + x^2\frac{-2/(m+2) - 1/(m+3)}{(m+2)^2(m+3)} + x^3\frac{-2/(m+2) - 2/(m+3) - 1/(m+4)}{(m+2)^2(m+3)^2(m+4)} + \cdots\right]. \quad (l)$$

By finding a few terms from (g) and from (l) with $m = -1$, we can indicate the answer in the form

$$y = c_0\left(1 + \frac{x}{1!2!} + \frac{x^2}{2!3!} + \frac{x^3}{3!4!} + \cdots\right) + c_1x^{-1}\ln x\left(x + \frac{x^2}{1!2!} + \frac{x^3}{2!3!} + \cdots\right) + c_1x^{-1}\left[1 - x + \frac{x^2}{1!2!}\left(-\frac{2}{1} - \frac{1}{2}\right) + \cdots\right]. \quad (m)$$

Observing that the second parenthesized expression in (m) is x times the quantity in the first parentheses, and generalizing, we can write (m) in the form

$$y = (c_0 + c_1\ln x)\sum_{n=0}^{\infty}\frac{x^n}{n!(n+1)!} + c_1x^{-1}\left[1 - x - \sum_{n=2}^{\infty}\frac{x^n}{(n-1)!n!}\left(\frac{1}{n} + \sum_{k=1}^{n-1}\frac{2}{k}\right)\right]. \quad (n)$$

Remark. To deal with equations of type (11), §103, for which the method of §103 fails, use a general series of type (*b*), write the general equation corresponding to (*f*) with the constant term $c(m - \beta)$, where β is the lesser root of the indicial equation, and then use the formula

$$y = A(Y)_{m=\alpha} + B\left(\frac{\partial Y}{\partial m}\right)_{m=\beta}. \tag{15}$$

A similar kind of procedure is effective for many differential equations of higher order.

EXERCISES

1. Using the regular procedure for $(x^2 - x)D^2y + xDy - y = 0$, obtain

$$Y = c_0x^m\left(1 + \frac{m-1}{m}x + \frac{m-1}{m+1}x^2 + \cdots + \frac{m-1}{m+n-1}x^n + \cdots\right). \quad (a)$$

Show that the roots of the indicial equation are 0, 1. Get one solution by substituting 1 for m in (*a*). Replace c_0 in (*a*) by c_0m, and use $y_2 = (\partial Y/\partial m)_{m=0}$ on the result to get a second solution.

2. For the equation $(x^3 + x^2)D^2y + xDy - 2xy = 0$, obtain

$$Y = c_0x^m\left[1 - \frac{m-2}{m+1}x + \frac{(m-2)(m-1)}{(m+1)(m+2)}x^2 + \sum_{n=3}^{\infty}\frac{(-1)^n(m-2)(m-1)mx^n}{(m+n-2)(m+n-1)(m+n)}\right].$$

Show that the roots of the indicial equation are 0, 0. Now, find the solution by using $y = Y_{m=0} + (\partial Y/\partial m)_{m=0}$.

Solve the following equations:

3. $xD^2y + Dy - xy = 0$.

4. $xD^2y - y = 0$.

5. $xD^2y + Dy + y = 0$.

6. $xD^2y + Dy - x^2y = 0$.

7. $xD^2y + 3Dy + xy = 0$.

★8. $x^3D^2y - y = 0$. Use a series having the form $y = x^m(c_0 + c_1x^{-1} + c_2x^{-2} + \cdots)$.

★9. $x^2D^4y + 6xD^3y + 6D^2y - y = 0$. Show that the roots of the indicial equation are 1, 0, 0, −1. Write an equation for Y in terms of m with $c_0(m + 1)$ taken as constant. The four parts of the solution are $Y_{m=1}$, $Y_{m=0}$, $(\partial Y/\partial m)_{m=0}$, $(\partial Y/\partial m)_{m=-1}$.

105. The gamma function

The **gamma function** is widely used in the applications of differential equations involving infinite series. For $p > 0$, we define gamma function $\Gamma(p)$ by

$$\Gamma(p) = \int_0^\infty x^{p-1}e^{-x}\,dx. \tag{16}$$

Applying integration by parts to the right-hand member, we get

$$\int_0^\infty x^{p-1}e^{-x}\,dx = [-x^{p-1}e^{-x}]_0^\infty + (p-1)\int_0^\infty x^{p-2}e^{-x}\,dx. \tag{17}$$

The first term in the left-hand member is zero if $p > 1$. Therefore, from (17) and (16) we get

$$\Gamma(\mathbf{p}) = (\mathbf{p} - \mathbf{1})\Gamma(\mathbf{p} - \mathbf{1}). \tag{18}$$

From (16), we get by direct integration

$$\Gamma(1) = 1. \tag{19}$$

Applying (18) repeatedly to $\Gamma(5)$, we obtain

$$\Gamma(5) = 4\Gamma(4) = 4 \cdot 3\Gamma(3) = 4 \cdot 3 \cdot 2\Gamma(2) = 4 \cdot 3 \cdot 2 \cdot 1 = 4!.$$

Evidently the same procedure for p a positive integer gives

$$\Gamma(p + 1) = p!.$$

The values of $\Gamma(p)$, where $0 < p \leqq 1$, have been computed from (16) by means of infinite series. A few values are shown in Table 1:

TABLE 1

p	0.1	0.2	0.3	0.4	0.5	0.6	0.7	0.8	0.9
$\Gamma(p)$	9.5	4.59	2.99	2.22	$\sqrt{\pi}$	1.49	1.30	1.16	1.07

The integral (16) does not define a value if $p \leqq 0$. However, we define the values of $\Gamma(p)$ for all real numbers as follows:

$\Gamma(p) = (p - 1)\Gamma(p - 1)$ *if* p *is neither zero nor a negative integer.*
$1/\Gamma(p) \to 0$ *as* p *approaches zero or a negative integer.*
$\Gamma(p)$ *is found from a table or computed directly from* (16) *if* $0 < p \leqq 1$.
Figure 1 shows the graph of $\Gamma(x)$.

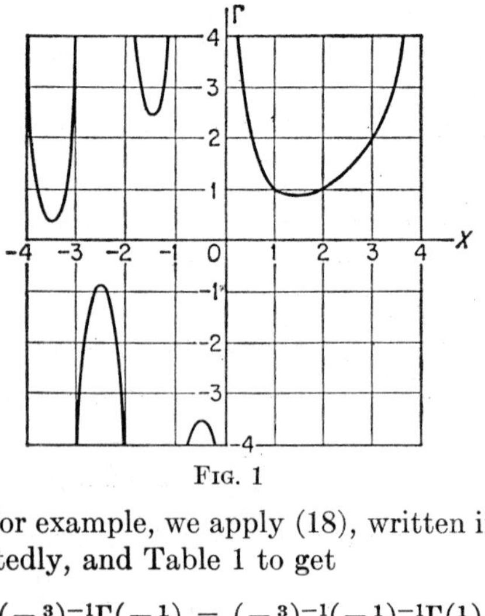

FIG. 1

To find $\Gamma(-\frac{3}{2})$, for example, we apply (18), written in the form $\Gamma(p) = p^{-1}\Gamma(p + 1)$ repeatedly, and Table 1 to get

$$\Gamma(-\tfrac{3}{2}) = (-\tfrac{3}{2})^{-1}\Gamma(-\tfrac{1}{2}) = (-\tfrac{3}{2})^{-1}(-\tfrac{1}{2})^{-1}\Gamma(\tfrac{1}{2}) = \tfrac{4}{3}\sqrt{\pi}.$$

EXERCISES

Evaluate:

1. $\Gamma(4)$. **2.** $\Gamma(2.2)$. **3.** $\Gamma(-\frac{1}{2})$. **4.** $\Gamma(-1.3)$.

Express in terms of t if t is not an integer:

5. $\Gamma(3 + t)$. **6.** $\Gamma(-3 + t)$. **7.** $\Gamma(-1 + t) \cdot \Gamma(1 + t)$.

Use (16), (18), and Table 1 to evaluate:

8. $\int_0^\infty t^{1.6}e^{-t}\,dt$. **9.** $\int_0^\infty t^{-0.5}e^{-t}\,dt$.

10. $\int_0^\infty t^2e^{-t^2}\,dt$. *Hint:* Let $x = t^2$.

11. Evaluate $\int_0^\infty x^{\frac{9}{2}}e^{-x^3}\,dx$. *Hint:* Let $t = x^3$.

12. For what integral values of t will

$$(t + 100)(t + 99)(t + 98) \cdots (t + 56) = \Gamma(t + 101)/\Gamma(t + 56)?$$

13. In what intervals is $\Gamma(t)$ negative?

14. By using reduction formulas, we can show that

$$\int_0^{\frac{1}{2}\pi} \sin^m \theta \cos^n \theta \, d\theta = \frac{\Gamma[\frac{1}{2}(m + 1)]\Gamma[\frac{1}{2}(n + 1)]}{2\Gamma[\frac{1}{2}(m + n + 2)]},$$

where m and n are integers with $m \geqq 0$, $n \geqq 0$. Using this formula and remembering that $\Gamma(\frac{1}{2}) = \sqrt{\pi}$, evaluate

(*a*) $\int_0^{\frac{1}{2}\pi} \sin^2 \theta \cos^4 \theta \, d\theta$. (*b*) $\int_0^{\frac{1}{2}\pi} \sin^3 \theta \cos^5 \theta \, d\theta$. (*c*) $\int_0^{\frac{1}{2}\pi} \sin^6 \theta \cos^8 \theta \, d\theta$.

106. Bessel's equation

Just as $d^2y/dx^2 + k^2y = 0$ defines the trigonometric functions and $x\,dy/dx = k$ the logarithmic functions, so also does

$$\mathbf{x^2 \frac{d^2y}{dx^2} + x \frac{dy}{dx} + (x^2 - k^2)y = 0} \tag{20}$$

define **Bessel's functions.** These have a wide field of applications; they are effective in solving the problems of flow of heat and of electricity in cylinders, the problems of the vibration of membranes, and many other problems. Volumes have been written on Bessel's functions and their applications, and extensive tables of their values have been computed. Some theory of these functions and of other outstanding functions will be developed in this chapter, and applications will be considered in later chapters.

The theory developed in §§102 to 104 may be used to solve (20). First get the indicial equation by substituting x^m for y in (20) and equating the coefficient of x^m to zero. This gives

$$m(m - 1) + m - k^2 = 0, \qquad \text{or} \qquad m = \pm k. \tag{21}$$

Next substitute $\sum_{r=0}^{\infty} c_r x^{m+r}$ for y in (20), equate the coefficient of x^{m+r} to zero, solve for c_r, and obtain

$$c_r = \frac{-c_{r-2}}{(m+r+k)(m+r-k)}. \tag{22}$$

Using this with $m = k$, we obtain as a solution of (20)

$$y_1 = c_0 x^k \left[1 - \frac{(x/2)^2}{1(1+k)} + \frac{(x/2)^4}{1 \cdot 2(1+k)(2+k)} - \cdots \right.$$
$$\left. + \frac{(-1)^r \Gamma(k+1)(x/2)^{2r}}{r!\Gamma(r+k+1)} + \cdots \right] = 2^k c_0 \sum_{r=0}^{\infty} \frac{(-1)^r \Gamma(k+1)(x/2)^{2r+k}}{r!\Gamma(r+k+1)}. \tag{23}$$

Similarly, if k is not an integer, we obtain from (23), with $m = -k$,

$$y_2 = 2^{-k} c_0 \sum_{r=0}^{\infty} \frac{(-1)^r \Gamma(1-k)(x/2)^{2r-k}}{r!\Gamma(r-k+1)}. \tag{24}$$

In this case, the solution is

$$y = c_1 y_1 + c_2 y_2. \tag{25}$$

If k is an integer, (24) fails to give a solution and the method of §104 may be applied. From (22) with $c_0 = m + k$, we get

$$Y = x^m \left[m + k + \sum_{r=1}^{\infty} \frac{(-1)^r (m+k) x^{2r}}{\prod_{n=1}^{r} (m+2n+k)(m+2n-k)} \right], \tag{26}$$

where the sign Π indicates the product of the $2r$ factors obtained by replacing n in the denominator of (26) by the numbers $1, 2, \ldots, r$ in succession. Observe that, when $r \geqq k$, the factor $m + k$ cancels. Hence, taking the partial derivative of (26) with respect to m, replacing m by $-k$ in the result, multiplying by $(k-1)!$, and simplifying, we get

$$\left(\frac{\partial Y}{\partial m}\right)_{m=-k}$$
$$= x^{-k} \ln x \sum_{r=k}^{\infty} \frac{2(-1)^{r+k-1}(x/2)^{2r}}{r!(r-k)!} + x^{-k} \sum_{r=0}^{k-1} \frac{(k-r-1)!(x/2)^{2r}}{r!}$$
$$+ x^{-k} \sum_{r=k}^{\infty} \left\{ \frac{2(-1)^{r+k}(x/2)^{2r}}{r!(r-k)!} \sum_{n=1}^{r} \left[\frac{1}{2n} + \frac{1}{2(n-k)} \right] \right\}, \tag{27}$$

where the n in $n - k$ takes on all integral values from 1 to r except k, and $0! = 1$. The solution for the case when $k = 0$ cannot be obtained from (27) by replacing k by zero. This case will be considered in exercise 2. The general solution of (20) when k is any integer not zero is

$$y = c_1y_1 + c_2(\partial Y/\partial m)_{m=-k}. \tag{28}$$

EXERCISES

1. Write the solution of (20) when (*a*) $k = \frac{1}{2}$; (*b*) $k = 3$.

2. Find the general solution of (20) when $k = 0$.

3. Note that the factor $m + k$ cancels from the coefficient of x^{2k} and all succeeding coefficients in (26). Let $m = -k$ in (26), consider k as a positive integer, and derive the solution

$$y_{(m=-k)} = x^{-k}\sum_{r=k}^{\infty}\frac{2(-1)^{r-k+1}(x/2)^{2r}}{r!(k-1)!(n-k)!} = \sum_{r=0}^{\infty}\frac{(-1)^{r+1}(x/2)^{2r+k}}{2^{k-1}(r+k)!(k-1)!r!}.$$

Is this dependent upon (23)?

107. Bessel's functions

The particular form of (23), §106, obtained by setting c_0 equal to $1/[2^k\Gamma(k+1)]$ is denoted by J_k. Hence,

$$\mathbf{J}_n(\mathbf{x}) = \sum_{r=0}^{\infty}\frac{(-1)^r(\mathbf{x}/2)^{2r+n}}{\mathbf{r}!\Gamma(\mathbf{r}+\mathbf{n}+1)}. \tag{29}$$

This is called **Bessel's function of the first kind,** and the function (27) is called **Bessel's function of the second kind.** Series (29) is absolutely convergent for all values of x, except $x = 0$ when $n < 0$.

Denote by $J_{-n}(x)$ the result of replacing n by $-n$ in the right-hand member of (29). Now, let $-n$ approach zero or a negative integer; then, by §105, $1/\Gamma(r - n + 1) \to 0$ when $r \leqq n - 1$, and we get

$$\mathbf{J}_{-n}(\mathbf{x}) = \sum_{r=0}^{\infty}\frac{(-1)^r(\mathbf{x}/2)^{2r-n}}{\mathbf{r}!\Gamma(\mathbf{r}-\mathbf{n}+1)} = \sum_{r=n}^{\infty}\frac{(-1)^r(\mathbf{x}/2)^{2r-n}}{\mathbf{r}!\Gamma(\mathbf{r}-\mathbf{n}+1)}. \tag{30}$$

When n is a positive integer, replace r by $s + n$ in this and obtain

$$J_{-n}(x) = \sum_{s=0}^{\infty}\frac{(-1)^{s+n}(x/2)^{2s+n}}{(s+n)!\Gamma(s+1)} = (-1)^nJ_n(x),$$

or, when n is an integer,

$$\mathbf{J}_{-n}(\mathbf{x}) = (-\mathbf{1})^n\mathbf{J}_n(\mathbf{x}). \tag{31}$$

$J_{\frac{1}{2}}(x)$ may be reduced to a simple and instructive form. Taking $n = \frac{1}{2}$ in (29), we get*

$$J_{\frac{1}{2}}(x) = \sum_{r=0}^{\infty} \frac{(-1)^r(x/2)^{2r+\frac{1}{2}}}{r!\Gamma(r + \frac{3}{2})} = \sum_{r=0}^{\infty} \frac{(-1)^r 2^{\frac{1}{2}}(x/2)^{2r+1}}{x^{\frac{1}{2}}r!(r + \frac{1}{2})(r - \frac{1}{2}) \cdots \frac{1}{2}\Gamma(\frac{1}{2})}. \tag{32}$$

From Table 1, §105, $\Gamma(\frac{1}{2}) = \sqrt{\pi}$. Then the denominator of the last fraction of (32) takes the form

$$x^{\frac{1}{2}}2^{-(2r+1)}2 \cdot 4 \cdots (2r)[1 \cdot 3 \cdot 5 \cdots (2r + 1)]\sqrt{\pi} = x^{\frac{1}{2}}2^{-(2r+1)}(2r + 1)!\sqrt{\pi}.$$

Using this value in (32) and recalling that $\sin x = x - x^3/3! + x^5/5! - \cdots$, we get

$$J_{\frac{1}{2}}(x) = \sqrt{\frac{2}{\pi x}} \sin x. \tag{33}$$

Similarly, we can show that

$$J_{-\frac{1}{2}}(x) = \sqrt{\frac{2}{\pi x}} \cos x. \tag{34}$$

From (33), we see that $n\pi$, where n represents integers not zero, are roots of $J_{\frac{1}{2}}(x)$. Also, from (34) it appears that $(2n + 1)\frac{1}{2}\pi$, n an integer, represents the roots of $J_{-\frac{1}{2}}(x)$. The roots of $J_{\frac{1}{2}}(x)$ lie between corresponding roots of $J_0(x)$ and $J_1(x)$ as indicated by Table 2. The difference between successive roots of $J_0(x)$ approaches π from below, and that for $J_1(x)$ approaches π from above. Figure 2 represents $J_0(x)$ and $J_1(x)$.

TABLE 2

Function	Roots				
$J_0(x)$	2.40	5.52	8.65	11.79	...
$J_{\frac{1}{2}}(x)$	3.14	6.28	9.42	12.57	...
$J_1(x)$	3.85	7.02	10.17	13.32	...

Some formulas, called recurrence formulas, are of basic importance.

* The series (32) is easily proved absolutely convergent for all real values of x.

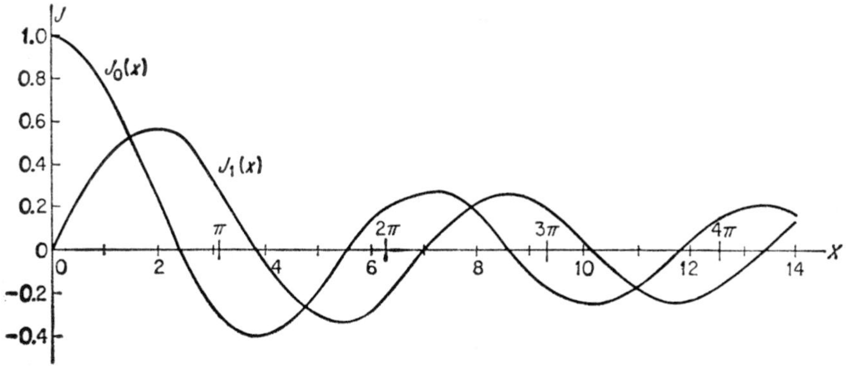

FIG. 2

We have

$$J_n'(x) = \sum_{r=0}^{\infty} \frac{(-1)^r \frac{1}{2}(2r+n)(x/2)^{2r+n-1}}{r!\Gamma(r+n+1)}$$

$$= \sum_{r=1}^{\infty} \frac{(-1)^r (x/2)^{2r+n-1}}{(r-1)!\Gamma(r+n+1)} + \sum_{r=0}^{\infty} \frac{(n/2)(-1)^r (x/2)^{2r+n}(x/2)^{-1}}{r!\Gamma(r+n+1)}$$

$$= \sum_{s=0}^{\infty} \frac{(-1)^{s+1}(x/2)^{2s+n+1}}{s!\Gamma(s+n+2)} + \frac{n}{x} J_n, \quad (35)$$

$$\frac{dJ_n(x)}{dx} = J_n'(x) = -J_{n+1}(x) + \frac{n}{x} J_n(x). \quad (36)$$

Also, from the first fraction of (35) we get

$$J_n' = \sum_{r=0}^{\infty} \frac{(-1)^r \frac{1}{2}(2r+2n-n)(x/2)^{2r+n-1}}{r!(r+n)\Gamma(r+n)} = \sum_{r=0}^{\infty} \frac{(-1)^r x^{2r+n-1}}{r!\Gamma(r+n)}$$

$$- \frac{n}{2}\left(\frac{x}{2}\right)^{-1} \sum_{r=0}^{\infty} \frac{(-1)^r (x/2)^{2r+n}}{r!\Gamma(r+n+1)} = J_{n-1} - \frac{n}{x} J_n,$$

or

$$\mathbf{J_n'(x) = J_{n-1}(x) - \frac{n}{x} J_n(x).} \quad \mathbf{(37)}$$

Adding (36) and (37) member by member, we get

$$\mathbf{2J_n'(x) = J_{n-1}(x) - J_{n+1}(x).} \quad \mathbf{(38)}$$

Eliminating J_n' between (36) and (37), we get

$$\mathbf{(2n/x)J_n(x) = J_{n-1}(x) + J_{n+1}(x).} \quad \mathbf{(39)}$$

Taking $n = 0$ in (36), we get

$$J_0'(x) = -J_1(x). \tag{40}$$

Example. Develop recurrence formulas for integrals involving $J_n(ax)$.

Solution. Equation (38) with x replaced by ax is

$$2\frac{dJ_n(ax)}{d(ax)} = J_{n-1}(ax) - J_{n+1}(ax).$$

From this, by integration and slight transformation, we get

$$\int_0^x J_{n+1}(ax)\,dx = \int_0^x J_{n-1}(ax)\,dx - (2/a)[J_n(ax) - J_n(0)]. \qquad (a)$$

To get a recurrence formula applying to $\int_0^x x^k J_{n+1}(ax)\,dx$, $k \geqq 0$, proceed as follows: Applying integration by parts to $\int_0^x x^k J_n'(ax)\,dx$, we get

$$\int_0^x x^k J_n'(ax)\,dx = \frac{1}{a}x^k J_n(ax) - \frac{k}{a}\int_0^x x^{k-1}J_n(ax)\,dx. \qquad (b)$$

In (36) replace x by ax, multiply the result through by $x^k\,dx$, equate the integrals of the members with limits 0 to x, replace the left-hand member of this second result by the right-hand member of (*b*), solve this last equation for $\int_0^x x^k J_{n+1}(ax)\,dx$, and obtain

$$\int_0^x x^k J_{n+1}(ax)\,dx = \frac{n+k}{a}\int_0^x x^{k-1}J_n(ax)\,dx - \frac{x^k}{a}J_n(ax), \quad k \geqq 1. \qquad (c)$$

Formulas (*b*) and (*c*) apply for $k \geqq 1$ and $n \geqq 0$, or n a negative integer.

The method of using formulas (*b*) and (*c*) will be suggested in the following exercises.

EXERCISES

Using formula (28), show that for the range $0 < x < 1$:

1. $J_2(x) \cong^* \frac{1}{8}x^2(1 - \frac{1}{12}x^2)$, $|\text{error}| \leqq x^6/[2^6(2!)(4!)]$. *Hint:* |Error| $\leqq$ (absolute value of first neglected term).

2. $J_3(x) \cong (x^3/48)[1 - x^2/16]$; $|\text{error}| < x^7/[2^7(2)!(5!)]$.

3. $J_4(x) \cong (x^4/384)[1 - x^2/20]$; $|\text{error}| < x^8/[2^8(2!)(6!)]$.

4. Find the values of $J_0(0)$, $J_k(0)$ when $k > 0$, and $J_{-2}(0.1)$ accurate to three decimal places.

5. Using (39), express $J_2(x)$, $J_3(x)$, and $J_4(x)$ in terms of $J_0(x)$ and $J_1(x)$. Show that the value of $J_n(x)$, n a positive integer, is determined by the values of $J_0(x)$ and $J_1(x)$.

* The symbol $\cong$ means *is approximately equal to.*

6. Express $J_{\frac{5}{2}}(x)$ in terms of $J_{\frac{1}{2}}(x)$ and $J_{-\frac{1}{2}}(x)$. Express $J_{\frac{7}{3}}(x)$ and $J_{-\frac{7}{3}}(x)$ in terms of $J_{\pm\frac{2}{3}}(x)$ and $J_{\pm\frac{1}{3}}(x)$. Is the value of $J_k(x)$ when $x \neq 0$ determined by the values of $J_m(x)$, $|m| \leqq 1$? Explain.

7. Using (36) to (39) and equations obtained by differentiating them, find in terms of $J_0(x)$ and $J_1(x)$: (a) $J_0''(x)$; (b) $J_1''(x)$; (c) $J_2'''(x)$. Are all values of $(d^s/dx^s)[J_k(x)]$ when $x \neq 0$ determined by the values of $J_m(x)$, $|m| \leqq 1$?

8. Using (38) and (39) and the fact that $J_0(1) \cong 0.765$ and $J_1(1) = 0.440$, find the approximate value of: (a) $J_1'(1)$; (b) $J_2'(1)$; (c) $J_2''(1)$.

9. Derive equation (34).

Using (33), (34), and (36) to (39), show that:

10. $J_{-\frac{3}{2}}(x) = [-\sqrt{2/(\pi x)}]\,(x^{-1}\cos x + \sin x)$.

11. $J_{-\frac{5}{2}}(x) = \sqrt{2/(\pi x)}\,[(1 - 15x^{-2})\sin x + (6x^{-1} - 15x^{-3})\cos x]$.

★12. $J''_{-\frac{3}{2}}(x) = \sqrt{2/(\pi x)}\,[(1 - \frac{15}{4}x^{-2})\sin x + (2x^{-1} - \frac{15}{4}x^{-3})\cos x]$.

13. Obtain, from (40), $\int_0^x J_1(ax)\,dx = [1 - J_0(ax)]/a$. Now, take $n = 0$ in equation (a) of the example, note that $J_{-1}(x) = -J_1(x)$, and get the same result.

Using equation (a) of the example, derive:

14. $\int_0^x J_2(ax)\,dx = \int_0^x J_0(ax)\,dx - (2/a)J_1(ax)$.

15. $\int_0^x J_3(ax)\,dx = [1 - J_0(ax) - 2J_2(ax)]/a$.

16. $\int_0^x J_4(ax)\,dx = \int_0^x J_0(ax)\,dx - 2[J_1(ax) + J_3(ax)]/a$.

17. $\int_0^x J_5(ax)\,dx = [1 - J_0(ax) - 2J_2(ax) - 2J_4(ax)]/a$.

Using equations (31), (40), and (c) of the example for various values of n and k, derive

$$\int_0^x xJ_{n+1}(ax)\,dx = \frac{n+1}{a}\int_0^x J_n(ax)\,dx - \frac{x}{a}J_n(ax),$$

and obtain from this equation:

18. $\int_0^x xJ_0(ax)\,dx = -(x/a)J_{-1}(ax) = (x/a)J_1(ax)$.

19. $\int_0^x xJ_1(ax)\,dx = \left[\int_0^x J_0(ax)\,dx - xJ_0(ax)\right]\Big/ a$.

20. $\int_0^x xJ_2(ax)\,dx = [2 - 2J_0(ax) - axJ_1(ax)]/a^2$.

21. $\int_0^x x^2J_{-1}(ax)\,dx = -(x^2/a)J_{-2}(ax)$, or $\int_0^x x^2J_1(ax)\,dx = (x^2/a)J_2(ax)$.

22. $\int_0^x x^2J_0(ax)\,dx = \left[-\int_0^x J_0(ax)\,dx + xJ_0(ax) + ax^2J_1(ax)\right]\Big/ a$.

23. $\int_0^x x^kJ_{k-1}(ax)\,dx = \int_0^x (-1)^{k+1}x^kJ_{1-k}(ax)\,dx = (x^k/a)J_k(ax)$, k a positive integer.

★24. Using equations (36) to (39), prove that $J_n(x)$ satisfies $x^2(d^2J_n/dx^2) + x(dJ_n/dx) + (x^2 - k^2)J_n = 0$.

★**25.** The *modified Bessel equation* is

$$x^2\frac{d^2y}{dx^2} + x\frac{dy}{dx} - (x^2 + n^2)y = 0.$$

Show that, when n is not an integer, the solution of this equation is

$$y = c_1I_n(x) + c_2I_{-n}(x) = c_1\sum_{r=0}^{\infty}\frac{(x/2)^{2r+n}}{r!\Gamma(r+n+1)} + c_2\sum_{n=0}^{\infty}\frac{(x/2)^{2r-n}}{r!\Gamma(r-n+1)}.$$

Also, show that

$$I_{\frac{1}{2}}(x) = (e^x - e^{-x})/\sqrt{2\pi x}, \qquad I_{-\frac{1}{2}}(x) = (e^x + e^{-x})/\sqrt{2\pi x}.$$

Conclude that $I_{\frac{1}{2}}(x)$ has no real root but that $\lim_{x\to 0} I_{\frac{1}{2}}(x) = 0$ and that $I_{-\frac{1}{2}}(x)$ has no real roots. If n is an integer, $I_n(x)$ is still a solution but $I_{-n}(x)$ is not an independent solution. Find another solution besides $I_n(x)$ when n is an integer. Also, deduce recurrence formulas for $I_n(x)$.

108. Expansion of functions in terms of Bessel's functions

A set of functions $f(n,x)$ are called **orthogonal functions** for the range a to b if

$$\int_a^b f(m,x)f(n,x)\,dx = 0, \qquad m \neq n. \tag{41}$$

For example, the functions sin nx, n *an integer*, are orthogonal for the range 0 to 2π since

$$\int_0^{2\pi} \sin mx \sin nx\,dx = 0, \qquad n \neq m.$$

We shall show that the functions $\sqrt{x}\,J_k(\alpha_n x)$, α_n a root of $J_k(x)$, are orthogonal for the range 0 to 1.

Denoting derivatives by primes and replacing x first by ax and then by bx in (20), §106, we get after slight simplification

$$x^2y'' + xy' + (a^2x^2 - k^2)y = 0, \tag{42}$$
$$x^2y'' + xy' + (b^2x^2 - k^2)y = 0. \tag{43}$$

Let

$$u = J_n(ax), \qquad v = J_n(bx). \tag{44}$$

Since $y = u(x)$ satisfies (42) and $y = v(x)$ satisfies (43), we have

$$x^2u'' + xu' + (a^2x^2 - k^2)u = 0, \tag{45}$$
$$x^2v'' + xv' + (b^2x^2 - k^2)v = 0. \tag{46}$$

Multiplying (45) through by v and (46) by u and subtracting the second result from the first, we obtain

$$x^2(u''v - v''u) + x(u'v - uv') + x^2(a^2 - b^2)uv = 0. \tag{47}$$

Note that

$$(d/dx)[x(u'v - uv')] = x(u''v - uv'') + u'v - uv'. \tag{48}$$

Divide (47) through by x, and integrate the result to obtain

$$(b^2 - a^2) \int_0^x xuv\, dx = x[u'v - uv']_0^x. \tag{49}$$

In (49), substitute for u and v their values from (44), and get

$$(b^2 - a^2) \int_0^x tJ_n(at)J_n(bt)\, dt = x[aJ_n'(ax)J_n(bx) - bJ_n(ax)J_n'(bx)]. \tag{50}$$

In this, let a and b be distinct roots of $J_n(x) = 0$ so that $J_n(a) = 0$, $J_n(b) = 0$, and take $x = 1$. Then the right member of (50) becomes

$$aJ_n'(a)J_n(b) - bJ_n(a)J_n'(b) = 0.$$

Therefore, *if a and b are roots of $J_n(x) = 0$ and $b \neq a$,*

$$\int_0^1 \mathbf{tJ_n(at)J_n(bt)\, dt = 0;} \tag{51}$$

accordingly, $\sqrt{x}\, J_n(mx)$, where $J_n(m) = 0$, $m = 0, 1, 2, \ldots, \infty$, represents an orthogonal set of functions for the range 0 to 1.

If $a = b$, (51) does not hold. Consider a as fixed, and let b approach a as a limit. Equating the derivatives of the members of (50) with respect to b and setting $b = a$, $x = 1$, and $J_n(a) = 0$ in the result, use (37) and (39), and get after slight simplification

$$\int_0^1 \mathbf{t[J_n(at)]^2\, dt = \tfrac{1}{2}J_n'^2(a) = \tfrac{1}{2}J_{n+1}^2(a), \qquad if\ J_n(a) = 0.} \tag{52}$$

Replacing n by zero in (52) and using the fact that $J_0'(a) = -J_1(a)$ from (40), we get

$$\int_0^1 \mathbf{t[J_0(at)]^2\, dt = \tfrac{1}{2}J_1^2(a), \qquad if\ J_0(a) = 0.} \tag{53}$$

Also, in (51) replace n by 0 to obtain

$$\int_0^1 \mathbf{tJ_0(at)J_0(bt)\, dt = 0, \qquad if\ J_0(a) = 0, \qquad J_0(b) = 0, \qquad a \neq b.} \tag{54}$$

Formulas (53) and (54) are used to expand functions in a series of Bessel's functions. Assume that for a given function $f(x)$ and the interval $0 \leqq x \leqq 1$

$$f(x) = a_1J_0(\alpha_1x) + a_2J_0(\alpha_2x) + \cdots + a_nJ_0(\alpha_nx) + \cdots, \tag{55}$$

where α_m, $m = 0, 1, 2, \ldots$, are roots of $J_0(x)$ and $\alpha_m < \alpha_{m+1}$. Also, assume that integration term by term of series (55) multiplied by $xJ_0(nx)$ is valid for the interval $0 \leqq x \leqq 1$. Then, by using (53) and (54), we get

$$\int_0^1 xf(x)J_0(\alpha_nx)\, dx = \int_0^1 \sum_{m=0}^{\infty} a_nxJ_0(\alpha_nx)J_0(\alpha_mx)\, dx = \tfrac{1}{2}a_nJ_1^2(\alpha_n),$$

or

$$a_n = \frac{2}{J_1^2(\alpha_n)} \int_0^1 xf(x)J_0(\alpha_nx)\, dx. \tag{56}$$

To expand $f(x) = 1$ in a series of type (55), replace $f(x)$ by 1 in (56) to obtain*

$$a_n = \frac{2}{J_1^2(\alpha_n)} \int_0^1 xJ_0(\alpha_n x)\, dx = \frac{2}{J_1^2(\alpha_n)} \left[\frac{x}{\alpha_n} J_1(\alpha_n x) \right]_0^1 = \frac{2}{\alpha_n J_1(\alpha_n)}. \quad (57)$$

Using this result in (55) with $n = 0, 1, 2, \ldots$, we get

$$1 = \sum_{n=0}^{\infty} 2J_0(\alpha_n x)/[\alpha_n J_1(\alpha_n)], \qquad 0 \leqq x < 1. \quad (58)$$

Evidently (58) does not hold when $x = 1$ for $J_0(\alpha_n) = 0$. It holds when $n = 0$; therefore, $\sum_{n=0}^{\infty} 1/[\alpha_n J_1(\alpha_n)] = \frac{1}{2}$.

EXERCISES

1. Expand x^2 in a series of form (55).
2. Expand x^4 in a series of form (55).
3. Expand x in a series of the form $\sum_{r=1}^{\infty} c_r J_1(\alpha_r x)$.
4. Using (51), (52), and $\int_0^x x^{k+1} J_k(ax)\, dx = (x^{k+1}/a)J_{k+1}(ax)$, show that

$$x^k = \sum_{r=1}^{\infty} \frac{2}{\alpha_r J_{k+1}(\alpha_r)} J_k(\alpha_r x),$$

where $J_k(\alpha_r) = 0$, k is zero or a positive integer, and $0 < x < 1$.

109. Legendre's functions

Legendre's functions are adapted to spherical coordinates. They are highly important in their applications to problems of physics, quantum mechanics, and engineering generally.

Legendre's equation has the form

$$(1 - x^2)D^2y - 2xDy + k(k + 1)y = 0. \quad (59)$$

We seek solutions in descending powers of x having the form

$$y = c_0 x^m + c_1 x^{m-1} + \cdots + c_r x^{m-r} + \cdots. \quad (60)$$

Setting $y = x^m$ in (59) and equating to zero the coefficient of x^m in the result, we get

$$-m^2 - m + k(k + 1) = 0, \qquad \text{or} \qquad m = k, -k - 1. \quad (61)$$

* $\int_0^x xJ_0(ax)\, dx = (x/a)J_1(ax)$. See exercise 18, §107.

Proceeding in the usual manner, we get

$$c_n = \frac{(m - n + 2)(m - n + 1)}{(m - n - k)(m - n + k + 1)} c_{n-2}. \tag{62}$$

Now, using (62), first with $m = k$ and then with $m = -k - 1$, and (60), we get

$$y_k = x^k \left[1 - \frac{k(k-1)}{2(2k-1)} x^{-2} + \frac{k(k-1)(k-2)(k-3)}{2 \cdot 4(2k-1)(2k-3)} x^{-4} + \cdots \right], \tag{63}$$

$$y_{-k-1} = x^{-k-1} \left[1 + \frac{(k+1)(k+2)}{2(2k+3)} x^{-2} + \frac{(k+1)(k+2)(k+3)(k+4)}{2 \cdot 4(2k+3)(2k+5)} x^{-4} + \cdots \right]. \tag{64}$$

The general solution is

$$y = c_1 y_k + c_2 y_{-k-1},$$

and this converges for all values of x satisfying $|x| \geqq 1$. Evidently, if k is zero or a positive integer, series (63) terminates. The polynomial solutions thus obtained, when multiplied by $(2k)!/[2^k(k!)^2]$, are called **Legendre polynomials** and are denoted by $P_k(x)$. Hence,

$$\mathbf{P_k(x) = \frac{(2k)!}{2^k(k!)^2} y_k}, \tag{65}$$

where k is zero or a positive integer. The coefficient $(2k)!/[2^k(k!)^2]$ was chosen so that

$$\mathbf{P_k(1) = 1.} \tag{66}$$

From (65) and (63), we can derive

$$P_k(x) = \sum_{r=0}^{L} \frac{(-1)^r(2k - 2r)!}{2^k r!(k - 2r)!(k - r)!} x^{k-2r} \tag{67}$$

where $L = (k - 1)/2$ if k is odd and $L = k/2$ if k is even. From (63) or (67), we easily obtain

$$\begin{gathered} P_0(x) = 1, \qquad P_1(x) = x, \qquad P_2(x) = \tfrac{1}{2}(3x^2 - 1), \\ P_3(x) = \tfrac{1}{2}(5x^3 - 3x), \qquad P_4(x) = \tfrac{1}{8}(35x^4 - 30x^2 + 3), \\ P_5(x) = \tfrac{1}{8}(63x^5 - 70x^3 + 15x). \end{gathered} \tag{68}$$

Another important property, permitting the expression of any function in Legendre polynomials, will now be considered.

The following proof shows that the Legendre polynomials constitute an orthogonal set in the interval $-1 \leqq x \leqq 1$ by demonstrating that

$$\int_{-1}^{1} \mathbf{P}_r(\mathbf{x})\mathbf{P}_k(\mathbf{x})\,\mathbf{dx} = \mathbf{0}, \qquad \mathbf{r} \neq \mathbf{k}. \tag{69}$$

Equation (59) may be written

$$\frac{d}{dx}[(1 - x^2)y'] + k(k + 1)y = 0.$$

In this, replace y by the solution $P_k(x)$, multiply through by $P_r(x)$, and integrate to obtain

$$\int_{-1}^{1} P_r(x) \frac{d}{dx}[(1 - x^2)P_k'(x)]\,dx + k(k + 1) \int_{-1}^{1} P_k(x)P_r(x)\,dx = 0.$$

Apply integration by parts to the first integral to get

$$[(1 - x^2)P_k'(x)P_r(x)]_{-1}^{1} - \int_{-1}^{1} (1 - x^2)P_r'P_k'\,dx + k(k + 1) \int_{-1}^{1} P_kP_r\,dx = 0. \tag{70}$$

The first term of this vanishes. Now write (70) with r and k interchanged to obtain

$$-\int_{-1}^{1} (1 - x^2)P_k'P_r'\,dx + r(r + 1) \int_{-1}^{1} P_rP_k\,dx = 0.$$

Subtract this from (70), member by member, to get

$$(k - r)(k + r + 1) \int_{-1}^{1} P_rP_k\,dx = 0.$$

Since $r \geqq 0$, $k \geqq 0$, and $k \neq r$, we see that $(k - r)(k + r + 1) \neq 0$. Therefore the integral must vanish and (69) holds true.

It can be proved that*

$$\varphi(s,x) = (1 + s^2 - 2xs)^{-\frac{1}{2}} = \sum_{k=0}^{\infty} P_ks^k. \tag{71}$$

The student may check this by expanding φ in powers of s in a Maclaurin series and equating the coefficients of like powers of s to obtain

$$P_0(x) = \varphi(0,x) = 1, \qquad P_1(x) = \frac{\partial\varphi(0,x)}{\partial s} = x,$$

$$P_2(x) = \frac{1}{2!}\frac{\partial^2\varphi(0,x)}{\partial s^2} = \frac{1}{2}(3x^2 - 1), \qquad \ldots .$$

* See Louis A. Pipes, "Applied Mathematics for Engineers and Physicists," 2d ed., pp. 367–368, McGraw-Hill Book Company, Inc., New York, 1958.

Relation (71) may be used to prove that

$$\int_{-1}^{1} \mathbf{P}_k^2(\mathbf{x})\,d\mathbf{x} = \frac{\mathbf{2}}{\mathbf{2k+1}}. \tag{72}$$

Equating the squares of the sides of (71), integrating these squares, using limits -1 to $+1$, and taking account of (69), we get

$$\int_{-1}^{1} \frac{dx}{1+s^2-2sx} = \sum_{k=0}^{\infty} s^{2k} \int_{-1}^{1} P_k^2(x)\,dx. \tag{73}$$

From the left member, we get

$$\int_{-1}^{1} \frac{dx}{1+s^2-2sx} = \left[-\frac{1}{2s}\ln(1+s^2-2sx)\right]_{-1}^{1}$$

$$= \frac{1}{s}\left[\ln(1+s) - \ln(1-s)\right]$$

$$= \frac{1}{s}\sum_{r=1}^{\infty}(-1)^{r+1}\frac{s^r}{r} + \frac{1}{s}\sum_{r=1}^{\infty}\frac{s^r}{r} = \sum_{k=0}^{\infty}\frac{2s^{2k}}{2k+1}.$$

Using this result in (73) and equating the coefficients of s^{2k}, we get (72). Equations (69) and (72) are used to expand functions $f(x)$* in terms of Legendre functions. Multiplying

$$f(x) = a_0P_0(x) + a_1P_1(x) + \cdots + a_nP_n(x) + \cdots \tag{74}$$

by $P_n(x)$, equating the integrals of the resulting members with limits -1 to $+1$, and taking account of (72) and (69), we get

$$\mathbf{a}_n = \frac{\mathbf{2n+1}}{\mathbf{2}} \int_{-1}^{1} \mathbf{f(x)P}_n\mathbf{(x)\,dx}. \tag{75}$$

Using these values in (74), we get

$$f(x) = \sum_{n=0}^{\infty}\left[\frac{2n+1}{2}\int_{-1}^{1} f(x)P_n(x)\,dx\right]P_n(x). \tag{76}$$

Example. Show that $\int_{-1}^{1} P_n(x)\,dx$ is 2 when $n = 0$ and is 0 when $n = 1, 2, \ldots.$ Show that $\int_{-1}^{1} xP_n(x)\,dx$ is 0 when $n = 0, 2, 3, \ldots$ and is $\frac{2}{3}$ when $n = 1$.

* Sufficient conditions for the expansion are that $f(x)$ and $f'(x)$ are sectionally continuous in $-1 \leq x \leq 1$.

Solution. Observing that $P_0(x) = 1$, $P_1(x) = x$, we have

$$\int_{-1}^{1} 1 \cdot P_0(x)\,dx = \int_{-1}^{1} P_0^2(x)\,dx = 2/(2\cdot 0 + 1) = 2, \qquad \text{by (72);}$$

$$\int_{-1}^{1} P_n(x)\,dx = \int_{-1}^{1} P_0(x)P_n(x)\,dx = 0, \qquad n = 1, 2, \ldots, \qquad \text{by (69);}$$

$$\int_{-1}^{1} xP_n(x) = \int_{-1}^{1} P_1(x)P_n(x)\,dx = 0, \qquad \text{when } n = 0, 2, 3, \ldots, \qquad \text{by (69);}$$

$$\int_{-1}^{1} xP_1(x)\,dx = \int_{-1}^{1} P_1^2(x)\,dx = 2/(2\cdot 1 + 1) = \tfrac{2}{3}, \qquad \text{by (72).}$$

EXERCISES

Assume that n represents a nonnegative integer in these exercises.

1. Check by direct operation that: (*a*) $P_0(1) = P_3(1) = P_5(1) = 1$; (*b*) $\int_{-1}^{1} P_1(x) P_2(x)\,dx = 0$, $\int_{-1}^{1} P_2^2(x)\,dx = 2/(2\cdot 2 + 1) = \frac{2}{5}$.

2. Find $P_6(x)$ by using (63) and (65).

3. Find $P_7(x)$ by using (67).

4. Using (67), find the degree of $P_k(x)$ in x.

5. Using (68), show that $1 = P_0$, $x = P_1$, $x^2 = \frac{1}{3}(2P_2 + 1)$, $x^3 = \frac{1}{5}(2P_3 + 3P_1)$, $x^4 = \frac{1}{35}(8P_4 + 20P_2 + 7)$. Show that the expression for x^n in terms of Legendre polynomials involves P_n but not P_k with $k > n$.

6. Express x^5 in terms of P_1, P_3, and P_5.

7. Using (69), (72), and exercise 5, find the values of: (*a*) $\int_{-1}^{1} x^2P_n(x)\,dx$; (*b*) $\int_{-1}^{1} x^3P_n(x)\,dx$; (*c*) $\int_{-1}^{1} x^4P_n(x)\,dx$.

8. Using (76), expand in terms of $P_k(x)$, $k = 0, 1, 2, \ldots$: (*a*) x^2; (*b*) x^3; (*c*) x^4; (*d*) $ax^2 + bx + c$.

9. Which of the functions $P_0(x), P_1(x), \ldots$ will not appear in the expansion of $x^n + 2x^{n-1} + 3x^{n-2} + \cdots + nx + n + 1$ in terms of Legendre functions?

10. Show that $\int_{-1}^{1} x^kP_{k+r}\,dx = 0$ if $r > 0$.

CHAPTER 13

NUMERICAL SOLUTIONS OF DIFFERENTIAL EQUATIONS

110. Introduction

By a numerical solution of a differential equation in x and y, we mean a table of values of y opposite corresponding values of x for a particular solution of the equation. The methods considered are step-by-step procedures which use at each stage the results previously obtained. They require much computation, but they can be applied when other methods fail, and the results are furnished in great detail. Moreover, the computation can be carried out by computing machines. Numerical methods are used for diverse purposes. A suggestion of their usefulness is given by the fact that at proving grounds giant computers and numerical methods of solving differential equations are used to plot the paths of projectiles fired from big guns.

111. Methods of successive approximations

The following two examples illustrate step-by-step procedures of approximating solutions of differential equations. They are very instructive but are not generally practical.

Example 1. Approximate the solution of

$$dy/dx = 0.3x + 0.45, \qquad (a)$$

passing through the point $(-1,-1)$.

Solution. A process of approximating a solution of $dy/dx = f(x,y)$ consists in starting at a point P_0, computing the slope at P_0,

$$\text{Slope at } P_0(x_0,y_0) = f(x_0,y_0),$$

drawing a short line P_0P_1 having slope $f(x_0,y_0)$, computing the slope $f(x_1,y_1)$ at P_1, drawing a short line P_1P_2 having slope $f(x_1,y_1)$, and continuing the process any desirable number of times. Figure 1 represents an approximate solution of equation (a) through $P_0(-1,-1)$. The slope at $(-1,-1)$ is $0.3(-1) + 0.45 = 0.15$. Through P_0, draw a

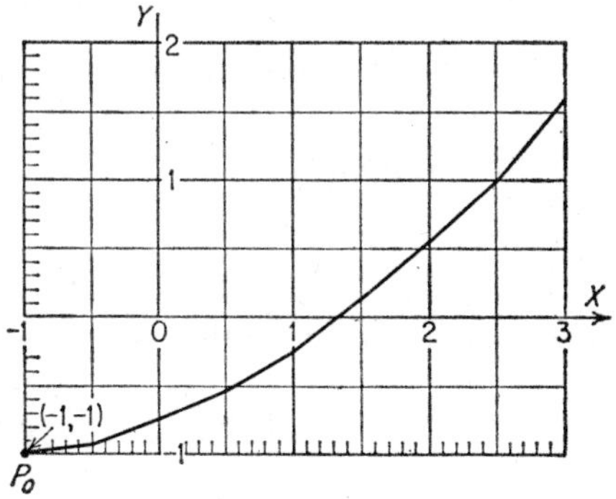

FIG. 1

straight line P_0P_1 with slope 0.15 so that x changes $\frac{1}{2}$. By (a), the slope at P_1 is $0.3(-\frac{1}{2}) + 0.45 = 0.30$. Draw P_1P_2 with slope 0.3 so that the change in x is $\frac{1}{2}$. The slope at P_2 is $0.3(0) + 0.45 = 0.45$; through P_2, draw P_2P_3 with slope 0.45, and so on. The exact solution passes through (3,2), whereas P_8 is (3,1.7). More accuracy would be obtained by using shorter line segments; theoretically, any desirable accuracy is attainable by the use of large scales and small line segments.

Example 2. Find approximately the solution of $(d^2y/dx^2) - 2x(dy/dx) = 2x$ which satisfies the initial conditions $y = 1$, $dy/dx = 0$ when $x = 0$.

Solution. Writing $D = d/dx$, $z = dy/dx$, $Dz = d^2y/dx^2$ in the statement of the problem, we have the system

$$Dy = z, \qquad Dz = 2x + 2xz \tag{a}$$

and the initial conditions

$$y = 1, \qquad z = 0 \qquad \text{when } x = 0. \tag{b}$$

The process to be performed repeatedly consists in substituting the approximations for y and z in terms of x in the right-hand members of (a), integrating the results, and determining the constants of integration by using (b).

Substituting the first approximation $y = 1$, $z = 0$ in the right-hand members of (a), we get

$$Dy = 0, \qquad Dz = 2x. \tag{c}$$

Integrating these equations and determining the constants of integration by using (b), we get

$$y = 1, \qquad z = x^2 \tag{d}$$

as the second approximation. Substituting these values in the right-hand members of (a), integrating, and determining the constants, we get the third approximation,

$$y = 1 + \frac{x^3}{3}, \qquad z = x^2 + \frac{x^4}{2}. \tag{e}$$

The fourth approximation is

$$y = 1 + \frac{x^3}{3} + \frac{x^5}{5 \cdot 2!}, \qquad z = x^2 + \frac{x^4}{2} + \frac{x^6}{3!}, \tag{f}$$

and the $(n + 2)$nd $(n > 1)$ approximation for y is found to be

$$\mathbf{y = 1 + \frac{x^3}{3} + \frac{x^5}{5 \cdot 2!} + \cdots + \frac{x^{2n+1}}{(2n + 1)n!}}. \tag{g}$$

Here again, the limit approached by the nth approximation, as n becomes infinite, is the series solution which satisfies the given initial conditions.

In general, the method applied to the system (*a*) of example 2 may be applied to approximate a solution of any system of n first-order equations in $n + 1$ unknowns, provided that the conditions of Theorem II of §95 are satisfied for the system.*

EXERCISES

1. Use the method of example 1 to approximate the solution of $y' = -0.2(x + 2) - 0.2$ which passes through $(-2,2)$. Extend the approximation from $(-2,2)$ to the point for which $x = 3$. Take one unit as the projection of each line segment on the X-axis. The point reached on line $x = 3$ should be $(3, -1.0)$. The exact solution passes through $(3, -1.5)$.

2. Solve exercise 1 by using as slope of each line segment the average (one-half the sum) of the values of y' at its ends instead of the slope at its initial point. The terminal point of your fifth line segment should be $(3, -1.5)$.

3. Using the method of example 2, find a five-term approximation to the solution of

$$\frac{d^2y}{dx^2} + 3x\frac{dy}{dx} - 6y = 0$$

for which $dy/dx = 1$, $y = 1$ when $x = 0$.

4. To approximate the solution of $dy/dx = xy$ which satisfies $y = 1$ when $x = 0$, proceed as follows: Take $y = 1$ as the first trial approximate solution, substitute 1 for y in the right member of $dy/dx = xy$, solve the resulting equation, determine the constant of integration so that $y = 1$ when $x = 0$, and obtain

$$y_2 = 1 + \tfrac{1}{2}x^2.$$

Now, replace y in the right-hand member of $dy/dx = xy$ by $1 + \frac{1}{2}x^2$, integrate the result, determine the constant of integration, and obtain

$$y_3 = 1 + \frac{x^2}{2} + \frac{x^4}{2^2(2!)}.$$

Repeat this process three more times, and then obtain by inspection the term of the solution containing x^{2n}.

5. Use the method of exercise 4 to derive the solution of $dy/dx = xy + 1$ through $(0,1)$.

112. Newton's interpolation formula

A widely used method of numerical approximation of solutions† of differential equations is based on one of Newton's interpolation formulas. This section relates to this formula.

A pair of values x and y will be referred to as the point (x,y). In Table 1, each point $(0,0)$, $(1,2)$, . . . , $(5,250)$ satisfies $y = 2x^3$, and each number in any column except the first two equals the adjacent number on its left minus the one immediately above the latter. Check the table.

* See E. L. Ince, "Ordinary Differential Equations," pp. 63–74.

† The development used in this text follows, in a general way, the plan set forth by James B. Scarborough in "Numerical Mathematical Analysis," 4th ed., Johns Hopkins Press, Baltimore, 1958.

TABLE 1

x	y	Δ_1	Δ_2	Δ_3	Δ_4	Δ_5
0	0					
1	2	2				
2	16	14	12			
3	54	38	24	12		
4	128	74	36	12	0	
5	250	122	48	12	0	0

A general table, called a horizontal difference table, suggested by Table 1, follows. For Table 2, we assume that the x values are equally

TABLE 2

x	y	Δ_1	Δ_2	Δ_3	Δ_4	Δ_n
x_0	y_0					
x_1	y_1	$\Delta_1 y_1$				
x_2	y_2	$\Delta_1 y_2$	$\Delta_2 y_2$			
x_3	y_3	$\Delta_1 y_3$	$\Delta_2 y_3$	$\Delta_3 y_3$		
x_4	y_4	$\Delta_1 y_4$	$\Delta_2 y_4$	$\Delta_3 y_4$	$\Delta_4 y_4$	
.	.	.	.	.	.	
.	.	.	.	.	.	
.	.	.	.	.	.	
x_n	y_n	$\Delta_1 y_n$	$\Delta_2 y_n$	$\Delta_3 y_n$	$\Delta_4 y_n$	$\cdots\ \Delta_n y_n$

spaced so that

$$x_1 - x_0 = x_2 - x_1 = x_3 - x_2 = \cdots = x_n - x_{n-1} = h \qquad (1)$$

and that *each element in any column except the first two is equal to the adjacent element on its left minus the element above the adjacent element.* Thus,

$$\Delta_1 y_1 = y_1 - y_0, \qquad \Delta_1 y_2 = y_2 - y_0, \qquad \ldots, \qquad \Delta_1 \mathbf{y}_k = \mathbf{y}_k - \mathbf{y}_{k-1}, \qquad \mathbf{(2)}$$

$$\begin{aligned} \Delta_2 y_2 = \Delta_1 y_2 - \Delta_1 y_1 = (y_2 - y_1) - (y_1 - y_0) = y_2 - 2y_1 + y_0, \\ \ldots, \qquad \Delta_2 \mathbf{y}_k = \mathbf{y}_k - \mathbf{2y}_{k-1} + \mathbf{y}_{k-2}, \end{aligned} \qquad \mathbf{(3)}$$

$$\begin{aligned} \Delta_3 y_3 = \Delta_2 y_3 - \Delta_2 y_2 = (y_3 - 2y_2 + y_1) - (y_2 - 2y_1 + y_0) \\ = y_3 - 3y_2 + 3y_1 - y_0, \\ \ldots, \qquad \Delta_3 \mathbf{y}_k = \mathbf{y}_k - \mathbf{3y}_{k-1} + \mathbf{3y}_{k-2} - \mathbf{y}_{k-3}, \end{aligned} \qquad \mathbf{(4)}$$

and so on. We now search for a polynomial $\varphi(x)$ such that (x_0,y_0), (x_1,y_1), . . . , (x_n,y_n) satisfies $y = \varphi(x)$. Take $\varphi(x)$ in the form

$$\begin{aligned} y = \varphi(x) = a_0 + a_1(x - x_n) + a_2(x - x_n)(x - x_{n-1}) + \cdots \\ + a_n(x - x_n)(x - x_{n-1})(x - x_{n-2}) \cdots (x - x_1). \end{aligned} \qquad (5)$$

Substituting in (5) the points (x_n,y_n), (x_{n-1},y_{n-1}), (x_{n-2},y_{n-2}), (x_{n-3},y_{n-3}), and taking account of (1), we obtain

$$\begin{aligned} y_n &= a_0, \\ y_{n-1} &= a_0 + a_1(x_{n-1} - x_n) = a_0 - a_1h, \\ y_{n-2} &= a_0 + a_1(-2h) + a_2(-2h)(-h), \\ y_{n-3} &= a_0 + a_1(-3h) + a_2(-3h)(-2h) + a_3(-3h)(-2h)(-h). \end{aligned} \tag{6}$$

The solution of equations (6) for a_0, a_1, a_2, and a_3 is

$$\begin{gathered} a_0 = y_n, \quad a_1 = (y_n - y_{n-1})/h, \quad a_2 = (y_n - 2y_{n-1} + y_{n-2})/(2!h^2), \\ a_3 = (y_n - 3y_{n-1} + 3y_{n-2} - y_{n-3})/(3!h^3), \quad \ldots . \end{gathered} \tag{7}$$

Comparing these values with (2), (3), and (4), and assuming, as can be proved, that the suggested law holds generally, we get

$$a_0 = y_n, \quad a_1 = \frac{\Delta_1 y_n}{h}, \quad a_2 = \frac{\Delta_2 y_n}{2!h^2}, \quad a_3 = \frac{\Delta_3 y_n}{3!h^3}, \quad \ldots, \quad a_n = \frac{\Delta_n y_n}{n!h^n}.$$

Substituting these values in (5), we obtain **Newton's interpolation formula**

$$\begin{aligned} \mathbf{y} = \varphi(\mathbf{x}) &= \mathbf{y}_n + \frac{\Delta_1 \mathbf{y}_n}{\mathbf{h}}(\mathbf{x} - \mathbf{x}_n) + \frac{\Delta_2 \mathbf{y}_n}{2!\mathbf{h}^2}(\mathbf{x} - \mathbf{x}_n)(\mathbf{x} - \mathbf{x}_{n-1}) \\ &+ \frac{\Delta_3 \mathbf{y}_n}{3!\mathbf{h}^3}(\mathbf{x} - \mathbf{x}_n)(\mathbf{x} - \mathbf{x}_{n-1})(\mathbf{x} - \mathbf{x}_{n-2}) + \cdots \\ &+ \frac{\Delta_n \mathbf{y}_n}{n!\mathbf{h}^n}(\mathbf{x} - \mathbf{x}_n)(\mathbf{x} - \mathbf{x}_{n-1}) \cdots (\mathbf{x} - \mathbf{x}_1). \end{aligned} \tag{8}$$

Observe that y_n and the Δ's are those of the last line of Table 2. But any line is the last one of a table with the ones below deleted, and therefore (8) applies to any line of Table 2. For example, applying (8) to the line in Table 1 beginning with 5, we use $h = 1$, $y_n = 250$, $x_n = 5$, $x_{n-1} = 4$, $x_{n-2} = 3$, $x_{n-3} = 2$, $x_{n-4} = 1$ and obtain

$$\begin{aligned} y = 250 + 122(x - 5) + \tfrac{48}{2}(x - 5)(x - 4) \\ + \tfrac{12}{6}(x - 5)(x - 4)(x - 3), \end{aligned} \tag{9}$$

a cubic satisfied by all points (x,y) of the table. In fact, it simplifies to $y = 2x^3$. Also, the result of substituting 2.5 for x in (9) is $y = 31.25$, and we say that 31.25 is the value of $\varphi(2.5)$ **interpolated** between $y = 16$ and $y = 54$. Also, (8), for the line beginning with 2, considered as a last line, is

$$y = 16 + 14(x - 2) + \tfrac{12}{2}(x - 2)(x - 1), \tag{10}$$

an equation satisfied by (2,16), (1,2), and (0,0), but not by (3,54). When $x = 1.3$ in (9), $y = 4.394$ and 4.394 is a value interpolated between $y = 2$ and $y = 16$.

Observe that *if all the kth differences $\Delta_k y_s$ are equal, all Δ's of higher order than k would be zero and the polynomial* (8) *would be of the kth order.*

Thus, in Table 1, all third differences are 12, and the corresponding polynomial obtained from (8) is a cubic. The converse is also true. In a table typified by Table 2 but derived from a polynomial of the kth degree, the differences of the kth order would be equal. Table 1 illustrates this fact.

EXERCISES

1. Apply (8) to the line of Table 1 beginning with 3, and simplify to get $y = 2x^3$. Do the same for the line beginning with 4.

2. From $y = 2x^2 + 4x$, find the values of y corresponding to the values of x, 2, 4, 6, 8, 10, make a horizontal difference table like Table 1 for the results, and compute differences. Apply (8) for the line beginning with 10 and also for the line beginning with 6. Find a value of y from this latter equation for $x = 5$ and one for $x = 4.5$.

3. Make a horizontal difference table for the points (0,2), (1,3), (2,18), (3,83), (4, 258), (5, 627), and (6, 1,298). The fourth differences should all be 24. Apply (8) for the line beginning with 4, and show that (6, 1,298) satisfies it. Apply (8) to the line beginning with 3, and show that (2,18), (1,3), and (0,2) satisfy it but that (4, 258) does not. Explain.

113. Interpolation

If a function $y = f(x)$ makes the association indicated by the points (x_0,y_0), $(x_0 + h, y_1)$, $(x_0 + 2h, y_2)$, . . . , $(x_0 + nh, y_n)$, then formula (8), §112, called an **interpolation formula of** $f(x)$, approximates $f(x)$. Finding values of y by applying (8), §112, is called **interpolation.** If $f(x)$ is continuous and finite in the interval of x considered, the errors of interpolation vary with h and approach zero as h approaches zero. If the kth differences are nearly constant, then formula (8), §112, with $n = k$ will generally give approximations as accurate as the values of y_i, $i = 1, 2, \ldots, n$, used. Thus, if third differences are nearly constant, a cubic polynomial will be employed.

A form of (8), §112, obtained by means of the substitution

$$\mathbf{x - x_n = uh}, \tag{11}$$

simplifies computation. From (11), we get

$$x - x_k = x - x_n + (x_n - x_k) = [u + (n - k)]h. \tag{12}$$

Making the substitution (12) in (8), §112, we get

$$\begin{aligned}\mathbf{y} = \varphi(\mathbf{x}) = \varphi(\mathbf{x}_n + \mathbf{uh}) &= \mathbf{y}_n + \frac{\Delta_1\mathbf{y}_n}{\mathbf{1!}}\mathbf{u} + \frac{\Delta_2\mathbf{y}_n}{\mathbf{2!}}\mathbf{u(u + 1)} \\ &+ \frac{\Delta_3\mathbf{y}_n}{\mathbf{3!}}\mathbf{u(u+1)(u+2)} + \cdots \\ &+ \frac{\Delta_n\mathbf{y}_n}{\mathbf{n!}}\mathbf{u(u+1)(u+2)} \cdots \mathbf{(u+n-1)}.\end{aligned} \tag{13}$$

Interpolating to find y when $x = x_n - \frac{1}{2}h$, that is, when $u = -\frac{1}{2}$, we get, from (13),

$$y\left(\text{at } u = -\frac{1}{2}\right) = y_n + \Delta_1 y_n\left(-\frac{1}{2}\right) + \frac{\Delta_2 y_n}{2!}\left(-\frac{1}{2}\right)\left(\frac{1}{2}\right)$$
$$+ \frac{\Delta_3 y_n}{3!}\left(-\frac{1}{2}\right)\left(\frac{1}{2}\right)\left(\frac{3}{2}\right) + \frac{\Delta_4 y_n}{4!}\left(-\frac{1}{2}\right)\left(\frac{1}{2}\right)\left(\frac{3}{2}\right)\left(\frac{5}{2}\right) + \cdots. \quad (14)$$

An illustration will indicate the interpolative power of formula (13). Table 3 is a horizontal difference table for $y = \log_{10} x$. In general, the

TABLE 3

x	$y = \log_{10} x$	Δ_1	Δ_2	Δ_3	Δ_4	Δ_5
4.0	0.6021					
4.2	0.6232	0.0211				
4.4	0.6435	0.0203	−0.0008			
4.6	0.6628	0.0193	−0.1010	−0.0002		
4.8	0.6812	0.0184	−0.0009	+0.0001	0.0003	
5.0	0.6990	0.0178	−0.0006	+0.0003	0.0002	−0.0001

accuracy of an interpolation in a table like Table 3 will not exceed that of the data, in this case four decimal places. However, the terms coming from (13) or (14) should be computed to five decimal places and their sum rounded to four decimal places. Applying (14) to the last line of Table 3, we get

$$\log_{10}\left[5 + \left(-\frac{1}{2}\right)(0.2)\right] = 0.6990 + 0.0178\left(-\frac{1}{2}\right) - \frac{0.0006}{2!}\left(-\frac{1}{2}\right)\left(\frac{1}{2}\right)$$
$$+ \frac{0.0003}{3!}\left(-\frac{1}{2}\right)\left(\frac{1}{2}\right)\left(\frac{3}{2}\right) + \frac{0.0002}{4!}\left(-\frac{1}{2}\right)\left(\frac{1}{2}\right)\left(\frac{3}{2}\right)\left(\frac{5}{2}\right)$$
$$- \frac{0.0001}{5!}\left(-\frac{1}{2}\right)\left(\frac{1}{2}\right)\left(\frac{3}{2}\right)\left(\frac{5}{2}\right)\left(\frac{7}{2}\right)$$
$$= 0.6990 - 0.0089 + 0.00008 - 0.00002 - 0 + 0 \text{ nearly} = 0.6902,$$

a result correct to four decimal places. Similarly, from (13) and Table 3 with $u = -\frac{3}{2}$ we get

$$\log_{10}[5 - \tfrac{3}{2}(0.2)] = \log_{10} 4.7 = 0.6721.$$

EXERCISES

1. Make a horizontal difference table for $y = \sin x$ from the data (0,0), $(\frac{1}{6}\pi, 0.50)$, $(\frac{2}{6}\pi, 0.87)$, $(\frac{3}{6}\pi, 1)$. Using (13), write an interpolation formula, and compute from it $\sin(\frac{5}{12}\pi)$ and $\sin(\frac{3}{12}\pi)$ by using in order $u = -\frac{1}{2}$ and $u = -\frac{3}{2}$. The respective results should be 0.97, 0.71.

2. Look up the logarithms to the base 10 of 3, 3.5, 4, 4.5, and 5 accurate to three figures, make a corresponding difference table, write the corresponding formula (13), and from this find in order logarithms to the base 10 of 4.75, 4.25, and 3.73.

3. If on a certain day the temperature T at time $t = 0$ (noon) was 80°, at 3 P.M. it was 90°, at 6 P.M. it was 80°, and at 9 P.M. it was 50°, find, by means of (12) and (13), an expression approximating T in terms of t.

114. Formulas for approximate integration*

The general plan of numerical integration of a function $y = f(x)$ consists in forming the approximating polynomial (13), §113, for $f(x)$ and integrating this polynomial. We shall derive some basic formulas by integrating the first five terms of polynomial (13), with y replaced by y', over various intervals of length h. From (11), $u = (x - x_n)/h$; therefore, $dx = h\,du$; when $x = x_n$, $u = 0$, and when $x = x_n + h$, $u = 1$. Hence, if $y' = \varphi(x)$ and if Y_n^{n+1} denotes $\int_{x_n}^{x_n+h} y'\,dx$, we get

$$Y_n^{n+1} = \int_{x_n}^{x_n+h} y'\,dx = h\int_0^1 y'\,du = h\int_0^1 \left[y'_n + \Delta_1 y'_n\,u + \frac{\Delta_2 y'_n}{2!}u(u+1) + \frac{\Delta_3 y'_n}{3!}u(u+1)(u+2) + \frac{\Delta_4 y'_n}{4!}u(u+1)(u+2)(u+3)\right]du, \quad (15)$$

or, evaluating the integral,

$$\mathbf{Y}_n^{n+1} = \mathbf{h}(\mathbf{y}'_n + \tfrac{1}{2}\Delta_1\mathbf{y}'_n + \tfrac{5}{12}\Delta_2\mathbf{y}'_n + \tfrac{3}{8}\Delta_3\mathbf{y}'_n + \tfrac{251}{720}\Delta_4\mathbf{y}'_n). \quad \mathbf{(16)}$$

Similarly, denote $\int_{x_{n-1}}^{x_n} y'\,dx = h\int_{-1}^{0} y'\,du$ by Y_{n-1}^n, evaluate the integral of (15) with limits 0 to 1 replaced by limits -1 to 0, and obtain

$$\mathbf{Y}_{n-1}^{n} = \mathbf{h}(\mathbf{y}'_n - \tfrac{1}{2}\Delta_1\mathbf{y}'_n - \tfrac{1}{12}\Delta_2\mathbf{y}'_n - \tfrac{1}{24}\Delta_3\mathbf{y}'_n - \tfrac{19}{720}\Delta_4\mathbf{y}'_n). \quad \mathbf{(17)}$$

Also, using (15) with limits 0 to 1 replaced by respective limits -2 to 0, -2 to -1, -3 to -2, and -4 to -3, obtain the following equations:

$$Y_{n-2}^{n} = 2h(y'_n - \Delta_1 y'_n + \tfrac{1}{6}\Delta_2 y'_n - \tfrac{1}{180}\Delta_4 y'_n), \quad (18)$$
$$Y_{n-2}^{n-1} = h(y'_n - \tfrac{3}{2}\Delta_1 y'_n + \tfrac{5}{12}\Delta_2 y'_n + \tfrac{1}{24}\Delta_3 y'_n + \tfrac{11}{720}\Delta_4 y'_n), \quad (19)$$
$$Y_{n-3}^{n-2} = h(y'_n - \tfrac{5}{2}\Delta_1 y'_n + \tfrac{23}{12}\Delta_2 y'_n - \tfrac{3}{8}\Delta_3 y'_n - \tfrac{19}{720}\Delta_4 y'_n), \quad (20)$$
$$Y_{n-4}^{n-3} = h(y'_n - \tfrac{7}{2}\Delta_1 y'_n + \tfrac{53}{12}\Delta_2 y'_n - \tfrac{55}{24}\Delta_3 y'_n + \tfrac{251}{720}\Delta_4 y'_n). \quad (21)$$

The two formulas in boldface are very important and are used regularly. The others are used only to check starting lines of a solution or a doubtful figure. The solution of a differential equation in the next section will illustrate methods of using them.

* For a more complete discussion of the derivation and use of formulas (15) to (21), consult James B. Scarborough's book on "Numerical Mathematical Analysis" (*ibid.*).

115. Illustration and discussion of formulas (16) to (21), §114

Consider a numerical solution accurate to four decimal places of

$$\frac{dy}{dx} = y' = 2x + y \tag{a}$$

from (0,2) to a point having abscissa 1.*

There are many ways of finding the first few lines of a solution. For example, we can often use an approximate formula got by deriving several terms of a Taylor's series or by the method of exercise 4, §111. The method used here applies repeatedly the formula

$$y_{x_0+h} \cong y_{x_0} + \tfrac{1}{2}(y'_{x_0} + y'_{x_0+h})h, \tag{22}$$

where a letter with a subscript p indicates the value of the letter when $x = p$ and $\cong$ means *equals approximately*. When $x = 0$, $y = 2$, and, from (a), $y'_0 = 2(0) + 2 = 2$. We now desire $y_{0.05}$. Estimate that $y_{0.05} = 2$, use (a) to get $y'_{0.05} = 2(0.05) + 2 = 2.1$, and then use (22) to get

$$y_{0.05} = 2 + \tfrac{1}{2}(2 + 2.1)(0.05) = 2.1025. \tag{b}$$

To get an improved approximation for $y_{0.05}$, take $y_{0.05} = 2.1025$, use (a) to get $y' = 2(0.05) + 2.1025 = 2.2025$, and then (22) to get

$$y_{0.05} \cong 2 + \tfrac{1}{2}(2 + 2.2025)(0.05) \cong \mathbf{2.1051}. \tag{c}$$

Now, use (22) again with $y_{0.05} = 2.1051$, $y'_{0.05} \cong 2.2051$ from (a), and get the same value 2.1051 as $y_{0.05}$ accurate to four decimal places. Therefore, we accept 2.1051 as the value of $y_{0.05}$.

To evaluate $y_{0.1}$, use (a) and (22) repeatedly as before with $x_0 = 0.05$ to obtain in succession

$$\begin{aligned} y_{0.1} &\cong 2.1051 + \tfrac{1}{2}(2.2051 + 2.4051)(0.05) = 2.2204, \\ y_{0.1} &\cong 2.1051 + \tfrac{1}{2}(2.2051 + 2.4204)(0.05) = \mathbf{2.2207}. \end{aligned} \tag{d}$$

Further trials yield the same result for $y_{0.1}$.

Again, using (a) and (22) repeatedly with $h = -0.05$, $y_{-0.05} = 2$, we obtain in succession

$$\begin{aligned} y_{-0.05} &\cong 2 + \tfrac{1}{2}(2 + 1.9)(-0.05) = 1.9025, \\ y_{-0.05} &\cong 2 + \tfrac{1}{2}(2 + 1.8025)(-0.05) = \mathbf{1.9049}. \end{aligned} \tag{e}$$

Further attempts to approximate $y_{-0.05}$ yield the same result. Similarly, using (a) and (22) twice with $x_0 = -0.05$, $y_{-0.05} = 1.9049$, $h = -0.05$, we get

$$y_{-0.1} \cong \mathbf{1.8193}. \tag{f}$$

* Equation (a) is easily solved by the method of §25. A simple problem was chosen to illustrate the process of numerical solution and avoid undue complication.

Using the values of the y's from (*c*), (*d*), (*e*), and (*f*) and the corresponding values for the y''s from (*a*), and computing differences, we get the first five lines of Table 4. To check these we use equations (21), (20), (19), (18), and (17) in that order. Observe that Y_m^n *is the increment which added to* y_m *(*y *in the mth line) gives* y_n.

TABLE 4

Line	x	y	y'	$\Delta_1 y'$	$\Delta_2 y'$	$\Delta_3 y'$	$\Delta_4 y'$
1	−0.1	1.8193	1.6193				
2	−0.05	1.9049	1.8049	0.1856			
3	0	2.0000	2.0000	0.1951	0.0095		
4	0.05	2.1051	2.2051	0.2051	0.0100	0.0005	
5	0.1	2.2207	2.4207	0.2156	0.0105	0.0005	0.0000
6	0.15	2.3474	2.6474	0.2267	0.0111	0.0006	0.0001
7	0.20	2.4857	2.8857	0.2383	0.0116	0.0005	−0.0001
8	0.25	2.6362	3.1362	0.2505	0.0122	0.0006	0.0001
9	0.30	2.7995	3.3995	0.2633	0.0128	0.0006	0.0000

Applying (21) to line 5 of Table 4, we get*

$$Y_1^2 = 0.05[2.4207 - \tfrac{7}{2}(0.2156) + \tfrac{53}{12}(0.0105) - \tfrac{55}{24}(0.0005) + 0] = 0.08556.$$

Adding 0.0856 to 1.8193 = y_1, we get 1.9049 = y_2, thus checking y_1. Applying (20) with $n = 5$ to line 5 of Table 4, we get

$$Y_2^3 = 0.05[2.4207 - \tfrac{5}{2}(0.2156) + \tfrac{23}{12}(0.0105) - \tfrac{3}{8}(0.0005) + 0] = 0.09508.$$

Adding 0.0951 to 1.9049 (= y_2), we get 2.0000, thus checking y_2. Similarly, using (19) on line 5, we get $Y_3^4 = 0.10510$ and this added to 2 (= y_3) gives 2.1051 = y_4. Also, using (17) on line 5, we get $Y_4^5 = 0.1156$, which added to 2.1051 (= y_4) gives 2.2207 = y_5. This completes the check of the first five lines of Table 4. The checks are important if one doubts the accuracy of his initial table.

To get a new line, use formulas (16) and (*a*) and then use (17) or (18) to check the new value of y. Desiring line 6 for Table 4, we use (16) with $n = 5$ on line 5 to obtain

$$Y_5^6 = 0.05[2.4207 + \tfrac{1}{2}(0.2156) + \tfrac{5}{12}(0.0105) + \tfrac{3}{8}(0.0005) + 0] = 0.12665.$$

Adding 0.1267 to 2.2207 (= y_5), we get 2.3474 = y_6. To complete the sixth line, use (*a*) to get $y_6' = 2(0.15) + 2.3474 = 2.6474$, and then com-

* We compute the numbers inside the brackets to five decimal places and round off final results to four decimal places.

plete the differences for this line. Now, applying (17) to line 6, we get

$$Y_5^6 = 0.05[2.6474 - \tfrac{1}{2}(0.2267) - \tfrac{1}{12}(0.0111) - \tfrac{1}{24}(0.0006) + 0] = 0.12665,$$

and, adding 0.1267 to 2.2207, obtain 2.6474 = y_6. As another check, use (18) on line 6 to obtain

$$Y_4^6 = 0.1[2.6474 - 0.2267 + \tfrac{1}{6}(0.0111) + 0] = 0.24225,$$

and adding 0.2423 to 2.1051 = y_4, obtain 2.3474 = y_6. Similarly, using (16), (17), and (18), we may compute and check lines 7, 8, and 9.

When the change for a new line due to third differences $\frac{3}{8}h\,\Delta_3 y'_n$ *is very slight, the interval h on x may be doubled.* Hence, we shall double the interval by writing the x's, y's, and y''s of the odd numbered lines of Table 4 and computing the differences. This gives the first five lines of Table 5. These lines may be checked by using formulas (21), (20), (19), and (17). The others may be found and checked by using (16), (17), and (18), just as we derived lines 6 to 9 of Table 4.

TABLE 5

Line	x	y	y'	y'	y'	y'	y'
1	−0.1	1.8193	1.6193				
2	0	2.0000	2.0000	0.3807			
3	0.1	2.2207	2.4207	0.4207	0.0400		
4	0.2	2.4856	2.8856	0.4649	0.0442	0.0042	
5	0.3	2.7994	3.3994	0.5138	0.0489	0.0047	0.0005
6	0.4	3.1673	3.9673	0.5679	0.0541	0.0052	0.0005
7	0.5	3.5949	4.5949	0.6276	0.0597	0.0056	0.0004
8	0.6	4.0885	5.2885	0.6936	0.0660	0.0063	0.0007
9	0.7	4.6550	6.0550	0.7665	0.0729	0.0069	0.0006
10	0.8	5.3022	6.9022	0.8472	0.0807	0.0078	0.0009
11	0.9	6.0385	7.8385	0.9363	0.0891	0.0084	0.0006
12	1.0	6.8732	8.8732	1.0347	0.0984	0.0093	0.0009

Observe that formulas (21), (20), (19), and (18) of §114 are used for checking the first five lines of a solution and that (16) and (17) are used for finding additional lines of the tabular solution. Formula (18) is simple to compute and may be used as an extra check. Of course, any of the formulas (15) to (20) may be used to check any part of a solution.

EXERCISES

1. Apply formulas (21), (20), (19), and (17) with $n = 5$ to line 5 of Table 5 to check the first five values of y.

2. Use (16) applied to line 5 of Table 5 to obtain y_6 for the sixth line, then compute y_6' by (*a*), and find the differences in line 6. Check y in line 6 by applying (17) to line 6. Also, check y_6 in line 6 by applying (18) to line 6, finding Y_4^6, and adding it to y_4.

3. Compute y_7 of Table 5 by using (16); then compute y_7' by using (21) and the differences of line 7. Then check y_7 by using (17) and also by using (16).

4. Compute a thirteenth line for Table 5.

5. To begin the numerical solution of

$$\frac{dy}{dx} = y' = x + 0.1y \tag{a}$$

through (0,1), take $h = 0.1$, use (22) as was done to find the first five lines of Table 4, and compute y_0, $y_{0.1}$, $y_{0.2}$, $y_{0.3}$, $y_{0.4}$ accurate to four decimal places.

6. Using the values obtained from exercise 5, compute $y_{0.1}'$, $y_{0.2}'$, $y_{0.3}'$, $y_{0.4}'$, and then make a five-line horizontal difference table for approximating the solution of $dy/dx = x + 0.1y$ through (0,1). Check your table by using (21), (20), (19), and (17) of §114 applied to the fifth line.

7. Compute and check four more lines by using (16), (17), and (18), and the result of exercise 6.

8. From the table of exercises 6 and 7, make a five-line horizontal difference table for doubling the interval and extend the table by three additional lines.

★9. Find by numerical methods the solution of $dy/dx = x + y$ for which $y = 1$ when $x = 0$. First use intervals of $h = 0.05$ for x. After finding nine lines of the tabular solution, double the interval and compute three lines in addition to the five lines copied from the first part of the problem.

★10. Find the solution of

$$\frac{dy}{dx} = 0.1x + \log_{10} y$$

if $y = 2$ when $x = 0$. First, find the values of y and y' for which x is 0.0, 0.1, 0.2, 0.3, 0.4. Then compute differences, and, using formulas (16) and (17), §114, compute four more lines of the table. Now, double the interval, and compute four new lines by using (16) and (17), §114.

★11. Use Maclaurin's series to show that the solution of $dy/dx = 0.1x + \log_{10} y$ through (0,2) is $y \cong 2 + 0.30103x + 0.08268x^2 + 0.004343x^3 + \cdots$. Use this series to check your result in exercise 10 for the values of x, 0.1, 0.2, 0.3, and 0.4.

116. Halving the interval h of x

When the effect, $\frac{251}{720}h\,\Delta_4 y_n'$, of the fourth difference is more than $\frac{1}{2}$ in the last figure of the computed values, it is well to shorten the interval. If $h = 0.1$ and the data are accurate to four decimal places we have

$$\text{If } \tfrac{251}{720}(0.1)\,\Delta_4 y_n' \geqq 0.00005, \qquad \Delta_4 y_n' > 14.$$

The usual method is to cut the interval from h to $\frac{1}{2}h$. An illustration will indicate the method of doing this.

Three lines of the solution of (*a*), §115, follow:

TABLE 6

x	y	y'	$\Delta_1 y'$	$\Delta_2 y'$	$\Delta_3 y'$	$\Delta_4 y'$
1.8	18.5986	22.1986	2.3028	0.2191	0.0207	0.0016
1.9	20.9436	24.7436	2.5450	0.2422	0.0231	0.0024
2.0	23.5562	27.5562	2.8126	0.2676	0.0254	0.0023

Now we apply the right member of interpolation formula (13), §113, with y replaced by y', y_n by y'_n, and u by $-\frac{1}{2}$, to the third line of Table 6. From this, we get as the value of y' at $x = 1.95$

$$y'_{1.95} = 27.5562 - \tfrac{1}{2}(2.8126) + (-\tfrac{1}{2})(\tfrac{1}{2})(0.2676)/2! \\ + (-\tfrac{1}{2})(\tfrac{1}{2})(\tfrac{3}{2})(0.0254)/3! + (-\tfrac{1}{2})(\tfrac{1}{2})(\tfrac{3}{2})(\tfrac{5}{2})(0.0023)/4! = 26.11477.$$

Similarly, we apply to the third line of Table 6 formula 13, §113, with y replaced by y', y_n by y'_n, and u by $-\frac{3}{2}$ to obtain $y'_{1.85} = 23.4393$. From (*a*), §115, we compute $y_{1.95} = y'_{1.95} - 2x = 26.11477 - 3.9 = 22.21477$, $y_{1.85} = 23.43929 - 3.7 = 19.73929$. Making a horizontal difference table from the values of x, y, y' just found and those in Table 6, and computing two new lines, we get Table 7.

TABLE 7

Line	x	y	y'	$\Delta_1 y'$	$\Delta_2 y'$	$\Delta_3 y'$	$\Delta_4 y'$
1	1.80	18.5986	22.1986				
2	1.85	19.7393	23.4393	1.2407			
3	1.90	20.9436	24.7436	1.3043	0.0636		
4	1.95	22.2148	26.1148	1.3712	0.0669	0.0033	
5	2.00	23.5562	27.5562	1.4414	0.0702	0.0033	0.0000
6	2.05	24.9716	29.0716	1.5154	0.0740	0.0038	0.0005
7	2.10	26.4647	30.6647	1.5931	0.0777	0.0037	−0.0001

Simpson's rule furnishes an excellent check. It may be written for our purposes

$$\int_a^{a+2kh} y'\,dx = \frac{h}{3}(y'_a + 4y'_{a+1} + 2y'_{a+2} + 4y'_{a+3} + \cdots + 4y'_{a+2k-1} + y'_{a+2k}) \\ = y_{a+2kh} - y_a. \quad (23)$$

For example, taking $a = 1.8$ and $k = 2$, we get from (23) and Table 7

$$\frac{0.05}{3}[22.1986 + 4(23.4393) + 2(24.7436) + 4(26.1148) + 27.5562] \\ = 4.9576,$$

and $$y_{2.00} - y_{1.80} = 23.5562 - 18.5986 = 4.9576.$$

EXERCISES

1. Using (23) with $a = 2.00$ and $k = 1$, make a check involving the last three lines of Table 7.

2. Using the last three lines of Table 5 and the right member of (14), §113, halve the interval; that is, construct a horizontal difference table for the five lines of the solution of $dy/dx = 2x + y$ through (0,2) associated with the values of x, 0.8, 0.85, 0.9, 0.95, 1.0. Check your table by means of (23) and also by means of formulas (16) to (21), §114.

3. Three lines in the solution of $dy/dx = 4x - y$ through (0,1) are given in Table 8.

TABLE 8

x	y	y'	$\Delta_1 y'$	$\Delta_2 y'$	$\Delta_3 y'$	$\Delta_4 y'$
1.0	1.8394	2.1606	0.4072	−0.0903	0.0197	−0.0049
1.2	2.3060	2.4940	0.3334	−0.0738	0.0165	−0.0032
1.4	2.8330	2.7670	0.2730	−0.0604	0.0134	−0.0031

Apply (23) with $a = 1.0$ and $k = 1$ as a check. Use (14), §113, to find y' when $x = 1.1$ and when $x = 1.3$. Now make a five-line horizontal difference table based on the interval 0.1, and check the table. Use (16), (17), and (18), §114, to compute and check two more lines of this table. Then check all seven lines by means of (23).

117. Numerical solution of a system of simultaneous equations

The general plan of solving numerically two equations having the form

$$\frac{dy}{dx} = f_1(x,y,z), \qquad \frac{dz}{dx} = f_2(x,y,z)$$

consists in computing two difference tables, one for y and one for z, by means of equations (15) to (21), §114, the results from each being used in the other as they become available. Consider the solution of the equation*

$$x\frac{d^2y}{dx^2} = y \tag{a}$$

for which $x = 1$, $y = 1$, $y' = 0$, or the equivalent set (§94)

$$y' = \frac{dy}{dx} = z, \qquad z' = \frac{dz}{dx} = \frac{y}{x}. \tag{b}$$

In beginning the solution, note that $y'_{x_0} + y'_{x_0+h} = z_{x_0} + z_{x_0+h}$, $z'_{x_0} + z'_{x_0+h} = (y/x)_{x_0} + (y/x)_{x_0+h}$, and use the formulas

$$y_{x_0+h} \cong y_{x_0} + \tfrac{1}{2}(z_{x_0} + z_{x_0+h})h, \tag{24}$$
$$z_{x_0+h} \cong z_{x_0} + \tfrac{1}{2}[(y/x)_{x_0} + (y/x)_{x_0+h}]h, \tag{25}$$

* The solution of this equation by §104 involves a complicated procedure and result, and the constants of integration involve difficulties. The solution by numerical methods is straightforward.

where, as in equation (22), §115, a letter with a subscript p indicates the value of the letter when $x = p$. For the first line of the solution, we have

$$x = 1, \quad y_1 = 1, \quad y_1' = z_1 = 0; \quad x_1 = 1, \quad z_1 = 0, \quad z_1' = 1. \quad (c)$$

Taking $h = 0.05$, $y_{1.05} = 1$, $x_1 = 1$, $z_1 = 0$, $x_{1.05} = 1.05$ in (25), we get $z_{1.05} \cong 0 + \frac{1}{2}[1 + (1/1.05)]0.05 = 0.04881$. Using $z = 0.04881$ in (24), we get $y_{1.05} \cong 1 + \frac{1}{2}(0 + 0.04881)(0.05) = 1.00122$.* Using $x = 1$, $y = 1.00122$, $h = 0.05$, $z = 0$ in (25), we get as a new estimate $z_{1.05} = 0 + \frac{1}{2}(1 + 1.00122/1.05)(0.05) = 0.0488$. Since this new estimate of z is the same as the old one, accurate to four decimal places, we accept it and the corresponding value of y. The new line then is

$$x = 0.05, \quad y = 1.0012, \quad z = 0.0488. \quad (d)$$

Now, assume that z changes by the same amount 0.0488 while x changes 0.05, and take $z_{1.1} = 0.0976$, $z_1 = 0.0488$, $y_1 = 1.0012$ in (24) to obtain $y = 1.0049$. Then use (25) with $z_{1.05} = 0.0488$, $(y/x)_{1.05} = 1.0012/1.05$, $(y/x)_{1.10} = 1.0049/1.1$, to obtain $z_{1.1} = 0.09552$. Another use of (24) with $z_{1.1} = 0.09552$ gives $y_{1.1} = 1.0048$. Further trials for $y_{1.1}$ and $z_{1.1}$ give the same value. Hence we accept $y_{1.1} = 1.0048$, $z_{1.1} = 0.0955$. The three lines thus computed with differences are given in Table 9. To get

TABLE 9

Line	x	y	z	$\Delta_1 z$	$\Delta_2 z$
1	1	1	0		
2	1.05	1.0012	0.0488	0.0488	
3	1.10	1.0048	0.0955	0.0467	0.0021

two more lines, we continue to use (24) and (25). However, if we assume that, for line 4, $\Delta_2 z = 0.0021$, we get $\Delta_1 z = 0.0467 - 0.0021 = 0.0446$, and $z_{1.15} = 0.0446 + 0.0955 = 0.1401$. Using this value for $z_{1.15}$ in (24) and proceeding as before, we find $y_{1.15} = 1.0107$ and then $z_{1.15} = 0.1403$. Now add the fourth line to Table 9, compute differences, and proceeding as before, compute the fifth line. To each value of z we find a value for dz/dx by using (b). Tables 10 and 11 exhibit the five lines thus computed with corresponding differences; applying formulas (21), (20), (19), and (17), we check the first five lines of these tables.

Now apply (16), §114, to the fifth line of Tables 10 and 11 to obtain $y_{1.25} = 1.0290$, $z_{1.25} = 0.2253$, enter $z_{1.25} = y'_{1.25} = 0.2253$ in Table 11,

* In the computation, we use five decimal places and then round off results to four places.

TABLE 10

Line	x	$z = y'$	$z' = y/x$	$\Delta_1 z'$	$\Delta_2 z'$	$\Delta_3 z'$	$\Delta_4 z'$
1	1	0.0000	1.0000				
2	1.05	0.0488	0.9535	−0.0465			
3	1.10	0.0955	0.9135	−0.0400	0.0065		
4	1.15	0.1403	0.8789	−0.0346	0.0054	−0.0011	
5	1.20	0.1835	0.8490	−0.0299	0.0047	−0.0007	0.0004
6	1.25	0.2253	0.8232	−0.0258	0.0041	−0.0006	0.0001
7	1.30	0.2659	0.8010	−0.0222	0.0036	−0.0005	0.0001
8	1.35	0.3054	0.7819	−0.0191	0.0031	−0.0005	0.0000
9	1.40	0.3441	0.7656	−0.0163	0.0028	−0.0003	0.0002

TABLE 11

Line	x	y	$y' = z$	$\Delta_1 y'$	$\Delta_2 y'$	$\Delta_3 y'$	$\Delta_4 y'$
1	1.00	1	0.0000				
2	1.05	1.0012	0.0488	0.0488			
3	1.10	1.0048	0.0955	0.0467	−0.0021		
4	1.15	1.0107	0.1403	0.0448	−0.0019	0.0002	
5	1.20	1.0188	0.1835	0.0432	−0.0016	0.0003	0.0001
6	1.25	1.0290	0.2253	0.0418	−0.0014	0.0002	−0.0001
7	1.30	1.0413	0.2659	0.0406	−0.0012	0.0002	0.0000
8	1.35	1.0556	0.3054	0.0395	−0.0011	0.0001	−0.0001
9	1.40	1.0718	0.3441	0.0387	−0.0008	0.0003	0.0002

compute $z'_{1.25} = 1.0290/1.25 = 0.8232$, and enter it in Table 10, compute differences for the sixth lines, and check by using (17), §114, on these sixth lines. Proceeding in the same way, compute and check lines 7, 8, and 9 of Tables 10 and 11.

EXERCISES

1. Compute lines 7, 8, and 9 of Tables 10 and 11.

2. Complete Table 9 by computing and adding lines 4 and 5 to it.

3. Check the value of $y_{1.4}$ and $z_{1.4}$ by applying Simpson's rule, formula (23), §116, to the second and third columns of Tables 10 and 11.

4. Double the interval from Tables 10 and 11, and compute and check lines for $y_{1.5}$, $z_{1.5}$, $y_{1.6}$, $z_{1.6}$.

5. To find an approximate solution of

$$y' = \frac{dy}{dx} = z, \qquad z' = \frac{dz}{dx} = y - xz, \tag{a}$$

satisfying $y = 1$, $z = 2$ when $x = 0$, use the formulas

$$y_{i+1} = 1 + \int_0^x z_i\,dx, \qquad z_{i+1} = 2 + \int_0^x (y_i - xz_i)\,dx, \tag{b}$$

where the subscripts i refer to ith approximations. For example,

$$y_1 = 1 + \int_0^x 2\,dx = 1 + 2x, \qquad z_1 = 2 + \int_0^x [1 + 2x - x(2)]\,dx = 2 + x. \quad (c)$$

To get y_2 and z_2, use (*b*) and (*c*) with $i = 1$. Similarly, find y_3 and z_3.

6. From the formulas derived in exercise 5, compute the values of Table 12. From

TABLE 12

x	-0.2	-0.1	0	0.1	0.2
y	0.6199	0.8050	1	1.2050	1.4199
z	1.8013	1.9002	2	2.0998	2.1987

this table, compute values for y' and z', make corresponding difference tables similar to Tables 10 and 11, and then using (16) and (17), §114, compute and check

$$y_{0.3},\ z_{0.3},\ y_{0.4},\ z_{0.4},\ y_{0.5},\ z_{0.5},\ y_{0.6},\ z_{0.6}.$$

118. The Runge-Kutta method

The method set forth in this section was devised by C. Runge about 1894 and extended by W. Kutta a few years later. It may well be used in obtaining the first few values required for a solution. It may be used for an extended solution also, but its use involves much computation.

Let x_0 and y_0 be initial values of the variables x and y for a solution of the equation

$$\frac{dy}{dx} = f(x,y). \tag{26}$$

A change h is made in x, and the corresponding change Δy in y is found by computing in order k_1, k_2, k_3, k_4, and Δy by means of the following formulas:

$$\begin{aligned}
k_1 &= f(x_0,y_0)h,\\
k_2 &= f\left(x_0 + \frac{h}{2}, y_0 + \frac{k_1}{2}\right)h,\\
k_3 &= f\left(x_0 + \frac{h}{2}, y_0 + \frac{k_2}{2}\right)h,\\
k_4 &= f(x_0 + h, y_0 + k_3)h,\\
\Delta y &= \tfrac{1}{6}(k_1 + 2k_2 + 2k_3 + k_4).
\end{aligned} \tag{27}$$

This gives the values $x_1 = x_0 + h$, $y_1 = y_0 + \Delta y$. To find a third pair of values, use the same formulas (27) with x_1 and y_1 taking the place of x_0 and y_0, respectively. When x_2 and y_2 are found, use (27) with x_0 and y_0 replaced by x_2 and y_2, etc.

Observe that the change Δy in y for a change h in x is an average of six values of $(dy/dx)h$. The first, k_1, is $(dy/dx)h$ evaluated at the beginning of the interval; the last, k_4, is $(dy/dx)h$ evaluated approximately at the end of the interval; and two other values, each doubled, are computed at mid-points of the segment from (x_0,y_0) to approximated end points. If f is a function of x only, the value Δy of (27) becomes

$$y = \tfrac{1}{6}h[f(x_0) + 4f(x_0 + \tfrac{1}{2}h) + f(x_0 + h)],$$

the value obtained by applying Simpson's rule to $y' = f(x)$ for the interval from x_0 to $x_0 + h$.

The error inherent in the Runge-Kutta method is roughly that of h^5.* The following example will illustrate the procedure in using the method.

Example. Find three pairs of values of x and y for the solution of $dy/dx = -x + y$ by means of formulas (27) if the initial values of the variables are $x = 0$, $y = 2$.

Solution. The first value pair is $x = 0$, $y = 2$. Take $h = 0.1$, $x_0 = 0$, $y_0 = 2$ in (27), keep five decimal places during the computation, but round off the value of Δy to four decimal places. This gives

$$\begin{aligned}
k_1 &= (-0 + 2)(0.1) = 0.2,\\
k_2 &= \left(-0 - \frac{0.1}{2} + 2 + \frac{0.2}{2}\right)(0.1) = 0.205,\\
k_3 &= \left(-0 - \frac{0.1}{2} + 2 + \frac{0.205}{2}\right)(0.1) = 0.20525,\\
k_4 &= (-0 - 0.1 + 2 + 0.20525)(0.1) = 0.21053,\\
\Delta y &= \tfrac{1}{6}[0.2 + 2(0.205) + 2(0.20525) + 0.21053] = 0.2052.
\end{aligned}$$

Hence, $$\mathbf{x_1 = 0.1, \quad y_1 = 2.2052.}$$

Substituting these values of x_1 and y_1 for x_0 and y_0 and 0.1 for h in (27), we obtain $k_1 = 0.21052$, $k_2 = 0.21605$, $k_3 = 0.21632$, $k_4 = 0.22215$, and $\Delta y = \frac{1}{6}(k_1 + 2k_2 + 2k_3 + k_4) = 0.21624$. Hence, the third pair of values of x and y is

$$\mathbf{x_2 = 0.2, \quad y_2 = 2.4214.}$$

The next pair of values could be computed by using x_2 and y_2 for x_0 and y_0 in (27).

EXERCISES

1. Check the values for x_2 and y_2 in the solution just given. Then compute $x_3 = 0.3$, $y_3 = 2.6499$ by using (27) with $x_0 = x_2$, $y_0 = y_2$, and $h = 0.1$. Finally, compute y when $x = 0.4$.

2. For the equation $dy/dx = -x + y$ of the example, find y'_0, $y'_{0.1}$, $y'_{0.2}$, $y'_{0.3}$, $y'_{0.4}$, make the corresponding horizontal difference table of x, y, and y', check this table by using (21), (20), (19), and (17) of §114, and then use (16) and (17), §114, to compute two new lines.

* See F. A. Willers, "Numerisches Integration," pp. 91–92. Also consult H. Levy and E. A. Baggott, "Numerical Solutions," Dover Publications, New York.

3. Find three value pairs of x and y by using (27) for the solution of $dy/dx = xy + 1$, in which $y = 1$ when $x = 0$. Use $h = 0.1$.

4. The Runge-Kutta equations for solving two simultaneous equations of the type

$$\frac{dy}{dx} = f(x,y,z), \qquad \frac{dz}{dx} = F(x,y,z)$$

are

$$k_1 = f(x_0,y_0,z_0)\,\Delta x, \qquad l_1 = F(x_0,y_0,z_0)\,\Delta x,$$

$$k_2 = f\left(x_0 + \frac{\Delta x}{2},\ y_0 + \frac{k_1}{2},\ z_0 + \frac{l_1}{2}\right), \qquad l_2 = F\left(x_0 + \frac{\Delta x}{2},\ y_0 + \frac{k_1}{2},\ z_0 + \frac{l_1}{2}\right),$$

$$k_3 = f\left(x_0 + \frac{\Delta x}{2},\ y_0 + \frac{k_2}{2},\ z_0 + \frac{l_2}{2}\right), \qquad l_3 = F\left(x_0 + \frac{\Delta x}{2},\ y_0 + \frac{k_2}{2},\ z_0 + \frac{l_2}{2}\right),$$

$$k_4 = f(x_0 + \Delta x,\ y_0 + k_3,\ z_0 + l_3), \qquad l_4 = F(x_0 + \Delta x,\ y_0 + k_3,\ z_0 + l_3),$$

$$\Delta y = \tfrac{1}{6}(k_1 + 2k_2 + 2k_3 + k_4), \qquad \Delta z = \tfrac{1}{6}(l_1 + 2l_2 + 2l_3 + l_4).$$

In using these equations, first find k_1 and l_1, then k_2 and l_2, then k_3 and l_3, then k_4 and l_4, and finally Δy and Δz. Use these equations to find the first five lines of the solution of

$$\frac{dy}{dx} = z - x, \qquad \frac{dz}{dx} = y + x$$

satisfying $y = 1$, $z = 1$ when $x = 0$. Use $h = 0.05$. Then use (16) and (17), §114, to compute two more lines.

CHAPTER 14

PARTIAL DIFFERENTIAL EQUATIONS

119. Introduction

Partial differential equations are likely to enter into any serious investigation involving more than two variables. We have already met them in the discussions of potential theory, envelopes of curves, exact differential equations, and existence theorems. They play a particularly important role in most sciences dealing with wave motions, such, for example, as heat, light, electricity, magnetism, radio, radar, television, and weather. This chapter will deal mainly with the theory of partial differential equations, and the next with their applications.

120. Solution of a partial differential equation

A **solution,** or **integral,** of a partial differential equation is a nondifferential relation among the variables which satisfies the equation. Its general form involves one or more arbitrary functions.* The following examples will illustrate these facts.

Example 1. Prove that

$$z = ax + a^2y^2 + b \tag{a}$$

is a solution of

$$\frac{\partial z}{\partial y} = 2y\left(\frac{\partial z}{\partial x}\right)^2. \tag{b}$$

Solution. Differentiating (a) partially with respect to x and with respect to y, we obtain

$$\frac{\partial z}{\partial x} = a, \qquad \frac{\partial z}{\partial y} = 2a^2y. \tag{c}$$

Substitution from (c) in (b) gives the identity

$$2a^2y = 2ya^2.$$

Example 2. Prove that

$$y = \varphi(ct - x) + \psi(ct + x), \tag{a}$$

* Throughout the chapters on partial differential equations, we shall assume that the arbitrary functions and their derivatives involved are continuous and single-valued in all regions under consideration.

where φ and ψ are arbitrary functions,* is a solution of

$$\frac{\partial^2 y}{dt^2} = c^2 \frac{\partial^2 y}{\partial x^2}. \tag{b}$$

Solution. It will be convenient to use the notation

$$\frac{d\varphi}{d(ct - x)} = \varphi', \qquad \frac{d^2\varphi}{[d(ct - x)]^2} = \varphi'',$$
$$\frac{d\psi}{d(ct + x)} = \psi', \qquad \frac{d^2\psi}{[d(ct + x)]^2} = \psi''.$$

Partial differentiation of (*a*) gives

$$\begin{aligned} \frac{\partial y}{\partial t} &= c\varphi' + c\psi', & \frac{\partial y}{\partial x} &= -\varphi' + \psi', \\ \frac{\partial^2 y}{\partial t^2} &= c^2\varphi'' + c^2\psi'', & \frac{\partial^2 y}{\partial x^2} &= \varphi'' + \psi''. \end{aligned} \tag{c}$$

Substituting from (*c*) in (*b*), we obtain the identity

$$c^2\varphi'' + c^2\psi'' = c^2\varphi'' + c^2\psi''.$$

Note: Throughout the chapters on partial differential equations, we shall use the notation

$$p = \frac{\partial z}{\partial x}, \quad q = \frac{\partial z}{\partial y}, \quad r = \frac{\partial^2 z}{\partial x^2}, \quad s = \frac{\partial^2 z}{\partial x\, \partial y}, \quad t = \frac{\partial^2 z}{\partial y^2}. \tag{1}$$

Example 3. Find the differential equation having as solution

$$\varphi(x^2 - z^2, x^3 - y^3) = 0 \tag{a}$$

where φ represents an arbitrary function.

Solution. Consider z as a function of x and y defined by (*a*), and let

$$x^2 - z^2 = u, \qquad x^3 - y^3 = v.$$

Differentiating (*a*) partially with respect to x and then partially with respect to y, we get

$$\frac{\partial \varphi}{\partial u}(2x - 2zp) + \frac{\partial \varphi}{\partial v}(3x^2) = 0, \tag{b}$$

$$\frac{\partial \varphi}{\partial u}(-2zq) + \frac{\partial \varphi}{\partial v}(-3y^2) = 0. \tag{c}$$

Equating $(\partial\varphi/\partial u)/(\partial\varphi/\partial v)$ from (*b*) to its value from (*c*), and simplifying slightly, we get

$$z(x^2q + y^2p) = xy^2. \tag{d}$$

* Equation (*a*) in example 2 represents a motion compounded of two wave motions having equal wavelengths and periods but opposite directions. Because of this fact, equation (*b*) of example 2 plays a very important role in mathematical physics.

EXERCISES

In the following exercises, φ and ψ represent arbitrary functions of the indicated variables.

Verify the fact that each equation on the left is a solution of the partial differential equation written opposite it:

1. $az = a^2x + y + b,$ $\qquad pq = 1.$
2. $2z = 2axe^y + a^2e^{2y} + b,$ $\qquad q = xp + p^2.$
3. $6az = x^3y + x\varphi(y) + \psi(y),$ $\qquad ar = xy.$
4. $z = \varphi(y/x) + \psi(xy),$ $\qquad x^2r - y^2t = qy - px.$
5. $x = \varphi(z) + \psi(y),$ $\qquad ps - qr = 0.$

Using the method of example 3, derive the differential equation having as solution

6. $z = \varphi(x + y).$
7. $z = x\varphi(x + y).$
8. $y = z\varphi(x + y).$
9. $y = \varphi(x) + \psi(z).$
10. $y = \varphi(x + y) + \psi(z).$
11. $z = \varphi(x + 2y) + \psi(x - y).$
12. $\varphi(x^2 + y^2, y^2 - z^2) = 0.$
13. $\varphi(x^2 - z^2, y^2 - z^2) = 0.$

14. Show that $q = 0$ for all cylindrical surfaces having their elements parallel to the Y-axis.

15. Show that, for all surfaces of revolution about the Z-axis, $yp = xq$ and, for all surfaces of revolution about the X-axis, $y + zq = 0$.

121. Equations easily integrable

Some partial differential equations may be solved by inspection. Thus, the equation

$$\frac{\partial z}{\partial x} = x^2 + y \tag{2}$$

evidently has as a solution

$$z = \frac{x^3}{3} + xy + \varphi(y), \tag{3}$$

where φ represents an arbitrary function. Since only differentiation with respect to x was indicated in (2), we got (3) from it by integrating with respect to x while treating y as a constant. Observe that $\varphi(y)$ plays the role of a constant since y was considered constant for the integration.

Again consider the equation

$$ys + p = 4xy, \tag{4}$$

where s and p have the meanings defined in (1) of §120. Writing this in the form

$$y\frac{\partial p}{\partial y} + p = 4xy,$$

we see that it is an ordinary linear equation of the first degree in p and

y if x is considered constant. Hence, its solution is

$$py = 2xy^2 + \varphi(x). \tag{5}$$

In (5), replace p by its equal $\partial z/\partial x$, and integrate again, considering y as a constant, to obtain

$$z = \int \left[2xy + \frac{1}{y}\varphi(x)\right] dx, \qquad y \text{ constant},$$

or

$$z = x^2y + \frac{1}{y}\varphi_1(x) + \psi(y).$$

Here, $\varphi_1(x)$ [$= \int \varphi(x)\,dx$] and $\psi(y)$ are arbitrary functions.

As a case requiring the solution of a second-order equation, consider

$$r - y^2z = xy^2. \tag{6}$$

Writing this in the form

$$\partial^2 z/\partial x^2 - y^2 z = xy^2,$$

integrating it, considering y as constant, and using functions of y as constants of integration, we get

$$z = \varphi_1(y)e^{xy} + \varphi_2(y)e^{-xy} - x.$$

These illustrations indicate how a large class of partial differential equations may be integrated by using the methods of solving ordinary differential equations. It is worthy of note that *the constant of integration consists of an arbitrary function of the variable considered constant during the integration.*

EXERCISES

1. $\dfrac{\partial z}{\partial x} = 3x^2 + y^2.$
2. $y\dfrac{\partial z}{\partial y} + z = x^2.$
3. $y\dfrac{\partial p}{\partial y} + p = 2x.$
4. $r = f(x,y).$
5. $ys = x + ay.$
6. $t - q = e^x + e^y.$
7. $p + r = xy.$
8. $xr + p = xy.$
9. $r + p^2 = y^2.$
10. $zp + z^2 = xy^2.$
11. $pr + p^2 = a.$
12. $\dfrac{\partial r}{\partial y} + \dfrac{\partial p}{\partial x} = 12.$

Using the plan of solution suggested for equation (6), solve the following equations:

13. $r - 4z = 8y^2.$
14. $t + 4z = 8x^2.$
15. $r - 2p - 3z = y^2(2 + 3x).$
16. $t + 2q - 3z = x^2(2 - 3y).$
17. $2r - 3yp - 5y^2z = y^2(3 + 5x).$
18. $t - 2xq + 5x^2z = 5x^3.$

122. Equations having the form $Pp + Qq = R$

In this section and elsewhere, we shall use the notation

$$\frac{\partial u}{\partial x} = u_x, \qquad \frac{\partial u}{\partial y} = u_y, \qquad \frac{\partial^2 u}{\partial x\,\partial y} = u_{xy}, \qquad \text{etc.} \tag{7}$$

THEOREM. *If $u(x,y,z) = a$, $v(x,y,z) = b$ are two independent integrals of the ordinary differential equations*

$$\frac{dx}{P(x,y,z)} = \frac{dy}{Q(x,y,z)} = \frac{dz}{R(x,y,z)}, \tag{8}$$*

then

$$\varphi(u,v) = 0 \quad or \quad v = \psi(u) \tag{9}$$

is a general solution of

$$Pp + Qq = R. \tag{10}$$

First, let us show that any solution $u(x,y,z) = c$ of (10) is also a solution of

$$Pu_x + Qu_y + Ru_z = 0, \tag{11}$$

and, conversely, any solution of (11) is also a solution of (10). From $u(x,y,z) = c$, we get

$$u_x + u_z p = 0, \qquad u_y + u_z q = 0. \tag{12}$$

Assume that $u_z \neq 0$. Then, substituting the values of p and q from (12) in (10) and simplifying slightly, we get (11). Similarly, we can derive (10) from (11) and (12).

Equating the ratios in (8) to λ, we get

$$dx = P\lambda, \qquad dy = Q\lambda, \qquad dz = R\lambda. \tag{13}$$

If $u(x,y,z) = c$ is a solution of (8) and $u_z \neq 0$, we get from (8) and (13)

$$0 = u_x\,dx + u_y\,dy + u_z\,dz = \lambda(u_xP + u_yQ + u_zR). \tag{14}$$

Hence, any solution of (8) is a solution of (11) and therefore of (10). If $w = a$ and $v = b$ are solutions of (8), we have from (8) $dw = 0$, $dv = 0$, and therefore, subject to (8),

$$d\varphi(w,v) = \varphi_w\,dw + \varphi_v\,dv = 0. \tag{15}$$

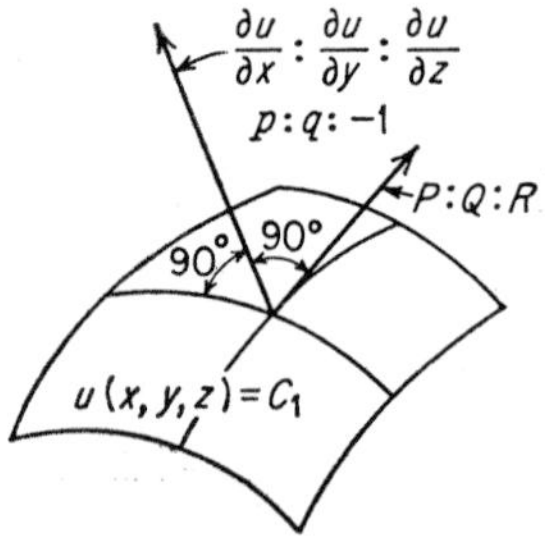

FIG. 1

From this we easily derive (14), with $u = \varphi(w,v)$, and therefore $\varphi(w,v) = 0$ satisfies (10).

We assumed that $u_z \neq 0$. However, any solution of (8) can be compounded of solutions of (8) each of which contains z and therefore has a derivative with respect to z. This completes the proof of the theorem.

Since $\partial u/\partial x$, $\partial u/\partial y$, $\partial u/\partial z$ are direction numbers of a normal to surface $u(x,y,z) = c$ at (x,y,z), equation (11) shows that *a line with direction numbers p, q, -1 is normal to a surface represented by an integral $u(x,y,z) = c$ of* (10), and (8) shows that *the surface is tangent at (x,y,z) to a line passing through (x,y,z) and having direction numbers P, Q, R.* Figure 1 is suggestive.

* The theory of §96 applies to solve equations of type (8).

By the same line of reasoning we could show that *if*

$$\mathbf{u}_i(\mathbf{x}_1,\mathbf{x}_2, \ldots ,\mathbf{x}_n,\mathbf{z}) = \mathbf{c}_i, \qquad \mathbf{i} = \mathbf{1}, \mathbf{2}, \ldots , \mathbf{n}, \tag{16}$$

are independent solutions of the differential equations

$$\frac{\mathbf{dx}_1}{\mathbf{P}_1} = \frac{\mathbf{dx}_2}{\mathbf{P}_2} = \cdots = \frac{\mathbf{dx}_n}{\mathbf{P}_n} = \frac{\mathbf{dz}}{\mathbf{R}}, \tag{17}$$

then $\varphi(u_1,u_2, \ldots ,u_n) = 0,$

φ representing an arbitrary function, is a solution of

$$\mathbf{P}_1\mathbf{z}_{x_1} + \mathbf{P}_2\mathbf{z}_{x_2} + \cdots + \mathbf{P}_n\mathbf{z}_{x_n} = \mathbf{R}. \tag{18}$$

Example 1. Solve $(y + z)p + (x + z)q = x + y.$

Solution. The first step is to find two integrals of

$$\frac{dx}{y + z} = \frac{dy}{x + z} = \frac{dz}{x + y}. \tag{a}$$

By the theory of proportion, we find from (*a*)

$$\frac{dx + dy + dz}{2x + 2y + 2z} = \frac{dx - dy}{-(x - y)} = \frac{dx - dz}{-(x - z)}. \tag{b}$$

Two integrals of (*b*) evidently are

$$\ln (x + y + z) + 2 \ln (x - y) = C_1,$$

or

$$(x + y + z)(x - y)^2 = c_1, \tag{c}$$

and $\ln (x - y) - \ln (x - z) = C_2,$ or $x - y = c_2(x - z).$ (*d*)

Hence, the solution required is

$$\varphi\left[(\mathbf{x} + \mathbf{y} + \mathbf{z})(\mathbf{x} - \mathbf{y})^2, \frac{\mathbf{x} - \mathbf{y}}{\mathbf{x} - \mathbf{z}}\right] = \mathbf{0},$$

or it may be written

$$\mathbf{x} - \mathbf{y} = (\mathbf{x} - \mathbf{z})\varphi[(\mathbf{x} + \mathbf{y} + \mathbf{z})(\mathbf{x} - \mathbf{y})^2].$$

Example 2. Solve

$$2xz_{xx} - yz_{xy} + 2x + 2z_x = 0. \tag{a}$$

Solution. In (*a*), let us set $z_x = p$ to obtain

$$2xp_x - yp_y = -2p - 2x. \tag{b}$$

Solving (*b*) for p by the method of this section, we get

$$2px + x^2 = \varphi(xy^2), \qquad \text{or} \qquad p = \frac{\partial z}{\partial x} = -\tfrac{1}{2}x + \tfrac{1}{2}x^{-1}\varphi(xy^2). \tag{c}$$

Integrating the second equation, considering y as constant, we get

$$\mathbf{z} = -\frac{x^2}{4} + \int \frac{1}{2xy^2}\varphi(xy^2)y^2\,dx = -\frac{\mathbf{x}^2}{\mathbf{4}} + \psi_1(\mathbf{xy}^2) + \psi_2(\mathbf{y}).$$

Here, $\psi_1(xy^2)$, being defined by $\psi'(xy^2) = [1/(2xy^2)]\varphi(xy^2)$, is an arbitrary function.

EXERCISES

Solve the following differential equations:

1. $p + q = z$.
2. $xp + yq = 2z$.
3. $xp + zq = y$.
4. $ap + bq = c$.
5. $xp + zq + y = 0$.
6. $xyq - x^2p = y^2$.
7. $x^2p + y^2q = axy$.
8. $yzp + xzq + 2xy = 0$.
9. $xy^2p - y^3q + axz = 0$.
10. $(x + y)(p - q) = z$.

11. If $R = 0$ in (10), show that $z = c$ is one solution.

12. Solve $xp + yq = 0$. Show that $z = c_1$ is a solution and $y/x = c_2$ is another. Check by direct substitution that $z = y^2/x^2$ and also $z = x/y$ are solutions.

13. Solve $x(1 + y)q = z$.

14. $y \dfrac{\partial^2 z}{\partial x\, \partial y} + \dfrac{\partial^2 z}{\partial x^2} = 4x$. *Hint:* First integrate with respect to x, treating y as constant. Observe that $\int^x \psi_1(ye^{-x})\, dx = \int^x \psi'(ye^{-x})(-ye^{-x}\, dx) = \psi(ye^{-x}) + \varphi(y)$.

15. $x \dfrac{\partial^2 z}{\partial x^2} + y \dfrac{\partial^2 z}{\partial x\, \partial y} + \dfrac{\partial z}{\partial x} = 2x + y$.

16. Determine the equations of the surfaces that cut orthogonally the system of ellipsoids $\frac{1}{5}x^2 + \frac{1}{3}y^2 + z^2 = c^2$. *Hint:* $P = \frac{2}{5}x$, $Q = \frac{2}{3}y$, $R = 2z$.

17. Find the equation of all surfaces whose normals intersect the line $x = y$, $z = 0$. *Hint:* $p/(x - a) = q/(y - a) = -1/z$. Eliminate a.

18. The condition that $u(x,y)$ be an integrating factor of $M(x,y)\, dx + N(x,y)\, dx = 0$ is $\partial(uM)/\partial y - \partial(uN)/\partial x = 0$. Show that this is equivalent to

$$Nu_x - Mu_y = u(M_y - N_x). \tag{a}$$

Using (*a*), find an integrating factor of

(*a*) $(y + y^2)\, dx - (x + y^2 + 2xy)\, dy = 0$.
(*b*) $(\ln x - 2xy)\, dx + (2xy - 2x^2)\, dy = 0$.

19. Use formula (*a*) of exercise 18 to find an integrating factor of $M\, dx + N\, dy = 0$ if $(\partial N/\partial x) - (\partial M/\partial y)$ is equal to

(*a*) $Mf(y)$. (*b*) $Nf(x)$. (*c*) $\dfrac{k(xM - yN)}{xy}$. (*d*) $\dfrac{axM - byN}{xy}$.

Read the solution of example 2, and then solve the following equations:

20. $xr - ys = 2y$.
21. $xr + ys = 0$.
22. $xs - yt = 2x$.
23. $xs - yt + q = 12xy$.
24. $xs - 2x^2t = q$.
25. $xs - 2yt = 2q + x$.
26. $r + ys = p$.
27. $xr + s + p = 0$.

123. Finding particular solutions satisfying given conditions

The solution of a differential equation

$$P(x,y,z)p + Q(x,y,z)q = R(x,y,z) \tag{19}$$

is generally determined by specifying that it satisfy two equations $I_1(x,y,z) = 0$, $I_2(x,y,z) = 0$, or, in other words, that it represent a surface containing a given space curve. *If $u = a$ and $v = b$ represent two independent solutions of* (19), *we may obtain the required particular solution by solving three of the equations*

$$u(x,y,z) = a, \quad v(x,y,z) = b, \quad I_1(x,y,z) = 0, \quad I_2(x,y,z) = 0 \tag{20}$$

for x, y, and z in terms of a and b, substituting these values in the fourth equation, and then replacing a by $u(x,y,z)$ and b by $v(x,y,z)$ in the result. The following example will illustrate the process:

Example. Find the solution of

$$xp + yq = z, \qquad (a)$$

which represents a surface through

$$x + y = 3, \qquad x^2 + y^2 + z^2 = 18. \qquad (b)$$

Solution. Two particular solutions of (a), found from

$$\frac{dx}{x} = \frac{dy}{y} = \frac{dz}{z}, \qquad (c)$$

are

$$x = az, \qquad y = bz. \qquad (d)$$

Solving (d) and the first equation of (b) for x, y, and z, we get

$$z = 3/(a + b), \qquad x = 3a/(a + b), \qquad y = 3b/(a + b). \qquad (e)$$

Replacing x, y, and z in the second equation of (b) by their values from (e), we get

$$9(a^2 + b^2 + 1)/(a + b)^2 = 18. \qquad (f)$$

In (f), replace a and b by their values from (d), and simplify to get

$$\mathbf{x^2 + y^2 + 4xy = z^2}. \qquad (g)$$

EXERCISES

1. Find the solution of $xp + yq = z$ which represents a surface through the curve $x^2 - y^2 = 4$, $y^2 + z^2 = 16$.

2. Find the solution of $xp - yq = 0$ which represents a surface through the curve: (a) $xy^2 = z$, $y + z = 10$; (b) $x^2y = z$, $xy + xz = 2y$; (c) $xz = 1$, $xy + 1 = 2y$.

3. Find the solution of $xp + yq = z$ which represents a surface through the curve: (a) $x + y = 1$, $x^2 + y^2 + z^2 = 25$; (b) $x - z = 1$, $x^2 + z^2 = 25$; (c) $xy = 2$, $z = y(1 + x^2 + x^4)$.

4. Find a solution of $p + q = z$ which represents a surface passing through the curve: (a) $z = \sin x$, $y = 0$; (b) $z = y^2$, $x = a$; (c) $x^2 + z^2 = a^2$, $y = 0$.

5. Find the equation of all surfaces having tangent planes with x-intercept 1. Also, find the equation of the particular surface passing through the circle $x = 0$, $y^2 + z^2 = 25$.

6. Find the equation of a surface for which

$$xyq - x^2p = y^2$$

and satisfying the condition $p = q$ when $x = 1$.

124. Separation of variables

In this section, we shall denote differentiation by subscripts. The process considered will be applied only to **linear partial differential equations,** that is, equations linear in a dependent variable and its partial derivatives with respect to independent variables. Thus,

$$A(x,y)z_{xx} + B(x,y)z_{xy} + C(x,y)z_{yy} = E(x,y)$$

is an equation in x, y, and z linear in z. Just as in §44, we can show that, if $z_i = f_i(x,y)$, $i = 1, 2, \ldots, n$, are solutions of an equation linear in z and having no term free of z, then $z = c_1f_1 + c_2f_2 + \cdots + c_nf_n$ is also a solution.

A process often used in the investigations of physical science is called **separation of variables.** The following example illustrates the process and the type of solutions obtained by using it:

Example. Solve

$$z_{xx} + 4z_{yy} = 0. \qquad (a)$$

Solution. Assume a solution having the form

$$z = XY, \qquad (b)$$

where X is a function of x only and Y a function of y only. Denoting derivatives by dots, we use such expressions as

$$\frac{dX}{dx} = \dot{X}, \qquad \frac{d^2X}{dx^2} = \ddot{X}, \qquad \frac{dY}{dy} = \dot{Y}, \qquad \text{etc.} \qquad (c)$$

Substituting z from (b) in (a), we obtain

$$\ddot{X}Y + 4\ddot{Y}X = 0. \qquad (d)$$

Dividing this by XY, we get

$$\frac{\ddot{X}}{X} + 4\frac{\ddot{Y}}{Y} = 0. \qquad (e)$$

This can be satisfied only if one member is a constant and the other the negative of this constant. Denoting the constant by k, we have

$$\ddot{X} = kX, \qquad 4\ddot{Y} = -kY. \qquad (f)$$

The solutions of these for $k > 0$ are

$$X = a_1e^{\sqrt{k}x} + a_2e^{-\sqrt{k}x}, \quad Y = a_3 \sin\left(\tfrac{1}{2}\sqrt{k}\,y\right) + a_4 \cos \tfrac{1}{2}\sqrt{k}\,y. \quad (g)$$

Now, z defined by (b) and (g) satisfies (a) for k any value. Hence, in accordance with the principle of adding solutions of linear equations, we may write as a solution of (*a*)

$$z = \sum^{k} X_k Y_k = \sum^{k} \{e^{\sqrt{k}x}[a_k \sin(\tfrac{1}{2}\sqrt{k}\,y) + b_k \cos(\tfrac{1}{2}\sqrt{k}\,y)] + e^{-\sqrt{k}x}[c_k \sin(\tfrac{1}{2}\sqrt{k}\,y) + d_k \cos(\tfrac{1}{2}\sqrt{k}\,y)]\}, \quad (h)$$

where k may take in succession the values of any finite set of positive numbers. If k takes the values $k_1, k_2, k_3, \ldots$, then equation (*h*), involving an infinite series, is a valid solution within its region of absolute convergence.

If k is negative, the sine-cosine part of the solution would go with X and the exponential part with Y. When $k = 0$, we have

$$X = c_1 x + c_2, \qquad Y = c_3 y + c_4.$$

Thus, it appears that the solution is made up of three types. For any application, appropriate types are used.

EXERCISES

Use the method of separation of variables to find the various types of solutions of equations 1 to 4:

1. $z_{xx} + z_{yy} = 0$.

2. $z_{xx} - z_y = 0$.

3. $z_x + z_y = 0$.

4. $z_x + z_y - 3z = 0$.

5. Solve $z_{xx} + z_{yy} + z = 0$, assuming that $\ddot{X}/X = k - 1$, where $k > 1$. What values of k will involve other types of solutions?

6. If, in solving $z_{xx} + z_{yy} + z_x + 2z_y = 0$, we use $\ddot{X}/X + \dot{X}/X = k$, state the ranges of k associated with oscillation of: (*a*) the x-factor; (*b*) the y-factor; (*c*) neither factor.

★7. For Laplace's equation* $(\partial^2 u/\partial x^2) + (\partial^2 u/\partial y^2) + (\partial^2 u/\partial z^2) = 0$, assume that $u = XYZ$, and obtain $\ddot{X}/X + \ddot{Y}/Y + \ddot{Z}/Z = 0$. This will be satisfied if

$$\frac{\ddot{X}}{X} = l, \qquad \frac{\ddot{Y}}{Y} = m, \qquad \frac{\ddot{Z}}{Z} = n, \qquad l + m + n = 0.$$

Find a solution, assuming that $l > 0$, $m > 0$, $n = -l - m$. How many different types of solutions, each associated with a set of values for l, m, and n, exist?

★8. Laplace's equation for two dimensions and polar coordinates is

$$\frac{\partial^2 u}{\partial \rho^2} + \frac{1}{\rho}\frac{\partial u}{\partial \rho} + \frac{1}{\rho^2}\frac{\partial^2 u}{\partial \theta^2} = 0.$$

Show that one solution has the form (*h*), of the illustrative example, with x replaced by θ and y by $\ln \rho$.

* This equation, called Laplace's equation, is of basic importance because it must hold for a flow of substance, such as heat, air, or water, if the quantity entering a region is equal to the quantity leaving it. Exercise 1 relates to Laplace's equation for two dimensions.

9. To solve $z_{xx} + z_{xy} + z_{yy} = 0$, let $z = XY$, and obtain

$$\frac{\ddot{X}}{X} + \frac{\dot{X}}{X}\frac{\dot{Y}}{Y} + \frac{\ddot{Y}}{Y} = 0.$$

Let $\dot{X}/X = k$, and solve for X; show that $\ddot{X}/X = k^2$; then solve for Y, and write a solution of the given equation.

10. Laplace's equation for cylindrical coordinates in space is

$$\frac{\partial^2 u}{\partial \rho^2} + \frac{1}{\rho}\frac{\partial u}{\partial \rho} + \frac{1}{\rho^2}\frac{\partial^2 u}{\partial \theta^2} + \frac{\partial^2 u}{\partial z^2} = 0.$$

Show that a solution of this has the form $u = R\Theta Z$, where

$$\frac{\ddot{Z}}{Z} = k_1, \qquad \frac{\ddot{\Theta}}{\Theta} = k_2, \qquad \rho^2\ddot{R} + \rho\dot{R} + (k_2 + k_1\rho^2)R = 0.$$

125. Hyperbolic, parabolic, elliptic equations

Partial differential equations of the second order are of great importance, as we shall see in the next chapter.

Consider a partial differential equation having the form

$$az_{xx} + bz_{xy} + cz_{yy} = f(x,y,z,z_x,z_y), \tag{21}$$

where a, b, and c represent continuous functions of x and y having all derivatives involved continuous and f represents a polynomial function in the indicated variables. Equation (21) is called

Hyperbolic if $b^2 - 4ac > 0$,
Parabolic if $b^2 - 4ac = 0$,
Elliptic if $b^2 - 4ac < 0$.

We shall derive simple forms, called **canonical forms,** of (21) for these cases and solve some particular examples.

Let us transform (21) by means of the substitution*

$$u = u(x,y), \qquad v = v(x,y). \tag{22}$$

Thinking of z as a function of u and v, we have, in accordance with the laws of transformation from calculus,

$$z_x = z_u u_x + z_v v_x, \qquad z_y = z_u u_y + z_v v_y. \tag{23}$$

Note that $z_{xx} = (z_x)_u u_x + (z_x)_v v_x$ and therefore, from (23), that

$$z_{xx} = (z_{uu}u_x + z_{uv}v_x)u_x + z_u u_{xx} + (z_{vu}u_x + z_{vv}v_x)v_x + z_v v_{xx}. \tag{24}$$

Note that $z_{uv} = z_{vu}$, change (24) slightly, and then derive expressions for z_{xy} and z_{yy} by the process applied for z_{xx}, and obtain

$$z_{xx} = z_{uu}u_x^2 + 2z_{uv}u_x v_x + z_{vv}v_x^2 + z_u u_{xx} + z_v v_{xx}, \tag{25}$$
$$z_{xy} = z_{uu}u_x u_y + z_{uv}(u_x v_y + u_y v_x) + z_{vv}v_x v_y + z_u u_{xy} + z_v v_{xy}, \tag{26}$$
$$z_{yy} = z_{uu}u_y^2 + 2z_{uv}u_y v_y + z_{vv}v_y^2 + z_u u_{yy} + z_v v_{yy}. \tag{27}$$

* We assume that $u_x v_y - v_x u_y \neq 0$ so that (22) may be solved for x and y in terms of u and v.

Substituting the values of z_{xx}, z_{xy}, z_{yy}, z_x, and z_y from (23), (25), (26), and (27) in (21), we get

$$\alpha z_{uu} + \beta z_{uv} + \gamma z_{vv} + \delta z_u + \epsilon z_v = F(u,v,z,z_u,z_v), \tag{28}$$

where

$$\alpha = au_x^2 + bu_xu_y + cu_y^2, \qquad \gamma = av_x^2 + bv_xv_y + cv_y^2, \tag{29}$$

$$\beta = 2au_xv_x + b(u_xv_y + u_yv_x) + 2cu_yv_y, \tag{30}$$

$$\delta = au_{xx} + bu_{xy} + cu_{yy}, \qquad \epsilon = av_{xx} + bv_{xy} + cv_{yy}, \tag{31}$$

and F is the result of transforming f by (22). In making a transformation, compute α, γ, β, δ, ϵ, and F by using (29), (30), and (31) and substituting the values thus obtained in (28).

Hyperbolic case. To get canonical forms we generally find the roots λ and μ of

$$ar^2 + br + c = 0, \tag{32}$$

and take

$$u_x/u_y = \lambda, \qquad v_x/v_y = \mu. \tag{33}$$

Since $r_1 = \lambda$ and $r_2 = \mu$ satisfy (32), we see that u_x/u_y and v_x/v_y from (33) satisfy $\alpha = 0$, $\gamma = 0$ of (29), and accordingly (28) is reduced to the canonical form

$$\beta z_{uv} = \varphi(u,v,z,z_u,z_v), \tag{34}$$

where $\varphi = F - \delta z_u - \epsilon z_v$. To get definite expressions for u and v, think of the curves, called **characteristics,** $u = c_1$, $v = c_2$, and consider that for these

$$-\frac{u_x}{u_y} = \frac{dy}{dx}, \qquad \frac{-v_x}{v_y} = \frac{dy}{dx},$$

or, *if λ and μ are the roots of* (32), *the solutions of*

$$\frac{dy}{dx} + \lambda = 0, \qquad \frac{dy}{dx} + \mu = 0 \tag{35}$$

may be taken as u and v.

Consider, for example,

$$z_{xx} + xz_{xy} - 6x^2z_{yy} = x^{-1}z_x. \tag{a}$$

Here $a = 1$, $b = x$, $c = -6x^2$, and the corresponding (32) and its roots λ and μ are

$$r^2 + xr - 6x^2 = 0, \qquad r_1 = 2x, \qquad r_2 = -3x.$$

Substituting these in (35) and integrating the results, we get $y + x^2 = c_1$, $y - \frac{3}{2}x^2 = c_2$, and

$$u = y + x^2, \qquad v = y - \tfrac{3}{2}x^2. \tag{b}$$

Note first that the right-hand member of (a) is

$$x^{-1}z_x = x^{-1}(z_uu_x + z_vv_x) = x^{-1}(2xz_u - 3xz_v) = 2z_u - 3z_v. \tag{c}$$

Substituting from (*b*) in (29), (30), and (31), we get

$$\alpha = \gamma = 0, \qquad \beta = -25x^2, \qquad \delta = 2z_u, \qquad \epsilon = -3z_v. \tag{d}$$

Substituting these values in (28), we get

$$-25x^2z_{uv} + 2z_u - 3z_v = 2z_u - 3z_v, \qquad \text{or} \qquad z_{uv} = 0.$$

From $z_{uv} = 0$, we easily get

$$z = \varphi(u) + \psi(v) = \varphi(y + x^2) + \psi(y - \tfrac{3}{2}x^2).$$

Parabolic case. For the parabolic case, we have $b^2 - 4ac = 0$. Hence, $ar^2 + br + c = 0$ has equal roots, λ, λ. Just as in the hyperbolic case, we take

$$\frac{dy}{dx} + \lambda = \frac{dy}{dx} - \frac{b}{2a} = 0 \tag{e}$$

and get as its solution $u = c_1$. When this value of u is used in (29) and (30), we see at once that $\alpha = 0$ and it happens that $\beta = 0$ also,* independently of the choice of v. Hence, *in the parabolic case* (28) *is reduced by the substitution derived from* (*e*) *to the canonical form*†

$$\gamma z_{vv} = \varphi(u,v,z,z_u,z_v). \tag{36}$$

Consider, for example, the equation

$$z_{xx} - 4xz_{xy} + 4x^2z_{yy} = 0. \tag{f}$$

Here the root of $r^2 - 4xr + 4x^2 = 0$ is $r = 2x$. Hence, we write

$$\frac{dy}{dx} + 2x = 0, \qquad y + x^2 = c. \tag{g}$$

Accordingly, we make the substitution

$$u = y + x^2, \qquad v = x, \tag{h}$$

where $v = x$, a simple substitution, was used, as v may be taken arbitrarily. Using (*h*) together with (23), (28), (29), (30), and (31), we get, from (*f*),

$$z_{vv} + 2z_u = 0. \tag{i}$$

This may be solved by separation of the variables to obtain

$$z = \sum^{k} e^{ku/2}(c_{1k} \sin \sqrt{k}\, v + c_{2k} \cos \sqrt{k}\, v)$$
$$= \sum^{k} e^{k(y+x^2)/2}(c_{3k} \sin \sqrt{k}\, x + c_{4k} \cos \sqrt{k}\, x). \tag{j}$$

* The proof that $\beta = 0$ is left for exercise 11.

† A substitution $v = v(x,y)$ based on $dy/dx + \lambda = 0$ would have led to $\alpha z_{uu} = \varphi(u,v,z,z_u,z_v)$.

Elliptic case. Since for this case $b^2 - 4ac < 0$, the roots of $ar^2 + br + c = 0$ will have the form $\lambda \pm i\mu$. Hence, the corresponding substitution based on

$$u_x/u_y = \lambda + i\mu, \qquad v_x/v_y = \lambda - i\mu \tag{37}$$

is like the hyperbolic case, but the solution involves imaginary functions. Accordingly, we derive functions u and v based on

$$\frac{dy}{dx} + \lambda + i\mu = 0, \qquad \frac{dy}{dx} + \lambda - i\mu = 0 \tag{38}$$

and then make the substitution

$$u_1 = \frac{1}{2}(u + v), \qquad v_1 = -\frac{i}{2}(u - v). \tag{39}$$

This leads to the canonical form (see exercise 12)

$$z_{uu} + z_{vv} = \varphi(u,v,z,z_u,z_v).$$

Consider the equation

$$z_{xx} + y^2 z_{yy} + y z_y = 0. \tag{k}$$

The roots of $r^2 + y^2 = 0$ are $\pm iy$. Hence, we derive from

$$\frac{dy}{dx} + iy = 0, \qquad \frac{dy}{dx} - iy = 0 \tag{l}$$

the function

$$u = ye^{ix} = y(\cos x + i \sin x), \qquad v = y(\cos x - i \sin x). \tag{m}$$

We now make the substitution

$$u_1 = \frac{1}{2}(u + v) = y \cos x, \qquad v_1 = -\frac{i}{2}(u - v) = y \sin x. \tag{n}$$

Proceeding in the usual manner to use the substitution (n) in (k) by means of (23), (29), (30), and (31), we get

$$y^2(z_{u_1u_1} + z_{v_1v_1}) = 0. \tag{o}$$

Solving this by the method of separation of the variables and replacing u_1 and v_1 by their values from (n), we get

$$z = \sum^{k} [c_{1k} \sin(\sqrt{k}\, y \cos x) + c_{2k} \cos(\sqrt{k}\, y \cos x)](c_{3k}e^{\sqrt{k}y \sin x} + c_{4k}e^{-\sqrt{k}y \sin x}).$$

EXERCISES

Use substitutions to solve the following equations:

1. $z_{xx} + z_{xy} - 2z_{yy} = 0$. *Hint:* The roots of $r^2 + r - 2 = 0$ are $r = 1, -2$; from $dy/dx + 1 = 0$, $dy/dx - 2 = 0$, obtain $u = y + x$, $v = y - 2x$. Now use (23), (28), (29), (30), and (31).

2. $z_{xx} - (m + n)z_{xy} + mnz_{yy} = 0$, m and n constants.

3. $z_{xx} + 2mz_{xy} + m^2z_{yy} = 0$. *Hint:* From $dy/dx + (-m) = 0$, obtain $u = y - mx$. Make the substitution $u = y - mx$, $v = x$.

4. $z_{xx} - 2z_{xy} + 5z_{yy} = 0$. *Hint:* Using (37), (38), and (39), deduce the substitution $u_1 = x + y$, $v_1 = 2x$.

5. $z_{xx} - 2mz_{xy} + (m^2 + n^2)z_{yy} = 0$.

6. $x^2z_{xx} + xyz_{xy} - 2y^2z_{yy} = \frac{4}{3}(yz_y - xz_x)$.

7. $z_{xx} - 4xz_{xy} + 4x^2z_{yy} = 2z_y$. **8.** $z_{xx} - 2yz_{xy} + 5y^2z_{yy} + 5yz_y = 0$.

9. $\rho^2 \dfrac{\partial^2 z}{\partial \rho^2} + \dfrac{\partial^2 z}{\partial \theta^2} + 2\rho \dfrac{\partial z}{\partial \rho} = 0$.

10. $x^2y^2z_{xx} + 2xyz_{xy} + z_{yy} = -x(1 + y^2)z_x$. *Hint:* Take $v = y$.

11. Show in the parabolic case that the equation $ar^2 + br + c$ has $-b/2a$ as a double root. Also, show that the substitution $u = u(x,y)$, $v = v(x,y)$ for which $u_x/u_y = -b/2a$ has $\beta = 0$ as a result provided that u and v are independent functions.

★12. Show in the elliptic case that the substitution (39) in (21) results in $\alpha = \gamma$ and $\beta = 0$. *Hint:* $u_{1x} = \frac{1}{2}(u_x + v_x), \ldots, v_{1y} = -\frac{1}{2}i(u_y - v_y)$. Also, remember that $au_x^2 + bu_xu_y + cu_y^2 = av_x^2 + bv_xv_y + cv_y^2 = 0$.

13. How could the canonical form $z_{uu} = \psi(u,v,z,z_u,z_v)$ be obtained for the parabolic case?

CHAPTER 15

APPLICATIONS OF PARTIAL DIFFERENTIAL EQUATIONS

126. Fourier series

Orthogonal functions have already been considered in §§106 to 109. Perhaps the most important set is the one based on sin nx and cos nx, where n is an integer. A series having the form

$$a_0 + a_1 \cos x + a_2 \cos 2x + \cdots + a_n \cos nx + \cdots \\ + b_1 \sin x + b_2 \sin 2x + \cdots + b_n \sin nx + \cdots \quad (1)$$

is called a **Fourier series.** First, let us assume that a certain function $f(x)$ can be expanded in a Fourier series

$$f(x) = a_0 + \sum_{n=1}^{\infty} (a_n \cos nx + b_n \sin nx), \quad (2)$$

which is uniformly convergent in the interval $-\pi \leqq x \leqq \pi$, and then attempt to find expressions for the coefficients a_n and b_n.

First, we find by direct evaluation of integrals

$$\int_{-\pi}^{\pi} \sin mx\, dx = \int_{-\pi}^{\pi} \cos mx\, dx = \int_{-\pi}^{\pi} \sin mx \cos nx\, dx = 0, \quad (3)$$

$$\int_{-\pi}^{\pi} \sin mx \sin nx\, dx = \int_{-\pi}^{\pi} \cos mx \cos nx\, dx = 0, \qquad m \neq n,$$

$$\int_{-\pi}^{\pi} \sin^2 mx\, dx = \int_{-\pi}^{\pi} \cos^2 mx\, dx = \pi, \quad (4)$$

where m and n represent integers.*

Since the right member of (2) multiplied by cos nx is uniformly continuous, term-by-term integration may be applied to integrate its right member. Multiplying (2) through by cos $nx\, dx$, equating the definite integrals of its members from $-\pi$ to π, and taking account of (3) and (4), we get

$$\int_{-\pi}^{\pi} f(x) \cos nx\, dx = a_n \int_{-\pi}^{\pi} \cos^2 nx\, dx = \pi a_n,$$

$$\mathbf{a_n = \frac{1}{\pi} \int_{-\pi}^{\pi} f(x) \cos nx\, dx.} \quad (5)$$

* Throughout this chapter, m and n represent integers unless the context indicates otherwise.

Similarly, multiplying (2) through by $\sin nx\,dx$ and proceeding as before, we obtain

$$b_n = \frac{1}{\pi}\int_{-\pi}^{\pi} f(x) \sin nx\, dx. \tag{6}$$

Also, in like manner, we get

$$a_0 = \frac{1}{2\pi}\int_{-\pi}^{\pi} f(x)\, dx. \tag{7}$$

It has been proved* that, *if $f(x)$ is single-valued and finite in the interval $-\pi < x < \pi$ and has only a finite number of discontinuities and of maxima and minima in this interval, then the Fourier series resulting from* (2) *by substituting in it the values of a_n, b_n, and a_0 from* (5), (6), *and* (7),

$$\begin{aligned} a_0 &= \frac{1}{2\pi}\int_{-\pi}^{\pi} f(x)\, dx, \qquad a_m = \frac{1}{\pi}\int_{-\pi}^{\pi} f(x)\cos mx\, dx, \\ b_m &= \frac{1}{\pi}\int_{-\pi}^{\pi} f(x)\sin mx\, dx, \qquad m = 1, 2, \ldots, \end{aligned} \tag{8}$$

is equal to $f(x)$ for all values of x in the interval $-\pi < x < \pi$ except at points of discontinuity. At a point of discontinuity where $x = a$, the value of the series is

$$\tfrac{1}{2}\lim_{\epsilon\to 0}\,[f(a-\epsilon) + f(a+\epsilon)], \qquad \epsilon > 0. \tag{9}$$

When $x = -\pi$ and when $x = \pi$, the value of the series for $f(x)$ is

$$\tfrac{1}{2}[f(-\pi) + f(\pi)]. \tag{10}$$

Both $\sin mx$ and $\cos mx$ have the period 2π, since $\sin m(x + 2k\pi) = \sin mx$ and $\cos m(x + 2k\pi) = \cos mx$, where m and k are integers. Hence,

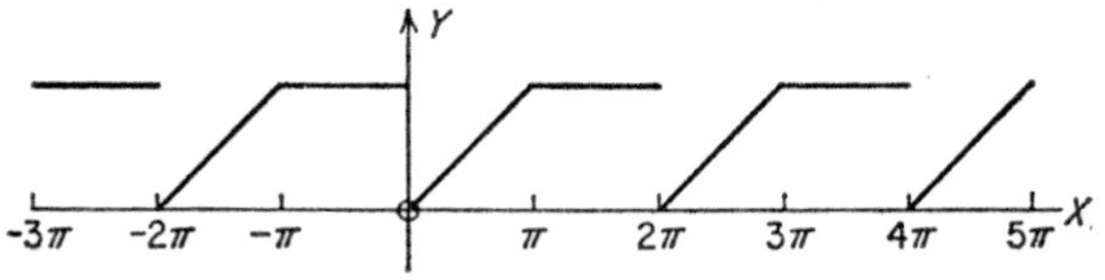

FIG. 1

the values assumed by series (2) *in the interval $-\pi < x < \pi$ are assumed by it in any other interval $(2k - 1)\pi < x < (2k + 1)\pi$. Otherwise stated,* (2) *together with* (8), (9), *and* (10) *defines a function $f(x + k2\pi)$, k an integer.* Figure 1 indicates this situation by showing the graph of a function from $-\pi$ to π and repetitions of it.

* Expansion in Fourier series is treated in books on advanced calculus. Consult R. Courant, "Differential and Integral Calculus," vol. I, pp. 437–456; W. E. Byerly, "Fourier's Series and Spherical Harmonics"; H. S. Carslaw, "Introduction to the Theory of Fourier's Series and Integrals."

The Fourier series representing $\int_{-\pi}^{x} f(x)\,dx$, $-\pi < x < \pi$, *may be obtained by integrating, term by term, the Fourier series for* $f(x)$, *but only under certain conditions* will the Fourier series for* $df(x)/dx$ *be obtained by differentiating the Fourier series for* $f(x)$, *term by term.*

Example. Expand x in a Fourier series. Find from the result by integration a Fourier series for x^2.

Solution. Using (7), (5), and (6) with $f(x) = x$, we get

$$a_0 = \frac{1}{2}\int_{-\pi}^{\pi} x\,dx = 0,$$

$$a_n = \frac{1}{\pi}\int_{-\pi}^{\pi} x\cos nx\,dx = \frac{1}{\pi}\left[\frac{x\sin nx}{n} + \frac{\cos nx}{n^2}\right]_{-\pi}^{\pi} = 0,$$

$$b_n = \frac{1}{\pi}\int_{-\pi}^{\pi} x\sin nx\,dx = \frac{1}{\pi}\left[-\frac{x\cos nx}{n} + \frac{\sin nx}{n^2}\right]_{-\pi}^{\pi} = \frac{-2\cos n\pi}{n}.$$

Substituting in (2) these values for a_0, a_n, and b_n and x for $f(x)$, we get

$$x = \sum_{n=1}^{\infty} \frac{-2\cos n\pi}{n}\sin nx = 2\sin x - \frac{2}{2}\sin 2x + \frac{2}{3}\sin 3x - \frac{2}{4}\sin 4x + \cdots. \quad (11)$$

Actually, (11) represents a function $\varphi(x)$ such that $\varphi(x + m2\pi) = f(x)$ and $\varphi(x) = x$ in $-\pi < x < \pi$, $f(-\pi) = 0$, $f(\pi) = 0$. Figure 2 shows the

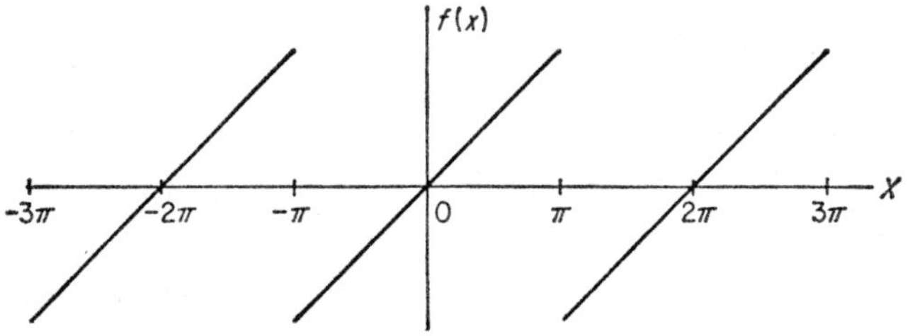

FIG. 2

graph of $f(x)$ for x in $-3\pi < x < 3\pi$. In Fig. 3, the straight line represents the graph of $y = x$, the dashed curve represents the first approximation $y = 2\sin x$, the light curve represents the approximation

$$y = 2\sin x - \sin 2x,$$

* If $f(x + 2\pi n) = f(x)$ and if $f'(x)$ is continuous and single-valued, and has only a finite number of maxima and minima in $-\pi < x < \pi$, then $f'(x)$ is represented for all values of x by the term-by-term derivative of the Fourier series for $f(x)$.

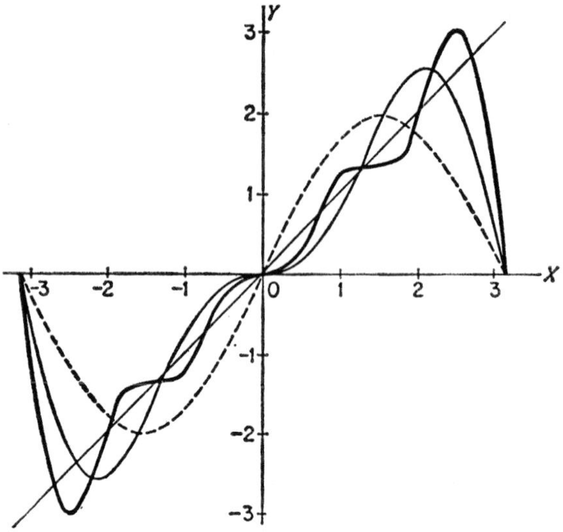

FIG. 3

and the heavy curve represents the four-term approximation

$$y = 2 \sin x - \sin 2x + \tfrac{2}{3} \sin 3x - \tfrac{1}{2} \sin 4x.$$

From (11), we get by integration

$$\int_{-\pi}^{x} x\,dx = \frac{x^2}{2} - \frac{\pi^2}{2} = a_0 + \sum_{n=1}^{\infty} \frac{2 \cos n\pi}{n^2} \cos nx. \tag{12}$$

By using (7) with $f(x) = \frac{1}{2}(x^2 - \pi^2)$, we get $a_0 = -\frac{1}{3}\pi^2$. Using this value of a_0 in (12) and transforming slightly, we obtain*

$$\mathbf{x}^2 = \tfrac{1}{3}\pi^2 - 4\left(\frac{1}{1^2} \cos \mathbf{x} - \frac{1}{2^2} \cos 2\mathbf{x} + \frac{1}{3^2} \cos 3\mathbf{x} - \cdots\right). \tag{13}$$

It is interesting to substitute 0 for x in (13), transform the result, and obtain

$$\tfrac{1}{12}\pi^2 = \frac{1}{1^2} - \frac{1}{2^2} + \frac{1}{3^2} - \frac{1}{4^2} + \cdots$$

and to substitute π for x in (13) and then derive

$$\tfrac{1}{6}\pi^2 = \frac{1}{1^2} + \frac{1}{2^2} + \frac{1}{3^2} + \cdots.$$

* Actually, (13) represents a function $\psi(x)$ such that $\psi(x + m2\pi) = \psi(x)$ and $\psi(x) = x^2$ in the interval $-\pi \leqq x \leqq \pi$.

EXERCISES

1. Substitute $\frac{1}{2}\pi$ for x in (11), and show that $\frac{1}{4}\pi = 1 - \frac{1}{3} + \frac{1}{5} - \frac{1}{7} + \cdots$.

2. Draw the part of the complete graph situated in the interval $-3\pi \leqq x \leqq 3\pi$ for the right member of (13).

3. Expand in a Fourier series the function $f(x)$ for which $f(x + m2\pi) = f(x)$, $f(x) = -1$ in $-\pi < x < 0$, $f(x) = 1$ in $0 < x < \pi$, $f(x) = 0$ when x is -1, 0, or 1. *Hint:* By (7), $a_0 = \frac{1}{2\pi}\int_{-\pi}^{0}(-1)\,dx + \frac{1}{2\pi}\int_0^\pi dx = 0$, $b_n = \frac{1}{\pi}\int_{-\pi}^{0} - \sin nx\,dx + \frac{1}{\pi}\int_0^\pi \sin nx\,dx = \frac{2}{n\pi}(1 - \cos n\pi)$.

4. Expand in a Fourier series the function $f(x)$ for which $f(x) = 0$ in the interval $-\pi < x < 0$, $f(x) = 1$ in the interval $0 < x < \pi$, $f(x) = \frac{1}{2}$ when $x = \pi$.

5. Find a Fourier series for $\sin \frac{1}{2}x$ by using (2), (5), (6), and (7). Does it represent $\sin \frac{1}{2}x$ for all values of x? Draw a figure representing the Fourier series in $-3\pi < x < 3\pi$.

6. If $f(x)$ is such that $f(x) = f(-x)$, that is, if $f(x)$ is an **even function,** show that the corresponding Fourier series defined by (2), (5), (6), and (7) contains no sine terms. State the nature of the Fourier series for a function $\varphi(x)$ if $\varphi(x) = -\varphi(-x)$, that is, for an **odd function.** Check your answer by means of series (11) and (13).

7. Equate $\int_{-\pi}^{x} x^2\,dx$ to the definite integral of the right member of (13) with limits $-\pi$ to x, and in the result replace the first term $\frac{1}{3}\pi^2 x$ in the right member by $\frac{1}{3}\pi^2$ times the series for x from (11), and then write the Fourier series for x^3.

127. Cosine series. Sine series

If $f(x)$ is an even function, that is, $f(x) = f(-x)$, then

$$\int_{-\pi}^{\pi} f(x)\,dx = \int_{-\pi}^{0} f(x)\,dx + \int_0^\pi f(x)\,dx = 2\int_0^\pi f(x)\,dx, \qquad f(x) \text{ even;}$$

for the elements $f(x_i)\,\Delta x_i$ and $f(-x_i)\,\Delta x_i$ in one kind of sum having the first integral as a limit are equal. Similarly, if $f(x)$ is an odd function, that is, $f(x) = -f(-x)$, then

$$\int_{-\pi}^{\pi} f(x)\,dx = \int_{-\pi}^{0} f(x)\,dx + \int_0^\pi f(x)\,dx = 0, \qquad f(x) \text{ odd;}$$

for a consideration of elements $f(x_i)\,\Delta x_i$ and $f(-x_i)\,\Delta x_i$ shows that they cancel. Taking account of the equations above and observing that $\cos mx$ is even and $\sin mx$ odd, we see that formulas (8), §126, may be written

$$a_0 = \frac{1}{\pi}\int_0^\pi f(x)\,dx, \qquad a_m = \frac{2}{\pi}\int_0^\pi f(x)\cos mx\,dx, \qquad b_m = 0. \tag{14}$$

$$a_0 = 0, \qquad a_m = 0, \qquad b_m = \frac{2}{\pi}\int_0^\pi f(x)\sin mx\,dx. \tag{15}$$

Any expansion based on (8), §126, (14), *or* (15) *will represent any function* $f(x)$ *on the interval* $0 < x < \pi$. *But, on the interval* $-\pi < x < 0$, *an expansion based on* (8), §126, *will represent* $f(x)$, *one based on* (14) *will represent* $f(-x)$, *and one based on* (15) *will represent* $-f(-x)$.

Note that, if $x = Lz/\pi$, $x = -L$ when $z = -\pi$ and L when $z = \pi$. Hence, *a Fourier expansion representing* $f(x)$ *on the interval* $-L < x < L$* *can be obtained by replacing* x *in* $f(x)$ *by* Lz/π,

$$\mathbf{x = \frac{Lz}{\pi},} \tag{16}$$

expanding $f(Lz/\pi)$ *by means of* (8), §126, *and replacing* z *by* $\pi x/L$ *in the result.* The same procedure may be employed with (14) and (15) to obtain an expansion relating to the interval $0 < x < L$.

Example 1. Expand $f(x) = 1$ in a sine series by using (2) and (15).

Solution. Using (15), we get

$$a_0 = 0, \qquad a_m = 0, \qquad b_m = \frac{2}{\pi}\int_0^\pi \sin mx\,dx = \frac{2(1 - \cos m\pi)}{\pi m}.$$

Substituting these values in (2), §126, we obtain

$$\mathbf{1 = \frac{4}{\pi}\left(\sin x + \frac{\sin 3x}{3} + \frac{\sin 5x}{5} + \cdots\right).} \tag{a}$$

Example 2. By using (14) and (2), §126, expand x in a cosine series over the range $0 < x < c$. Define completely the function represented by the expansion.

Solution. Let $x = cz/\pi$, and apply (14) to obtain

$$a_0 = \frac{1}{\pi}\int_0^\pi \frac{c}{\pi} z\,dz = \frac{c}{2},$$

$$a_m = \frac{2}{\pi}\int_0^\pi \frac{cz}{\pi}\cos mz\,dz = \frac{2c}{\pi^2 m^2}(\cos m\pi - 1), \qquad b_m = 0.$$

Substitute these values in (2) to get

$$\frac{cz}{\pi} = \frac{c}{2} + \frac{2c}{\pi^2}\left(\frac{-2\cos z}{1^2} - \frac{2\cos 3z}{3^2} - \frac{2\cos 5z}{5^2} - \cdots\right),$$

or, replacing z by $\pi x/c$ and simplifying slightly,

$$\mathbf{x = \frac{c}{2} - \frac{4c}{\pi^2}\left(\frac{1}{1^2}\cos\frac{\pi x}{c} + \frac{1}{3^2}\cos\frac{3\pi x}{c} + \cdots\right).} \tag{b}$$

Denoting by $f(x)$ the right-hand member of (*b*), $f(x) = x$ on $0 \leqq x \leqq c$, $f(x) = -x$ on $-c \leqq x \leqq 0$, $f(x + m2\pi) = f(x)$.

* Here $f(x)$ on the range $-L < x < L$ is subject to the limitations of $f(x)$ on $-\pi < x < \pi$ specified in §126. Also, the expansions represent a function $F(x)$ for which $F(x) = f(x)$ on $0 < x < \pi$ and $F(x + m2\pi) = F(x)$.

EXERCISES

1. (*a*) Replace x by Lz/π, expand Lz/π by (15), and then replace z by $\pi x/L$ in the result. (*b*) Using integration on the expansion of (*a*) and also the fact that $a_0 = (1/\pi)\int_0^\pi (L^2z^2/\pi^2)\,dz = L^2/3$, obtain an expansion of x^2 in a series of cosines. (*c*) Define in terms of x^2 the function $F(x)$ represented by the expansion from (*b*). (*d*) Use the result from (*b*) to deduce that $\pi^2/6 = 1/1^2 + 1/2^2 + 1/3^2 + \cdots$.

2. Using (15), expand x^2 in a series of sines. If $F(x)$ represents the expansion obtained, define $F(x)$ in terms of x^2 for all values of x.

3. Show that for the interval $0 < x < L$

$$mx(L - x) = \frac{8L^2m}{\pi^3}\left(\frac{1}{1^3}\sin\frac{\pi x}{L} + \frac{1}{3^3}\sin\frac{3\pi x}{L} + \frac{1}{5^3}\sin\frac{5\pi x}{L} + \cdots\right).$$

If $F(x)$ represents the expansion, define $F(x)$ in terms of $mx(L - x)$ for all values of x.

4. Find a Fourier series representing $mx(L^2 - x^2)$ on the range $-L < x < L$.

★5. Expand $f(x) = |\pi + \frac{1}{2}x|$ in a Fourier series representing $|\pi + \frac{1}{2}x|$ on the interval $-4\pi < x < 4\pi$. *Hint:* $|\pi + \frac{1}{2}x| = -\pi - \frac{1}{2}x$ if $x < -2\pi$, and $|\pi + \frac{1}{2}x| = \pi + \frac{1}{2}x$ if $x > -2\pi$ (see Fig. 4). Use $x = 4z$ and (2), (5), (6), and (7), §126.

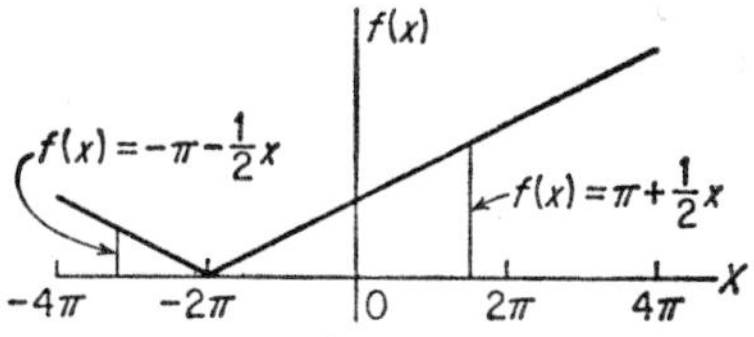

FIG. 4

6. Show that $F(x) = \alpha(x) + \alpha(-x)$ is an even function and that $G(x) = \alpha(x) - \alpha(-x)$ is an odd function.

128.* Application to nuclear fission

Atoms consist essentially of positively charged **nuclei** and negatively charged **electrons,** or particles of electricity. The **nucleus** contains **protons** and **neutrons.** A proton carries a positive charge of electricity which may bind a charge of electrons of equal magnitude. The neutrons carry no charge. Energy, called **nuclear energy,** may be released by a redistribution of the particles of a nucleus.

Fission is a process in which atoms capture neutrons and then split into parts different from the original atoms and release nuclear energy. Radioactive materials, such as thorium, radium, and uranium, disintegrate and emit various kinds of particles. These are used to bombard other materials, such as uranium 235, with neutrons and cause fission. If an atom absorbs a neutron, other neutrons are released. When for a given arrangement of materials in a reactor the number of neutrons lost by leakage and absorption equals the number released by fission, the arrangement is called **critical.**

The following equation is basic in nuclear theory:

$$\frac{\partial^2\psi(x,y,z)}{\partial x^2} + \frac{\partial^2\psi(x,y,z)}{\partial y^2} + \frac{\partial^2\psi(x,y,z)}{\partial z^2} + B^2\psi(x,y,z) = 0, \qquad (17)$$

* There are many excellent books treating nuclear-reactor theory. Consult, for example, Samuel Glasstone, "Elements of Nuclear Reactor Theory."

where B^2 is a positive constant called **buckling** and $\psi(x,y,z)$, called the **neutron flux,** is the sum of the distances traveled per second per cubic centimeter at (x,y,z) by bombarding neutrons. For a certain value of B^2, called **material buckling,** the arrangement of material is critical. Our problem will be to deduce relations among dimensions and minimum volumes of reactors filled with materials subject to (17).

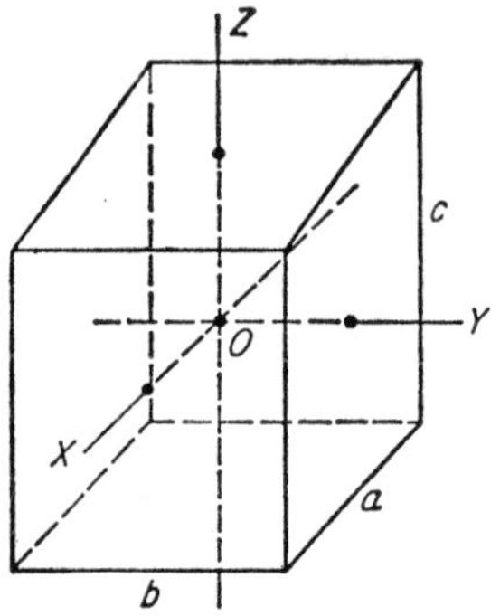

FIG. 5

First, consider a reactor in the shape of a rectangular box having dimensions a, b, and c as indicated in Fig. 5. Take the origin of coordinates at the center of the box and the coordinate axes parallel to its edges as indicated. Since there is no flux outside the reactor, we have as boundary conditions

$$\psi = 0 \text{ at } x = \pm\tfrac{1}{2}a, \qquad y = \pm\tfrac{1}{2}b, \qquad z = \pm\tfrac{1}{2}c. \tag{18}$$

Also, assume symmetry of $\psi(x,y,z)$ with respect to the coordinate planes. Applying the method of separation of the variables, §124, to solve (17), we let

$$\psi(x,y,z) = X(x) \cdot Y(y) \cdot Z(z), \tag{19}$$

substitute this value of ψ in (17), divide through by XYZ, and obtain

$$\frac{d^2X/dx^2}{X} + \frac{d^2Y/dy^2}{Y} + \frac{d^2Z/dz^2}{Z} + B^2 = 0. \tag{20}$$

Equating the first fraction to $-\alpha^2$ and solving the resulting equation, we get

$$X = c_1 \cos \alpha x + c_2 \sin \alpha x.$$

The condition $\psi = 0$ when $x = \pm\frac{1}{2}a$ demands, because of (19) and symmetry, that $X = 0$ when $x = \pm\frac{1}{2}a$; therefore, we must take $c_2 = 0$ and $\alpha = (2n + 1)\frac{1}{2}(\pi/a)$. Hence, choosing $\frac{1}{2}\pi/a$ for α, the least positive value,* we have

$$X = c_1 \cos \frac{\pi}{a} x.$$

Applying the same process to each of the fractions, we get

$$X = c_1 \cos \frac{\pi}{a} x, \qquad Y = d_1 \cos \frac{\pi}{b} y, \qquad Z = e_1 \cos \frac{\pi}{c} z, \tag{21}$$

* A little reflection indicates that a more complicated arrangement of material in the reactor would be represented by a value for α like $3\pi/a$ or $5\pi/a$ since this would mean a number of planes parallel to the YZ-plane on which ψ would vanish.

and, from (19),

$$\psi(x,y,z) = A \cos\frac{\pi}{a}x \cos\frac{\pi}{b}y \cos\frac{\pi}{c}z. \tag{22}$$

The constant A depends on the power output of the reactor. Substituting from (22) in (20), we get

$$B^2 = \frac{\pi^2}{a^2} + \frac{\pi^2}{b^2} + \frac{\pi^2}{c^2}. \tag{23}$$

For a given value of B^2, the volume of the reactor will be minimum if it has the shape of a cube. In this case, we see, from (23), that

$$a = b = c = \frac{\pi\sqrt{3}}{B}, \qquad \text{Vol } v = \frac{\pi^3 3\sqrt{3}}{B^3} = \frac{161}{B^3}. \tag{24}$$

The arrangement will be critical if B^2 has a certain value called the *material buckling*.

EXERCISES

1. For a spherical reactor we use spherical coordinates (see Fig. 6) so that

$$x = r\sin\theta\cos\varphi, \qquad y = r\cos\theta\cos\varphi, \qquad z = r\cos\theta.$$

In these coordinates, (17) takes the form

$$\frac{\partial^2\psi}{\partial r^2} + \frac{2}{r}\frac{\partial\psi}{\partial r} + \frac{1}{r^2\sin\theta}\frac{\partial}{\partial\theta}\left(\sin\theta\frac{\partial\psi}{\partial\theta}\right) + \frac{1}{r^2\sin^2\theta}\frac{\partial^2\psi}{\partial\varphi^2} + B^2\psi = 0, \tag{25}$$

where $\psi(r,\theta,\varphi)$ is the neutron flux. Assuming uniform and symmetrical distribution of material, so that ψ depends only upon r, delete all terms from (21) involving θ and φ to get

$$\frac{\partial^2\psi}{\partial r^2} + \frac{2}{r}\frac{\partial\psi}{\partial r} + B^2\psi = 0. \tag{26}$$

Show that the solution of this is

$$\psi = \frac{c_1}{r}\sin Br + \frac{c_2}{r}\cos Br.$$

Assume as initial conditions

$$\psi(a) = 0, \qquad \psi(r) \text{ is bounded,}$$

and deduce that

$$\psi(r) = \frac{A}{r}\sin\frac{\pi r}{a}, \qquad (\text{Vol})_{\min} = \frac{130}{B^3}. \tag{27}$$

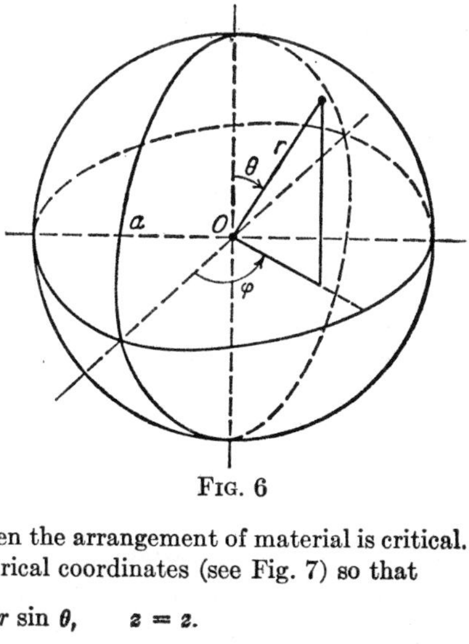

FIG. 6

If B^2 is properly determined, (27) applies when the arrangement of material is critical.

★**2.** For a cylindrical reactor, we use cylindrical coordinates (see Fig. 7) so that

$$x = r\cos\theta, \qquad y = r\sin\theta, \qquad z = z.$$

In cylindrical coordinates, (17) takes the form

$$\frac{\partial^2\psi}{\partial r^2} + \frac{1}{r}\frac{\partial\psi}{\partial r} + \frac{1}{r^2}\frac{\partial^2\psi}{\partial\theta^2} + \frac{\partial^2\psi}{\partial z^2} + B^2\psi = 0. \tag{28}$$

Assuming that ψ depends only on r and z, delete from (28) the term involving θ, and obtain

$$\frac{\partial^2\psi}{\partial r^2} + \frac{1}{r}\frac{\partial\psi}{\partial r} + \frac{\partial^2\psi}{\partial z^2} + B^2\psi = 0. \tag{29}$$

Solve this by *separation of the variables*, using

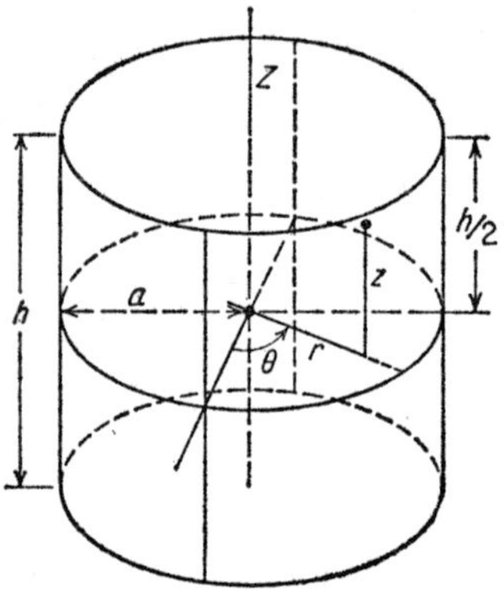

FIG. 7

$$\psi = R(r)Z(z),$$

and use the initial conditions

$$\psi \text{ is bounded,}$$

$$\psi = 0 \qquad \text{when } z = \pm\tfrac{1}{2}h \text{ or } r = a$$

to obtain

$$Z = c_1 \cos\frac{\pi}{h}z,\ R = c_2 J_0\left(\frac{2.405r}{a}\right),$$

where 2.405 is the smallest positive root of $J_0(x)$. Now, deduce that

$$\psi(r,z) = A\cos\frac{\pi}{h}z\,J_0\left(\frac{2.405r}{a}\right), \tag{30}$$

$$B^2 = \left(\frac{\pi}{h}\right)^2 + \left(\frac{2.405}{a}\right)^2, \tag{31}$$

and then that, for given B^2 and minimum volume $V_{\min}$ of the cylindrical reactor,

$$2B^2a^2 = 3(2.405)^2, \qquad B^2h^2 = 3\pi^2, \qquad V_{\min} = 148.2/B^3. \tag{32}$$

Hint: $u = AJ_0(nr)$ is a solution of $d^2u/dr^2 + (1/r)\,du/dr + n^2u = 0$.

129. Vibrations of a string

Sums, differences, and constant multiples of the following formulas may be used to construct desired ones:

$$1 = \frac{4}{\pi}\left(\sin\frac{\pi x}{L} + \frac{1}{3}\sin\frac{3\pi x}{L} + \frac{1}{5}\sin\frac{5\pi x}{L} + \cdots\right), \tag{A}$$

$$x = \frac{2L}{\pi}\left(\frac{1}{1}\sin\frac{\pi x}{L} - \frac{1}{2}\sin\frac{2\pi x}{L} + \frac{1}{3}\sin\frac{3\pi x}{L} - \frac{1}{4}\sin\frac{4\pi x}{L}\cdots\right), \tag{B}$$

$$x^2 = \frac{2L^2}{\pi^3}\left[\left(\frac{\pi^2}{1} - \frac{4}{1^3}\right)\sin\frac{\pi x}{L} - \frac{\pi^2}{2}\sin\frac{2\pi x}{L} + \left(\frac{\pi^2}{3} - \frac{4}{3^3}\right)\sin\frac{3\pi x}{L} - \frac{\pi^2}{4}\sin\frac{4\pi x}{L} + \cdots\right]. \tag{C}$$

Figure 8 represents a string L units long fastened at A and B. Assume that the vibrations are so small that the tension T in the string may be considered constant, that the weight of the string is small in comparison with T,* that the length of the string may be considered as a constant L

* Assume in this section that all strings considered are tightly stretched.

for each of its positions, and that each point in the string moves parallel to the Y-axis. Consider the motion of a small piece PQ (see Fig. 8) of the string Δx units long. Two forces of magnitude T act at its ends, one inclined θ and the other $\theta + \Delta\theta$ to the X-axis. Since θ is small, $\sin\theta = \tan\theta = \partial y/\partial x$, approximately. Therefore, applying Newton's

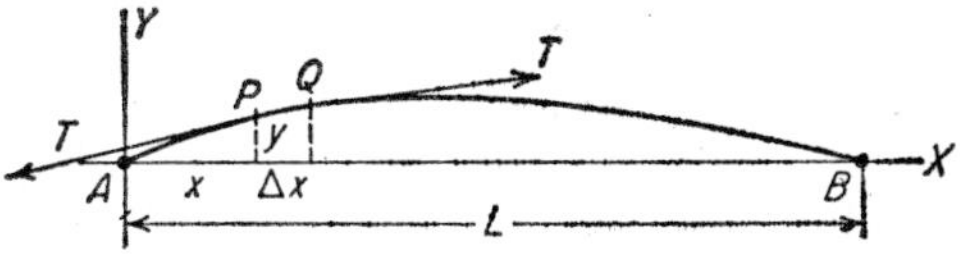

FIG. 8

law parallel to the Y-axis, we get

$$T[\sin(\theta + \Delta\theta) - \sin\theta] = T\left[\frac{\partial y(x + \Delta x, t)}{\partial x} - \frac{\partial y(x,t)}{\partial x}\right]$$
$$= \frac{\rho\,\Delta x}{g}\frac{\partial^2 y}{\partial t^2}, \tag{33}$$

where ρ is the weight per unit length of the string. Dividing (33) through by $\rho\,\Delta x/g$ and equating the limits of its members, we have

$$\mathbf{a}^2\frac{\partial^2\mathbf{y}(\mathbf{x},\mathbf{t})}{\partial\mathbf{x}^2} = \frac{\partial^2\mathbf{y}}{\partial\mathbf{t}^2}, \qquad \mathbf{a}^2 = \frac{\mathbf{Tg}}{\rho}. \tag{34}$$

By trial, we see that a solution of (34) is

$$y = \varphi(x + at) + \psi(x - at), \tag{35}$$

where φ and ψ* represent arbitrary functions. Let the position and velocity of points on the string be such that

$$y_{t=0} = \alpha(x), \qquad \left(\frac{\partial y}{\partial t}\right)_{t=0} = a\frac{d\beta(x)}{dx}, \qquad \text{when } t = 0. \tag{36}$$

From (35) and (36), we get

$$\varphi(x) + \psi(x) = \alpha(x), \tag{37}$$
$$a\varphi'(x) - a\psi'(x) = a\beta'(x),$$

or
$$\varphi(x) - \psi(x) = \beta(x) + c. \tag{38}$$

The solution of (37) and (38) for φ and ψ is

$$\varphi(x) = \tfrac{1}{2}[\alpha(x) + \beta(x) + c], \qquad \psi(x) = \tfrac{1}{2}[\alpha(x) - \beta(x) - c].$$

* An equation of the form $e = \varphi(x - \omega t)$ represents a wave motion, because the value of e associated with any point in the line at any instant is taken on at each point as the time t increases. If $e = m$ at point x_1 and time t_1, then e will equal m provided that $x - mt = x_1 - mt_1$; that is, as x varies with the time, the condition $e = m$ moves along the line like the crest of a wave. Observe that $e = \varphi(x + \omega t)$ represents waves moving in a direction opposite to that of the motion represented by $e = \varphi(x - \omega t)$.

Finding $\varphi(x + at)$ and $\varphi(x - at)$ from these functions, substituting them in (35), and rearranging, we get

$$y = \tfrac{1}{2}[\alpha(x + at) + \alpha(x - at)] + \tfrac{1}{2}[\beta(x + at) - \beta(x - at)]. \qquad (39)$$

If, for example, $\alpha(x) = cL^2 \sin (\pi x/L)$ and $\beta(x) = 0$, (39) becomes

$$\begin{aligned} y &= \tfrac{1}{2}cL^2\{\sin [\pi(x + at)/L] + \sin [\pi(x - at)/L]\} \\ &= cL^2 \sin (\pi x/L) \cos (\pi at/L). \end{aligned} \qquad (40)$$

Note that $y = 0$ and $\partial y/\partial t = 0$ when $x = 0$ and when $x = L$. Also, note from (40) that $y(x,t) = y(x + k2L, t)$; therefore, it may be thought of as describing the motion of an infinite string.

The following solution will present a new method of approach and throw more light on formula (39).

Example. A string is stretched along the X-axis, to which it is attached at $x = 0$ and at $x = L$. Find y in terms of x and t, assuming that $y = mx(L - x)$ when $t = 0$.

Solution. Using the method of separation of variables, §124, substitute

$$y = X(x)T(t) \qquad (a)$$

in (34), and divide the result by XT to obtain

$$\frac{a^2\, d^2X/dx^2}{X} = \frac{d^2T/dt^2}{T}. \qquad (b)$$

Equating each member of (b) to $-\omega^2$ and solving the resulting equations, obtain

$$X = c_1 \sin \frac{\omega x}{a} + c_2 \cos \frac{\omega x}{a}, \qquad (c)$$

$$T = c_3 \sin \omega t + c_4 \cos \omega t. \qquad (d)$$

It now appears from (a), (c), and (d) that solutions of (34) for y can consist of sums of terms having the forms

$$\begin{aligned} &A \cos \frac{\omega}{a} x \cos \omega t, \qquad B \cos \frac{\omega}{a} x \sin \omega t, \\ &C \sin \frac{\omega}{a} x \cos \omega t, \qquad F \sin \frac{\omega}{a} x \sin \omega t. \end{aligned} \qquad (e)$$

The initial conditions are

$$y = 0 \quad \text{when } x = 0 \quad \text{and} \quad y = 0 \quad \text{when } x = L, \qquad (f)$$

$$y = mx(L - x) \quad \text{when } t = 0. \qquad (g)$$

Conditions (f) will be satisfied, provided that we take

$$\omega = \frac{n\pi a}{L}, \qquad n \text{ an integer}, \qquad (h)$$

and restrict ourselves to terms having the form of those in the last line of (*e*). From exercise 3, §127, we have

$$mx(L - x) = \frac{8L^2m}{\pi^3}\left(\sin\frac{\pi x}{L} + \frac{1}{3^3}\sin\frac{3\pi x}{L} + \frac{1}{5^3}\sin\frac{5\pi x}{L} + \cdots\right). \qquad (i)$$

Hence, conditions (34), (*f*), and (*g*) are satisfied by

$$y = \frac{8L^2m}{\pi^3}\left(\frac{1}{1^3}\cos\frac{a\pi t}{L}\sin\frac{\pi x}{L} + \frac{1}{3^3}\cos\frac{3\pi at}{L}\sin\frac{3\pi x}{L} + \cdots\right). \qquad (j)$$

Observe that, if for (39) $\alpha(x)$ is the right-hand member of (*i*) and $\beta = 0$, (39) is the solution (*j*).

EXERCISES

1. If the string of the illustrative example is 3 ft long and weighs $\frac{1}{30}$ lb, if $T = 10$ lb and $m = 0.01$, find the equation of the moving string. Find the time frequency of the first harmonic, that is, the first term.

2. If, for (39), $\beta(x) = a\sin(3\pi x/L)$ and $\alpha(x) = 0$, find displacement y in terms of x and t. For what points in the interval $0 < x < L$ is $y = 0$ for all values of t?

3. If, when $t = 0$, the particles of the string of the illustrative example have velocities defined by $(\partial y/\partial t)_{t=0} = A\sin(\mu\pi x/L)$, find y in terms of x and t.

4. For a certain motion of an infinite, tightly stretched string, (34) holds. If $y = 0.02\sin(\frac{1}{2}\pi x/L)$ and $\partial y/\partial t = 0$ when $t = 0$, find y in terms of x and t.

5. If the string of exercise 3 is at rest when $t = 0$ on the lines defined by $y(x) = mx$ on $0 < x < \frac{1}{2}L$, and $y(x) = m(L - x)$ on $L/2 < x < L$, find y in terms of x and t. Use a Fourier series for $y(x)$ on $0 < x < L$ and (39). At what time after $t = 0$ will the string be in the position it had at time $t = 0$?

6. In the illustrative example, replace $y = mx(L - x)$ by $y = mx(L^2 - x^2)$, and solve the resulting problem. Use the answer to exercise 4, §127. If t is time in seconds, how often will the string return to the position it had at time $t = 0$?

130. Vibrations of a rod

Figure 9 represents a straight, elastic, homogeneous rod of density ρ, modulus of elasticity E, length L, and cross-sectional area A. It

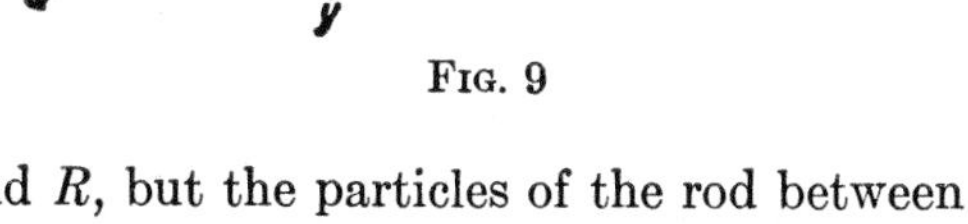

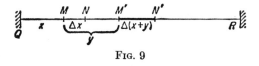

FIG. 9

is fixed at Q and R, but the particles of the rod between Q and R move along the line QR. It is assumed that the pressure on any cross section is uniformly distributed and that all particles on any cross section have the same velocity. Let y be the displacement at time t of a particle that is distant x from Q when the rod is at rest. Then, Δy is the change in length of the part of the rod marked Δx in Fig. 9. Now, by Hooke's law,

$$E = \frac{P}{A(l_1/L)}, \qquad \text{or} \qquad l_1 = \frac{PL}{AE}, \tag{41}$$

where l_1 is the amount that a rod of length L and cross-sectional area A is stretched by force P. Applying this equation to the piece MN in Fig. 9, we obtain

$$\Delta y = \frac{P(x_1,t)}{AE}\,\Delta x, \tag{42}$$

where x_1 satisfies $x < x_1 < x + \Delta x$. Dividing by Δx and equating the limits of the two members, we get

$$\frac{\partial y(x,t)}{\partial x} = \frac{P(x,t)}{AE}. \tag{43}$$

Now, apply Newton's law of motion to the part $M'N'$ of the rod. This gives

$$P(x + \Delta x, t) - P(x,t) = \frac{A\rho\,\Delta x}{g}\,\frac{\partial^2 y_1}{\partial t^2},$$

where y_1 satisfies $y < y_1 < y + \Delta y$. Now, divide by Δx, and equate limits to get

$$\frac{\partial P}{\partial x} = \frac{A\rho}{g}\,\frac{\partial^2 y}{\partial t^2}, \tag{44}$$

and eliminate P between (43) and (44) to obtain

$$\mathbf{a}^2\,\frac{\partial^2 \mathbf{y}(\mathbf{x},\mathbf{t})}{\partial \mathbf{x}^2} = \frac{\partial^2 \mathbf{y}(\mathbf{x},\mathbf{t})}{\partial \mathbf{t}^2}, \qquad \mathbf{a}^2 = \frac{\mathbf{Eg}}{\rho}. \tag{45}$$

Note that this equation has the same form as (34) in §129 and therefore has the solutions marked (*e*) in §129. Also, equation (39) holds, but it has a different interpretation.

EXERCISES

1. What meaning attaches to $\alpha(x)$ and $a\beta(x)$ in equation (39), §129, when it relates to a rod?

2. If at time $t = 0$ displacements of points on the rod of Fig. 9 are given by $m \sin(\pi x/L)$ and their velocities by $ac\pi/L \sin(\pi x/L)$, find the displacements and velocities at time t. At what times will the velocities be the same as at time $t = 0$, and when will both displacements and velocities be the same as at time $t = 0$?

3. For a steel rod $\rho = 490$ lb/ft³, $E = 4.3 \times 10^9$ lb/ft², $g = 32$ ft/sec². Using the initial conditions $y(0,t) = 0$, $y(3,t) = 0$, $y(x,0) = 0.0001x(3 - x)$, $(\partial y/\partial t)_{t=0} = 0$, find the corresponding solution of (45), and give the frequency of the harmonic represented by the first term.

131. Flow of heat

Let $\theta(x,y,z,t)$ represent the temperature at any point in space at time t, and assume that *the heat flows in the direction of decreasing tem-*

perature and that *the rate (in calories per second) across any infinitesimal square is proportional to the area of the square and to* $\partial\theta/\partial s$, *where s is measured normal to the square.* Also, assume that *the quantity of heat in a small body is proportional to its mass and to its temperature* θ.

To get the partial differential equation of heat flow, express in mathematical symbols the relation that *rate at which heat enters the small block of Fig.* 10 *minus the rate at which it leaves is equal to the rate of increase of heat in the block.* The rate at which heat leaves through face AB is $k[\partial\theta(x,y_1,z_1,t)/\partial x]\,\Delta y\,\Delta z$, where k (in calories per centimeter per degree per second) is a constant and point (x,y_1,z_1) is a certain point in face AB. Similarly, the rate at which heat enters through face CD is approximately $k[\partial\theta(x+\Delta x, y_1, z_1, t)/\partial x]\,\Delta y\,\Delta z$. Hence, the rate at which heat enters through the faces of the block perpendicular to the X-axis is

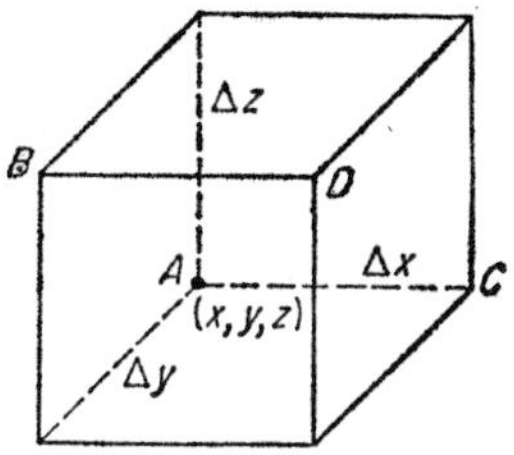

FIG. 10

$$k\left[\frac{\partial\theta(x+\Delta x, y_1, z_1, t)}{\partial x} - \frac{\partial\theta(x,y_1,z_1,t)}{\partial x}\right]\Delta y\,\Delta z. \tag{46}$$

Similarly, the rate at which heat enters the block through faces perpendicular to the Y-axis is

$$k\left[\frac{\partial\theta(x_2, y+\Delta y, z_2, t)}{\partial y} - \frac{\partial\theta(x_2,y,z_2,t)}{\partial y}\right]\Delta x\,\Delta z, \tag{47}$$

and the rate for the faces perpendicular to the Z-axis is

$$k\left[\frac{\partial\theta(x_3, y_3, z+\Delta z, t)}{\partial z} - \frac{\partial\theta(x_3,y_3,z,t)}{\partial z}\right]\Delta y\,\Delta x. \tag{48}$$

The rate of increase of heat in the block is

$$c\rho\,\Delta x\,\Delta y\,\Delta z\,\frac{\partial\theta(x_4,y_4,z_4,t)}{\partial t}, \tag{49}$$

where ρ (in grams per cubic centimeter) is the density, c (in calories per gram per degree) is the specific heat, and (x_4,y_4,z_4) is a certain point in the block.

The limit of (46) divided by $\Delta x\,\Delta y\,\Delta z$ as $\Delta x \to 0$ is

$$\lim_{\Delta x\to 0} k\left[\frac{\dfrac{\partial\theta(x+\Delta x, y_1, z_1)}{\partial x} - \dfrac{\partial\theta(x,y_1,z_1)}{\partial x}}{\Delta x}\right] = k\,\frac{\partial^2\theta(x,y_1,z_1)}{\partial x^2},$$

and similar statements apply to expressions (47) and (48). Also, as Δx, Δy, and Δz approach zero, all the points (x,y_1,z_1), (x_2,y,z_2), (x_3,y_3,z), and (x_4,y_4,z_4) approach point (x,y,z). Equating the sum of expressions

(46) to (48) to expression (49), dividing the result through by $\Delta x \, \Delta y \, \Delta z$, and equating the limits of the two members as Δx, Δy, and Δz approach zero, we obtain

$$k\left(\frac{\partial^2\theta}{\partial x^2}+\frac{\partial^2\theta}{\partial y^2}+\frac{\partial^2\theta}{\partial z^2}\right)=c\rho\frac{\partial\theta}{\partial t}. \tag{50}$$

To get the equation of heat flow in a plate with insulated surfaces, omit $\partial^2\theta/\partial z^2$ from (50) to obtain

$$k\left(\frac{\partial^2\theta}{\partial x^2}+\frac{\partial^2\theta}{\partial y^2}\right)=c\rho\frac{\partial\theta}{\partial t}, \tag{51}$$

and to get the equation for the flow in an insulated rod, omit $\partial^2\theta/\partial y^2$ from (51) to get

$$k\frac{\partial^2\theta}{\partial x^2}=c\rho\frac{\partial\theta}{\partial t}. \tag{52}$$

After heat has flowed until the temperature at any point is constant, the steady state is reached. *To obtain the equations for flow of heat in the steady state, replace $\partial\theta/\partial t$ by zero in* (50) *to* (52). Thus, for steady-state flow we get from (50)

$$\frac{\partial^2\theta}{\partial x^2}+\frac{\partial^2\theta}{\partial y^2}+\frac{\partial^2\theta}{\partial z^2}=0. \tag{53}$$

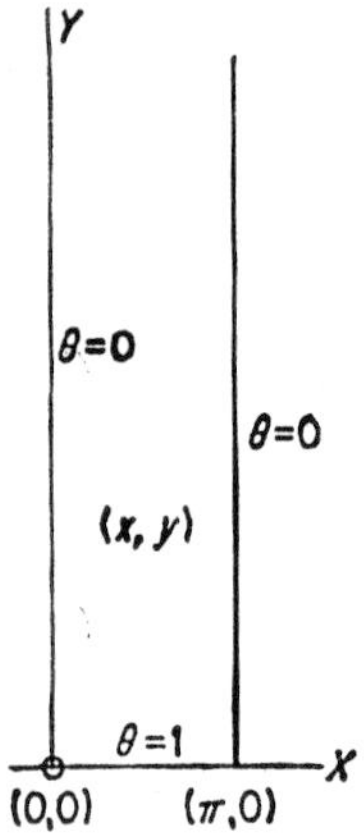

FIG. 11

Example. Fourier's problem is to find the temperature θ at any point (x,y) of a thin plate (see Fig. 11), π units wide and infinitely long, assuming (1) the steady state so that

$$\frac{\partial^2\theta}{\partial x^2}+\frac{\partial^2\theta}{\partial y^2}=0, \tag{a}$$

from (51) with $\partial\theta/\partial t = 0$; (2) perfectly insulated surfaces; (3) the short edge constantly at temperature unity; (4) the long edges at temperature zero.

Solution. Taking the Y-axis along an infinite edge and the X-axis along the short edge, we have the boundary conditions: (α) temperature $\theta = 0$, when $x = 0$; (β) $\theta = 0$ when $x = \pi$; (γ) $\theta = 0$ when $y = \infty$; (δ) $\theta = 1$ when $y = 0$.

To solve (a), substitute $\theta = X(x)Y(y)$ in it, and divide by XY to obtain

$$\frac{d^2X/dx^2}{X}+\frac{d^2Y/dy^2}{Y}=0.$$

Equating the first term to $-\omega^2$ and the second to ω^2, solving the resulting equations for X and Y, and forming $\theta = XY$, obtain

$$\theta=(c_1e^{\omega y}+c_2e^{-\omega y})(c_3\sin\omega x+c_4\cos\omega x). \tag{b}$$

Hence, any one of the terms

$$Ae^{\omega y}\sin \omega x, \qquad Be^{\omega y}\cos \omega x, \qquad Ce^{-\omega y}\sin \omega x, \qquad Ge^{-\omega y}\cos \omega x \tag{c}$$

is a solution of (a), and any sum of such terms is a solution. It remains to choose such a sum that the initial conditions will be satisfied by it. Conditions (α) and (β) will be satisfied by

$$\theta = \sum_{\omega=1}^{\infty} (c_{1\omega}e^{\omega y} + c_{2\omega}e^{-\omega y}) \sin \omega x, \tag{d}$$

and condition (γ) will also be satisfied by (d) if $c_{1\omega} = 0$. The expansion of unity in a Fourier series is

$$1 = \frac{4}{\pi}\left(\sin x + \frac{1}{3}\sin 3x + \frac{1}{5}\sin 5x + \cdots\right). \tag{e}$$

Hence, conditions (α), (β), (γ), and (δ) are satisfied by

$$\theta = \frac{4}{\pi}\left(\frac{1}{1}e^{-y}\sin x + \frac{1}{3}e^{-3y}\sin 3x + \frac{1}{5}e^{-5y}\sin 5x + \cdots\right).$$

EXERCISES

1. Solve the problems obtained from the illustrative example by replacing condition (3) by: (a) the short edge has temperature $\theta(x,0) = A \sin 3x$; (b) $\theta(x,0) = Ax$.

2. In the example, replace π units wide by L units wide, and solve the resulting problem.

3. In the example, replace π units wide by L units wide and condition (3) by: the temperature at point $(x,0)$ is mx when $0 \leqq x \leqq \frac{1}{2}L$ and is $m(L - x)$ when $\frac{1}{2}L \leqq x \leqq L$. Solve the resulting problem.

132. One-dimensional heat flow

The temperature θ in an insulated rod through which heat is flowing parallel to the axis of the rod satisfies equation (52) in §131, namely,

$$a^2 \frac{\partial^2\theta(x,t)}{\partial x^2} = \frac{\partial\theta(x,t)}{\partial t}, \qquad a^2 = \frac{k}{c\rho}. \tag{54}$$

To find solutions of (54), substitute in it

$$\theta = X(x)T(t), \tag{55}$$

and divide by XT to obtain

$$\frac{a^2\, d^2X/dx^2}{X} = \frac{dT/dt}{T}.$$

Equate each member to $-a^2\omega^2$, solve the resulting equations for X and T, substitute the solutions in (55), and conclude that solutions of (54) may consist of sums of terms having the forms

$$Ae^{-a^2\omega^2 t} \sin \omega x, \qquad Be^{-a^2\omega^2 t} \cos \omega x. \tag{56}$$

The following example will illustrate a method of solving simple problems relating to the flow of heat:

Example. A rod L cm long with insulated lateral surface is initially at temperature 20°C throughout. If one end is kept at 10°C and the other at 100°C, find the temperature θ as a function of time t and distance x from the end at 10°C.

Solution. The boundary conditions are

$$\theta(0,t) = 10, \qquad \theta(L,t) = 100, \qquad \theta(x,0) = 20. \tag{a}$$

A sum $\varphi(x,t)$ of terms having the first form of (56) will satisfy the condition $\varphi(0,t) = 0$, $\varphi(n\pi/\omega,t) = 0$, n an integer. Also, $\theta = A + Bx$ satisfies (54). Now, let the required solution be

$$\theta(x,t) = A + Bx + \varphi(x,t), \tag{b}$$

where

$$\varphi(x,t) = \sum_{n=1}^{\infty} A_n e^{-a^2n^2\pi^2t/L^2} \sin \frac{n\pi}{L} x. \tag{c}$$

Using the conditions (a) with (b) and (c), we obtain

$$\begin{gathered} 10 = A + \varphi(0,t) = A, \qquad 100 = A + BL + \varphi(L,t) = A + BL, \\ 20 = A + Bx + \varphi(x,0). \end{gathered} \tag{d}$$

Solve (d) for A, B, and $\varphi(x,0)$ to get

$$A = 10, \qquad B = \frac{90}{L}, \qquad \varphi(x,0) = 10 - \frac{90}{L} x. \tag{e}$$

Next, expand $\varphi(x,0)$ in a Fourier series for the interval $0 < x < L$, to obtain

$$\begin{aligned} \varphi(x,0) = 10 - \frac{90x}{L} = -\frac{4}{\pi}\biggl(\frac{35}{1} \sin \frac{\pi x}{L} - \frac{45}{2} \sin \frac{2\pi x}{L} \\ + \frac{35}{3} \sin \frac{3\pi x}{L} - \frac{45}{4} \sin \frac{4\pi x}{L} + \cdots\biggr). \end{aligned} \tag{f}$$

To form $\varphi(x,t)$, write in front of the first, second, . . . terms in (f) the respective results of setting $n = 1, 2, \ldots$ in $e^{-n^2a^2\pi^2t/L^2}$. Then, $\theta(x,t)$ from (b) is given by

$$\begin{aligned} \theta(x,t) = 10 + \frac{90x}{L} - \frac{4}{\pi}\biggl(\frac{35}{1} e^{-a^2\pi^2t/L^2} \sin \frac{\pi x}{L} \\ - \frac{45}{2} e^{-4a^2\pi^2t/L^2} \sin \frac{2\pi x}{L} + \cdots\biggr). \end{aligned} \tag{g}$$

EXERCISES

By a *rod* in the following problems, we shall mean a straight rod with insulated lateral surface and with ends A and B. The letter θ will refer to temperature at a point in the rod, and x will refer to the distance of a point in the rod from end A.

1. Observe that in the steady state of heat flow for a rod $\partial\theta/\partial t = 0$ and θ does not contain t. Hence, $d^2\theta/dx^2 = 0$, and $\theta = Ax + B$. End A of a rod 120 cm long is kept at 56° and the other at 200°; find the temperature x cm from A if the steady state prevails. If end A of a rod L ft long is kept at $P°$ and end B at $Q°$, find the temperature x cm from end A.

2. At time $t = 0$, a rod 100 cm long has temperature $4x + 20$ at x cm from end A. If the temperature at A is suddenly changed to and kept at 56° and that at B is changed to and kept at 200°, find θ at x cm from A at time t.

3. The temperature at end A of a rod 100 cm long is 20°, and that at end B is 200°, and the flow is in the steady state. At time $t = 0$, the temperatures at A and B are suddenly changed to and kept at 60° and 160°, respectively; find θ in terms of x and t at time t.

4. Assume that the rod of exercise 3 is cast iron, and find the temperature at $x =$ 50 cm, $t =$ 1,000 sec. For cast iron, $k = 0.17$ cal/cm deg sec, $c = 0.113$ cal/g deg, $\rho = 7.20$ g/cm³.

5. At time $t = 0$, a rod AB 40 cm long has temperature $20x$ for the range $0 < x <$ 20 cm and temperature $800 - 20x$ for the range $20 < x < 40$ cm, where x is measured from A. Also, at time $t = 0$, the ends A and B are changed to and kept at 800° and 0°, respectively. Find temperature θ in terms of x and t.

133. Vibrations of a membrane

Think of a right-circular cylindrical drum having axis vertical and having as top a tightly stretched, thin, homogeneous membrane. The membrane is depressed symmetrical to a vertical line through its center. Assume that the depression at all times is so slight that we may think of the particles of the membrane as moving vertically and of the tension T g/cm across a line in the surface as being constant and directed at right angles to the line. The problem is to find the equation of the motion of the membrane.

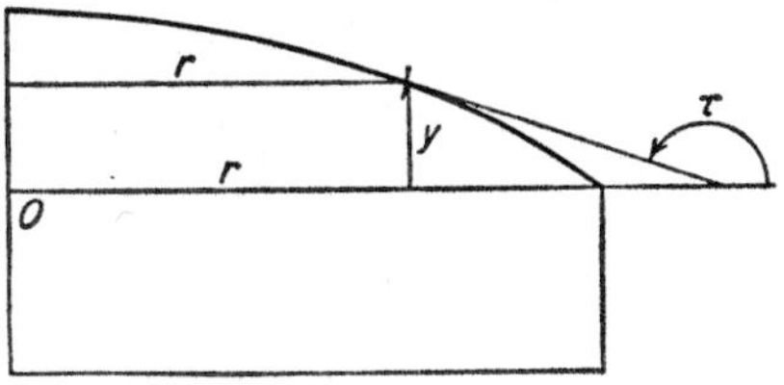

FIG. 12

Let (r,θ,y) be coordinates of points in the membrane, where r and θ are polar coordinates of a system in the drum head with pole O at its center and y designates displacement from the drum head. Observe that y is independent of θ from symmetry and that for any curve cut out of the membrane (see Fig. 12) by a vertical plane through the center O, and having a tangent of inclination τ, we may use the approximate equations

$$\sin \tau = \tan \tau = \frac{\partial y}{\partial r} = \frac{T_v}{T}, \tag{57}$$

where T_v is the vertical component of radial tension at a point. The vertical component of force on a small element $r\,\Delta\theta$ of a circle on the moving membrane y units above the drum head, from (57), is $T(\partial y/\partial r)r\,\Delta\theta$, and on the complete circle it is

$$F_v = 2\pi Tr\,\partial y/\partial r.$$

The vertical force on the zone of radial width Δr is then

$$\frac{\partial F_v}{\partial r}\Delta r = 2\pi T\,\Delta r\left(r_1\frac{\partial^2 y}{\partial r^2} + \frac{\partial y}{\partial r}\right), \tag{58}$$

where r_1 is between r and $r + \Delta r$. The mass times the acceleration of the zone is $\rho 2\pi r_2\,\Delta r\,\partial^2 y/\partial t^2$, where ρ is the mass per square unit of the membrane and r_2 is between r and $r + \Delta r$. Now, using Newton's law of motion for the zone, equate the limits of the right member of (58) divided by Δr and $2\pi r_2\,\Delta r(\partial^2 y/\partial t^2)/\Delta r$, and obtain

$$2\pi T\left(r\frac{\partial^2 y}{\partial r^2} + \frac{\partial y}{\partial r}\right) = 2\pi\rho r\frac{\partial^2 y}{\partial t^2}.$$

Dividing this through by $2\pi rT$, we get

$$\frac{\partial^2 y}{\partial r^2} + \frac{1}{r}\frac{\partial y}{\partial r} = a^2\frac{\partial^2 y}{\partial t^2}, \tag{59}$$

where $a^2 = \rho/T$. In (59), substitute $y = R(r)Z(t)$ for y, divide by RZ, and obtain

$$\frac{1}{R}\left(\frac{d^2R}{dr^2} + \frac{1}{r}\cdot\frac{dR}{dr}\right) = a^2\frac{d^2Z}{dt^2}\cdot\frac{1}{Z}. \tag{60}$$

In this, take $(d^2Z/dt^2)/Z = -\omega^2$, and obtain

$$Z = c_1 \sin \omega t + c_2 \cos \omega t. \tag{61}$$

The other equation obtained from (60) is

$$\frac{d^2R}{dr^2} + \frac{1}{r}\frac{dR}{dr} + a^2\omega^2 R = 0. \tag{62}$$

In this, substitute $w/(a\omega)$ for r, and obtain after a slight simplification

$$\frac{d^2R}{dw^2} + \frac{1}{w}\frac{dR}{dw} + R = 0, \qquad w = a\omega r, \qquad a^2 = \frac{\rho}{T}. \tag{63}$$

This is Bessel's equation with $n = 0$. Its basic solutions (see exercise

2, §106) are

$$J_0(w) = \sum_{n=0}^{\infty} \frac{(w/2)^{2n}(-1)^n}{(r!)^2},$$

$$Y_0(w) = \ln w \sum_{n=0}^{\infty} \frac{(w/2)^{2n}(-1)^n}{(n!)^2} + \sum_{n=1}^{\infty} \frac{(x/2)^{2n}(-1)^{n+1}}{(n!)^2} \sum_{m=1}^{n} \frac{1}{m},$$

and $$R = c_1J_0(w) + c_2Y_0(w), \qquad w = a\omega r, \qquad a = \sqrt{\rho/T}. \tag{64}$$

EXERCISES

1. Why must c_2 in (64) be taken as zero generally? Might c_2 be different from zero if the membrane had the shape of a plane area bounded by two concentric circles?

2. If $\bar{R}$ is the radius of the circular membrane and $c_2 = 0$ in (64), why must $J_0(a\bar{R}) = 0$? Three roots of $J_0(w)$ are $w_1 = 2.40$, $w_2 = 5.52$, $w_3 = 8.65$. State three corresponding values that $\bar{R}$ may have.

3. If $\bar{R} = 5.52/a$, Fig. 13 indicates the shape of a cross section of the moving membrane at time $t = 0$. The complete membrane would be generated by revolving

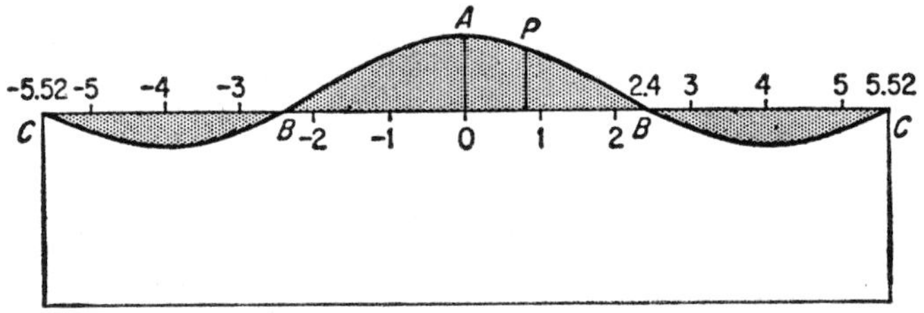

FIG. 13

curve $APBC$ about the Y-axis. Considering (61), state what happens as t varies from 0 to $2\pi/\omega$: (a) to point A; (b) to point P; (c) to points B;* (d) to points C.

4. Draw a figure analogous to Fig. 13 for the situation when: (a) $\bar{R} = 2.40/a$; (b) $\bar{R} = 8.65/a$.

★5. If the vertical cross section through the center of the membrane at time $t = 0$ has the equation $y = m(L - x)$, where L is the radius of the drum, show that

$$y(r,t) = \sum_{i=1}^{\infty} \left[\frac{-mL}{\alpha_i^2} \int_0^1 J_0(\alpha_i z)\, dz\right] J_0\left(\frac{\alpha_i r}{L}\right) \cos \frac{\alpha_i}{aL} \frac{t}{\frac{1}{2}J_1^2(\alpha_i)}, \qquad J(\alpha_i) = 0.$$

First expand $m(L - Lz)$ in an infinite series by the method of §108 and in the result replace z by r/L.

134. Telephone, telegraph, and radio equations

Figure 14 represents a long line carrying electricity. The current goes out through AB and returns through the ground from C to D. Let L (in henrys per mile) be the inductance of the line AB, let R (in

* Points such as B on the complete surface lie at rest on a circle called the nodal circle.

ohms per mile) be its resistance, let C (in farads per mile) be its capacitance to ground, and let G (in mhos per mile) be the leakage of current or conductance to ground. Let $e(x,t)$ and $i(x,t)$ represent the voltage and current at a point in the line AB x miles from A, and derive relations between e and i by considering the flow of electricity in a small portion PQ of the cable having length Δx. The drop Δe in potential along PQ will be

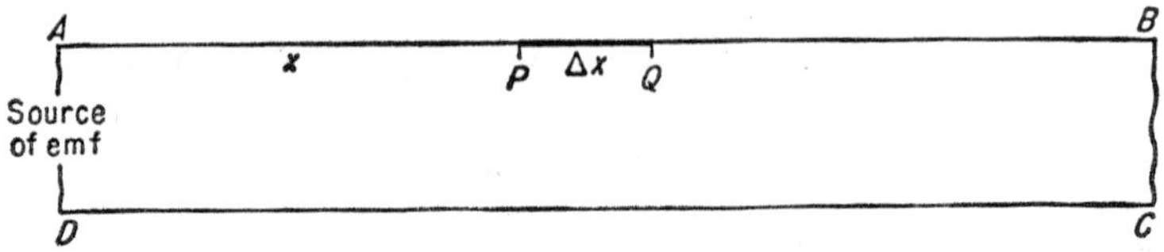

FIG. 14

approximately

$$\Delta e = -R\,\Delta x i(x_1,t) - L\,\Delta x\,\frac{\partial i(x_1,t)}{\partial t}, \tag{65}$$

where $x < x_1 < x + \Delta x$. Dividing this equation through by Δx and equating the limits approached by its members as Δx approaches zero, we get

$$\frac{\partial e}{\partial x} = -Ri(x,t) - L\,\frac{\partial i(x,t)}{\partial t}. \tag{66}$$

Here, changes in e due to leakage and capacitance to ground are of second order and therefore have nothing to do with equation (66).

Similarly, the drop in current along PQ is approximately

$$\Delta i = -G\,\Delta x e(x_1,t) - C\,\Delta x\,\frac{\partial e(x_1,t)}{\partial t}.$$

Dividing this through by Δx and equating the limits approached by its members as Δx approaches zero, we obtain

$$\frac{\partial i}{\partial x} = -Ge - C\,\frac{\partial e}{\partial t}. \tag{67}$$

Equations (66) and (67) are basic equations. Three important sets will be derived from them.

Eliminate i between (66) and (67) by equating the partial derivatives with respect to x of the two members of (66), replacing $\partial i/\partial x$ in the result by its value from (67) and $\partial^2 i/(\partial x\,\partial t)$ by its value obtained from (67) by partial differentiation with respect to t, and simplifying; the result is

$$\frac{\partial^2 e}{\partial x^2} = RGe + (RC + LG)\,\frac{\partial e}{\partial t} + LC\,\frac{\partial^2 e}{\partial t^2}. \tag{68}$$

Similarly, eliminate e between (66) and (67) to get

$$\frac{\partial^2 i}{\partial x^2} = RGi + (RC + LG)\frac{\partial i}{\partial t} + LC\frac{\partial^2 i}{\partial t^2}. \tag{69}$$

The equations (66) to (69) are known as the *telephone equations.*

In many applications to telegraph signaling, G and L are negligible. Replacing G and L by 0 in equations (66) to (69), we obtain the telegraph equations which follow:

$$\begin{aligned}\frac{\partial e}{\partial x} &= -Ri,\\ \frac{\partial i}{\partial x} &= -C\frac{\partial e}{\partial t},\\ \frac{\partial^2 e}{\partial x^2} &= RC\frac{\partial e}{\partial t},\\ \frac{\partial^2 i}{\partial x^2} &= RC\frac{\partial i}{\partial t}.\end{aligned} \tag{70}$$

For high frequencies, we may place $G = R = 0$ in (66) to (69) to obtain the radio equations which follow:

$$\begin{aligned}\frac{\partial e}{\partial x} &= -L\frac{\partial i}{\partial t},\\ \frac{\partial i}{\partial x} &= -C\frac{\partial e}{\partial t},\\ \frac{\partial^2 e}{\partial x^2} &= LC\frac{\partial^2 e}{\partial t^2},\\ \frac{\partial^2 i}{\partial x^2} &= LC\frac{\partial^2 i}{\partial t^2}.\end{aligned} \tag{71}$$

EXERCISES

1. Substitute $e = X(x)T(t)$ in the third of the radio equations (71) and, by the usual procedure, deduce that it is satisfied by the expressions for e

$$\begin{array}{ll}\cos(\omega\sqrt{LC}\,x)\cos\omega t, & \cos(\omega\sqrt{LC}\,x)\sin\omega t,\\ \sin(\omega\sqrt{LC}\,x)\sin\omega t, & \sin(\omega\sqrt{LC}\,x)\cos\omega t.\end{array} \tag{72}$$

If i and e are to satisfy the four radio equations (71) and $e = A\sin(\omega\sqrt{LC}\,x)\cos\omega t$, show that i must have the form $i = -A\sqrt{C/L}\cos(\omega\sqrt{LC}\,x)\sin\omega t + B$, where B is a constant.

2. If $i = A\cos(\omega\sqrt{LC}\,x)\sin\omega t$, find e so that i and e satisfy the radio equations (71).

3. Substitute $e = X(x)T(t)$ in the third equation of (70), and, by the regular procedure, deduce that some solutions of (70) have the form*

$$A\epsilon^{-(\omega^2/RC)t}\cos\omega x, \qquad B\epsilon^{-(\omega^2/RC)t}\sin\omega x. \tag{73}$$

* In this section, $\epsilon = 2.7183$ approximately.

4. (*a*) If $e = A\epsilon^{-(\omega^2/RC)t} \cos \omega x$, find a corresponding function $i(x,t)$ such that e and i satisfy (70). (*b*) If $i = A\epsilon^{-(\omega^2/RC)t} \sin \omega x$, find $e(x,t)$ such that i and e will satisfy (70).

5. In a steady-state condition for which i and e are functions of x only, solve (70). Since i and e depend on x only, $\partial i/\partial t$ and $\partial e/\partial t$ are zero.

6. In Fig. 14, take L miles as the length of AB, and solve the corresponding telegraph equations (70). Use as initial conditions $e(0,t) = 0$, $e(L,t) = 0$, $e(x,0) = 2 + 3x/L$. Formulas (A), (B), and (C) of §129 may be used to save time.

7. If $u = x + t/\sqrt{LC}$, $v = x - t/\sqrt{LC}$, show that $i = \varphi(u) + \psi(v)$ satisfies the fourth equation of (71). Then, derive $e = \sqrt{L/C}\,[\psi(v) - \varphi(u)] + H$, H constant, from equations (71).

8. A line is called distortionless if $LG = RC$, or $G/C = R/L$. Make the substitution

$$e = E(x,t)\epsilon^{-Gt/C}, \qquad i = I(x,t)\epsilon^{-Gt/C}$$

in (66) to (69) to obtain equations having the form (71) of the radio equations for a distortionless line. Also, check directly that (68) is satisfied by

$$e = A\epsilon^{-Gt/C} \sin (\omega \sqrt{LC}\, x) \cos \omega t,$$

when $G/C = R/L$, and find the corresponding $i(x,t)$ to satisfy (66) and (67).

135. Fluid motion

Because of the importance of fluid motion, as exemplified by the flow of air over airplane wings and the flow of water near ships, and because the solution of fluid-motion problems involves partial differential equations, a brief introduction to the subject will be given.

Consider the motion of a homogeneous fluid with continuous structure and no viscosity.* In this case all forces exerted by the fluid on a surface will be normal to the surface. For simplicity, think of a fluid moving between two parallel planes, and assume that any particle remains in a plane parallel to the bounding planes and that the motions in all such planes are the same. The flow will then be two-dimensional.

The motion of the fluid will be due to pressure in the fluid and a force proportional to the mass like the pull of gravity. Thus, the pressure p in the fluid will be a function of x, y, and t, and the force per unit mass will have components $X(x,y,t)$ and $Y(x,y,t)$ parallel to the coordinate axes. Also, let $u(x,y,t)$ and $v(x,y,t)$ be the x- and y-components of the velocity at time t.

From calculus, we have for the x- and y-components of acceleration

$$\begin{aligned} a_x &= \frac{du}{dt} = \frac{\partial u}{\partial x} u + \frac{\partial u}{\partial y} v + \frac{\partial u}{\partial t}, \\ a_y &= \frac{dv}{dt} = \frac{\partial v}{\partial x} u + \frac{\partial v}{\partial y} v + \frac{\partial v}{\partial t}. \end{aligned} \tag{74}$$

Now apply Newton's law of motion to the element of fluid represented

* All fluids are viscous, but many, water for example, are only slightly viscous.

by $ABCD$ in Fig. 15. The forces at time t on the faces represented by AD and BC may be expressed as an average pressure multiplied by the area $h\,\Delta y$, where h is the distance between the bounding planes. Accordingly, we write as the total force due to pressure on the surfaces represented by AD and BC

$$h\,\Delta y\,p(x,y_1,t) - h\,\Delta y\,p(x + \Delta x, y_1, t), \quad (75)$$

where $y < y_1 < y + \Delta y$. Also, the force proportional to mass acting on the element in the x-direction may be expressed by

$$\frac{h}{g}\,\Delta y\,\Delta x\,\bar{\rho}X(x_2,y_2,t), \quad (76)$$

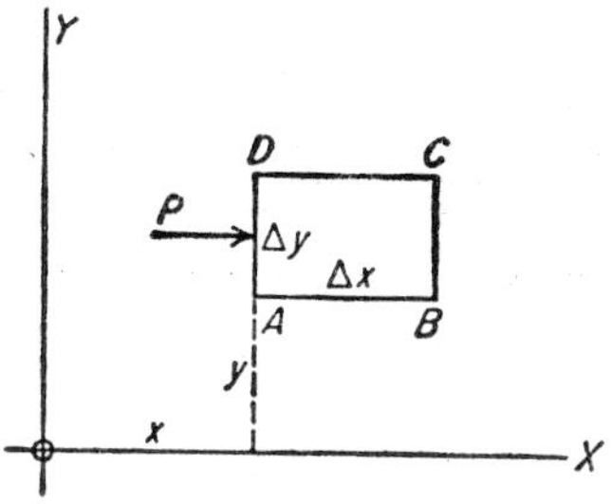

Fig. 15

where $\bar{\rho}$ is the average density of the fluid in the element and (x_2,y_2) is a point properly chosen in the element. Hence, we have

$$h\,\Delta y\,p(x,y_1,t) - h\,\Delta y\,p(x + \Delta x, y_1, t) + \frac{h}{g}\,\Delta y\,\Delta x\,\bar{\rho}X(x_2,y_2,t)$$
$$= \frac{\bar{\rho}h\,\Delta y\,\Delta x}{g}\,\frac{du(x_3,y_3,t)}{dt}, \quad (77)$$

where (x_3,y_3) is a properly chosen point in the element. Dividing through by $\Delta x\,\Delta y$, equating the limits of the two members as Δx and Δy approach zero, and simplifying slightly, we get

$$\frac{du}{dt} = X - \frac{g}{\rho}\frac{\partial p}{\partial x}. \quad (78)$$

Applying Newton's law parallel to the Y-axis, we obtain in a like manner

$$\frac{dv}{dt} = Y - \frac{g}{\rho}\frac{\partial p}{\partial y}. \quad (79)$$

Finally, express the condition that the rate of change of amount of fluid in the element is the rate at which fluid enters minus the rate at which it leaves. The rate of change of the quantity is

$$\frac{\partial}{\partial t}\,[h\,\Delta x\,\Delta y\,\rho(x_1,y_1,t)] = h\,\Delta x\,\Delta y\,\frac{\partial\bar{\rho}}{\partial t}. \quad (80)$$

The rate of entering minus the rate of leaving is approximately

$$h\,\Delta y[\overline{\rho u}(x,y_1,t) - \overline{\rho u}(x + \Delta x, y_1, t)] + h\,\Delta x[\overline{\rho v}(x_1,y,t) - \overline{\rho v}(x_1, y + \Delta y, t)]. \quad (81)$$

Equating the limit of (81) divided by $\Delta x\,\Delta y$ as Δx and Δy approach zero to the limit of (80) divided by $\Delta x\,\Delta y$, we get

$$-\frac{\partial(\rho u)}{\partial x}-\frac{\partial(\rho v)}{\partial y}=\frac{\partial \rho}{\partial t}. \tag{82}$$

Equations (78), (79), and (82) are the differential equations of fluid flow for the special case considered.

To understand the simplest case, the idea of *rotation* will be required. Figure 16 shows positions $A'B'C'D'$, after Δt units of time, of four fluid particles originally at corners A, B, C, and D of a rectangle having side AB parallel to the x-axis and side AD parallel to the y-axis. Disregarding

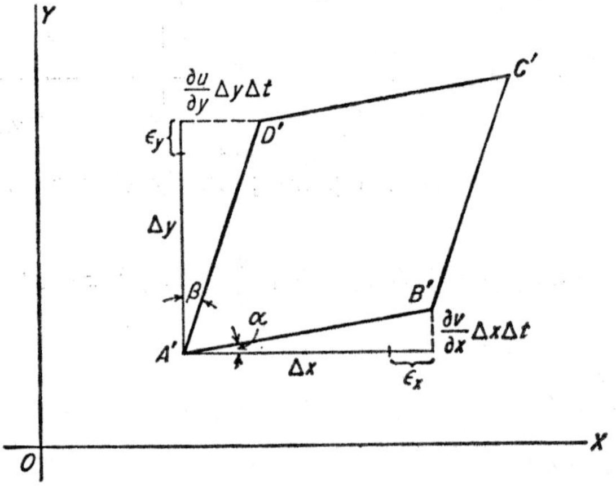

FIG. 16

infinitesimals of higher order than the first, we get for the angular velocity ω_x of $A'B'$

$$\omega_x=\frac{(\partial v/\partial x)\,\Delta x\,\Delta t}{\Delta t\,\Delta x}=\frac{\partial v}{\partial x}, \tag{83}$$

and for the angular velocity ω_y of $A'D'$

$$\omega_y=\frac{-(\partial u/\partial y)\,\Delta y\,\Delta t}{\Delta t\,\Delta y}=\frac{-\partial u}{\partial y}. \tag{84}$$

One-half the sum of the velocities ω_x and ω_y is called the *rotation* of the fluid, that is,

$$\text{Rotation}=\frac{1}{2}\left(\frac{\partial v}{\partial x}-\frac{\partial u}{\partial y}\right). \tag{85}$$

Now, consider the motion of a fluid for which the rotation is zero, that is,

$$\frac{\partial v}{\partial x}=\frac{\partial u}{\partial y}; \tag{86}$$

the fluid is incompressible, that is,

$$\rho=\text{constant}; \tag{87}$$

the fluid is in the steady state, that is, u and v are functions of x and y only; and the force is conservative, that is, there exists a force function $U(x,y)$ such that

$$\frac{\partial U}{\partial x} = X, \qquad \frac{\partial U}{\partial y} = Y. \tag{88}$$

From (74), (86), and the fact that the steady state exists,

$$\frac{du}{dt} = \frac{\partial u}{\partial x}u + \frac{\partial u}{\partial y}v = \frac{\partial u}{\partial x}u + \frac{\partial v}{\partial x}v. \tag{89}$$

Hence, taking account of (86) to (89), we may write (78) in the form

$$u\frac{\partial u}{\partial x} + v\frac{\partial v}{\partial x} = \frac{\partial U}{\partial x} - \frac{g}{\rho}\frac{\partial p}{\partial x}. \tag{90}$$

The integral of (90) is

$$\frac{u^2 + v^2}{2} = U - \frac{g}{\rho}p + C. \tag{91}$$

EXERCISES

1. From (86), deduce that in steady-state irrotational fluid motion there is a *velocity potential* $\varphi(x,y)$ such that

$$\frac{\partial \varphi}{\partial x} = u, \qquad \frac{\partial \varphi}{\partial y} = v.$$

The curves $\varphi(x,y) = c$ are called *curves of constant velocity potential.*

2. A streamline of a fluid in motion is a curve at each of whose points the direction of the velocity is the same as that of the curve. Hence, along streamlines, $dy/dx = v/u$, or

$$v\,dx - u\,dy = 0.$$

Show that, for steady-state irrotational motion of an incompressible fluid, this equation is exact because of (82), which, for the case in question, simplifies to $\partial u/\partial x + \partial v/\partial y = 0$. Hence, show that there are streamlines represented by

$$\psi(x,y) = C, \qquad \frac{\partial \psi}{\partial x} = v, \qquad \frac{\partial \psi}{\partial y} = -u.$$

Also, show that the streamlines $\psi(x,y) = C$ are the orthogonal trajectories of the velocity potential curves considered in exercise 1.

3. If $f(z) = v(x,y) + iu(x,y)$, where u and v are real functions of x and y, is analytic, then

$$\frac{\partial v}{\partial x} = \frac{\partial u}{\partial y}, \qquad \frac{\partial u}{\partial x} = -\frac{\partial v}{\partial y}.$$

These are equivalent to (86) and (82) for steady-state irrotational motion of an incompressible fluid.

(*a*) Using $f(z) = (x + iy)^2 = x^2 - y^2 + 2ixy$, take $v = x^2 - y^2$, $u = 2xy$, and find the corresponding equations of the streamlines and curves of constant velocity potential. Also, assuming that $X = 0$, $Y = -g$, find p in terms of x and y. (*b*) Carry out the same process for $f(z) = 1/z$, assuming $X = 0$, $Y = -g$.

ANSWERS

§2, page 3

1. 1, 1. **2.** 1, 2. **3.** 1, 6. **4.** 2, 1. **5.** 2, 1. **6.** 2, 2. **7.** 3, 2. **8.** 2, 2.

§4, page 6

1. (*a*) 0. (*b*) -2. (*c*) y_0. **2.** $\frac{1}{2}x = m$. **5.** (*a*) $y = x^2 + x$. (*b*) $y = x^2 - 2x$. (*c*) $y = x^2 - x$. (*d*) $y = x^2 - \frac{4}{3}x$. (*e*) $y = x^2 - 3x$.

§7, page 10

In these answers, primes are used to denote derivatives.

1. $y' = 3x^2$. **2.** $xy' = 2y$. **3.** $xy' = y - 3$. **4.** $(x + 2)y' = y$. **5.** $y' = y$. **6.** $(x^2 + x)y' = (2x + 1)y$. **7.** $xy' + (y')^2 = y$. **8.** $xy'' = y'$. **9.** $y''x^2 - 2y'x + 2y = 0$. **10.** $y'' - y = 0$. **11.** $y'' + 4y = 0$. **12.** $y'' + 4y = 3 \sin x$. **13.** $y''' = 0$. **14.** $x^2y'^2 - 2xyy' + (1 + x^2)y^2 = x^4$. **15.** $xy' = y$. **16.** $yy' + x = 0$. **17.** $y'' = 0$. **18.** $y'(y^2 - x^2 + 2x) + 2y(x - 1) = 0$. **19.** $(y - x)^2(1 + y'^2) = (1 + y')^2$.

§8, page 13

1. $x^2 + y^2 = c$. **2.** $x + y = c$. **3.** $x^3 + y^3 = c$. **4.** $xy = c$. **5.** $\rho\theta = c$. **6.** $1 + y^2 = c(1 + 2x^2)$. **7.** $\rho = ce^{\theta}$. **8.** $xy = 3x + c$. **9.** $x(y + \sqrt{1 + y^2}) = c$. **10.** $15 - 16S = ce^{-16t}$. **11.** $i = ce^{-Rt/L}$. **12.** $3e^x + e^{-3y} = c$. **13.** $3xy = y^3 + c$. **14.** $(1 - x^2)y^2 = cx^2$. **15.** $y = c(y + 2)e^{2x}$. **16.** $\sin^{-1} x - \sin^{-1} y = c$. **17.** $6xy = -1$. **18.** $r = 3\theta$. **19.** $e^{-x} + e^{-y} = 2$. **20.** $\rho = 2 \sin \theta$. **21.** $2y + 1 = 2e^{2/x}$. **22.** $(2 + x)y^4 - 3x + 6 = 0$. **23.** $xy = 2(x - 1)e^{2/x}$. **24.** $3ky^2 - 2x = 3kb^2 - 2a$. **25.** $y = be^{(x-a)/k}$. **26.** $y = (2k)^{-1}(x - a \pm 2kb)$. **27.** $y(x - a - k/b) + k = 0$.

§9, page 13

1. 1, 3. **2.** 1, 3. **3.** 2, 4. **4.** 2, 3. **9.** $y = xy' + (y')^3$. **10.** $y' = 5y$. **11.** $y'' + 2y' - 15y = 0$. **12.** $y'' - y = 2 - x^2$. **13.** $yy'' + y'^2 + 1 = 0$. **14.** $y''' = 0$. **15.** $y^2(1 + y'^2) = 1$. **16.** $xy'' = y' + y'^3$. **17.** $y = xy' - y'^2$. **18.** $4x + 2y' = y'(4x - y'^2)$. **19.** $3y = 5x$. **20.** $2x - 3y = 12$. **21.** $xy^2 = 3$. **22.** $2y + \ln(\frac{2}{5}x - \frac{1}{5}) = 0$. **23.** $(y - 1)(x + 1) = 2$. **24.** $(x - 2)^2 + 2(y + 3)^2 = c$. **25.** $(a + x)^{1-a} = cy$. **26.** $x + y - 2xy = 0$. **27.** $x = \ln[y/(y + 1)]$. **28.** $x^2(1 + y^2) = 17$. **29.** $27 \cot y = (1 + e^x)^3$. **30.** $x - a = 2k \ln |y/b|$. **31.** $(2y - 3b)x^2 = -a^2b$. **32.** $(6y^2 - 7b^2)x^6 + a^6b^2 = 0$. **33.** (*a*) $2\sqrt{y} = x + c$. (*b*) $\sqrt{y} = m$. (*e*) $y = m^2 \geqq 0$. **34.** (*a*) $y^2 = 2x + c$. (*b*) $y = 1/m$. (*e*) No.

§11, page 17

1. (*a*) $y = x^2 - 2x + 1$. (*b*) $(x - 1)^2 + (y + 1)^2 = 29$. (*c*) $(x - 1)(y - 1) = 6$. **3.** (*a*) $y = ce^x$. (*b*) $y = ce^{6x}$. (*c*) $y = 4 + ce^x$. **4.** $y = cx$. **5.** $xy = c$. **6.** $2y^2 + x^2 = c$. **7.** $3x^2 + 2y^2 = c$. **8.** Because the orthogonality must apply for curves crossing at any point and therefore must be independent of c. **9.** $x^2 + y^2 = c$.

10. $2y^2 + x^2 = c$. **11.** $xy = c$. **12.** $y^2 = \pm x^2 + c$. **13.** $y = ce^{x/k}$. **15.** $y = ce^{x/k}$. **16.** $y^3 = 6kx + c$. **17.** $x^2 - y^2 = c$. **18.** $y = cx^2$. **19.** $x = cy^2$. **20.** $3x^2 + y^2 = c$. **21.** $y^3 = cx^2$. **22.** $xy^{2a} = c$.

§12, page 20

1. $\rho = c \cos \theta$. **2.** $\rho = c(\sin \theta + \cos \theta)$. **3.** $\rho^4 = c \cos 2\theta$. **4.** $\rho^2 = c \sin \theta$. **5.** $\rho^n = c \cos \theta$. **6.** $\rho(1 - \cos \theta) = c$. **7.** $\rho = ae^{\theta \cot \alpha}$. **8.** (*a*) $\rho^n = c \sin n\theta$. (*b*) $\rho = c \sin^2 \frac{1}{2}\theta$, $\rho = c \csc^4 (\frac{3}{4}\pi - \frac{1}{4}\theta)$. **9.** (*a*) $\rho = a\theta + c$. (*b*) $\rho(c + \theta) + a = 0$. **10.** $\rho = ce^{-\theta^2/2}$, $0 < \theta < 2\pi$.

§13, page 21

1. $x^2 + y^2 = 13$. **2.** $2x^3 + y^2 = 25$. **3.** $x + 4 = 3 \ln y$.

§15, page 23

1. $T = 100(0.9)^{t/20}$; 22.4 min; 62.2°C. **2.** $T = 20 + 80(\frac{7}{8})^{t/20}$; 23.0 min; 63.9°C. **3.** $q = (0.5)^{0.222(10)^{-9}t}$; $q = (0.5)^{1.14(10)^{-9}t}$; $q = 0.5^{3.70(10)^{-6}t}$. **4.** 1.91 hr. **5.** $i = 30(\frac{11}{30})^{100t}$. **6.** $p = 14.7e^{0.0000375h}$; 8.37 lb/in.^{2} **7.** (*a*) 1.062 dollars. (*b*) 1.822 dollars. **8.** 11.55 years. **9.** 42,511 dollars. **10.** 25,285 dollars.

§16, page 25

3. $v = 20/(1 + 6t)$, $\frac{20}{61}$ ft/sec; $v = 20e^{-0.3s}$. **4.** (*a*) $7.5(1 - e^{-0.2t})$. (*b*) 6.5 ft/sec. (*c*) 7.5 ft/sec. **5.** (*a*) $v = \frac{15}{4}(1 - e^{-0.4t})$. (*b*) 3.68 ft/sec. (*c*) $\frac{15}{4}$ ft/sec. **6.** 32,000 ft/sec or about 6 miles/sec; limiting speed about 7 miles/sec. **7.** $v = 35(1 - e^{-t/5})$, $s = 35(t + 5e^{-t/5}) - 175$, 30.3 ft/sec, 198.7 ft. **8.** $s = 625 \ln [H^2/(H^2 - v^2)]$, 249 ft. **10.** $v = 3t^2$, $s = t^3$, $s = (1/\sqrt{27})v^{\frac{3}{2}}$.

§17, page 29

1. 1.37×10^8 cal. **2.** 1.66×10^6 cal. **3.** (*a*) 1 min 44 sec. (*b*) 1 min 48 sec. **4.** 26 min 28 sec. **5.** (*a*) 190 lb. (*b*) 200 lb. (*c*) 23.10 min. **6.** 117.2 lb. **7.** 54.4 lb. **8.** $r = -\frac{1}{600}t + \frac{1}{20}$. **9.** $\frac{80}{81}$. **10.** About 19.5 min. **11.** 1.18 gal.

§18, page 30

1. $x + y - xy = 7$. **2.** $x^2 + 5y^2 = c$. **3.** $y^2 = \ln cx$. **4.** $\rho = ce^{-\theta^2/4}$. **5.** $\frac{1}{32}$. **6.** $pv^k = c$. **7.** $\rho = c \sin \theta$, $\rho = c \csc \theta$. **8.** $\rho = a \sec (\theta + c)$. **9.** $\rho = c/(1 + \cos \theta)$. **10.** $\rho \cos \theta = c$, $\rho \sec \theta = c$. **11.** $\rho = ce^{\theta/(2k)} \csc \theta$. **12.** 44,880 dollars. **13.** 35.5 years (nearly). **14.** (*c*) 858 sec. **15.** 0.124 per cent. **17.** $v = 173(1 - e^{-gt/173})$; 151 ft/sec. **18.** 9.33×10^5 cal, 7.21×10^4 cal, 1.17×10^5 cal. **19.** 7 min 59 sec. **20.** 112 sec. **21.** 43 min 50 sec. **22.** $\frac{1}{2}kwl$.

§19, page 34

1. $2x - \ln (2x - 2y + 1) = c$. **2.** $\ln (2x + 3y - 3) + y = c$. **3.** $(x + y)^2 - 4y = c$. **4.** $x + y + 6 \ln (6 - 2x - y) = c$. **5.** $(x - 2y)^2 + 10(x - 2y) + 2y = c$. **6.** $x - \tan^{-1} (x + \frac{1}{2}y) = c$. **7.** $y^2(x^2 - 3y^2) = 1$. **8.** $(x^2 + y^2)(10 - 9x) = 5x$. **9.** $(st - 2)^3t = cs$. **10.** $x(x^2 + 3y^2) = 14$. **11.** $x(x^3 + 4y^3) = 5$. **12.** $\rho^3\theta^3(c - e^\theta) = 1$. **13.** $(2y + cx)(x + y)^2 + x = 0$. **14.** $x^2y^2 = c(x^2 + y^2)$.

§20, page 36

2. $x^2 - 3xy - y^2 = c$. **3.** $3x^2 + 4xy = c$. **4.** $xy^2 + y^3 = c$. **5.** $2x^3 - 7xy^2 = c$. **6.** $3\theta^2 + 4\rho\theta - 4\rho^2 = c$. **7.** $y^3 = 3x^3 \ln x$. **8.** $2x + y \ln x = 3y$. **9.** $2y^2 \ln (y^3/x^2) + 2xy + x^2 = cy^2$. **10.** $y + \sqrt{y^2 + x^2} = cx^2$. **11.** $\ln x + \cos (y/x) = c$. **13.** $x^2 + y^2 = cy$.

§21, page 38

1. $(x + y - 2)^3 = c(x - y + 2)$. **2.** $(y - 2x - 3)^4 = c(x + 1)^3$. **3.** $(y + 2x - 4)^2 = c(x + y - 1)$. **4.** $5x - 10y + \ln(10x + 5y - 2) = c$. **5.** $x + 6y + \ln(2x - 3y) = c$. **6.** $4x^2 + 6xy - 7y^2 - 14x + 8y = c$. **7.** $\ln[(y - x)^2 + (x - 1)^2] + 2\tan^{-1}[(y - x)/(x - 1)] = c$.

§22, page 39

1. $2x\,dx + 2y\,dy$. **2.** $(x\,dy - y\,dx)/x^2$. **3.** $3\,dx/x + 3\,dy/y$. **4.** $x^3y^4(4y\,dx + 5x\,dy)$. **5.** $x^{m-1}y^{n-1}(my\,dx + nx\,dy)$. **6.** $(x\,dy - y\,dx)/(x^2 + y^2)$. **7.** $e^{mx}(dy + my\,dx)$. **8.** $y^{-1-n}e^{mx}(-n\,dy + my\,dx)$. **9.** $3x^2y\,dx + (x^3 - 6y)\,dy = 0$. **10.** $ye^{ax}(2\,dy + ay\,dx) = 0$. **11.** $3y^2(x\,dy - y\,dx)/x^4 = 0$. **13.** $x^2y + 2x^2 + 3x + y^2 - 5y + c$. **14.** $x^2 - xy + 2x + \ln y + c$. **15.** $y/x + c$. **16.** $xy - \cos x - 2\sin y + c$. **17.** $xy^{-2} + yx^{-1} - 2y + c$. **18.** $-\frac{1}{2}x^{-2}y^{-2} + y^2 + c$.

§23, page 41

1. $2x^2 - 2xy + 5x + y^2 = c$. **2.** $x^3 + \frac{3}{2}x^2y^2 - y^3 + y^2 = c$. **3.** $a^2x - x^2y - xy^2 - \frac{1}{3}y^3 = c$. **4.** $ax^2 + bxy + ey^2 + gx + hy = c$. **5.** $x = cy$. **6.** $y = cx$. **7.** $y^2 - x^3 = cx$. **8.** $y\ln(2x - 2) + \ln y = c$. **9.** $\cos y \ln(5x + 15) + \ln y = c$. **10.** $\rho^2(\sec 2\theta + 2) = c$. **11.** $\rho\sin 2\theta - \rho^2\cos 2\theta = c$. **12.** $\ln x + 2x\ln 5y = c$. **13.** $3ye^{2x} = x^3 + c$. **14.** $ye^{x^2} = x^3 + c$. **15.** $4x + x^4y = cy$. **16.** $x + \sqrt{x^2 + y^2} = c$. **17.** $x^2y^2(x^2 - y^2) = c$. **18.** $y^3(1 + \cos 2x) = c$. **19.** $y^2\ln[5x/(x + 3)] - 3\cos y = c$.

§24, page 44

1. $xy = x^3 + c$. **2.** $(xy)^{-2} = 2/x + c$. **3.** $3\ln(y/x) = y^3 + c$. **4.** $y = x^2 + 3 + cx$. **5.** $y^2 + 3 + x + cy = 0$. **6.** $\ln[(x + 2y)/(x - y)] = 3x + c$. **7.** $\tan^{-1}(y/x) = \frac{1}{4}y^4 + c$. **8.** $\tan^{-1}(x/y) = \frac{1}{4}(x^2 + y^2)^2 + c$. **9.** $xy = \frac{1}{3}(x^2 + y^2)^{\frac{3}{2}} + c$. **10.** $\tan^{-1}(3y/2x) = 6\sqrt{4x^2 + 9y^2} + c$. **11.** $2\tan^{-1}(y/x) = \ln(x^2 + y^2) + c$. **12.** $y^3(x^2 - 1) = c$. **13.** $x^3(y^4 - x^2) = c$. **14.** $2y^4 + x = cx^3$. **15.** $5y = x^2(y^5 + c)$. **16.** $3\ln(xy^2) = x^3 + c$. **17.** $3\ln(x^2y^{-1}) = y^3 + c$. **18.** $x^2y(y^2 + c) + 2 = 0$. **19.** $11x^{\frac{3}{2}} - yx^{\frac{11}{2}} = cy$. **20.** $y^2 + x^4 = cx^6$. **21.** $6\tan^{-1}(x/y) + (x^2 + y^2)^{-3} + c = 0$. **22.** $\ln|(ay - x)/(2ay - x)|^2 = a(x^2 + y^2) + c$. **23.** $5\ln(xy^{-2}) = y^5 + c$. **24.** $\sqrt{6}\tan^{-1}[\sqrt{\tfrac{3}{2}}\,(y/x)] = (2x^2 + 3y^2)^3 + c$. **25.** (a) $x = ce^{x/y}$. (b) $y^3 + 3x^3\ln cx = 0$. **26.** (a) $x^{\frac{1}{3}}(7y^4 + x^3) = c$. (b) $x^5 + x^3y + x^2y^2 = c$.

§25, page 47

1. y. **2.** y. **3.** x. **4.** Nonlinear. **5.** x. **6.** Nonlinear. **7.** $y = \frac{1}{5}x^4 - \frac{3}{2}x + cx^{-1}$. **8.** $15x^2y = 3x^5 + 10x^3 + c$. **9.** $y = x^2\ln x + 2x^2 - x$. **10.** $x = \frac{2}{5}y^2 + cy^{-3}$. **11.** $x = 3y^2\ln y + 1$. **12.** $y = x^3 + 2x^2 - x^{-1}$. **13.** $4x^3y + 2x\cos 2x = c + \sin 2x$. **14.** $2x = y^4(y^2 + 7)$. **15.** $x = \sin^2 y(c - \cot y)$. **16.** $2x + 4y = 1 - 5e^{-2x}$. **17.** $x = e^{y^2} + 4e^{y^2/2}$. **18.** $2s = e^{3t}(t^3 + ct)$. **19.** $2t = e^{-s^2}(s^2 + c)$. **20.** $4x + 2y = 1 - 5e^{-2y}$. **21.** $y = ax + 2a\sqrt{1 + x^2}$. **22.** $\rho = \sin\theta - 1 + ce^{-\sin\theta}$. **23.** $3y = f(x) + c[f(x)]^{-2}$. **24.** $2xf^3(y) = f^2(y) + c$.

§26, page 49

1. $xy(c - \frac{3}{2}x^2) = 1$. **2.** $1 = ye^x(c - x^2)$. **3.** $xy^{-2} + x^5 = c$. **4.** $x^{-3}y^{-3} + x^2 = c$. **5.** $x^{-1}y^{-2} = c - 2y$. **6.** $x^{-2}e^{2y^2} = c - 4y^3$. **7.** $y^{\frac{1}{2}} = c(x - 2)^{-\frac{1}{2}} + (x - 2)^2$. **8.** $y^{-2}e^{2x/3} = c - e^{2x}$. **9.** $y^{-1}e^{-x} = 13 - 12e^x$. **10.** $y^3(x + 1) = \frac{8}{3}[(x + 1)^3 - 1]$. **11.** $2y^{-1}(x + 1)^{-1} = 3 - [\ln(x + 1)]^2$. **12.** $6yx^{-2} - 4\ln(3yx^{-2} + 2) = 3x^2 + c$. **13.** $\ln[\ln(ye^{\cos x})] = x + c$. **14.** $x^2\sin^2 y + 2\ln(x\sin y) = \sin^2 y + c$.

§27, page 51

1. $x = t^2 + c_1$, $y = c_1t + c_2$. **2.** $x = c_1e^{-t} + c_2$, $y = (t + c_1)e^{-t}$. **3.** $x = 1{,}000t + c_1$, $y = 500t - 8t^2 + c_2$. **4.** $\rho = \frac{1}{2}e^t + c_1e^{-t}$, $\theta = \frac{1}{2}e^t - c_1e^{-t} + c_2$. **5.** $x = 6t^2 + 2c_1t$, $y = -2t^3 + (6 - c_1)t^2 + 2c_1t + c_2$. **6.** $x = t + c_1t^{-1}$, $y = c_1 \ln t - t - c_1t^{-1} + c_2$. **7.** $x^2 = t^2(2 \ln t + c_1)$, $2y = t^3(2 \ln t + c_1 - 1) + c_2t$. **8.** $x = 4e^t(t - 1) + 2e^{2t} + c_1$, $y = 4e^t - e^{2t}(2t - 1) + c_2$. **9.** $\rho = c_1t$, $\theta = (c_1 + 1)t \ln t + c_2t$. **10.** $x = c_1 \cos (at + c_2)$, $y = c_1 \sin (at + c_2)$.

§28, page 52

1. $xy \ln (cx/y) = x + y$. **2.** $3y(x^2 + 3) + 5x^3 = c$. **3.** $\ln x + \tan^{-1} [(y + x)/2x] = c$. **4.** $4x - 2y = \ln [c(x + y - 1)/(x + y + 1)]$. **5.** $y \sec^3 x = 2 \tan x + c$. **6.** $2x = y(c - x^2)$. **7.** $x^3 + x^2y + \sin y = 1$. **8.** $y = x(1 + \ln y)$. **9.** $x + y = \ln (cxy)$. **10.** $y \ln cx = \pm 1$. **11.** $5x^{-3}y^{-3} = c - 3y^5$. **12.** $8y^{-1} = 1 - 2x^2 + ce^{-2x^2}$. **13.** $x^{-1} = \frac{1}{2} + ce^{y^2}$. **14.** $y \ln 3x + x + y^2 = c$. **15.** $\ln (x^3y^5) = \frac{1}{3}y^3 + c$. **16.** $(xy)^{-2} + 2 \ln (2x^2 + y^2 - 3) = c$. **17.** $y = cx$, $y^2 - 2x^2 = c$. **18.** $2x^3 + xy^2 = 2x \ln y + 5x - 2$. **19.** $xy + 1 = 4.946e^{-x/y}$. **20.** $5y^2 = 8 \cos x + 4 \sin x - 4e^{\pi - 2x}$. **21.** $x^3y = 8xy - 16$. **22.** $x + y + c = 4 \ln (2x + 3y + 7)$. **23.** $5xy^2 = 18(y^2 - x^2)$. **24.** $xy = 3(x^2 - 1)^3 - 21(x^2 - 1)$. **25.** $6x^2y + 6xy^2 + a^2y + b^2x = c$. **26.** $\ln xy + y \ln [(x - 1)/(x + 1)] = c$. **27.** $(x + y + 5)^2 = 16x + 20$. **28.** $(2x + y - 5)^2 = (3x + 2y - 2)^2 + c$. **29.** $(x^2 - y)^4 = 3\sqrt{x^2 - y^2} + c$. **30.** $xy(y - x) = c(y + x)$. **31.** $4y = \ln \{[c(4x - 3y - 3)]/(4x - 3y + 1)\}$. **32.** $25y^3 + 8(1 + 2y)^2(1 - y)e^{3x^2/2}$. **33.** $x^2 + y^2 + c = \ln (3x^2 + 4y^2 - 2)$. **34.** $y(\sec x + \tan x) = x + c$. **35.** $xy(x^2 + y^2 - 1) + 1 = 0$. **36.** $y^2 + x(\ln x - 4) = 0$. **37.** $y = x + x \ln [(x + y)/4]$. **38.** $(x + y - 3)^3 = 125(x - y - 1)$. **39.** $3x^2 + 2xy - y^2 = c$. **40.** $6\rho\theta - 2\rho^3 + 3 \sin^2 \theta = c$. **41.** $x(x + y)^3 = 3my + cx$. **42.** $(y - x^2 - xy)(x + y)^3 = c(y + 2x^2 + 2xy)$. **43.** $xy(x^2 - xy + y^2) = c$. **44.** $x^2\sqrt{y} + \ln cx = 0$. **45.** $x^{\frac{3}{2}}(x^2 + y^2) + y^{\frac{3}{2}} = c$. **46.** $x[c - (y - 2x)^2] = 2y - 10x \tan^{-1} (y/x)$. **47.** $x = (t + 3c_1)e^{3t}$; $9y = (12t + 36c_1 - 1)e^{3t} + c_2$. **48.** $x - y = t - c_1$, $x \ln x - y = c_2x$. **49.** $xy = t^2 + c_1$, $x + y = \ln (2t^2 + c_1) + c_2$. **50.** $y^2 = 2x + c_1$, $y\sqrt{y^2 + 1} + \ln (y + \sqrt{y^2 + 1}) \pm 10t = c_2$. **51.** $2y = 3x^2 - x + c_1$, $2t = x^3 + c_1x + c_2$. **52.** $xyt = c_1$, $xy + yt + tx = c_2$.

§29, page 54

1. $4x^3 + 12xy^2 - 3y^4 = 204$. **2.** $x + c = 2\sqrt{2x + 3y} - 4 \ln (2 + \sqrt{2x + 3y})$. **3.** $y^2 = 2cx + c^2$. **4.** The part above the x-axis or the part below the x-axis of any straight line. **5.** $2nk\rho^{n-2} = (n - 2)\theta$, $0 \leq \theta \leq 2\pi$. **6.** $x + ky^2 = cy$. **7.** $(x^2 + y^2)^{1-n/2} = (2 - n)(kx + c)$. **8.** $x^2 + y^2 = cx$. **9.** $t = 10.91 \ln [(4 - x)/(4 - 2x)]$; 2. **10.** $t = 19.14 \{\ln [(12 - 4x)/(12 - 3x)] + 1/(3 - x) - \frac{1}{3}\}$; 3. **11.** $t = 22.4 \ln [\frac{15}{16}(4 - x)^2/(x^2 - 8x + 15)]$; 3. **13.** $18\frac{1}{3}$ lb. **14.** A parabola. **15.** $x^2 + y^2 = cx$. **16.** $a\rho^{-1} = \sin \theta + ce^{\theta \cot \alpha}$. **17.** $c\rho^2 = a - \rho \sin \theta$. **18.** $\sqrt{l^2 - y^2} + l \ln [(l - \sqrt{l^2 - y^2})/y] = c \pm x$.

§30, page 58

1. $x = (t + 1)^2$, $y = 2(t + 1)$. **4.** $x = 50{,}000(1 - e^{-0.032t})$, $y = 81{,}250(1 - e^{-0.032t}) - 1{,}000t$. **5.** $6\frac{2}{3}$ lb. **6.** 19.38 lb. **8.** $x^2y = -1$, $x = (2 - t)^{-1}$, $y = -(2 - t)^2$. **10.** $x = \frac{1}{2}t + \frac{25}{2}t^{-1}$, $y = \frac{1}{2}t - \frac{25}{2}t^{-1}$. **11.** $x = y = \text{R}e^{4t}$. **12.** Since $\ln [M/(M - kt)]$ must be real, $M - kt > 0$, or $t < M/k$. The rocket would be dissipated completely when $t = (M/k) \cdot c \ln 10$. **13.** $0.670cM/k$. **14.** $v = c \ln [M/(M - kt)] - gt$; $c \ln 10 - 0.9Mg/k$; $x = (c/k)(M - kt) \ln [(M - kt)/M] + ct - \frac{1}{2}gt^2$; $(cM/k)0.670 - \frac{1}{2}(0.81)gM^2/k^2$.

§31, page 60

1. $q_\infty = 0$, $q_{t=RC} = 0.368q_0$, $q_{t=2RC} = 0.135q_0$, $t_{q=0.01q_0} = 4.61RC$. **2.** $0.368I_0$, $0.135I_0$, 0. **3.** (a) $i = (E/R)[1 - e^{-(R/L)t}]$, starting from 0, rapidly approaches E/R. (b) $i = E/(R^2 + L^2\omega^2)(R \sin \omega t - \omega L \cos \omega t + \omega L e^{-(Rt/L)})$ starting, from zero, rapidly approaches $E/(R^2 + L^2\omega^2)(R \sin \omega t - \omega L \cos \omega t)$. **7.** $q = q_0 \cos (t/\sqrt{LC})$, $i = (-q_0/\sqrt{LC}) \sin (t/\sqrt{LC})$.

§32, page 61

1. 1.05 lb/in.^{2} **2.** $(p_0^{\frac{2}{7}} - \frac{2}{7}k^{-\frac{5}{7}}h)^{3.5}$, $\frac{7}{2}p_0^{\frac{2}{7}}k^{\frac{5}{7}}$. **3.** 98,000 ft.

§33, page 66

1. $x^2 + y^2 = c$, $y = cx$. **2.** $x^2 - y^2 = c$, $xy = c$. **3.** $xy = c$, $y^2 - x^2 = c$. **4.** $3x^2y - y^3 = c$, $3xy^2 - x^3 = c$. **5.** $\tan^{-1}(y/x) = c - 2y$, $\ln (x^2 + y^2) = c - 4x$. **6.** $x^3 + 3xy^2 = c$, $y^2 - x^2 = cy$. **7.** $10x - 32y = c$, $32x + 10y = c$. **8.** $x^2 + y^2 = c$, $y = cx$. **9.** $x^2 + y^2 = c$, $y = cx$. **11.** (b) $3x^2y - y^3 = c$, $x^3 - 3xy^2 = c$; $x^3y - y^3x = c$, $x^4 - 6x^2y^2 + y^4 = c$. **12.** (a) $y = cx$, $x^2 + y^2 = c$. (b) $3 \tan^{-1}(y/x) = c - 2y$, $3 \ln (x^2 + y^2) = c - 4x$. (c) $x^2 + y^2 = cy$, $x^2 + y^2 = cx$. **13.** $r_1 - r_2 = cr_1r_2$, $\cos \theta_1 - \cos \theta_2 = c$. **14.** y^{n-2}.

§34, page 68

1. $ax^3 + bx^2y - exy^2 - fy^3 = am^3$. **2.** $2\rho = \theta + \theta^3$. **3.** $x^2 + y^2 = cy$. **4.** $\rho = c(\sin \theta - 6 \cos \theta)$. **5.** 40 lb. **6.** $38\frac{3}{4}$ lb, $28\frac{1}{8}$ lb. **8.** $\rho = 9/(5 + 4 \cos \theta)$. **9.** $s = \pm \sin t$. **10.** $s = 4 - 4 \cos 4t$. **11.** $q = 0.02(1 - e^{-500t})$, $q \to \frac{1}{50}$ coulomb, $i \to 0$. **12.** $q = 10^{-3}[13 \sin 380t - 9.7(\cos 380t - e^{-500t})]$, $i = dq/dt$. **13.** $\ln (2Li + Rq) + Rq/(2Li + Rq) = c$. **14.** 52,700 ft. **15.** $\tau(1 + \mu^2) = \rho R[(1 - \mu^2) \sin \theta - 2\mu \cos \theta] + ce^{\mu\theta}$. **16.** (c) $2\sqrt{2}\,\mu = (1 - 2\mu - \mu^2)e^{3\pi\mu/4}$. **17.** $y^2x^3 = c$, $2x^2 - 3y^2 = c$. **18.** $y^{-2} = 4x^2 - 2 + ce^{-2x^2}$, $x^{-2} = 4y^2 + 2 + ce^{2y^2}$. **19.** $\ln (x^3y + x^3\sqrt{x^2 + y^2}) - 10y = c$, $\sqrt{x^2 + y^2} = 5x^2 + 4y + c$. **20.** $\sqrt{x^2 + y^2} = c + x$, $\sqrt{x^2 + y^2} = c - x$. **21.** $y^2 - x^2 + \ln (x^2 + y^2) = c$, $xy - 2 \tan^{-1}(y/x) = c$.

§36, page 71

1. $(9y - x^3 + c)(9y + x^3 + c) = 0$. **2.** $(y - x^3 - c)(\ln y^2 - x^2 - c)(y^{-1} + x - c) = 0$. **3.** $(3y + c)^2 = 25x^3$. **4.** $(\ln y + 2x - c)(\ln y - 2x + c) = 0$, $y = 0$. **5.** $1 - a^2y^2 = (a^2x + c)^2$. **6.** $ay^2 = (x - c)^3$, $y = 0$. **7.** $(y^2x - c)(yx^2 - c) = 0$. **8.** $(2y - x^2 - c)(a^2y + ax - 1 - ce^{-ax}) = 0$. **9.** $2cy = c^2x^2 - 1$. **10.** $(y - c)(x + y - c)(x^2 + xy + y^2 - c) = 0$. **11.** $(2y + bx^2 - c)[x - a \sin (y + c)] = 0$. **12.** Each family of the new system will be the orthogonal trajectories of one family of the old system. **13.** (a) $y = \pm\sqrt{k^2 - x^2} \pm k \ln |(\sqrt{k^2 - x^2} - k)/x| + c$. (b) $(x - c)^2 + y^2 = k^2$.

§37, page 75

2. $2y = \pm x$. **3.** $x^2 + y^2 + x = 0$. **4.** $x^2 = 4y^3$. **5.** $x = \pm 1$.

§38, page 77

3. No. **4.** $y^2 - x^2 = 0$. Yes. **6.** $y = -x^2$. **7.** None. **8.** $y = 0$. **9.** $y = \dfrac{-1}{64}x^8$.

§39, page 79

1. $2y = c^2 + 2cx - x^2$, $y = -x^2$. **2.** $2cy = c^2x^2 + 3$, $y^2 = 3x^2$. **3.** $y = cx - x^2 + c^2$, $4y + 5x^2 = 0$. **4.** $xy = c^2x + c$, $4x^2y + 1 = 0$. **5.** $3x = 2p + cp^{-\frac{1}{2}}$, $3y = p^2 - cp^{\frac{1}{2}}$. **6.** $x = 2p + cp^{-2}$, $y = p^2 + 2cp^{-1}$. **7.** $x = p(-2 + ce^{-p^2/2})$, $y = (p^2 + 1)ce^{-p^2/2} -$

$p^2 - 2$. **8.** $y = cx + c^3$, $27y^2 = -4x^3$. **10.** $y = -2x^2 - 3(x/4)^{\frac{4}{3}}$. **11.** $y = c \ln x - \frac{1}{2}x^2 + \phi(c)$, $y = -\frac{1}{4}(\ln x)^2 - \frac{1}{2}x^2$.

§40, page 81

1. $cx = e^y + 4c^3$, $x = 3e^{2y/3}$. **2.** $x = y + \ln(1 + ce^{-y})$. **3.** $4cx = 2y^2 + c^3$, $64x^3 = 27y^4$. **4.** $(x + c)^2 = 2cy - c^2$, $x^2 + 2xy - y^2 = 0$. **5.** $2cx = 2 \sin y + c^3$, $2x = 3(\sin y)^{\frac{2}{3}}$. **6.** $x = c - 2p - 2\ln(p - 1)$, $y = c - p^2 - 2p - 2\ln(p - 1)$. **7.** $x = p^{-2} + 2cp$, $y = 2p^{-1} + cp^2$. **8.** $x = (3c)^{-1}y^3 + \phi(c)$. **9.** $x = (1/c)e^y + \phi(c)$. **10.** $3x = 4e^{3y/4}$.

§41, page 82

1. $(3x - \ln y - c)(y - 2x^2 - c) = 0$. **2.** $(x - \ln y - c)(x + y + c)(y - x^2 - c) = 0$. **3.** $y = cx + c^2$, $x^2 + 4y = 0$. **4.** $y = cx - c^3$, $27y^2 = 4x^3$. **5.** $y = cx - 3x^2 + \frac{1}{2}c^2$, $2y + 7x^2 = 0$. **6.** $y^2 = 2cx + c^3$, $27y^4 = -32x^3$. **7.** $y = c \ln x + \frac{1}{4}c^2$, $y = -(\ln x)^2$. **8.** $cx = e^y + \frac{1}{3}c^3$, $4x^3 = 9e^{2y}$. **9.** $3cx = y^3 + 3c\phi(c)$. **10.** $y = c \ln(\sin x) + \phi(c)$. **11.** $y^2 + (c - x)^2 = c$, $x + \frac{1}{4} = y^2$. **12.** $y(y - 3)^2 = (x - c)^2$; $y = 0$. $y = 1$ is a tac locus. $y = 3$ is a nodal locus along which $\partial f(x,y,p)/\partial x = 0$, $\partial f(x,y,p)/\partial y = 0$. **13.** $512y^3 + 27x^4 = 0$. **14.** (*a*) $4p(y - px) = 1$, $27y^2 = 2(2x - 1)^3$. (*b*) $2p(y - px) = 2p^2 + 1$, $27y^2 = 8x^3$. **15.** $3x = p^{-\frac{2}{3}}(1 + 4p^2)$, $6y = p^{-\frac{4}{3}}(5 + 2p^2)$.

§42, page 86

1. $2x$. **2.** $8x^2 + 16x$. **3.** $-2x^3 + 3x^2$. **4.** $12x^2$. **5.** $27e^{3x}$. **6.** $2e^{5x}$. **7.** $-2a^2 \sin ax$. **8.** 0. **9.** 0. **10.** 0. **11.** 0. **12.** $(1 - x)\cos x - x \sin x$. **13.** $2e^{-x}$. **14.** $2e^{-2x}$. **15.** 0. **16.** $y = c_1 + c_2e^{2x}$. **17.** $y = c_1e^{2x} + c_2e^{-2x}$. **18.** $y = c_1 + c_2e^{2x} - \frac{3}{2}x^2 - \frac{3}{2}x$. **19.** $y = c_1e^{3x} + c_2e^{-4x} - 1$. **20.** $y = c_1 + c_2e^{3x} - \frac{1}{2}e^x$. **21.** $y = c_1e^{2x} + c_2e^{-2x} + \frac{1}{5}e^{3x}$. **22.** $y = c_1 + c_2x + c_3e^{-3x} + \frac{1}{6}e^{-x}$. **23.** $y = c_1e^x + c_2e^{2x} + c_3e^{3x}$. **24.** $y = (c_1 + \frac{1}{3}x)e^x + c_2e^{-2x}$. **25.** $y = c_1x + c + x^4$. **26.** $y = (c_1 + c_2x)e^{2x} + x^2e^{2x}$. **27.** $y = 2 + 3e^{-3x}$. **28.** $y = 3e^{-2x} - 2e^{2x}$. **29.** $y = e^x(x^2 - 3x + 3)$.

§43, page 87

1. $-11(x^2) + 11x^2 = 0$.

§45, page 90

1. $y = c_1e^x + c_2e^{2x}$. **2.** $y = c_1e^x + c_2e^{-5x}$. **3.** $y = c_1e^{-3x} + c_2e^{-x}$. **4.** $y = e^{\frac{5}{2}x}(c_1e^{\frac{1}{2}\sqrt{13}x} + c_2e^{-\frac{1}{2}\sqrt{13}x})$. **5.** $y = c_0 + c_2e^{\frac{1}{2}\sqrt{5}x} + c_3e^{-\frac{1}{2}\sqrt{5}x}$. **6.** $y = c_1 + c_2e^{-x} + c_3e^x$. **7.** $y = c_1e^{kx} + c_2e^{-kx}$. **8.** $y = c_1e^x + c_2e^{-x} + c_3e^{3x}$. **9.** $y = c_1e^x + c_2e^{2x} + c_3e^{-3x}$. **10.** $y = c_1 + c_2e^{3x} + e^{-x}(c_3e^{\sqrt{2}x} + c_4e^{-\sqrt{2}x})$.

§47, page 91

1. $y = e^{3x}(c_1 + c_2x)$. **2.** $y = e^{-2x}(c_1 + c_2x)$. **3.** $y = c_1 + c_2x + c_3e^x$. **4.** $y = c_1 + c_2x + c_3x^2 + c_4e^{2x} + c_5e^{-2x}$. **5.** $y = c_0 + e^x(c_1 + c_2x)$. **6.** $y = c_1 + c_2x + c_3x^2$. **7.** $y = e^x(c_1 + c_2x) + c_3e^{-x}$. **8.** $y = e^x(c_1 + c_2x + c_3x^2)$. **9.** $y = c_1 + c_2x + e^{2x}(c_3 + c_4x) + e^{-2x}(c_5 + c_6x)$. **10.** $y = c_1 + c_2x + e^{2x}(c_3 + c_4x) + c_5e^{-4x}$. **11.** $y = (5 - 14x)e^x$. **12.** $y = e^{-x}$. **13.** $y = x + 2e^x$. **14.** $y = 2x + 4e^{-x}$. **15.** $y = 1 + 2xe^{2x}$. **16.** $y = e^{-x} + (2x - 1)e^x$.

§48, page 93

1. $y = e^x(c_1 \sin x + c_2 \cos x)$. **2.** $y = c_0 + e^{2x}(c_1 \sin x + c_2 \cos x)$. **3.** $y = c_1e^{2x} + e^{-x}(c_2 \sin 3x + c_3 \cos 3x)$. **4.** $y = c_1 \sin 2x + c_2 \cos 2x$. **5.** $y = (c_1 + c_2x)\sin 2x + (c_3 + c_4x)\cos 2x$. **6.** $y = c_1 + c_2x + c_3 \sin x + c_4 \cos x$. **7.** $y = c_1 + c_2x + (c_3 + c_4x)\sin \sqrt{3}\,x + (c_5 + c_6x)\cos \sqrt{3}\,x$. **8.** $y = c_0e^{-ax} + e^{ax/2}[c_1 \sin(\frac{1}{2}\sqrt{3}\,ax) + c_2$

$\cos(\frac{1}{2}\sqrt{3}\,ax)]$. **9.** $y = \sin x - \cos x$. **10.** $y = 2\sin 3x$. **11.** $y = e^{-x}\sin x$. **12.** $y = 1 + e^x \sin x$. **13.** $y = 4e^x \sin x - 2e^{-2x}$. **14.** $y = 4\cos 2(x-1)$.

§49, page 95

1. $y = c_1e^{2x} + c_2e^{-2x} - 3$. **2.** $y = c_1e^{-3x} + c_2e^x + 2e^{4x}$. **3.** $y = c_1e^x + c_2e^{-2x} + 3x$. **4.** $y = c_1e^{2x} + c_2e^{-x} - 3e^x$. **5.** $y = c_1 \sin x + c_2 \cos x + 3 + 3e^x$. **6.** $y = e^{-2x}(c_1 + c_2x) + \frac{1}{4}(x - 1 + 2e^{2x})$. **7.** $y = c_1 + c_2e^{-x} - 1.2\sin 2x - 0.6\cos 2x$. **8.** $y = c_1 + c_2x + c_3e^x + \cos x - \sin x$. **9.** $y = c_1 \sin x + c_2 \cos x + e^x(2\sin x - 4\cos x)$. **10.** $y = c_1e^x + c_2e^{-x} - 2x^2 - 4$. **11.** $y = e^{3x} - 1 - \cos 3x$. **12.** $y = 3e^{-3x} + 2x$. **13.** $y = 1 + 2e^{-x} + \frac{1}{2}e^x$. **14.** $y = xe^x - \frac{3}{4}e^x - 2$. **15.** $y = e^{2x} + e^x + 2e^{-x}$.

§50, page 97

1. $y = c_1 + c_2e^{-x} + 2x^2 - 4x$. **2.** $y = c_1e^x + c_2e^{-x} + \frac{5}{2}xe^x$. **3.** $y = -xe^{-x}$. **4.** $y = -\frac{1}{2}x\cos x$. **5.** $y = -\frac{1}{2}xe^{-x}$. **6.** $y = x - \frac{4}{3} + \frac{1}{2}xe^{-x}$. **7.** $y = 3 + \frac{1}{2}x^2e^x$. **8.** $y = \frac{1}{4}x \sin 2x$. **9.** $y = 2x^2 - 2x - \frac{1}{2}xe^{-2x}$. **10.** $y = x - x\cos 2x$. **11.** $y = 2x + \frac{1}{34}(15\sin 2x + 60\cos 2x)$. **12.** $y = -\frac{1}{2}xe^x \cos x$.

§51, page 98

1. 0. **2.** $32a^5e^{ax}$. **3.** 0. **4.** $-120e^{-3x}$. **5.** $5!e^{ax}$. **6.** 0. **7.** $\sin xe^{2x}$. **8.** 0. **10.** $y = (c_1 + c_2x + \frac{1}{6}x^3)e^{-ax}$. **11.** $y = (c_1 + c_2x + c_3x^2 + x^4/24)e^{-2x}$. **12.** $y = (\frac{2}{5}\cos x - \frac{1}{5}\sin x)e^{-2x} + c_1e^{-2x} + c_2$. **13.** $y = c_1 + (c_2 + c_3x)e^{-x} - 6x^2e^{-x}$. **14.** $y = (\frac{1}{3}\sin x + c_1 \sin 2x + c_2 \cos 2x)e^{-2x}$.

§52, page 103

1. $\frac{1}{4}x^4$. **2.** $2e^{2x}$. **3.** $\frac{1}{6}x^3e^x$. **4.** $-\frac{3}{5}\cos 3x$. **5.** $x^4 - 4x^3 + 12x^2 - 24x + 24$. **6.** $-1/1{,}728 \cos 4x$. **7.** $\frac{1}{3}x^3 - \frac{1}{3}x^2 + \frac{2}{9}x - \frac{2}{27}$. **8.** $\frac{1}{2}\sin xe^{2x}$. **9.** $y = 8x^3e^{3x}$. **10.** $y = e^{-x}\ln(2x+3)$. **11.** $y = (8x^2 - 4x + 1)e^{3x}$. **12.** $y = \frac{1}{9}\sin 2x$. **13.** $y = -\frac{1}{3}\sin 2x - \frac{1}{8}\cos 3x$. **14.** $y = -e^x \sin x$. **15.** $y = \frac{9}{17}e^x(\sin 2x - 4\cos 2x)$. **16.** $y = e^x(-7\cos 3x + 3\sin 3x)$. **17.** $y = \frac{1}{2}\sin x(e^{2x} - 2e^x)$. **18.** $y = \frac{1}{17}e^x(\sin 2x - 4\cos 2x)$. **19.** $y = -2e^x(\sin x + \cos x)$. **20.** $y = \frac{1}{4}e^{3x}(2x^2 - 6x + 7)$. **21.** $y = \frac{9}{32}e^{2x}(8x^3 - 6x^2 + 3x)$. **22.** $y = e^{3x}(2x^2 - x + \frac{1}{4})$. **23.** $y = x^2e^{2x}$. **24.** $\frac{1}{2}x^2 + \frac{1}{2}x - \frac{3}{4}$. **25.** $2x^3 - 12x^2 + 54x - 120$. **26.** $x^3 - 2x^2 - 12x + 2$. **27.** $y = \cos x + 2x\sin x$. **28.** $y = \sin 3x - 6x\cos 3x$. **29.** $y = (4x^2 - 2)\sin x + 4x\cos x$. **30.** $y = 12x \sin 2x + (3 - 8x^2)\cos 2x$. **32.** $y = e^{2x}/41$.

§53, page 105

1. $y = c_1 \sin x + c_2 \cos x - \cos x \ln(\sec x + \tan x)$. **2.** $y = (c_1 + x)\sin x + (c_2 + \ln \cos x)\cos x$. **3.** $y = c_1 \sin 2x + c_2 \cos 2x + \sin 2x \ln(\csc 2x - \cot 2x)$. **4.** $y = e^{-x}(c_1 + x)\sin x + e^{-x}(c_2 + \ln \cos x)\cos x$. **5.** $y = e^{2x}\left[c_1 + c_2x + \frac{x^{n+2}}{(n+1)(n+2)}\right]$, $n \neq -1$, $n \neq -2$; $y = e^{2x}(c_1 + c_2x + x\ln x)$, $n = -1$; $y = e^{2x}(c_1 + c_2x - \ln x)$, $n = -2$. **6.** $y = e^{-2x}(c_1 + c_2x - \ln x)$. **7.** $y = e^{-x}[c_1 + c_2x - \ln x - \frac{1}{2}(\ln x)^2]$. **8.** $y = e^x(c_1 + c_2x + c_3x^2 - 3x^{-1}\ln x - \frac{11}{2}x^{-1})$. **9.** $y = c_1 + c_2x^2 - 2\ln x$. **10.** $y = c_1x + c_2e^x - 1 - x\ln x$. **11.** $y = c_1e^{1/x} + c_2e^{-1/x} + 2e^{3/x}$.

§54, page 107

1. $x = 2 - (c_1 + c_2 + c_2t)e^t$, $y = (c_1 + c_2t)e^t - 2t - 4$. **2.** $x = e^{2t}(c_1 - 4t)$, $2y = (4t - c_1 + 2)e^{2t} + c_2$. **3.** $x = c_1e^t + c_2e^{-t} + c_3 \sin t + c_4 \cos t - 1$, $y = c_1e^t + c_2e^{-t} - c_3 \sin t - c_4 \cos t$. **4.** $x = (2c_1 + 2c_2t)e^t + (2c_3 + 2c_4t)e^{-t}$, $y = (c_2 - c_1 - c_2t)e^t - (c_3 + c_4 + c_4t)e^{-t}$. **5.** $x = (6c_2 - 2c_1 - 2c_2t)e^t - \frac{1}{3}(c_3e^{-3t/2} + 2)$, $y = (c_1 + c_2t)e^t + c_3e^{-3t/2} - t$. **6.** $y = c_1e^{\sqrt{3}t} + c_2e^{-\sqrt{3}t} + c_3 \sin(t/\sqrt{3}) + c_4 \cos(t/\sqrt{3}) + 2e^t$, $x =$

$-16e^t + (5D - 3D^3)y$. **7.** $2x = (23 - 13t)e^t + (23 + 13t)e^{-t} - 46$, $4y = (-36 + 13t)e^t - (36 + 13t)e^{-t} + 72$. **8.** $x = c_1 - 3c_2e^{2t} - 3c_3e^{-2t}$, $y = -2c_2e^{2t} + 2c_3e^{-2t}$, $z = c_2e^{2t} + c_3e^{-2t} + c_1$. **9.** $x = c_1e^{2t} + c_2e^{-t} + \frac{1}{2}$, $y = c_1e^{2t} - 2c_2e^{-t} + t - \frac{1}{2}$, $z = -2c_1e^{2t} + c_2e^{-t}$. **10.** $x = c_1e^t + c_2e^{-t} + \frac{1}{4}te^t$, $2y = -c_1e^t + (c_3 - c_2)e^{-t} - \frac{1}{4}te^t$, $z = c_1e^t - (c_2 + c_3)e^{-t} + \frac{1}{4}te^t + \frac{1}{4}e^t$.

§55, page 108

1. $y = c_1 \sin kx + c_2 \cos kx$. **2.** $y = c_1e^{ax} + c_2e^{-ax} + c_3 \sin ax + c_4 \cos ax$. **3.** $y = c_1e^{2x} + c_2e^{-2x} - 4$. **4.** $y = (c_1 + c_2x)e^{-x} + \frac{1}{2}x^2e^{-x}$. **5.** $y = c_1 + c_2x + c_3e^x$. **6.** $y = e^x(c_1 + c_2x + c_3x^2) + e^{-2x}(c_4 + c_5x)$. **7.** $y = e^{-x}(c_1 \sin \sqrt{2}\, x + c_2 \cos \sqrt{2}\, x)$. **8.** $y = c_1 + c_2x + c_3e^{3x} - (3x^3 + 3x^2)$. **9.** $y = c_1 + c_2e^{-2x} + c_3e^x - 2x^2 - 2x$. **10.** $y = ce^{-4x} + c_2e^{2x} - 2x + 1$. **11.** $y = 3e^{2x}$. **12.** $y = -x^2 + x + 1$. **13.** $y = x^2 + x + xe^x$. **14.** $y = e^{-x} - \frac{1}{2} \sin x$. **15.** $y = -5e^{2x} + 5e^{3x}$. **16.** $y = 1 + \cos x + \sin 2x$. **17.** $y = e^x(1 - 2 \sin x - \cos x)$. **18.** $y = e^{-x} + e^x(2x - 5)$. **19.** $y = e^{-x} - 6x - \sin 5x$. **20.** $y = e^x \cos 2x - e^{-x} \cos x$. **21.** $y = -2x \sin 2x + c_1 + c_2 \cos 2x + c_3 \sin 2x$. **22.** $y = \frac{1}{42}x^7e^x + (c_1 + c_2x)e^x$. **23.** $y = (8x^2 - 4x)e^{2x} + c_1e^{2x} + c_2e^{-2x}$. **24.** $y = e^x(c_1 \sin x + c_2 \cos x) - 3e^x \sin 3x$. **25.** $y = e^x[c_1 + c_2 \cos x + c_3 \sin x - x \cos x + \sin x \ln \cos x + \ln (\sec x + \tan x)]$. **26.** $y = e^x[c_1 \sin x + c_2 \cos x + \sin x \ln (\csc x - \cot x) - \cos x \ln (\sec x + \tan x)]$. **27.** $y = 3xe^x - 4xe^{-3x/2} + c_1e^x + c_2e^{-3x/2}$. **28.** $y = \frac{1}{6}e^x(x^3 - 3x^2) + c_1 + (c_2 + c_3x)e^x$. **29.** $y = e^x[(c_1 + c_2x) \cos \sqrt{2}\, x + (c_3 + c_4x) \sin \sqrt{2}\, x] + e^x \cos x$. **30.** $y = c_1 \sin 3x + c_2 \cos 3x + 2x \sin 3x$. **31.** $y = (c_1 + 6x^2) \sin 3x + (c_2 + 2x) \cos 3x$. **32.** $y = e^x(c_1 \sin x + c_2 \cos x) - 2xe^x \cos x$. **33.** $y = e^{-2x}(c_1 \cos x + c_2 \sin x) + 6xe^{-2x} \sin x$. **34.** $y = 2 \sin 2x \ln (\sec 2x + \tan 2x) - 4 + c_1 \sin 2x + c_2 \cos 2x$. **35.** $y = e^{2x} \ln x + c_1e^{2x} + c_2e^{-4x}$. **36.** $y = c_1 \sin x + c_2 \cos x + \sin x \ln x$. **37.** $y = c_1 \sin x + c_2 \cos x + \sin x \tan x$. **38.** $y = c_1x + c_2x^3 + 2/x$. **39.** $y = c_1e^{x^2} + c_2e^{-x^2} + 2e^{2x^2}$. **40.** $x = c_1e^{4t} - c_2e^{8t}$, $y = 3c_1e^{4t} + c_2e^{8t}$. **41.** $x = c_1e^{3t} + c_2e^{-t} + 0.4 \sin t - 0.2 \cos t$, $y = -2c_1e^{3t} + 2c_2e^{-t} + \frac{2}{5} \cos t + \frac{1}{5} \sin t$. **42.** $x = e^t(1 - c_2 - 2t) + c_3$, $y = e^t(4t + 2c_2 - 1) - c_3$, $z = e^t(1 - c_2 - 2t) + c_1$.

§58, page 114

1. $1/p + 6/p^4$. **2.** $\frac{1}{2}(2 + p)/(p^2 + 4)$. **3.** $(15 - 4p)/(p^2 - 9)$. **4.** $[4 - 3(p - 3)]/[(p - 3)^2 + 4]$. **5.** $[4 - 3(p - 2)]/[(p - 2)^2 + 16]$. **6.** $[7 + (p + 2)]/[(p + 2)^2 + 49]$. **7.** $\frac{1}{144}t^6 + 7e^{at}$. **8.** $3e^{mt} + 4e^{-mt}$. **9.** $\sin 3t$. **10.** $\cosh 3t$. **11.** $\sin 5t + 5 \cos 5t$. **12.** $e^{2t}(\cos 3t + \frac{2}{3} \sin 3t)$.

§59, page 116

7. $e^{mt} \cosh at$. **8.** $(1/a)e^{mt} \sinh at$. **9.** $e^{-mt} \cos at$. **10.** t^6e^{2t}. **11.** $e^{3t} \cos 4t$. **12.** $3e^{-5t} \sin 7t$. **13.** $\frac{1}{128}e^{3t}(\sin 4t - 4t \cos 4t)$. **14.** $te^{2t} \cos 4t$. **15.** $e^{-ct}[\cos at + \{(m - c)/a\} \sin at]$. **18.** $2/(p - a)^3$. **19.** $(6ap^2 - 2a^3)/(p^2 + a^2)^3$. **20.** $(6ap^2 + 2a^3)/(p^2 - a^2)^3$. **25.** $be^{at} \cos kt$. **26.** t^5e^{5t}. **27.** $\frac{7}{5}e^{-3t} \sinh 5t$. **28.** $e^{2t}(2 \cos 6t + 3 \sin 6t)$. **29.** $-\frac{1}{3}te^{-7t/3}(\cos \frac{1}{3}t + \sin \frac{1}{3}t)$. **30.** $-t^3e^{2t}(2 \cosh 4t + \frac{9}{2} \sinh 4t)$. **31.** $3/(p^2 + 9)$. **32.** $3/[(p + 2)^2 + 9]$. **33.** $-6(p + 2)/[(p + 2)^2 + 9]$. **34.** $1/p^4$. **35.** $1/(p - 5)^4$. **36.** $-4/(p - 5)^5$. **37.** $1/(p^2 - 1)$. **38.** $1/[(p + 1)^2 - 1]$. **39.** $[2(p + 1)^3 + 6(p + 1)]/[(p + 1)^2 - 1]^3$. **40.** $(p + 4)/[(p + 4)^2 - 1]$. **41.** $-[(p + 4)^2 + 1]/[(p + 4)^2 - 1]^2$. **42.** $[2(p + 4)^3 + 6(p + 4)]/[(p + 4)^2 - 1]^3$. **43.** $4/(p - 3)^3 + (36 + 24p - 4p^2)/(p^2 + 9)^2$.

§60, page 120

1. $\frac{1}{9}(e^{3t} - 3t - 1)$. **2.** $e^{4t} - 8t^2 - 4t - 1$. **3.** $e^{3t} - (t + 1)e^{2t}$. **4.** $\frac{1}{2}t - \frac{1}{4} \sin 2t$. **5.** $\frac{4}{9}e^{3t} - \frac{4}{9} - \frac{1}{3}t$. **6.** $\frac{3}{4}t + \frac{1}{2} - \frac{1}{2} \cos 2t + \frac{1}{8} \sin 2t$. **7.** $e^t + e^{2t}(\frac{1}{6}t^3 - \frac{1}{2}t^2 + t - 1)$. **8.** $\cos t - \frac{1}{2}t \sin t$. **9.** $\frac{1}{2}t \cos 2t + \cos 2t + \frac{1}{4} \sin 2t$. **10.** $1 - \cos 2t + \frac{3}{2} \sin 2t$. **11.**

$$\frac{1}{a^n} e^{at}\left[\frac{(at)^{n-1}}{(n-1)!} - \frac{(at)^{n-2}}{(n-2)!} + \frac{(at)^{n-3}}{(n-3)!} - \cdots + \frac{(-1)^{n-1}(at)^0}{0!}\right] + \frac{(-1)^n}{a^n}.$$ **12.** $$\frac{-ne^{at}(at)^n}{a^{n+1}n!} + \frac{(n+at)e^{at}}{a^{n+1}}\left[\frac{(at)^{n-1}}{(n-1)!} - \frac{(at)^{n-2}}{(n-2)!} + \cdots + \frac{(-1)^{n-1}(at)^0}{0!}\right] + \frac{(-1)^n(at+n)}{a^{n+1}}.$$ **13.** $\sin t - \cos t + e^{-2t}(\sin t + \cos t)$. **14.** $6 \cos 2t - 4 \sin 2t + \frac{1}{3}e^t(-18 \cos 3t + 14 \sin 3t)$.

§61, page 122

1. $e^t + 1 + t$. **2.** $\frac{7}{4}e^{2t} + \frac{1}{20}e^{-2t} - \frac{9}{5}e^{3t}$. **3.** $3t + 5 - 3 \sin t - 5 \cos t$.

§62, page 124

2. $y = 2e^t - 2$. **3.** $y = 2e^{-3t} - 2e^t$. **4.** $y = 3 + 3 \cos 2t - \frac{3}{2} \sin 2t$. **5.** $y = \frac{5}{9} - \frac{5}{9} \cos 3t$. **6.** $y = \frac{5}{2} \sin t - \frac{5}{2}t \cos t$. **7.** $y = 2t \sin 3t + 2 \cos 3t + \frac{5}{3} \sin 3t$. **8.** $y = 2 + e^{3t}(4 \sin 2t - 2 \cos 2t)$. **9.** $y = 3 + e^{3t}(\sin 2t - 2 \cos 2t)$. **10.** $y = 2e^{-t} \cos t + te^{-t} \sin t$. **11.** $y = 12e^t - (2t^3 + 6t^2 + 12t + 12)$. **12.** $y = e^{-t}(t^3 + 7t + 2)$. **13.** $y = 2 \cos t + \sin t$. **14.** $y = e^{3t}(\frac{36}{5}t - \frac{21}{25}) - \frac{54}{25}e^{-2t}$. **15.** $y = e^{2t}(\frac{1}{6}t + \frac{23}{72}) + \frac{5}{9}e^{-t} - \frac{7}{8}e^{-2t}$. **16.** $y = -\frac{2}{5}e^{-t} + \frac{2}{5} \cos 2t + \frac{4}{5} \sin 2t$. **17.** $y = -6 \cos 3t - 4 \sin 3t + e^{-t}(8 \cos 2t + 10 \sin 2t)$.

§63, page 125

2. $x = t - 2 \sin t$, $y = 2t + 2 \cos t$. **3.** $x = e^t$, $y = t$. **4.** $x = 3t + 2$, $y = \sin t$. **5.** $x = 2t$, $y = 2t - 2$. **6.** $x = t + 2e^t$, $y = 3e^t$. **7.** $x = te^t$, $y = e^t$. **8.** $x = 1 + \sin t$, $y = \cos t$. **9.** $x = 1 + t \sin t$, $y = t \cos t$. **10.** $x = Em/(H^2e)[1 - \cos (He/m)t]$, $y = (E/H)t - Em/(H^2e) \sin He/mt$.

§64, page 128

1. $-2e^t + 4e^{2t}$. **2.** $\frac{3}{2} - e^{-t} - \frac{1}{2}e^{-2t}$. **3.** $-\frac{4}{5} + \frac{9}{5}e^{5t}$. **4.** $\frac{7}{4}e^{2t} + \frac{1}{4}e^{-2t}$. **5.** $1 - 3e^t + 3e^{2t}$. **6.** $\frac{1}{5}e^{2t} - e^{-2t} + \frac{9}{5}e^{-3t}$. **7.** $-1 + \frac{5}{2}e^{-t} - \frac{3}{2}e^{-3t}$. **8.** $\frac{5}{12}e^{2t} - \frac{1}{3}e^t + \frac{1}{3}e^{-t} - \frac{5}{12}e^{-2t}$. **9.** $e^{-2t} - \frac{1}{2}e^{-3t/2}$. **10.** $-1 + \frac{1}{7}e^{2t} + \frac{13}{7}e^{-3t/2}$. **11.** $(1/m)(bm - an)/(mr - ln)e^{-nt/m} + (1/l)(bl - ar)/(ln - mr)e^{-rt/l}$. **12.** $y = 2e^{3t} + 3e^{-2t}$. **13.** $y = 2e^{-3t} + e^{-t}$. **14.** $y = 2e^t - e^{-4t}$. **15.** $y = 4 - 4e^{-2t} + 2e^{-4t}$. **16.** $x = 4e^{-t} + e^t$. **17.** $x = e^t + 3$, $y = 2e^t + 4$. **18.** $x = 4 - e^{2t}$, $y = 2e^{2t}$.

§65, page 130

1. (b) $$\frac{e^{rt}}{1}\left[\frac{(N/M)_r}{1!}\frac{t^3}{3!} + \frac{(N/M)_r^{(1)}}{1!}\cdot\frac{t^2}{2!} + \frac{(N/M)_r^{(2)}}{2!}\frac{t}{1!} + \frac{(N/M)_r^{(3)}}{3!}\cdot\frac{1}{1}\right].$$ **2.** $e^t(\frac{2}{3}t^3 + \frac{5}{2}t^2 + 4t + 1)$. **3.** $-2t^2 + 4t - 2 + 2e^{-2t}$. **4.** $-\frac{1}{4} + e^{2t}(\frac{2}{3}t^4 - \frac{1}{2}t^2 - \frac{1}{2}t + \frac{1}{4})$. **5.** $y = e^{2t} + te^t$. **6.** $y = 2 - 4t + e^{2t}$. **7.** $y = 1 - e^{-t}(\frac{1}{2}t^2 + t - 1)$. **8.** $y = (t^3 + 2t)e^{-2t}$. **9.** $y = e^t(6t^2 + 4t - 6) + 2t + 6$. **10.** $x = te^{-t}$, $y = 3t$.

§66, page 132

1. $e^{2t}(\cos 2t - 2 \sin 2t)$. **2.** $\frac{1}{2}(e^{2at}/a) \sin 2at$. **3.** $(e^{at}/b)[bm \cos bt + (ma + n) \sin bt]$. **4.** $1 - 2e^{-t} \sin t$. **5.** $e^{-t}(2 \cos t - 3) + 1$. **6.** $\frac{1}{4}e^t + e^t(\frac{3}{4} \cos 2t + \sin 2t)$. **7.** $e^{-t}[(t - 4) \cos t - (\frac{3}{2}t + 1) \sin t + 4]$. **8.** $\frac{1}{2}e^t(1 + t) \sin 2t$. **9.** $\frac{1}{2}(t \cos t + \sin t)$. **10.** $A_1 + iB_1 = [(N/M)/(p - a + bi)^3]^{(2)}_{a+bi}$, $A_2 + iB_2 = [(N/M)/(p - a + bi)^3]^{(1)}_{a+bi}$, $A_3 + iB_3 = [(N/M)/(p - a + bi)^3]_{a+bi}$. **11.** $y = 3 \sin t$. **12.** $y = 1 - \cos 2t + 2 \sin 2t$. **13.** $y = e^{2t}(\frac{7}{4} \cos 2t - 3 \sin 2t + \frac{1}{4})$. **14.** $y = -3t \cos 2t + \frac{3}{2} \sin 2t$. **15.** $y = t \sin 3t + \cos 3t$. **16.** $y = \frac{1}{8}e^{-3t}(5 \sin 2t - 26t \cos 2t)$. **17.** $y = 2(\cos t + \sin t) - 2 \cos 2t - \frac{1}{2} \sin 2t$. **21.** $\frac{1}{145}e^{-t}(4 \cos 3t - \frac{1}{3} \sin 3t) + \frac{1}{145}e^t(-4 \cos 2t + \frac{9}{2} \sin 2t)$.

§67, page 133

3. $(1/a^2)(1 - \cos at)$. **4.** $(1/a^4)(1 - \frac{1}{2}at \sin at - \cos at)$. **5.** $(e^{ct}/a^4)(1 - \frac{1}{2}at \sin at - \cos at)$. **6.** $(e^{ct}/a^5)(at + \frac{1}{2}at \cos at - \frac{3}{2} \sin at)$. **7.** $\frac{d^2}{dp^2} \frac{p}{p^2 + k^2}$. **8.** $\frac{k^2 - p^2}{p(p^2 + k^2)^2}$. **9.** $\frac{2k}{p^3(p^2 + k^2)}$. **10.** $y = 2e^t - 2t^2$. **11.** $2e^t \sin 3t + 2 \cos 3t$. **12.** $y = 4t^2 + 3 \cos t$. **13.** $y = 2 - 2e^{-2t} \sin 3t$. **14.** $y = 3t \cos 4t + 2t$. **15.** $y = 2te^{-t} \sin 3t + 4e^{-t} \cos 3t$. **16.** $y = t^6 - 6t^5 + 30t^4 - 120t^3 + 360t^2 - 720t + 721 - 721e^{-t}$. **17.** $y = te^{-t} + 3e^{3t} + 2e^{-3t}$. **18.** $y = -2t \sin 2t - 3 \cos 2t$. **19.** $x = 2 - (1 + 3t)e^t$, $y = (-2 + 3t)e^t - 2t - 4$. **20.** $x = 2te^t + (4 - 2t)e^{-t}$, $y = (1 - t)e^t - (1 - t)e^{-t}$.

§68, page 137

1. 5 ft, $\frac{1}{6}$ sec, 6 cycles/sec, $\frac{5}{72}$ sec, $\frac{11}{72}$ sec. **2.** $\pi/16$ sec, $16/\pi$ cycles/sec, 13 ft. **3.** $y = 5 \sin 10t + 10 \cos 10t$, $5/\pi$ cycles/sec, $\pi/5$ sec, $\sqrt{125}$ ft. **4.** $\frac{1}{60}$ sec, 60 cycles/sec. **5.** $k^2 < 120$. **6.** 1.99 sec, $e^{-0.05t}$, 13.9 sec. **7.** $b = \frac{1}{5}$, $c = (120\pi)^2$ nearly. **8.** $b = 0.046$, $c = 400\pi^2$ nearly.

§69, page 138

1. (*a*) 4. (*b*) 1. (*c*) 5. **2.** (*a*) Damped. (*b*) Critical. (*c*) Overdamped. **3.** (*a*) ± 8. (*b*) $-4\pi 10^6$, $4\pi 10^6 + \frac{1}{2}\pi$.

§72, page 144

2. $s = 0.4 \cos 10t + 0.32$, 0.4 ft, $\pi/5$ sec, $f = 5/\pi$ cycles/sec. **3.** $x = e^{-0.01t}(0.0004 \sin 10t + 0.4 \cos 10t) + 0.32$, $\pi/5$ sec, $5/\pi$ cycles/sec, $e^{-0.01t}$, 69.3 sec. **4.** (*a*) $x = -0.6 \sin 10t + 0.4 \cos 10t + \sin 6t + 0.32$. (*b*) $\pi/5$ sec, $\pi/3$ cycles/sec, π. (*c*) 0.210 ft. **5.** $x = a \cos \sqrt{g/h}\, t$. **6.** $x = 4 \sin (\sqrt{3g}\, t) - 3.46 \sin (2 \sqrt{g}\, t)$, 3.80 ft. **7.** $x = \frac{1}{2} \sin (2 \sqrt{g}\, t) - \sqrt{g}\, t \cos (2 \sqrt{g}\, t)$, 157 ft below initial position. No. **8.** $2\pi(\sqrt{I/k})$. **9.** $I = g/(16\pi^2)$ lb-ft². **10.** $\theta = e^{-0.0693t}(c_1 \sin 12.6t + c_2 \cos 12.6t)$, 0.5 sec. **11.** 656 lb. **12.** 0.886 sec, $0.886\rho^{-\frac{1}{2}}$ sec. **13.** $2\pi \sqrt{l/g}$. **14.** $x = e^{-1.08t}(0.111 \sin 9.77t + \cos 9.77t)$, 0.643 sec. **15.** 21.1 min. **16.** (*a*) 5.4×10^7 ton-ft². (*b*) 9.9 sec. **17.** $x = 48 \sin 10t + 2\sqrt{6} \sin \sqrt{600}\, t$, $y = 24 \sin 10t - 4\sqrt{6} \sin \sqrt{600}\, t$. **19.** (*c*) k small. (*d*) Decreased. (*e*) Violent.

§73, page 149

1. $x = v_0 \cos \varphi \cdot t$, $y = v_0 \sin \varphi \cdot t - \frac{1}{2}gt^2$. **2.** $x = 130{,}000(1 - e^{-0.02t})$, $y = 155{,}500(1 - e^{-0.02t}) - 1{,}610t$, maximum y = 22,000 ft. **3.** $x = 49{,}800(1 - e^{-0.04t})$, $y = 174.3t - 16.1t^2$. **4.** $x = 347t$, $y = 118{,}000(1 - e^{-0.0268t}) - 1{,}200t$, 30,000 ft, 27,000 ft. **5.** $x = a \cos (\sqrt{k/m}\, t)$, $y = v_0 \sqrt{m/k} \sin (\sqrt{k/m}\, t)$. **6.** (*a*) $x = 3 \sin t$, $y = 2 \cos t - 2$. (*b*) $x = 2.12 \sin t$, $y = 2.12 \sin t + 2 \cos t - 2$. **7.** 2,120 ft. **8.** 300 ft/sec, 10,600 ft.

§75, page 154

2. $q = CE[1 - \cos (t/\sqrt{LC})]$, $i = CE/\sqrt{LC} \sin (t/\sqrt{LC})$, $2\pi \sqrt{LC}$, CE, $2\pi \sqrt{LC}$, $E \sqrt{C/L}$. **5.** $q = \epsilon^{-5t}/1{,}600(-\sin 200t - 40 \cos 200t) + \frac{1}{40}$, $i = 5.00\epsilon^{-5t} \sin 200t$, 0.460 sec, $\frac{1}{40}$, 0. **6.** $q = 200\epsilon^{-\frac{1}{2}t}(-2 - t) + 400$, $i = 100t\epsilon^{-\frac{1}{2}t}$. **7.** $q = q_0 \cos (t/\sqrt{LC})$, $i = dq/dt$. **8.** $q = -CE \cos (t/\sqrt{LC}) + CE$, $i = E\sqrt{C/L} \sin (t/\sqrt{LC})$. **9.** $q = (q_0/\omega_1)e^{-at}(\omega_1 \cos \omega_1 t + a \sin \omega_1 t)$, $i = dq/dt$.

§77, page 156

2. $i = -E/Z^2(X \cos \omega t - R \sin \omega t)$. **3.** $q = -0.00275(3 \sin 400t + \cos 400t)$, $i = 1.10(\sin 400t - 3 \cos 400t)$; 0.0087 coulomb, 3.48 amp. **4.** (a) $i = -E/(L\omega) \cos \omega t$. (b) $i = E/R \sin \omega t$. (c) $q = CE \sin \omega t$. (d) $q = EC/(1 + R^2C^2\omega^2)(\sin \omega t - RC\omega \cos \omega t)$, $i = EC\omega/(1 + R^2C^2\omega^2)(\cos \omega t + RC\omega \sin \omega t)$. (e) $i = E/(R^2 + L^2\omega^2)(R \sin \omega t - L\omega \cos \omega t)$. (f) $q = CE/(1 - LC\omega^2) \sin \omega t$, $i = CE\omega/(1 - LC\omega^2) \cos \omega t$. **5.** $i = 10 \sin 500t(1 - \epsilon^{-5t})$, 0.0067 sec. **6.** 4.2×10^{-7} farad, 1.000018.

§78, page 159

1. $i_2 = E/R \sin \omega t$, $i_1 = E/(L\omega)(1 - \cos \omega t)$, $i = i_1 + i_2$. **2.** $i_1 = E/R \sin \omega t$, $q = CE \sin \omega t$, $i_2 = CE\omega \cos \omega t$, $i = i_1 + i_2$. **4.** $i_2 = 2 \sin 400t$. $160{,}100q = 40\epsilon^{-10t} + \sin 400t - 40 \cos 400t$, $i_1 = dq/dt$. **6.** $i = \frac{1}{12}(1 - \cos 300t) + 10t \sin 300t$. **7.** $i = [(C_1E_1 + C_2E_2)\omega]/[1 - L(C_1 + C_2)\omega^2][\cos \omega t - \cos t/\sqrt{L(C_1 + C_2)}]$. **9.** (a) 100 per cent nearly. (b) 100 per cent nearly. (c) 89 per cent. (d) Less than 20 per cent. **10.** $q_1 = a/[\omega_1(\omega_1^2 - \omega^2)](\omega_1 \sin \omega t - \omega \sin \omega_1 t)$, $i_2 = Ma\omega/[L_2(\omega^2 - \omega_1^2)](\cos \omega t - \cos \omega_1 t)$.

§79, page 161

1. 2π sec, $\frac{1}{2}\pi^{-1}$ cycle/sec, 5 ft. **2.** $x = 2e^{-t/2} \sin 3t$, 2.09 sec, 0.223. **3.** $a = 2$, $x = 2e^{-t/3} \sin 3t$, 2.09 sec. **4.** $b = 13.86$, $c = 14{,}400\pi^2$ nearly. **5.** $c = 0.000025$. **6.** (a) $b^2 - |4ac| > 0$. (b) $b^2 - 4ac = 0$. (c) $b^2 - 4ac < 0$. (d) $b = 0$. **8.** $w/20$, 93.7 ft. **9.** Rises 2.02 sec, then falls. Speed approaches 80.5 ft/sec downward. **10.** 0.815 sec. **11.** $q = q_0 \cos (t/\sqrt{LC})$, $i = -(q_0/\sqrt{LC}) \sin (t/\sqrt{LC})$. **12.** $q = 0.05\epsilon^{-5t} \cos 200t$, $i = \epsilon^{-5t}(-10 \sin 200t - 0.25 \cos 200t)$, $\frac{1}{100}\pi$, 0, 0. **13.** $q = 1 - \frac{1}{2}\epsilon^{-t/2}(2 - t)$. **14.** $i = \epsilon^{-50t}(3.04 \sin 312t - \cos 312t) + 1$. **15.** $y = 2(\sin 2t - 4 \cos 2t) + \epsilon^{-t}(-2 \sin 2t + 8 \cos 2t)$. **16.** $i_1 = E/(L_1\omega)(1 - \cos \omega t) + L_2E/(R_2L_1) \sin \omega t$, $i_2 = -[ME/(L_1R_2)] \sin \omega t$. **17.** $x = g/192(-\cos 8t - 8 \cos 4t + 9)$, $y = g/96(\cos 8t - 4 \cos 4t + 3)$.

§81, page 164

1. $y = 2x^3 + c_1x + c_2$. **2.** $y = 6 \ln x + c_1x^2 + c_2x + c_3$. **3.** $y = c_1 \ln x + c_2$. **4.** $y = c_1x + c_1^2 \ln (x - c_1) + c_2$. **5.** $y = -4x^3 + 2x - 26$. **6.** $y = \frac{1}{5}(3x^5 - 5x^4 + 10x - 8)$. **7.** $y = a^3 \sinh x/a - 2a^2x$.

§82, page 166

1. $y^2 = c_1x + c_2$. **2.** $x = c_1y - \ln y + c_2$, $y = c_3$. **3.** $y^3 = c_1x + c_2$, $y = c$. **4.** $e^y(y - 1) = Rx + c$. **5.** $\sqrt{cs^2 - 1} = \pm ct + c_1$. **6.** $\ln (8e^s + \sqrt{64e^{2s} - c}) = \pm 8t + c_1$. **7.** $y = 1 + \sin \sqrt{8}\, x$. **8.** $10e^s + \sqrt{576 + 100e^{2s}} = 36e^{10t}$. **9.** $e^{-\frac{1}{2}y} = \cos (x/2)$. **11.** $y = \cosh x$.

§83, page 168

3. $xy = c_1(x^2 - 2x + 2) + c_2e^{-x}$. **4.** $(D + x + 1)(D - x)$. **5.** $(xD - 2)(xD + x + 1)$. **6.** $y + 12x = c_1x^2 + c_2$. **7.** $y = 12x^2 + c_1x \ln x + c_2x$. **8.** $xy = (x + c_1)e^x + c_2$. **9.** $x^2y = (x^2 + c)e^{x^2} + c_1$. **10.** $y = 2x^2 - 2x + 1 + c_1(2x - 1) + c_2e^{-2x}$. **11.** $y = c_1(2x - 1) + c_2e^{-2x}$. **12.** $y = c_1(x + 1)e^{-3x} + c_2e^{-2x}$. **13.** $(xD + 1)(D + x)$. **14.** $y \sin x = \frac{1}{2}e^x(\sin x - \cos x) + c_1e^{-x}(\sin x + \cos x) + c_2$.

§84, page 170

1. $y = c_1x^{-1} + c_2x^{-2} + c_3x^3$. **2.** $y = c_1x^3 + c_2x^{-3} + [1/(n^2 - 9)]x^n$. **3.** $y = c_1(x - 1) + c_2(x - 1)^2 + c_3(x - 1)^{-2} + \ln [e(x - 1)]$. **4.** $y = c_1 + c_2x + c_3 \ln x$.

§85, page 171

1. $y = c_1x + c_2\sqrt{x^2 - 1}$. **2.** $xy = c_1e^{-x}(x^2 + 2x + 2) + c_2$. **3.** $y = c_1(x^2 - 1) + c_2x + 3x^2 + x^4$. **4.** $y = (x^4 + c_2)e^x + c_1(x^3 + 3x^2 + 6x + 6)$. **5.** $y = \sin x \ln [c_1 \sin x(\csc x - \cot x)^c]$.

§86, page 171

1. $y = x^4 + c_1 \ln x + c_2$. **2.** $y = c_1xe^x + c_2$. **3.** $4y = 5 \ln (1 + 3 \tan \frac{1}{2}x) - \ln (\tan \frac{1}{2}x + 3)$. **4.** $y = \ln |2.6 \cos (\tan^{-1} 2.4 - 10x)|$. **5.** $y = 1 - e^{-x}$. **6.** $y = a^2 \sinh (x/a) - 2ax$. **7.** $y = c_1x + (c_2 - x^2)xe^{-x^2}$. **8.** $y = (x^2 + c_1x + c_2)e^{x^2}$. **9.** $y = (x + c_1e^{-x} + c_2)e^{x^2/2}$. **10.** $xy = c_1(x^2 - 2x + 2) + c_2e^{-x}$. **11.** $y = c_1x^{\frac{4}{3}} + c_2x^{-1} - 4 \ln x + \frac{4}{3}$. **12.** $y = c_1 + c_2 \sin (\sqrt{3} \ln x) + c_3 \cos (\sqrt{3} \ln x) - \frac{1}{6} (\ln x) \sin (\sqrt{3} \ln x)$. **13.** $y = c_1\{4x^2 \ln [x/(2x + 1)] + 2x - \frac{1}{2}\} + c_2x^2$. **14.** $y = ce^{-4x}(7x + 1) + c_2e^{3x}$. **15.** $(v - v_1)/(v - v_0) = [r_0(r - r_1)]/[r_1(r - r_0)]$.

§87, page 174

1. $(x - c_1)^2 + y^2 = c_2^2$. **2.** $y = c_1 \cosh (x/c_1 + c_2)$. **3.** $(c_1x + c_2)^2 = k(c_1y^2 - 1)$. **4.** $c_1x = \cosh (c_1y + c_2)$. **5.** $x^2 + (y - c_1)^2 = c_2^2$. **6.** $(y - c_1)^2 = 4c_2(x - c_2)$. **7.** $(x - c_1)^2 + (y - c_2)^2 = a^2$. **8.** $e^{x/a} = c_1 \sin (y/a + c_2)$.

§88, page 175

1. $2Hy = wx^2$. **2.** $H(d^2y/dx^2) = w_1 + w_2\sqrt{1 + (dy/dx)^2}$. **3.** $y = c \cosh \sqrt{w/H}\, x$. **4.** $2Hy = wlx^2$. **6.** $y = a \cosh \sqrt{w/H}\, x$. **7.*** $y = (c + kt) \cosh (\sqrt{w/H}\, x) - kt$. **8.*** $x = w \int_c^y \frac{(c^2 + 2H/w - y^2)\, dy}{\sqrt{4H^2 - w^2(c^2 + 2H/w - y^2)^2}}$. **9.*** Like Ans. (8) with y replaced by $y + kt$. **10.** $x_0 = a \tanh^{-1} (b/l)$, $y_0 = l \coth (c/a) - a$, where a satisfies $l^2 - b^2 = a^2 \sinh^2 (c/a)$.

§89, page 179

1. $y = w/(24EI)(2lx^3 - x^4 - l^3x)$; maximum deflection $= 5wl^4/(384EI)$. **2.** $y = P/(EI)(\frac{1}{12}x^3 - \frac{1}{16}l^2x)$; maximum deflection $= Pl^3/(48EI)$. **3.** $5wl^4/(384EI) + \frac{1}{48}Pl^3/(EI)$. **4.** (a) 0.889 in. (b) 1.067 in. (c) 1.956 in. **5.** (a) $y = P/(6EI)(-3lx^2 + x^3)$. (b) $y = -w/(24EI)(x^4 - 4lx^3 + 6l^2x^2)$. (c) y equals the sum of the y's from (a) and (b). **6.** $y = -w/(48EI)(2x^4 - 5lx^3 + 3l^2x^2)$; 0.578. **7.** $y = P/(48EI)(4x^3 - 3lx^2)$. **8.** $y_1 = Px/(18EI)(x^2 - 8a^2)$, $y_2 = P/(18EI)[x^3 - 3(x - 2a)^3 - 8a^2x]$, $(16\sqrt{6}\, Pa^3)/(81EI)$. **9.** $\frac{16}{147}Pa^3$. **10.** $kl^5/(30EI)$. **11.** $y = Pb^2x^2/(6l^3EI)[(3a + b)x - 3al]$, $x \leqq a$.

§90, page 182

2. Equation of graph $y = G/P[1 - \cos (4\pi x/l)]$ from $x = 0$ to $x = l$. **4.** Equation of graph $y = -a[1 - \cos (\frac{3}{2}\pi x/l)]$, $0 \leqq x \leqq l$.

§91, page 185

1. $\frac{1}{3}a^{\frac{3}{2}}(2 - 1/\sqrt{2})$. **2.** $a^2/\sqrt{k}$. **4.** $\rho = 2e^{2t} - e^{-2t} - \frac{1}{4}$, $\theta = 2t$; $a_\theta = 16e^{2t} + 8e^{-2t}$. **5.** $\rho = t + 1$, $\theta = 2t/(t + 1)$, $F_\rho = 4W/g(t + 1)^3$. **7.** $\rho = 2/(1 + \cos \theta)$. **8.** $\rho = 1/[n - (n - 1) \cos \theta]$. (a) Ellipse. (b) Parabola. (c) Hyperbola. (d) Straight line perpendicular to the initial line. (e) Circle of radius 1. (f) Hyperbola. (g) Ellipse. **9.** $\rho = 2b/[(2 - n) \cos \theta + n]$. (a) Parabola. (b) Circle. **10.** (a) $x = 30{,}000/g \ln (154g/30{,}000t + 1)$, $y = -30{,}000/g \ln \cosh (gt/\sqrt{30{,}000})$. (b) 15.3 sec. (c) 1,170 ft.

* c is the depth of material over the highest point of the arch, and t is the thickness of the top layer.

§92, page 186

1. $e^{-r} = c_1 + c_2\theta$. **2.** $y = 5t^2, x = 5(t\sqrt{1-t^2} + \sin^{-1} t)$. **3.** $EIy = \frac{1}{360}wx(-7l^4 + 10l^2x^2 - 3x^4)$. **4.** (a) $EIy = \frac{1}{240}wx^2(-7l^3 + 9l^2x - 2x^3)$. (b) $EIy = \frac{1}{120}wx^2(-2l^3 + 3l^2x - x^3)$. **6.** For highest point $t = 2c^{-\frac{3}{2}}[\frac{1}{2}v_0Rc^{\frac{1}{2}} + gR^2 \sin^{-1}(v_0/\sqrt{2gR})]$, where $c = 2Rg - v_0^2$. **7.** $\rho^{n+1} \cos[(n+1)\theta + c_1] = c_2$.

§94, page 188

1. (a) $dy/dx = z, dz/dx = -x^2z - x^3y$. (b) $dx/1 = dy/z = dz/(-Pz - Qy)$. (c) $x_1 = dx/dt, y_1 = dy/dt, y_2 = dy_1/dt, dx_1/dt = 3x - 3y - 2y_2, dy_2/dt = 3x - y_2$. **3.** $y = -\frac{1}{2}x^2 \ln x - \ln x + c_1x^2 + c_2$. **4.** $y = -x + \int c_1e^{-x^2/2}\,dx + c_2$. **5.** $y_1 = dy/dx$; $y_i = dy_{i-1}/dx$, $i = 2, 3, \ldots, n-1$; $a_0\,dy_{n-1}/dx = -a_1y_{n-1} - a_2y_{n-2} - \cdots - a_ny - f(x) = 0$. n constants.

§95, page 190

2. No. $dy/dx = y/x$ is not defined when $x = 0$. **3.** $y = 0$. **4.** dy/dx undefined and $\frac{\partial}{\partial y}\left(\frac{dy}{dx}\right)$ undefined. No, for $3y/x$ has no value at (0,0). **5.** Yes. $y = 2x + 5$, $z + 2e^x + 3x + 8 = 0$. **6.** No. **7.** There is a unique solution $y = \varphi(x)$ through (x_0,y_0) which has dy/dx at (x_0,y_0) equal to $\varphi'(x_0)$, provided that $Q(x)/P(x)$ and $R(x)/P(x)$ are continuous and single-valued in $|x - x_0| < b, b > 0$. **8.** If an initial condition requires that $y = y_0$ and $d^2y/dx^2 = 0$ when $x = x_0$, then $c_1 = -2x_0$. d^3y/dx^3 does not exist when $x = x_0$ and $c = -2x_0$.

§96, page 193

1. $x^2 - y^2 = c_1, x + y = c_2z$. **2.** $bx^2 - ay^2 = c_1, cy^2 - bz^2 = c_2$. **3.** $y = c_1x, 2x - 2y = z^2 + c_2$. **4.** $y^2 + z^2 = c_1, \ln c_2x = \tan^{-1}(y/z)$. **5.** $x - y = c_1(x - z) = c_2(y - z)$. **6.** $x^2 - y^2 = c_1, (x + y)(z - 1) = c_2(z + 1)$. **7.** $x^2 + y^2 + z^2 = c_1y, y = c_2z$. **8.** $x + y + z = c_1, xyz = c_2$. **9.** $xy - z = c_1, x^2 - y^2 + z^2 = c$. **10.** $x - y - z = c_1, x^2 - y^2 = cz^2$. **11.** $lx + my + nz = c_1, x^2 + y^2 + z^2 = c_2$. **12.** $x + y - z = c_1, xy - z^{-1} = c_2$. **13.** $x^2 - y^2 = c_1, z^2 - w^2 = c_2, x + y = c_3(z + w)$. **14.** $x - y = c_1, x + y + z + w = c_2, x^2 + y^2 + z^2 + w^2 = c_3$. **15.** $y = c_1 \sin 2x + c_2 \cos 2x + \frac{5}{2}, 5z = (2c_1 + c_2) \cos 2x + (c_1 - 2c_2) \sin 2x - 10x + \frac{5}{2}$. **16.** $y = c_1 + c_2e^{2x} - 4e^x, z = -c_1 + c_2e^{2x} - 2e^x$. **17.** $y = c_1e^{2x} + c_2e^{-2x} - 3x, 3z = 3c_1e^{2x} - c_2e^{-2x} - 3 - 3x - 6x^2$. **18.** $y = c_1 \sin x + c_2 \cos x - \frac{1}{3}a \sin 2x, 2z = (c_1 - c_2) \cos x - (c_1 + c_2) \sin x - \frac{2}{3}a(\cos 2x + \sin 2x)$. **19.** Sufficient conditions that a solution through (x_0,y_0,z_0) exist are $y' = (P_2R_1 - P_1R_2)/(Q_1R_2 - Q_2R_1)$ and $z' = (P_1Q_2 - P_2Q_1)/(Q_1R_2 - Q_2R_1)$, and their partial derivatives with respect to y and to z are continuous and single-valued in regions defined by $|x - x_0| \leqq a$, $|y - y_0| \leqq b$, $|z - z_0| \leqq c$, where a, b, and c are positive constants.

§97, page 197

1. $y = x(z^2 + c)$. **2.** $2y - z = ce^{-x/2}$. **3.** $4xy = 2z - 1 + ce^{-2z}$. **4.** $y = xz^2(3z + c)$. **5.** $(x^2 + y^2)e^z + z = c$. **6.** $x^2y^2z + y = c$. **7.** $(x^2 - xyz)e^z = c$. **8.** $z^2(x + y) = z \cos z - \sin z + c$. **9.** $xy(1 + z)^2 = 2z^2 + \frac{4}{3}z^3 + c$. **10.** $x \sin z + y \cos z = (c + \ln \cos z)e^{-z}$. **11.** $xy + xz + yz = cx$. **12.** (a) $M_y - N_x = MN_z - NM_z$. (b) $M_y = N_x$. **13.** $ax^2 + 2(a + 2b)xy + 2by^2 - 2cx = c_1$.

§99, page 200

1. $z = mx, z = ny$. **2.** $xz = m, z^3y = n$. **3.** $x^3y^2 = m, x^2z = n$. **4.** $x^2 - y^2 = m, z^2 - y^2 = n$. **5.** $x^2 + xy + yz = c$. **6.** $z^2x - y = cx$. **7.** $xy = c(3 - z)$, and $z = 3$.

8. $y = cx^2$. **9.** $x^2 + y^2 - z^2 = c$. **10.** $x^2 = cy^3$, $z^3x = c$; $3x^2 + 2y^2 - z^2 = c$. **11.** $bx^2 - ay^2 = c_1$, $cx^2 - az^2 = c_2$; $x^a y^b z^c = c_1$. **12.** $x = c_1 y$, $z + 2x^2 + 2y^2 = c_2 y^3$; $8(x^2 + y^2) = 3 - 12z + ce^{-4z}$. **13.** $bx^2 - ay^2 = c_1$, $cx^2 - az^2 = c_2$; $x^a y^b z^c = c_1$. **14.** (a) $r_1 + r_2 = cr_1r_2$, where r_1 and r_2 are the respective distances of (x,y) from $(-a,0,0)$ and $(+a,0,0)$. (b) $r_1 - r_2 = cr_1r_2$. **15.** $(x + a)r_2 + (x - a)r_1 = c_1r_1r_2$, $z = c_2y$.

§100, page 200

1. $y_1 = Dy$, $y_2 = Dy_1$, $Dz = z_1$, $Dz_1 = -(x-3)y_2/(x-4)$, $Dy_2 = [x(3-x)y_2 + (y+2z)(4-x)]/[x(x-2)(x-4)]$; 0, 2, 4. **2.** (a) Yes. (b) No. (c) No. (d) Yes. **3.** (a), (b), (d). **4.** (b) $(x-y)^2 = 3\cos z + \sin z + ce^{-3z}$. (d) $x^2y^3 = cz$. **5.** $x(y + z^3) = cz^2$. **6.** $x + y + z = c_1$, $x^2 + y^2 + z^2 = c_2$. **7.** $y = c_1e^x + c_2e^{-x} - x - 1$, $z = c_1e^x - c_2e^{-x} - x - 1$. **8.** $y = e^x(c_1 \sin x + c_2 \cos x) + x + 2$, $z = e^x(c_1 \cos x - c_2 \sin x) - 3x - 1$. **9.** $y = c_1 z^{\sqrt{2}} + c_2 z^{-\sqrt{2}}$, $x = c_1(1 + \sqrt{2})z^{\sqrt{2}} + c_2(1 - \sqrt{2})z^{-\sqrt{2}}$; $x^2 + 2xy - y^2 + z^2 = c$. **10.** $x = c_1y^3$, $y^2(4z^2 - 3x^2 - 4y^2) = c_2$; $(6x^2 + 4y^2)z^2 = z^4 + c$. **11.** $y = cz$, $2x\sqrt{y^2 + z^2} = c_1(x^2 - y^2 - z^2 - a^2)$; $(x^2 + y^2 + z^2 + a^2)^2 - 4a^2x^2 = c$. **12.** $z = c_1y$, $r_2^3[2(x+a)^2 + 3y^2 + 3z^2](x + a) + r_1^3[2(x-a)^2 + 3y^2 + 3z^2](x - a) = c_2r_1^3r_2^3(y^2 + z^2)^2y^{-4}$; $r_1^{-3} + r_2^{-3} = c$.

§101, page 203

1. $5/(n+5)!$. **6.** (a) $-3 < x < 3$. (b) $|x - 3| < 2$ or $1 < x < 5$. (c) All values.

§102, page 207

1. $y = c_0\left(1 + x + \frac{x^2}{2!} + \cdots + \frac{x^n}{n!} + \cdots\right) = c_0 \sum_{n=0}^{\infty} \frac{x^n}{n!}$. **2.** $y = c_0 \sum_{n=0}^{\infty} \frac{x^{2n}}{n!}$.

3. $y = c_0\left(1 + \frac{x^4}{3 \cdot 4} + \frac{x^8}{3 \cdot 4 \cdot 7 \cdot 8} + \cdots\right) + c_1\left(x + \frac{x^5}{4 \cdot 5} + \frac{x^9}{4 \cdot 5 \cdot 8 \cdot 9} + \cdots\right)$.

4. $y = c_0 \sum_{n=0}^{\infty} (-1)^n(2n+1)x^{2n} + c_1 \sum_{n=0}^{\infty} (-1)^n(2n+2)x^{2n+1}$. **5.** $y = c_1(x - x^3) + c_2 \sum_{n=0}^{\infty} \frac{3}{(2n-1)(2n-3)} x^{2n}$. **6.** $y = c_0x^2 + c_1x^3$. **7.** $y = c_0 \sum_{n=0}^{\infty} (2n+1)(x-1)^{2n} + c_1 \sum_{n=0}^{\infty} (n+1)(x-1)^{2n+1}$. **8.** $y = c_0 \sum_{n=0}^{\infty} (n+1)(2n+1)(x+1)^{2n} + c_1 \sum_{n=0}^{\infty} (n+1)(2n+3)(x+1)^{2n+1}$. **9.** $y = c_0 + c_1x + \frac{c_0x^2}{2!} + \frac{(c_1 + c_0)x^3}{3!} + \frac{(3c_0 + 2c_1)x^4}{4!} + \cdots$.
10. $y = c_0 + c_1x - \frac{1}{6}(c_0 + c_1)x^3 - \frac{1}{12}c_1x^4 + \frac{3}{40}(c_0 + c_1)x^5 + \cdots$. **11.** $y = -x^{-3} - x^{-4} + 24 \sum_{n=5}^{\infty} (-1)^{n-1} \frac{x^{-n}}{n!}$. **12.** $c_0e^{-x^2/2}$, $c_2(1 - 2x^2)e^{-x^2/2}$, $c_3(x - \frac{2}{3}x^3)e^{-x^2/2}$. **13.** $y = c_0 \sum_{n=0}^{\infty} \frac{(-1)^n 2^n n!}{(2n)!} x^{2n} + c_1x + \frac{1 - 3c_1}{3} \sum_{n=1}^{\infty} \frac{(-1)^{n+1}x^{2n+1}}{2^n n!}$.

§103, page 209

1. $y = a_0 \sum_{n=0}^{\infty} \frac{(4x)^n}{(2n)!} + a_1 x^{\frac{1}{2}} \sum_{n=0}^{\infty} \frac{(4x)^n}{(2n+1)!}$. **2.** $y = A(1 + 2x^2 + 3x^4 + 4x^6 + \cdots) + Bx^{-1}(1 + 3x^2 + 5x^4 + 7x^6 + \cdots)$. **3.** $y = A\left(\frac{1}{2} + \frac{1 \cdot 4}{5!}x^3 + \frac{1 \cdot 4 \cdot 7}{8!}x^6 + \cdots\right) + Bx^{-2}\left(1 + \frac{2x^3}{3!} + \frac{2 \cdot 5}{6!}x^6 + \cdots\right)$. **4.** $y = Ax^2\left(1 - \frac{2 \cdot 2}{5}x + \frac{3 \cdot 2^2}{5 \cdot 6}x^2 - \cdots\right) + B\left(\frac{1}{x^2} - \frac{4}{3x} + \frac{2}{3}\right)$. **6.** $y = Ax^{-1} + B\left(1 + \frac{x^2}{3} + \frac{x^4}{5} + \cdots\right)$. **7.** $y = A(x + 1) + B(x^2 + x^3 + x^4 + \cdots)$. **8.** $y = A\left(1 - \frac{x^{-2}}{3!} - \frac{x^{-4}}{5!} - \frac{3x^{-6}}{7!} - \cdots\right) + B(x - x^{-1})$.

12. $$y = A\left(1 - \frac{2a^3x^3}{5!} + \frac{2a^6x^6}{8!} - \cdots\right) + Bx^{-1}\left(1 - \frac{a^3x^3}{4!} + \frac{a^6x^6}{7!} - \cdots\right) + Cx^{-2}\left(1 - \frac{a^3x^3}{3!} + \frac{a^6x^6}{6!} + \cdots\right).$$

13. $$y = x^{\frac{3}{2}} \sum_{n=0}^{\infty} \frac{4^{n+1}x^{2n}}{[1 \cdot 5 \cdot 9 \cdots (4n+1)]^2(4n+5)}.$$

§104, page 213

1. $$y = c_0x - c_1x \ln x + c_1\left(1 + x - \sum_{n=2}^{\infty} \frac{x^n}{n-1}\right).$$

2. $$y = (c_0 + c_1 \ln x)(1 + 2x + x^2) + c_1\left[-3x - 3x^2 + \sum_{n=3}^{\infty} \frac{(-1)^n 2x^n}{n(n-1)(n-2)}\right].$$

3. $$y = (c_0 + c_1 \ln x) \sum_{n=0}^{\infty} \left(\frac{x}{2}\right)^{2n} \frac{1}{(n!)^2} - c_1 \sum_{n=1}^{\infty} \left(\frac{x}{2}\right)^{2n} \frac{1}{(n!)^2} \sum_{k=1}^{n} \frac{1}{k}.$$

4. $$y = (c_0 + c_1 \ln x) \sum_{n=1}^{\infty} \frac{x^n}{(n-1)!n!} + c_1\left[1 - \sum_{n=1}^{\infty} \frac{x^n}{(n-1)!n!}\left(\frac{1}{n} + \sum_{k=1}^{n-1} \frac{2}{k}\right)\right].$$

5. $$y = (c_0 + c_1 \ln x) \sum_{n=0}^{\infty} \frac{(-1)^n x^n}{(n!)^2} - c_1 \sum_{n=1}^{\infty} \frac{(-1)^n x^n}{(n!)^2} \sum_{k=1}^{n} \frac{2}{k}.$$

6. $$y = (c_0 + c_1 \ln x) \sum_{n=0}^{\infty} \frac{x^{3n}}{3^{2n}(n!)^2} - 2c_1 \sum_{n=1}^{\infty} \frac{x^{3n}}{3^{2n}(n!)^2} \sum_{k=1}^{n} \frac{1}{3k}.$$

7. $$y = \left(c_0 - \frac{1}{2}c_1 \ln x\right)\sum_{n=0}^{\infty}\left(\frac{x}{2}\right)^{2n}\frac{(-1)^n}{n!(n+1)!}$$
$$+ c_1x^{-2}\left[1 + \frac{1}{4}x^2 - \sum_{n=2}^{\infty} 2\left(\frac{x}{2}\right)^{2n}\frac{(-1)^n}{n!(n-1)!}\left(\frac{1}{2n} + \sum_{k=1}^{n-1}\frac{1}{k}\right)\right].$$

8. $$y = (A - B\ln x)\sum_{n=0}^{\infty}\frac{x^{-n}}{n!(n+1)!}$$
$$+ Bx\left[1 - x^{-1}\sum_{n=1}^{\infty}\frac{x^{-n}}{(n-1)!n!}\left(\frac{1}{n} + \sum_{k=1}^{n-1}\frac{2}{k}\right)\right].$$

9. $$y = (c_1x + c_3x\ln x)\sum_{n=0}^{\infty}\frac{x^{2n}}{(2n+1)!(2n+2)!}$$
$$+ (c_2 + c_4\ln x)\sum_{n=0}^{\infty}\frac{x^{2n}}{(2n)!(2n+1)!} + c_3x^{-1}\left[1 - \sum_{n=1}^{\infty}\frac{x^{2n}}{(2n-1)!(2n)!}\right.$$
$$\left.\left(\sum_{j=1}^{2n-1}\frac{2}{j} + \frac{1}{2n}\right)\right] + c_4\left[1 - \sum_{n=1}^{\infty}\frac{x^{2n}}{(2n)!(2n+1)!}\left(\frac{1}{2n+1} + \sum_{j=2}^{2n}\frac{2}{j}\right)\right].$$

§105, page 215

1. 6. **2.** 1.10. **3.** $-2\sqrt{\pi}$. **4.** 3.33. **5.** $(2+t)(1+t)t\Gamma(t)$. **6.** $(-3+t)^{-1}(-2+t)^{-1}(-1+t)^{-1}\Gamma(t)$. **7.** $[t/(t-1)]\Gamma^2(t)$. **8.** 1.43. **9.** 1.77. **10.** 0.443. **11.** 0.310. **12.** $t > -56$. **13.** $-(2n+1) < t < -2n$, where n is zero or a positive integer. **14.** (a) $\frac{1}{32}\pi$. (b) $\frac{1}{24}$. (c) $(5/4{,}096)\pi$.

§106, page 217

1. (a) $$y = c_1x^{\frac{1}{2}}\left(1 - \frac{x^2}{3!} + \frac{x^4}{5!} - \cdots\right) + c_2x^{-\frac{1}{2}}\left(1 - \frac{x^2}{2!} + \frac{x^4}{4!} - \cdots\right).$$

(b) $$y = c_1x^3\sum_{r=0}^{\infty}\frac{(-1)^r(x/2)^{2r}3!}{r!(r+3)!} + c_2\left(x^{-3}\ln x\sum_{r=3}^{\infty}2\frac{(x/2)^{2r}(-1)^r}{r!(r-3)!}\right.$$
$$\left.+ 2x^{-3} + \frac{x^{-1}}{4} + \frac{x}{32} + x^{-3}\sum_{r=3}^{\infty}\left\{2\frac{(-1)^{r+1}(x/2)^{2r}}{r!(r-3)!}\sum_{n=1}^{r}\left[\frac{1}{2n} + \frac{1}{2(\bar{n}-3)}\right]\right\}\right),$$

where $\bar{n}$ does not take the value 3 but takes all the other values from 1 to r.

2. $$y = c_1\sum_{r=0}^{\infty}\frac{(x/2)^{2r}(-1)^r}{(r!)^2} + c_2\left[\ln x\sum_{r=0}^{\infty}\frac{(x/2)^{2r}(-1)^r}{(r!)^2}\right.$$
$$\left.+ \sum_{r=1}^{\infty}\frac{(x/2)^{2r}(-1)^{r+1}}{(r!)^2}\sum_{n=1}^{r}\frac{1}{n}\right].$$

3. Yes.

§107, page 220

4. 1, 0, 0.0012. **5.** $2x^{-1}J_1 - J_0$; $8x^{-2}J_1 - 4x^{-1}J_0 - J_1$; $48x^{-3}J_1 - 24x^{-2}J_0 - 8x^{-1}J_1 + J_0$. Here $x \neq 0$, but the formula holds as $x \to 0$. **6.** $(3/x^2 - 1)J_{\frac{1}{2}} - (3/x)J_{-\frac{1}{2}}$; $(\frac{16}{9}x^{-2} - 1)J_{\frac{1}{3}} - \frac{8}{3}x^{-1}J_{-\frac{2}{3}}$; $(\frac{16}{9}x^{-2} - 1)J_{-\frac{1}{3}} + \frac{8}{3}x^{-1}J_{\frac{2}{3}}$. **7.** (*a*) $-J_0 + x^{-1}J_1$. (*b*) $(2x^{-2} - 1)J_1 - x^{-1}J_0$. (*c*) $(-1 + 12x^{-2} - 48x^{-4})J_1 + (-3x^{-1} + 24x^{-3})J_0$. **8.** (*a*) 0.325. (*b*) 0.210. (*c*) 0.135. **25.** $2I'_n = I_{n+1} + I_{n-1}$, $I_{n+1} = I_{n-1} - (2n/x)I_n$.

§108, page 224

1. $x^2 = \sum_{n=1}^{\infty} 2(\alpha_n^{-1} - 4\alpha_n^{-3})J_0(\alpha_n x)/J_1(\alpha_n)$, $J_0(\alpha_n) = 0$.

2. $x^4 = \sum_{n=1}^{\infty} (128\alpha_n^{-5} - 32\alpha_n^{-3} + 2\alpha_n^{-1})J_0(\alpha_n x)/J_1(\alpha_n)$.

3. $x = \sum_{n=1}^{\infty} - 2\alpha_n^{-1}J_0(\alpha_n)J_1(\alpha_n x)/J_2^2(\alpha_n)$, $J_1(\alpha_n) = 0$.

§109, page 228

2. $\frac{21}{16}(11x^6 - 15x^4 + 5x^2 - \frac{5}{21})$. **3.** $\frac{1}{16}(429x^7 - 693x^5 + 315x^3 - 35x)$. **4.** k. **6.** $\frac{3}{7}P_1 + \frac{4}{9}P_3 + \frac{8}{63}P_5$. **7.** (*a*) $\frac{2}{3}$ if $n = 0$, $\frac{4}{15}$ if $n = 2$, otherwise zero. (*b*) $\frac{2}{5}$ if $n = 1$, $\frac{4}{35}$ if $n = 3$, otherwise zero. (*c*) $\frac{2}{5}$ if $n = 0$, $\frac{8}{35}$ if $n = 2$, $\frac{16}{315}$ if $n = 4$, otherwise zero. **8.** (*a*) $\frac{1}{3} + \frac{2}{3}P_2$. (*b*) $\frac{3}{5}P_1 + \frac{2}{5}P_3$. (*c*) $\frac{7}{35} + \frac{4}{7}P_2 + \frac{8}{35}P_4$. (*d*) $(\frac{1}{3}a + c)P_0 + bP_1 + \frac{2}{3}aP_2$. **9.** $P_k(x)$, $k > n$.

§111, page 231

3. $y = 1 + x + 3x^2 + \frac{1}{2}x^3 - \frac{3}{40}x^5 + \cdots$. **4.** $y = 1 + \frac{1}{2}x^2 + (1/2!)x^4/2^2 + \cdots + (1/n!)x^{2n}/2^n + \cdots$. **5.** $y = 1 + x + x^2/2 + x^3/3 + x^4/(2 \cdot 4) + x^5/(3 \cdot 5) + x^6/(2 \cdot 4 \cdot 6) + x^7/(3 \cdot 5 \cdot 7) + \cdots$.

§112, page 234

2. 70, 58.5.

§113, page 235

2. 0.677, 0.628, 0.572. **3.** $T = 50 - 10(t - 9) - \frac{10}{9}(t - 9)(t - 6)$.

§115, page 239

4. $y = 7.8167$, $y' = 10.0167$, etc. **5.** $y_0 = 1$, $y_{0.1} = 1.0151$, $y_{0.2} = 1.0403$, $y_{0.3} = 1.0759$, $y_{0.4} = 1.1219$, etc. **6.** $y_{0.5} = 1.1784$, $y_{0.6} = 1.2455$, $y_{0.7} = 1.3233$, $y_{0.8} = 1.4120$, etc. **7.** $y_{1.4} = 2.1773$, etc. **9.** $y_{0.1} = 1.1104$. **10.** $y_{0.1} = 2.0309$, $y_{0.2} = 2.0635$, $y_{0.3} = 2.0979$, $y_{0.4} = 2.1339$.

§116, page 242

2. $y'_{0.85} = 7.3587$, $y_{0.85} = 5.6587$. **3.** $y'_{1.1} = 2.3356$, $y_{1.1} = 2.0644$.

§117, page 244

4. $y_{1.5} = 1.100$, $z_{1.5} = 0.4193$, $y_{1.6} = 1.1556$, $z_{1.6} = 0.4924$. **5.** $z_3 = 2 + x - x^3/3! + 3x^5/5!$, $y_3 = 1 + 2x + \frac{1}{2}x^2 - x^4/4! + 3x^6/6!$. **6.** $y_{0.6} = 2.3748$, $z_{0.6} = 2.5659$.

§118, page 246

1. $y_{0.4} = 2.8918$. **2.** $y_{0.5} = 3.1488$, $y_{0.6} = 3.4222$. **3.** (0.1, 1.1053), (0.2, 1.2229) (0.3, 1.3552). **4.** (0.05, 1.0501, 1.0525), (0.1, 1.1004, 1.1100), (0.15, 1.1511, 1.1725), (0.25, 1.2552, 1.3128), (0.3, 1.3091, 1.3907).

§120, page 250

6. $p = q$. **7.** $x(p - q) = z$. **8.** $y(q - p) = z$. **9.** $pt = qs$. **10.** $q(r - s) + p(t - s) = 0$. **11.** $2r + s - t = 0$. **12.** $xy = z(xq - yp)$. **13.** $xy = z(xq + yp)$.

§121, page 251

1. $z = x^3 + xy^2 + \varphi(y)$. **2.** $yz = x^2y + \varphi(x)$. **3.** $yz = x^2y + \varphi(x) + \psi(y)$. **4.** $z = \int\int f(x,y)\,dx^2 + x\varphi(y) + \psi(y)$. **5.** $2z = x^2 \ln y + 2axy + \varphi(x) + \psi(y)$. **6.** $z = -ye^x + e^y[y + \varphi(x)] + \psi(x)$. **7.** $2z = x^2y - 2xy + \varphi(y) + e^{-x}\psi(y)$. **8.** $4z = x^2y + \varphi(y) \ln x + \psi(y)$. **9.** $z = \ln [e^{xy}\varphi(y) - e^{-xy}] + \psi(y)$. **10.** $2z^2 = (2x - 1)y^2 + \varphi(y)e^{-2x}$. **11.** $\pm z = \sqrt{a - \varphi(y)e^{-2x}} + \sqrt{a} \ln [\sqrt{ae^{2x} - \varphi(y)} - \sqrt{a}\, e^x] + \psi(y)$. **12.** $z = 6x^2 + e^{-y}\varphi(x) + x\psi(y) + \theta(y)$. **13.** $z = \varphi_1(y)e^{2x} + \varphi_2(y)e^{-2x} - 2y^2$. **14.** $z = \varphi_1(x) \cos 2y + \varphi_2(x) \sin 2y + 2x^2$. **15.** $z = \varphi_1(y)e^{3x} + \varphi_2(y)e^{-x} - xy^2$. **16.** $z = \varphi_1(x)e^{-3y} + \varphi_2(x)e^y + x^2y$. **17.** $z = \varphi_1(y)e^{5xy/2} + \varphi_2(y)e^{-xy} - \frac{1}{5}(5x + 3 - 3y^{-1})$. **18.** $z = e^{xy}[\varphi_1(x) \sin 2xy + \varphi_2(x) \cos 2xy] + x$.

§122, page 254

1. $z = e^x\varphi(x - y)$. **2.** $z = x^2\varphi(y/x)$. **3.** $y + z = x\varphi[x(y - z)]$. **4.** $az = cx + \varphi(bx - ay)$. **5.** $\tan^{-1}\dfrac{y}{z} = \ln x + \varphi(z^2 + y^2)$. **6.** $3xz = y^2 + \varphi(xy)$. **7.** $z(y - x) = axy \ln (y/x) + (y - x)\varphi[(x - y)/(xy)]$. **8.** $x^2 - y^2 = \varphi(z^2 + 2y^2)$. **9.** $3y^2 \ln z + ax = 3y^2\varphi(xy)$. **10.** $(x + y) \ln z - x = \varphi(x + y)$. **12.** $z = \varphi(y/x)$. **13.** $z = (1 + y)^{1/x}\varphi(x)$. **14.** $3z = 2x^3 + \varphi(ye^{-x}) + \psi(y)$. **15.** $2z = x^2 + xy + \varphi(y/x) + \psi(y)$. **16.** $z = y^3\varphi(x^5/y^3)$. **17.** $(y - x)^2 + 2z^2 = \varphi(x + y)$. **18.** (a) $(y + y^2)^{-2}$. (b) x^{-1}. **19.** (a) $e^{\int f(y)\,dy}$. (b) $e^{-\int f(x)\,dx}$. (c) $(xy)^k$. (d) x^by^a. **20.** $yz + 2xy^2 = \varphi(xy) + \psi(y)$. **21.** $z = y\varphi(x/y) + \psi(y)$. **22.** $xz - 2x^2y = \varphi(xy) + \psi(x)$. **23.** $x^2z - 6x^3y^2 = \varphi(xy) + \psi(x)$. **24.** $z = x\varphi(y + x^2) + \psi(x)$. **25.** $z + xy = \varphi(x^2y) + \psi(x)$. **26.** $z = y\varphi(e^x/y) + \psi(y)$. **27.** $z = \varphi(e^y/x) + \psi(y)$.

§123, page 255

1. $5y^2 + z^2 = 4x^2$. **2.** (a) $z(1 + xy) = 10xy$. (b) $z(x^2y^2 + z^2) = 2x^3y^3$. (c) $1 + xy = 2xyz$. **3.** (a) $x^2 + y^2 + z^2 = 25(x + y)^2$. (b) $x^2 + z^2 = 25(x - z)^2$. (c) $yz = y^2 + 2xy + 4x^2$. **4.** (a) $z = e^y \sin (x - y)$. (b) $z = (a - x + y)^2e^{x-a}$. (c) $z^2 = [a^2 - (x - y)^2]e^{2y}$. **5.** $\varphi\left(\dfrac{x - 1}{y}, \dfrac{z}{y}\right) = 0$, $y^2 + z^2 = 25(x - 1)^2$. **6.** $z = \dfrac{1}{3}\dfrac{y^2}{x} + \dfrac{1}{6}x^2y^2 + xy + \ln (xy - 1) + c$.

§124, page 257

1. $z = \sum^k (a_ke^{\sqrt{k}x} + b_ke^{-\sqrt{k}x})(c_k \sin \sqrt{k}y + d_k \cos \sqrt{k}y)$; same with x and y interchanged; $z = c_1xy + c_2x + c_3y + c_4$. **2.** $z = \sum^k e^{ky}(a_ke^{\sqrt{k}x} + b_ke^{-\sqrt{k}x})$; $z = \sum^k e^{-ky}(a_k \sin \sqrt{k}x + b_k \cos \sqrt{k}x)$; $z = c_1 + c_2x$. **3.** $z = \sum^k c_ke^{k(x-y)}$. **4.** $z = \sum^k c_ke^{k(x-y)+3y}$.

5. $z = \sum^{k} (a_k e^{\sqrt{k-1}x} + b_k e^{-\sqrt{k-1}x})(c_k \sin \sqrt{k}y + d_k \cos \sqrt{k}y)$; $k = 1, 0 < k < 1, k = 0, k < 0$. **6.** (a) $k < -\frac{1}{4}$. (b) $k > 1$. (c) $-\frac{1}{4} \leqq x \leqq 1$. **7.** $u = \sum^{k,l,m} (a_k e^{\sqrt{l}x} + b_k e^{-\sqrt{l}x})(c_k e^{\sqrt{m}y} + d_k e^{-\sqrt{m}y})(g_k \sin \sqrt{l + mz} + f_k \cos \sqrt{l + mz})$; 13 types. **9.** $z = \sum^{k} e^{kx - ky/2}[a_k \sin (\frac{1}{2} \sqrt{3ky}) + b_k \cos (\frac{1}{2} \sqrt{3ky})]$.

§125, page 261

1. $z = \varphi(y + x) + \psi(y - 2x)$. **2.** $z = \varphi(y + mx) + \psi(y + nx)$. **3.** $z = x\varphi(y - mx) + \psi(y - mx)$. **4.** $z = \sum^{k} [c_{1k} \sin \sqrt{k}\,(x + y) + c_{2k} \cos \sqrt{k}\,(x + y)](c_{3k}e^{2\sqrt{k}x} + c_{4k}e^{-2\sqrt{k}x})$. **5.** $z = \sum^{k} [c_{1k} \sin \sqrt{k}\,(y + mx) + c_{2k} \cos \sqrt{k}\,(y + mx)](c_{3k}e^{2\sqrt{k}nx} + c_{4k}e^{-2\sqrt{k}nx})$. **6.** $z = y^{\frac{1}{3}}x^{-\frac{2}{3}}\varphi(xy) + \psi(yx^{-2})$. **7.** $z = x\varphi(y + x^2) + \psi(y + x^2)$. **8.** $z = \sum^{k} [c_{1k} \cos (\sqrt{k}\, ye^{x} \cos 2x) + c_{2k} \sin (\sqrt{k}\, ye^{x} \cos 2x)](c_{3k}e^{\sqrt{k}ye^{x} \sin 2x} + c_{4k}e^{-\sqrt{k}ye^{x} \sin 2x})$. **9.** $z = \sum^{k} \rho^{-\frac{1}{2}}(c_{1k} \sin \sqrt{k}\,\theta + c_{2k} \cos \sqrt{k}\,\theta)(c_{3k}\rho^{\sqrt{k+\frac{1}{4}}} + c_{4k}\rho^{-\sqrt{k+\frac{1}{4}}})$. **10.** $z = y\varphi(xe^{-y^2/2}) + \psi(xe^{-y^2/2})$. **13.** By using the substitution u arbitrary and finding v from the solution of $dy/dx - b/2a = 0$.

§126, page 267

3. $1 = (4/\pi)(\frac{1}{1} \sin x + \frac{1}{3} \sin 3x + \frac{1}{5} \sin 5x + \cdots)$. **4.** $\frac{1}{2} + (2/\pi)(\sin x + \frac{1}{3} \sin 3x + \frac{1}{5} \sin 5x + \cdots)$. **5.** $\frac{8}{\pi}\left(\frac{\sin x}{1.3} - \frac{2 \sin 2x}{3.5} + \frac{3 \sin 3x}{5.7} - \cdots\right)$. **7.** $\left(\frac{2}{1}\pi^2 - \frac{12}{1^3}\right) \sin x - \left(\frac{2}{2}\pi^2 - \frac{12}{2^3}\right) \sin 2x + \left(\frac{2}{3}\pi^2 - \frac{12}{3^3}\right) \sin 3x - \cdots, -\pi < x < \pi$.

§127, page 269

1. (a) $x = 2L/\pi[\sin (\pi x/L) - \frac{1}{2} \sin (2\pi x/L) + \frac{1}{3} \sin (3\pi x/L) - \cdots]$. (b) $x^2 = L^2/3 - 4L^2/\pi^2[1/1^2 \cos (\pi x/L) - 1/2^2 \cos (2\pi x/L) + 1/3^2 \cos (3\pi x/L) - \cdots]$. (c) $F(x + k2L) = F(x)$, $F(x) = x^2$ on $-L \leqq x \leqq L$. **2.** $x^2 = 2/\pi[(\pi^2/1 - 4/1^3) \sin x - \pi^2/2 \sin 2x + (\pi^2/3 - 4/3^3) \sin 3x - \pi^2/4 \sin 4x + \cdots]$. **3.** $F(x) = mx(L - x)$ on $0 \leqq x \leqq L$, $F(x) = mx(L + x)$ on $-L \leqq x \leqq 0$, $F(x + k2L) = F(x)$. **4.** $mx(L^2 - x^2) = 12mL^3/\pi^3[1/1^3 \sin (\pi x/L) - 1/2^3 \sin (2\pi x/L) + 1/3^3 \sin (3\pi x/L) - \cdots]$, $-L \leqq x \leqq L$. **5.** $|\pi + \frac{1}{2}x| = \frac{5}{4}\pi + \sum_{m=1}^{\infty} \left[\frac{4 \cos m\pi - 4 \cos (m\pi/2)}{\pi m^2} \cos \frac{mx}{4} + \frac{4 \sin (m\pi/2) - 2\pi m \cos m\pi}{\pi m^2} \sin \frac{mx}{4}\right]$.

§129, page 275

1. $y = 0.0232[\cos 178t \sin (\pi x/3) + 1/3^3 \cos (3 \cdot 178t/3) \sin (3\pi x/3) + \cdots]$; about 28 vibrations per second. **2.** $y = a \sin (3\pi x/L) \cos (3\pi at/L)$. Points $(\frac{1}{3}L,0)$, $(\frac{2}{3}L,0)$,

(0,0), and (L,0) are at rest. **3.** $y = \frac{1}{2}[\alpha(x + at) + \alpha(x - at)] + AL/(\mu\pi a) \sin(\mu\pi x/L) \sin(\mu\pi at/L)$. **4.** $y = 0.02 \sin(\frac{1}{2}\pi x/L) \cos(\frac{1}{2}\pi at/L)$. **5.** $y = 4mL/\pi^2 \sum_{n=1}^{\infty} (-1)^{n+1}1/(2n - 1)^2 \sin[(2n - 1)\pi x/L] \cos[(2n - 1)\pi at/L]$; $t = 2L/a$ units of time. **6.** $y = 12mL^3/\pi^3 \sum_{n=1}^{\infty} (-1)^{n+1}/n^3 \sin(n\pi x/L) \cos(n\pi at/L)$; $2L/a$ sec.

§130, page 276

1. $\alpha(x)$ relates to displacement of points from the position of equilibrium and $\beta(x)$ relates to velocity of points, all at time $t = 0$. **2.** $y = \sin(\pi x/L)[m \cos(\pi at/L) + c \sin(\pi at/L)]$; L/a, $2L/a$. **3.** $y = 0.0072/\pi^3 \sum_{n=1}^{\infty} (2n - 1)^{-3} \sin[(2n - 1)\pi x/3] \cos[(2n - 1)\pi 17{,}000t/3]$; 2,800 oscillations per second.

§131, page 279

1. (*a*) $\theta(x,y) = Ae^{-3y} \sin 3x$. (*b*) $2A \sum_{n=1}^{\infty} (-1)^{n+1}n^{-1}e^{-ny} \sin nx$.

2. $\theta = 4/\pi \sum_{n=1}^{\infty} (2n - 1)^{-1}e^{-\pi(2n-1)y/L} \sin[(2n - 1)\pi x/L]$.

3. $\theta = 4mL/\pi^2 \sum_{n=0}^{\infty} (2n - 1)^{-2}e^{-(2n-1)\pi y/L} \sin[(2n - 1)\pi x/L]$.

§132, page 281

1. $\theta = 1.2x + 56$ deg; $\theta = (Q - P)L^{-1}x + P$. **2.** $\theta = 56 + 1.44x - (144/\pi) \sum_{n=1}^{\infty} (2n - 1)^{-1}e^{-(2n-1)^2\pi^2a^2t/100^2} \sin[(2n - 1)\pi x/100] + 512/\pi \sum_{n=1}^{\infty} (-1)^{n+1} e^{-n^2\pi^2a^2t/100^2} \sin(n\pi x/100)$. **3.** $\theta = 60 + x - (160/\pi) \sum_{n=1}^{\infty} (2n - 1)^{-1}e^{-a^2(2n-1)^2\pi^2t/100^2} \sin[(2n - 1)\pi x/100] + 160/\pi \sum_{n=1}^{\infty} (-1)^{n-1}(n)^{-1}e^{-n^2a^2\pi^2t/100^2} \sin(n\pi x/100)$. **4.** 110°. **5.** $\theta(x,t) =$

$$800 - 20x + \sum_{n=1}^{\infty} \left(\frac{3{,}200}{n^2\pi^2} \sin\frac{n\pi}{2} - \frac{1{,}600}{n\pi}\right) e^{-a^2n^2\pi^2t/40^2} \sin\frac{n\pi x}{40}.$$

§133, page 283

1. $Y_0(w)$ is infinite at $w = r = 0$. Yes. **2.** $y = 0$ at the boundary of the drum head. $2.40/a$, $5.52/a$, $8.65/a$. **3.** (*a*) It makes a complete oscillation up and down with maximum amplitude. (*b*) Same as (*a*) but with different amplitude. (*c*) Remain fixed. (*d*) Remain fixed.

§134, page 285

2. $e = -A\sqrt{L/C}\sin(\omega\sqrt{LC}\,x)\cos\omega t + B$. **4.** (a) $i = (A\omega/R)e^{(-\omega^2/RC)t}\sin\omega x$. (b) $e = (AR/\omega)e^{(-\omega^2/RC)t}\cos\omega x + B$. **5.** $e = Ax + B$, $i = -A/R$. **6.** $e = -2/\pi$ $[7e^{-at}\sin(\pi x/L) - \frac{3}{2}e^{-4at}\sin(2\pi x/L) + \frac{7}{3}e^{-9at}\sin(3\pi x/L) - \frac{3}{4}e^{-16at}\sin(4\pi x/L) + \cdots]$, $i = 2/(RL)[7e^{-at}\cos(\pi x/L) - 3e^{-4at}\cos(2\pi x/L) + 7e^{-9at}\cos(3\pi x/L) - 3e^{-16at}\cos(4\pi x/L) + \cdots]$, where $a = \pi^2/(L^2RC)$, $t > 0$. **8.** $i = -A\sqrt{C/L}\,e^{-(G/C)t}\cos(\omega\sqrt{LC}\,x)\sin\omega t$.

§135, page 289

3. (a) $x^3 - 3xy^2 = c$, $3x^2y - y^3 = c$, $p = \rho/g[c - gy - \frac{1}{2}(x^2 + y^2)^2]$. (b) $x^2 + y^2 = c$, $y = cx$, $p = \rho/g[c - gy - \frac{1}{2}(x^2 + y^2)^{-1}]$.

INDEX

Acceleration, 24, 139, 140
  expressed, in polar coordinates, 183
    in rectangular coordinates, 183
Adiabatic law, 61
Aerial velocity, 185
Air condition, 29, 31
Air pressure, 23, 60, 61
Amperes, 59, 151
Answers, 291–311
Approximate integration, 237–247
  beginning a solution, 237, 238, 242, 243, 245, 246
  doubling interval, 239
  formulas for, 236–244
  halving interval, 240, 241
  Runge-Kutta method of, 245–247
  of simultaneous equations, 242–244
  when to change interval, 239, 240
Approximate-integration formulas, 236
Arbitrary functions, 249
Arch, shape of, 175
Archimedes' principle, 145
Atmosphere, height of, 61
Attraction, 183
Auxiliary equation, roots of, distinct, 89
    imaginary, 92
    repeated, 90

Bailey, R. P., 182
Barnes, John L., 110
Beams, 176–180
  cantilever, 180
  deflection of, 179
  elastic curve of, 177
Bedell, F., 151
Bending moment, 177
Bernouilli's equation, 48
Bessel function, of first kind, 217
  of second kind, 217
Bessel's equation, 215, 282
  modified, 222
  solutions of, 216, 217
Biggott, E. A., 246
Boyle's law, 61
Brachistochrone, 166
Buckling, material, 270
Buckling stress, 181, 182
Byerly, W. E., 264

c-discriminant, 74
Cables, 174, 176
Calories, 27
Canonical forms of second-order linear equations, 259–261
Cantilever beam, 180
Capacitance, 59
  to ground, 284
Capacitor, 59, 152
  in parallel, 160
Carslaw, H. S., 110, 264
Catenary, 166, 174
Cauchy, Augustin, 66
Cauchy's ratio test, 203
Chain, on cylinder, 67, 69
  friction of, 67, 69
Characteristics, 259
Chemical reactions, 54, 55, 58
Churchill, Ruel V., 110
Circuits, electric, 59, 151–161
Clairaut's equation, 79, 80
Columns, 181
Complementary function, 94
Complex numbers, 66, 69, 92, 102
  expressing fluid flow, 289
Components, of acceleration, 183
  of force, 62
Compound-interest law, 22
Conductivity, 27

Conservative force, 289
Constants of integration, 91
Coulomb, 59, 151
Coupled circuits, 161
Courant, R., 115, 203, 264
Crehore, A. C., 151
Critical arrangement, 269
Current of electricity, 59, 161
Current leakage, 284
Curvature, 186
  radius of, 173
Cuspidal locus, 77
Cycloid, 166

Damping, 135–138
  constant, 136
  critical, 138
  over-, 138
Damping factor, 136
Deflection, 177
Degree, 2
Dependent variable absent, 163
Difference of potential, 151
Differential equations, definition of, 2
  degree of, 2
  exact, 38–41
  from general solution, 8
  integro-, 123
  linear, 45
  order of, 2
  ordinary, 2
  partial (*see* Partial differential equations)
  solution of, 3, 7, 8
  total, 194–197
Differentials, exact, 38
Dimensions, 26
Discriminant, *c*-, 74
  p-, 76
Distortionless line, 286

Easily integrable partial differential equations, 250–251
Elastic curve, 176
Electrical analogue, 153
Electricity, 59
Electromotive force (emf), 59
  constant, 153
  sinusoidal, 154
Electromotive force law, 152
Electron, 151, 269
Elliptic equations, canonical form of, 261
emf (*see* Electromotive force)
Envelope, 72–77
  from *c*-discriminant, 74
  from differential equation, 75
  equations of, 73, 76
  from *p*-discriminant, 76
Epoch, angle of, 135
Equations, equivalent systems of, 187, 188
  of first order and first degree, 191–193
  having form $P_p + Q_q = R$, 251–253
  of higher degree, 70–82
    factorable, 70
    solvable, for x, 80
      for y, 78
  homogeneous, 35–37
  hyperbolic, 258–259
  of motion, 140, 141
  radio, telegraph, telephone, 283, 285
  (*See also* Differential equations; Linear equations; Simultaneous equations)
Equipotential curves, 63
Equipotential surfaces in space, 199
Equivalent systems of equations, 187, 188
Euler's linear equation, 169
Evolute, 82
Exact differential equation, 38–40
  condition for, 40
Exact differentials, 38
Existence Theorem I, 188
Existence Theorem II, 189
Existence theorems, 7, 188–190
Expansions in terms of Bessel's functions, 222–224
Exponential order, 111

Factorization of operator, 166–168
  method based on, 85
Falling bodies, 26, 31
Farad, 59, 152
Fields of force, in a plane, 62
  in space, 198–200
Fission, nuclear, 269–272
Flow, of heat, 276–279
  through an orifice, 28, 32

Fluid motion, 286–289
  steady state for, 289
Force function, 289
Forced motion, 141, 143
Forces, 24, 61–66, 139
  addition of, 62
  components of, 62
  conservative, 289
  field of, 62
  lines of, 62
Formulas, for approximate integration, 236
    use of, 237–244
  from figures, 15, 19
Fourier series, 263–268
  basic formulas for, 263–264, 267, 272
  change of limits for, 268
  of cosines, 267–268
  expansion in, 264–268
  graph of, representing x, 266
  of sines, 267–268
Fourier's problem, solution of, 278
Fractional precipitation, 58
Free motion, 141
Frequency, 135, 136

Galvanometer, 160
Gamma function, 213–215
  definition of, 214
Gardner, Murray F., 110
Generating function, 226
Geometric considerations, 5–7
Geometrical interpretations, 5, 6, 198, 252
Glasstone, Samuel, 269
Gravitational field, 62, 66

Half-lives of isotopes, 23
Harmonic motion, 135
  amplitude of, 135
  frequency of, 135
  period of, 135
  simple, 135
Heat flow, 276–279
  general equations of, 278
  law of, 277
  one-dimensional, 279, 280
Heat loss, 27, 31
Heaviside, Oliver, 110
Henry, 59, 152
Higher-degree equations (*see* Equations)
Homogeneous equations, 35–36
  reducible to, 37
Hooke's law, 177, 276
Horizontal difference table, 232
Hyperbolic equations, 258, 259
  canonical form of, 259

Ice boat, motion of, 26
Imaginary numbers, 66, 69, 92
Impedance, 155
  coil, 158
Ince, E. L., 231
Independent variable absent, 165
Indicial equation, 208
  roots differing by an integer, 210–213
Inductance, 59, 152
Integral, 39, 248
Integrating factor, 42–43, 46, 48
Integration in series, 202–217
Integration constants, 91
Integrodifferential equations, 123
Interpolation, 233, 235, 241
  Newton's formula for, 234
Inverse transforms, 112, 117, 118
Irrotational motion, 289
Isoclines, 5
Isotopes, half-lives of, 23

J_n, n an integer, 217, 218
  expansions in terms of, 222–224
  recurrence formulas of, 218, 219
Jaeger, J. C., 110

Keuffel and Esser, 22
Kirchhoff's laws, 151, 152
  current, 151
  emf, 151
  networks and, 156–161
Kutta, W., 245

Laplace, Pierre Simon, 66
Laplace transforms, 110–134
  definition of, 110
  derivatives of, 115
  deriving relations from, 114–116

Laplace transforms, inverse, 112, 117, 118
  properties of, 111–114
  solving equations by, 122–125
  table, 113, 116
Laplace's equation, 257
  in cylindrical coordinates, 258
  in polar coordinates, 257
  in rectangular coordinates, 257, 258
Law of gravitation, 183
  (*See also* Newton's law)
Leakage of current, 284
Legendre polynomials, 225
  expansion in terms of, 226–228
Legendre's functions, 224–228
Levy, H., 246
Light, absorption of, 29
Light reflection, 55
Like terms, 95
Limits, use of, 20
Linear equations, 45–47, 88, 89
  Euler's 169
  homogeneous, 88, 89
  reducible to, 45
  second-order, 170
  theorem of, 89
Linear independence of functions, 86, 87
Linear partial differential equations, 256
Lines of force, 63, 199

Maclaurin series, 206, 207
Mass, 24
Maxwell, Clerk, 1
Membrane, vibrations of, 281–283
  general equation, 282
Mhos, 284
Mixture problems, 28, 29
Modulus of elasticity, 177
Moment of inertia, 177
Moments, 139, 140
  bending, 177
Momentum, change of, 57
Motion, of a comet, 68
  fluid, 286–289
  forced, 141, 143
  free, 141
  harmonic (*see* Harmonic motion)
  of ice boat, 26
  Newton's law of, 24, 31, 57
  oscillatory, 141
Motion, of a particle in a plane, 182
  periodic, 135, 136
  of a planet, 68
  of rocket, 57, 58
  space, 184–186
  string, 272
  wave, 249, 273
  of weights, 27, 69, 142, 162

Networks and Kirchhoff's laws, 156–161
Neutron flux, 270
Neutrons, 269
Newton, Isaac, 1
  interpolation formula, 234
Newton's law, of cooling, 23
  of gravitation, 183
  of motion, 24, 31, 57
Nodes, 74
Normals to a surface, 252
Nuclear energy, 269
Nuclear fission, 269
Nuclear reactor theory, 269
Nucleus, 269
Numerical solution of systems of equations, 242–244
Numerical solutions of differential equations, 229–247

Ohm, 59, 152
One-dimensional heat flow, 279
  example of, 280
Operators, 83–86
  basic theorem of, 97
  D^k, basic theorem of, 97, 98
    methods using, 98–102
    obey laws of algebra, 84
  definition of, 83
  inverse, 99
  methods using, 99–102
  obey laws of algebra, 84
  product of, 83
  sum of, 83
  symbolic, 98–103
Order, 2
Orthogonal functions, 222, 263
Orthogonal trajectories, 16, 19, 65
Oscillator, 207
Oscillatory motion, 141

p-discriminant, 76
Parabolic equations, canonical form of, 260
Parachute, 31
Parallel capacitors, 160
Parallel conductances, 160
Parameters, variation of, 103–106
Parametric equation, 78
Partial differential equations, 248–262
  easily integrable, 250–251
  integral of, 248
  linear, 256
  solution of, 248, 250–254, 256–261
    particular, 254–255
Partial fractions and transforms, 126–132
  roots of denominator, complex, 130–132
    different, 127
    repeated, 128–129
Particular solution, 94
  of partial differential equations, 254–255
Pendulum, 145, 146
Perfect gas, 61
Periodic motion, 135, 136
Periods of ships, 146
Phase, 135
Pierce, G. W., 151
Pipes, Louis A., 226
Plane motion, 140, 147–150
Polar coordinates, 18, 19, 31
Potential, 63
  difference of, 151
Projectiles, 147, 149, 150
Protons, 269

Quantum mechanics, 207

Radio equations, 283, 285
Radium, 22, 163, 269
Radius of curvature, 173
Rate problems, 27–29
Ratio test, Cauchy's, 203
Reactance, 155
Reactor, shape of, 271, 272
    cylindrical, 272
    rectangular, 271
    spherical, 271
Recurrence formulas, for integral of J_n, 220
  of J_n, 218, 219
Reduction of order, 163
Reflector, 55
Resistance, electrical, 59
  proportional to velocity, 26, 31
Resonance, 137, 155, 156
  current, 156
Riemann, Georg Frederich Bernhard, 66
Right-hand member not zero, 94
Rocket, motion of, 57, 58
Rotation of a fluid, 288
Runge, C., 245
Runge-Kutta method, 245–247
  for equations, 247
  error in, 246
  for simultaneous equations, 247

Scarborough, James B., 231, 236
Sears, F. W., 151
Second-order linear equation, 170
  conical forms of, 259–261
Sectionally continuous function, 111
Separation of variables, 256, 257
Series, Fourier, 263
  general type of, 208–213
Series solutions, 202–217
Simple circuit, 59
Simple harmonic motion, 135
Simpson's rule, 241
Simultaneous equations, 49–51, 106, 107
  applications of, 56–58
Singular points, 74
Singular solution, 8, 76, 79
Slug, 140
Snow-ball law, 22
Solution, general, 8
  particular, 8
  singular, 8, 76, 79
Solving systems of equations by transforms, 121–125
Space motion, 184–186
Special case of right member, 96
Springs, motion caused by, 142–145
Steady state, 144, 155
  for heat flow, 278

Stream lines, 64, 200
String motion, 272
Substitutions, 33, 34, 43, 46, 48, 163–165, 169, 170, 258–261
Successive approximations, method of, 229–231
Summation notation, 202
Superposition, 88
Suspension bridge, 175
Symbolic operator, 98–103

Tac-locus, 76
Tangent lines of a surface, 249
Taylor's formula, 73
Telegraph equations, 283, 285
Telephone equations, 283, 285
Thorium, 269
Torque, 140, 141
Total differential equations, 194–197
  condition of integrability, 195
  method of solution, 196
Trajectory, orthogonal, 16, 19, 68
Transforms, of derivatives, 121, 122
  Laplace, 110–134
    inverse, 112, 117, 118
Transient, 144, 155
Trial solution, 95

Undetermined coefficients, method of, 94
Uranium, 269

Variables, separable, 11, 12
  separation of, 256, 257
Variation of parameters, 103–106
Vector, components of, 139
  direction of, 139
  magnitude of, 139
Velocity, 24, 61
Velocity field, 64
Velocity potential, 289
Vibrations, of a membrane, 281–283
  of a rod, 275, 276
    general equation for, 276
  of a string, 272, 275
    equation for, 273
    example of, 274, 275
Vibratory disturbances, 147
Viscosity, 286
Volt, 59, 151
Voltage, 151

Wave motions, 249, 273
Willers, F. A., 246
Wronskians, 87